Awards

William K. Durr
Jean M. LePere
John Pescosolido
Rita M. Bean
Nicholas A. Glaser

Consultant
Hugh Schoephoerster

HOUGHTON MIFFLIN COMPANY   BOSTON

Atlanta   Dallas   Geneva, Illinois   Hopewell, New Jersey   Palo Alto   Toronto

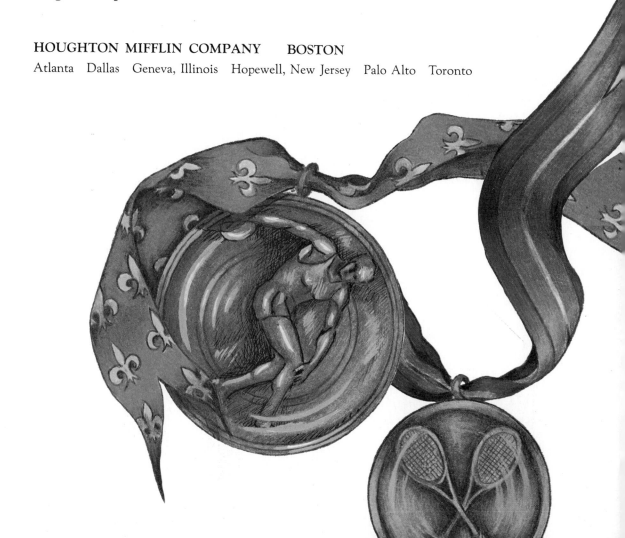

Acknowledgments

Grateful acknowledgment is given for the contributions of Paul McKee.

For each of the selections listed below, grateful acknowledgment is made for permission to adapt and/or reprint original or copyrighted material, as follows:

"African Proverbs," from *Speak to the Winds*, by Kofi Asare Opoku: "Introduction," adapted, and 11 proverbs. Copyright © 1975 by Kofi Asare Opoku. By permission of Lothrop, Lee & Shepard Company. One proverb "Even the greatest bird . . . a tree to roost upon." From *A Story Like the Wind*, by Laurens van der Post (William Morrow & Company, 1972).

"The Ballad of Mulan," from *The Flying Horses*, by Jo Manton and Robert Gittings. Copyright © 1977 by Jo Manton and Robert Gittings. The alterations have been approved by the authors. Adapted and reprinted by permission of Holt, Rinehart and Winston, Publishers, and Methuen Children's Books Ltd., publishers.

"Before the Forty-Niners," from *Chicano Roots Go Deep*, by Harold Coy. Copyright © 1975 by Harold Coy. Reprinted by permission of Dodd, Mead & Company.

"Bert Breen's Barn," from *Bert Breen's Barn*, by Walter D. Edmonds. Copyright © 1975 by Walter D. Edmonds. Reprinted by permission of Little, Brown and Co.

"Billie Jean King," adapted from *Women Who Win*, by Francene Sabin. Copyright © 1975 by Francene Sabin. Reprinted by permission of Random House, Inc.

"Billy Beans Lived Here," from *Deep Where the Octopi Lie*, by Jean McCord. Copyright © 1958 by Jean McCord. Used by permission of Atheneum Publishers.

"A Blessing," from *The Branch Will Not Break*, by James Wright. Copyright © 1961 by James Wright. First appeared in *Poetry*. Reprinted by permission of Wesleyan University Press.

"Blue Beach," from *Carlota*, by Scott O'Dell. Copyright © 1977 by Scott O'Dell. Reprinted by permission of Houghton Mifflin Company, and McIntosh and Otis, Inc.

"The Boy Who Predicted Earthquakes," by Margaret St. Clair. Copyright © 1950 by Margaret St. Clair. Adapted by permission of McIntosh and Otis, Inc.

"Canada Geese," from *Canada Geese*, by Jack Denton Scott. Copyright © 1976 by Jack Denton Scott. Adapted by permission of G. P. Putnam's Sons, the author, and Raines & Raines.

"The Case of the Punjabi Ruby," by Frank Willment. Reprinted by permission from *Plays, The Drama Magazine for Young People*. Copyright © by Plays, Inc. This play is for reading purposes only. For permission to produce this play, write to Plays, Inc., 8 Arlington St., Boston, MA 02116.

"Chino's Tale," by Mary Stolz. Copyright © 1974 by Mary Stolz. Reprinted by permission of Roslyn Targ Literary Agency, Inc.

Copyright © 1981 by Houghton Mifflin Company

Printed in the U.S.A.

ISBN: 0-395-27832-5

3

Contents

MAGAZINE TWO

MAGAZINE THREE

MAGAZINE FOUR

Awards

MAGAZINE ONE

Contents

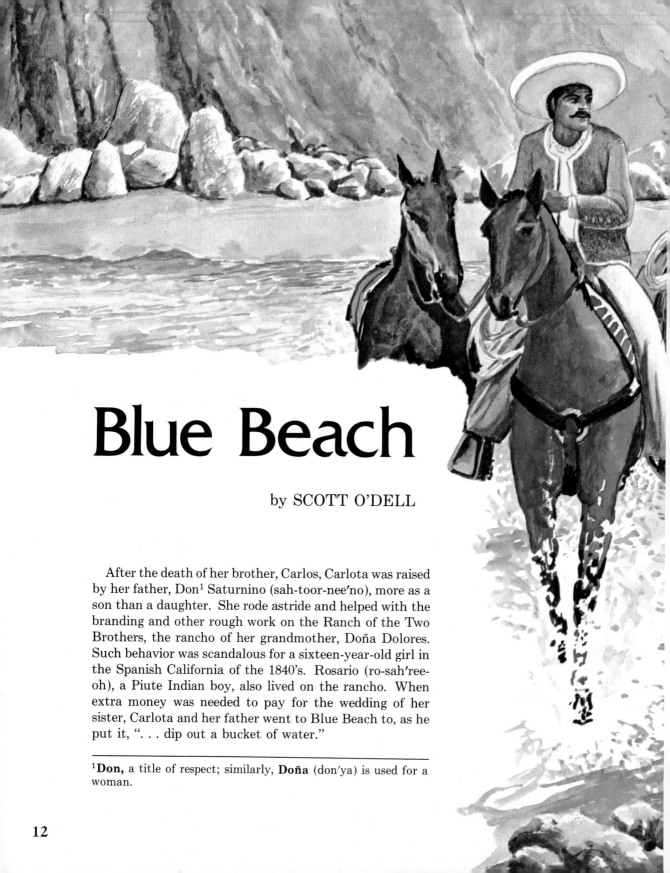

Blue Beach

by SCOTT O'DELL

After the death of her brother, Carlos, Carlota was raised by her father, Don[1] Saturnino (sah-toor-nee′no), more as a son than a daughter. She rode astride and helped with the branding and other rough work on the Ranch of the Two Brothers, the rancho of her grandmother, Doña Dolores. Such behavior was scandalous for a sixteen-year-old girl in the Spanish California of the 1840's. Rosario (ro-sah′ree-oh), a Piute Indian boy, also lived on the rancho. When extra money was needed to pay for the wedding of her sister, Carlota and her father went to Blue Beach to, as he put it, ". . . dip out a bucket of water."

---

[1]**Don,** a title of respect; similarly, **Doña** (don′ya) is used for a woman.

My father wore the heaviest of his leather breeches, his thickest jacket, and a pair of high horsehide boots. It was gear for the wild country that lay between the Ranch of the Two Brothers and Blue Beach. He carried his best musket, his tinderbox, and his powder horn. I dressed accordingly, but carried no weapon except a knife.

There were four horses saddled and waiting for us. I rode my stallion, Tiburón (tee-boo-rahn'), and I rode astride.

The river would still be running a torrent. It was much easier to cross close to the ranch and go down the south bank, but we had no desire to get soaked so early on the journey.

Accordingly, we chose the north bank and followed it through heavy chaparral and patches of cactus until we had ridden for two hours.

Where the river widened and ran knee-deep, we crossed to the south bank. It was still a good hour's ride from the Blue Beach. But it was here that we took the first precaution.

My father and I had been coming to Blue Beach for two years. On the three journeys we had made, we had always been followed. Sometimes by one or two Indians, sometimes by more. But to this day, no one had followed us farther than this west crossing. Here we had managed to elude them.

One thing that helped was that we never told anyone our secret — the story of the Blue Beach.

We told none of the vaqueros[2] or the *mayordomo*.[3] Nor Rosario, though Rosario could be trusted. Nor my sister, who could not be. Nor even Doña Dolores, whom we could trust most of all. Dolores you could hang by her thumbs and still not hear one word that she did not wish to speak.

There was no way to find the Blue Beach except by following the river, either down from the mountains or up from the sea. From the sea no one would ever find it because of a series of lagoons. From the direction of the mountains you would need to be very lucky, as lucky as we had been in the beginning.

The river at this point, where it fanned out into the deep lagoons, ran narrow, between two sheer walls of granite, where even a mountain goat would be lost. At the bottom of these cliffs were two beaches, one facing the other across a distance of a hundred steps.

The beaches were strips of fine sand, finer than the sand you find on the sea beach itself. Both had a bluish cast, like pebbles you see through clear-running water. But they also had another color, a lighter blue that had a look of metal, as if there were copper deposits in the cliffs that had been washed down by the river and the rain and had mixed with the lighter color.

Someone might call the beaches green or the color of turquoise, but to us they were blue, and this is what we called them — the Blue Beaches, more often, the Blue Beach.

On this day, as on the three other journeys we had made to the Blue Beach, we tied our horses and climbed up from the stream to a towering rock. This was where we took our second precaution, for from this high place we could survey the trails, one coming along the river, and one from the sea.

"What do you see?" my father said. He liked to test my eyesight. "Are we followed?"

"I see nothing on the trail," I said, "either from the river or from the sea."

"What is the brown spot among the oaks?"

"Where?"

[2] **vaqueros** (bah-kay′rohs), cowhands or herders.
[3] **mayordomo** (mayr′doh-mo), manager of a ranch.

"Up the river about a hundred *varas*." [4]

"I see nothing."

"Look once more."

"Does it move?"

"Judge for yourself. But first you need to find it."

I looked hard and at last made out the brown spot among the oaks. "It is a cow grazing," I said.

"There are two, and one is not a cow but a yearling fawn. What do you hear?"

"The stream."

"What else?"

"A crow somewhere."

"Is that all?"

"Yes."

"Listen."

"A woodpecker behind us."

"Yes. And what else do you hear?"

"Nothing."

"Besides the stream and the surf at the mouth of the river and gulls fishing?"

"You have good ears."

"And you will have them someday."

"Never so good as yours."

"Better. *Mucho más.*" [5]

Don Saturnino was silent for a while. Then he said, "Tomorrow is Carlos's birthday. He would have been eighteen had he lived."

---

[4] **varas** (vah'rahs). A *vara* is a unit of measure that approximates a yard.
[5] **Mucho más** (moo'choh mahs): Much better.

"He would have liked these journeys," I answered.

"Perhaps. Perhaps not. Who knows? It is sufficient that you like them. You do like them, Carlota?"

"Everything, Father," I said. "Everything."

Here we sat for an hour, to make sure that we had not been followed.

When the sun was overhead, we crawled down from the pinnacle. We reached the Blue Beach and took off our boots and stepped out into the middle of the stream. We made our way for a distance of some fifty paces, leaving no tracks behind us. A clump of willows grew amidst a pile of driftwood and boulders at this place. Here the river divided and ran in two smaller streams on both sides of the willows.

The boulders could not be seen at high tide. But the tide was low now and they stuck up in two crescents, facing each other and leaving a clear space between them. The water was cold, both the sea water that met the river at this point and likewise the river water itself.

Stripped to my singlet, I splashed water on my legs, on my arms and chest. I had found that the best way to approach cold water was by small shivers, suffered one at a time.

Throwing out my arms, I took in a great gulp of air, held it for a minute, counting each second. Then I let out all the air in a quick whoosh.

Then I raised my arms again and took in a greater gulp.

This air I held for two minutes, still counting the seconds in my mind — one second, two seconds, and so forth. I repeated this three times. The third time I counted up to four minutes.

It had taken me two years to build up to where I could hold my breath for this length of time. My father had heard of pearl divers in La Paz who could hold their breath for five minutes and even longer. I had tried this but had fainted.

Carefully we stepped into the wide pool between the two crescents of stone, beneath the canopy of willows. We inched our way to the center of the pool, cautious not to rile the sand.

As my foot touched a smooth slab of stone, I stooped down, lifted it with much care, and set it to one side. Beneath it was a rock-lined hole filled with water, the size of my body and twice its height.

At the bottom of this hole was something that, when we first saw it, seemed to be the trunk of a tree — a tree washed down from the mountains. Undoubtedly, it once had risen above the water, but over the years floods had worn it away to a worm-eaten stump.

It had been the mainmast of a ship, which my father said was some seventy feet in length. It had the wide beam, the high stern, of the galleons that two centuries before had sailed the seas between China and the coast of California and Mexico.

These ships, my father said, came on favorable winds and currents to northern California, then along the coast south to the ports of San Blas and Acapulco (ah'kuh-pool'ko). They carried great treasures from the Indies, these galleons, so great that they became the prey of American and English pirates.

But when it was once inside, something happened to the ship and it never returned to the sea."

Hidden in the galleon's hold, near the stump of the mainmast, were two chests filled with coins. The coins were of pure gold. They showed three castles and the two flying doves that meant they had been struck in the mint at Lima (lee'muh), Peru. The date marked upon each coin that we carried away on the trips we had made was the year of Our Lord 1612.

The two chests — each made of hard wood banded with iron straps and sealed with a hasp that had rusted and fallen off — were well beneath the surface of the water, whether at low tide or in the summer, when the stream ran low. This was fortunate, for had the chests been exposed, some passing Indian or vaquero would have discovered them.

There were many things to do before the chests could be reached. Usually it took me half a day to bring up a pouch of coins from the sunken ship.

The place where I dove, which was surrounded by jagged rocks and driftwood, was too narrow for my father. He had tried to squeeze through when we first discovered the galleon, but partway down he got stuck and I had to pull him back. It was my task, therefore, to go into the cavelike hole. My father

Some of these treasure ships had been captured. On some, their crews had died of scurvy. Others had run aground through careless navigation. Others were driven ashore by storms. Still others had sought refuge from their pursuers by hiding in lagoons such as the one at Blue Beach.

"This must have been a large lagoon at one time," my father said when we first discovered the galleon. "A good place to hide a ship.

stood beside it and helped me to go down and to come up.

I buckled a strong belt around my waist and to it tied a riata[6] that was ten *varas* long and stout enough to hold a stallion. I fastened my knife to my wrist — a two-edged blade made especially for me by our blacksmith — to protect myself against spiny rays and the big eels that could sting you to death. In the many dives I had made, I never had seen a shark.

Taking three deep breaths, I prepared to let myself down into the hole. In one hand I held a sink-stone, heavy enough to weigh me down. I let out all the air in my chest, took a deep breath, and held it. Then I began the descent.

The sink-stone would have taken me down fast, but the edges of the rocky hole were sharp. I let myself down carefully, one handhold at a time. It took me about a minute to reach the rotted deck where the chests lay. I now had two minutes to pry the coins loose and carry them to the surface. We had tried putting the coins in a leather sack and hoisting them to the surface. But we had trouble with this because of the currents that swept around the wreck.

The coins lay in a mass, stuck together, lapping over each other and solid as rock. They looked,

[6] **riata** (ree-ah′tuh), a long rope or leather thong.

when I first saw them, like something left on the stove too long. I always expected to find them gone, but now as I walked toward the chests, with the stone holding me down, I saw that they were still there. No one had come upon them during the seven months since our last visit.

The first time I had dived and brought up a handful of coins, I said to my father that we should empty both the chests and take the coins home.

"Then everyone would talk," Don Saturnino said. "As soon as they saw the gold coins the news would spread the length of California."

"We don't need to tell anyone. I can hide them in my chest at home."

"The news would fly out before the sun set. At the ranch there are many eyes."

I still thought it was a better idea to empty the chests before someone else did, but I could see that my father enjoyed these days, when the two of us went to the Blue Beach, so I said no more.

The sun was overhead and its rays slanted down through the narrow crevice. There were many pieces of debris on the deck and I had to step carefully. With my knife I pried loose a handful of coins. They were of a dark green color and speckled here and there with small barnacles. I set the coins aside.

My lungs were beginning to hurt, but I had not felt the tug of the riata yet, the signal from my father that I had been down three minutes. I pried loose a second handful and put my knife away. Before the tug came I dropped my sink-stone and took up the coins. Gold is very heavy, much heavier than stones of the same size.

Fish were swimming around me as I went up through the hole of rocks and tree trunks, but I saw no sting rays or eels. I did see a shark lying back on a ledge, but he was small and gray, a sandshark, which is not dangerous.

On my third trip down, I hauled up about the same number of coins as the other times. The pouch we had brought was now full. I asked my father if we had enough.

"Are you tired?" he said.

"Yes, a little."

"Can you go down again?"

"Yes."

"Then go."

I dived twice more. It was on the last dive that I had the trouble. The tug on the riata had not come, but I was tired, so I started away from the chest with one handful of coins. Close to the chests, between them and the hole, I had noticed what seemed to be two pieces of timber covered with barnacles. They looked as if they might be part of a third and larger chest.

I still held my knife and I thrust it at a place where the two gray timbers seemed to join. It was possible that I had found another chest filled with coins.

As the knife touched them, the two timbers moved a little. Instantly, I felt pressure upon my wrist. I drew back the hand that held the knife. Rather, I tried to draw it back, but it would not move. The tide had shifted the timbers somehow and I was caught. So I thought.

I felt a tug upon the riata fastened to my waist. It was the signal from my father to come to the surface. I answered him with two quick tugs of the leather rope.

Now I felt a hot pain run up my arm. I tried to open my fingers, to drop the knife, but my hand was numb. Then as I stared down into the murky water I saw a slight movement where my hand was caught. At the same moment I saw a flash of pink, a long fleshy tongue sliding along my wrist.

I had never seen a burro clam, but I had heard the tales about them, for there were many on our coast. Attached to rocks or timbers, they grew to half the height of a man, these gray, silent monsters. Many unwary fishermen had lost their lives in the burros' jaws.

The pain in my arm was not so great now as the hot pains in my chest. I gave a long, hard tug on the riata to let my father know that I

was in trouble. Again I saw a flash of pink as the burro opened its lips a little, and the fat tongue slid back and forth.

I dropped the coins I held in my other hand. The burro had closed once more on my wrist. But shortly it began to open again, and I felt a sucking pressure, as if the jaws were trying to draw me inside the giant maw.

Putting my knees against the rough bulge of the shell, as the jaws opened and then began to close, I jerked with all my strength. I fell slowly backward upon the ship's deck. My hand was free. With what breath I had I moved toward the hole. I saw the sun shining above and climbed toward it. The next thing I saw was my father's face and I was lying on the river's sandy bank. He took my knife in his hand.

After I told him what had happened, my father said, "The knife saved your life. The burro clamped down upon it. See the mark here. The steel blade kept its jaws open. Enough to let you wrench yourself free."

He pulled me to my feet and I put on my leather pants and coat.

"Here," he said, passing the reins of his bay gelding to me, "ride Santana. He goes gentler than Tiburón."

"I'll ride my own horse," I said.

"Good, if you wish it."

"I wish it," I said, knowing that

he didn't want me to say that my hand was numb.

"Does the hand hurt?"

"No."

"Some?"

"No."

"You were very brave," he said.

My father wanted me to be braver than I was. I wanted to say I was scared, both when the burro had hold of me and now, at this moment, but I didn't because he expected me to be as brave as Carlos.

It was at times like this that I was angry at my father and at my dead brother, too.

"It was good fortune," I said.

"Fortune and bravery often go together," Don Saturnino said. "If you do not hurt, let us go."

You may wish to read the book **Carlota,** *in which "Blue Beach" appears, to find out how courageous Carlota proves herself to be.*

DISCUSSION

1. Do you believe that Carlota was a person who enjoyed meeting challenges? Give details from the story to support your answer.

2. Where and when did the story take place? How was Carlota's behavior scandalous for a girl her age living at the time?

3. What was Carlota's main reason for behaving as she did?

4. What secret had Carlota and her father kept for two years? Why did they take special precautions during their journey to the Blue Beach?

5. What evidence is there in the story that Don Saturnino took pride in Carlota's achievements? Why, do you think, did he like to test her eyesight and hearing?

6. Why did galleons like the one found by Don Saturnino and Carlota often become the prey of American and English pirates? What treasure did Carlota discover in the galleon's hold?

7. Why did Carlota, rather than her father, have to do the diving? What kind of warning system was devised for Carlota's dives? Do you think that the system was reliable? Why or why not?

8. How long had it taken Carlota to develop her diving ability? Why was precise timing of such importance in each dive for the coins?

9. What part did good luck, or good fortune, play in Carlota's escape from the burro clam? What do you think Don Saturnino meant when he said, "Fortune and bravery often go together"? Would you agree or disagree? Give reasons for your answer.

10. What qualities of character did Carlota show in the episodes involving her survey of the trails, her escape from the burro clam, and her decision to ride back on her own horse?

11. At the end of the story, why did Carlota avoid telling her father that she was hurt and frightened? Do you agree with her father's idea that a brave person does not openly express feelings of pain or fear? Give reasons for your answer.

12. How do you know that at times Carlota resented having her father treat her as if she were his lost son, Carlos? Do you think that Carlota's resentment was justified? Tell why you think as you do.

AUTHOR

Scott O'Dell's first book for young people, *Island of the Blue Dolphins,* won the Newbery Medal, and his other books have received many different awards and honors. Mr. O'Dell was the first American to win the Hans Christian Andersen Medal, the highest international recognition for a body of work by an author of books for young people. In 1978 he received the Regina Medal from the Catholic Library Association for "continued distinguished contribution to children's literature."

Mr. O'Dell was born in Los Angeles, California. He grew up in that area, "never far from the sound of the sea," and he says that is why the sound of the sea is in his books. He attended universities in California, Wisconsin, and Italy and worked in the motion-picture industry and as a book editor for a Los Angeles newspaper before he began to devote his time to writing books.

The story you have just read is from his book *Carlota.* Other books of his that you may enjoy are *The Cruise of the Arctic Star, The 290,* and *The Dark Canoe.*

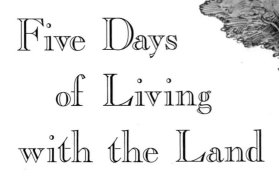

Five Days of Living with the Land

by SARAH BROWN

Have you ever raced rabbits across a field? Picked daisies and then put them in a canteen vase on your table — a rock? Eaten grasshoppers? I have!

In many ways, I have had a very comfortable life. My main challenge has been the battle for grades in school. I have been protected, in a way, and have never really had to rely on my own abilities — in fact, I have been unsure just what my abilities were.

Many of my happiest hours have been spent watching animals, identifying plants, walking in the woods, and exploring the fields and orchards of my grandparents' farm. I am a romantic and have devoured many books about survival in the woods, living off the land, and the idealism of it all. And I've dreamed and hoped.

This past summer, my dreams materialized. With the invaluable help of Dan DeWolf — naturalist, teacher, and friend — I finally felt ready to take the big step: to take only essentials into a "wild" area away from human contact and to live off the land or, in better words, to live *with* the land.

This, then, is an account of my five days (and four long nights) on my own in the woods. This experience gave me not only confidence in my own capabilities but also time to develop a philosophy of life and to find a peace within myself.

The area I chose for my "survival week" was the Town Forest and land belonging to Dan DeWolf in Holliston, Massachusetts. This totaled about two hundred acres of virtually uninhabited land. The woods were logged in the mid-1930's, so the trees are relatively young. They are mainly red and white oak, and hickory. There are also swamps, with maple trees dominant, and some deserted overgrown farmlands, where sassafras, cedar, birch, and white pine have grown up.

23

A few ground rules were laid out at the beginning of the week. I had with me Nick, Dan DeWolf's huge Great Dane. He was to be with me at all times, and if I lost him, I was to come out of the woods immediately.

I also left daily notes on a signpost by the trail. Dan picked these up as indications of my safety.

I obtained all water from an old well, probably once belonging to a farm that has since disappeared. This water was tested before I used it.

Generally, I was more cautious about everything than I usually am.

MONDAY, AUGUST 10

I am in the woods!

It's impossible for me to explain how much those words mean and how much lies behind them. It's been a long road that's led me here — but I *am* here, and I'm going to make it!

At 8:30 this morning, it was as though I'd never seen any of this — everything seemed totally unfamiliar. It was a scary feeling! But my camp is set up, lunch is eaten, and supper is all ready to be cooked. Already I feel sure about myself in a way I never have before! All that I have to rely on this week is myself — success or failure is dependent only on my own capabilities. I've never been in a position like this before — and that's a big part of why I'm here. I have some idea of just what it is that makes me Sarah Brown instead of someone else, and I have some idea of what Sarah Brown can do — but I need to know better before I can assert myself as an individual. These woods are my path to that knowledge of myself.

I've got my mosquito netting hung, my sleeping bag unrolled, a fire ring built, canteens filled — everything's neat and convenient. I'm on top of a small slope that ends in a swamp. There are several large, prominent rocks around. The trees are young and scattered. It's a pretty spot.

Setting up took such a short time that, since I was feeling ambitious, I decided to go fishing. So Nick and I walked about two miles to Weston Pond.

Although I am not good at fishing, with a grub out of a log and a lot of luck, I finally pulled in a sunfish. I did a miserable job of cleaning it, and then Nick and I walked back.

The sunfish was delicious, stuck on a stick and cooked right in the fire, but I don't know if it was really worth the trouble.

I just got back from the field down the road, where I've been collecting my supper. I've got a bunch of day-lily tubers, some small, rather wormy apples, and a lot of blueberries. The tubers are good raw, but I'm going to try boiling them.

7:00 P.M.   I have such an incredible feeling of peace inside of me!

B.T.S.   I don't feel like writing any more about food, but the tubers were

(*By The* good boiled in salted water.

Sun!)   Nick is a comfortable pillow — and I'm tired — so good night.

25

6:30 A.M.   There were no stars last night (I know because I was awake most of it!), and the sky is very gray this morning. I'm afraid it's going to rain — but that's not going to stop me. I will let it be a challenge!

I'd better get going.

12:30 P.M.   I've won! It's raining hard — and I'm warm and dry — and proud.

I was really panicked this morning, but I explored around for shelter and found a beautiful place. I'm about twenty-five yards away from where I was before. There's a boulder set into the side of the hill so that one side of it is buried. The boulder has split in half, forming a crack between the halves that's about eight feet long, five feet deep, and three and one-half feet wide — my house.

I placed several long sticks across the top of the crack and draped my poncho and ground cloth across the boulder halves. With the sides held down by stones, it makes a very secure shelter. The sleeping bag is spread on the floor, my pack is leaning against a wall, and Nick is lying at the opening. Everything is dry and comfortable, and I'm really pretty proud of myself.

Oh — I also made a fast trip to the field, and I have day-lily tubers, sheep sorrel, blueberries, apples, and wintergreen as well as water. What else could I possibly want?

I've also got a lot of time to use — and a lot of thinking and writing to fill it with.

It's amazing how much adjusting I've had to do just in a day and a half. I've changed my eating habits — I now eat whenever I find food, although I try to collect for one big meal a day. I've changed my sight. I'm looking more carefully and seeing more things than I ever have before. In fact, all my senses are sharpening and adjusting to quiet sounds and subtle smells and a much more sensual atmosphere than my usual one. It's an exciting thing!

These are our roots — the woods, the smell and feel of the earth, the closeness of animals. They are basic to us all. And if you look back at the common bases and at the fact that it takes differences to make a place livable, then it seems as though things should or could be so simple — it seems as though treating another human being as a *person* should be one of the easiest things in the world. But it's not, and I don't know why. Knowing this, though, I can try!

Nick is asleep with his head on my knees. What a beautiful dog he is! And also what a good friend! I'm going to miss him a lot. I talk to him, I sing to him, I hug him, I get protection and companionship from him — he's better than a person! I've never really liked a dog before — but then, Nick is a lot more than a dog.

I'm going to take a walk!

6:00 P.M.   It's still raining — even harder, as a matter of fact. But it's nice. I had a beautiful walk — everything was shiny and clean. I sang at the top of my lungs and got soaking wet — and fantastically happy!

I came back here and changed into my dry set of clothes. I'll have to string up a clothesline tomorrow.

I am very tired. I think I'll eat now and then go to bed.

WEDNESDAY, AUGUST 12

9:00 A.M.   I feel deliciously good! I slept deeply and easily last night — I was warm, dry, and comfortable, in spite of the rain.

So, I'm rested, not hungry, and it's a bright, sunny day.

I had a visitor! Dan showed up early this morning to see if I had survived the rain. I was annoyed at first — I had given him strict orders to stay away, and besides, why shouldn't I have survived? But I can't stay mad at him, so I showed him my shelter — very proudly I must say — and asked him to leave off a book or two at the signpost, and then he left.

I realized after he had gone that I honestly don't miss people at all.

I've got rope strung up between two trees, and my poncho and ground cloth and clothes are waving in the breeze. My mosquito netting is also hanging up to dry, so it's sort of hard to walk around without bumping into something. The sun and breeze are warm, though, so things shouldn't take long to dry.

I've got to go collecting.

I'm going to feast tonight. I went over to the field and got baby milkweed pods and leaves, apples, and about two dozen grasshoppers.

Dan did leave a couple of books on the signpost, so I got those, and then I went for water.

I filled all three canteens and picked (and ate) some blueberries and wintergreen on the way back.

I'm not going to eat for the rest of the afternoon — that way I'll be good and hungry tonight.

Here is a fantastic dinner recipe:

1. Boil milkweed pods and leaves in slightly salted water for several minutes; then change the water and boil for several more minutes. Drain.
2. Slice several apples almost all the way through, put honey between the sections, wrap in aluminum foil, and bake in the coals.
3. Place grasshoppers on a stick and hold them in the flames for about a minute, until they're dark brown and crisp. Eat everything but the legs.
4. Add honey to blueberries. Then eat!

You can finish the whole thing off with wintergreen leaves. I'm very full!

I took one of my canteens that had just a little bit of water left in it, propped it up on my table rock, and put my daisies in it. They look nice. It's been a good day.

Good night.

Thursday, August 13

It's a beautiful, lazy sort of day — sunny, with a light breeze. I don't feel like sitting still.

Nick — you and I are going on an expedition!

5:00 P.M.   Nick is flopped over on his side, sound asleep, and I'm going to be the same way very soon. I'm completely worn out.

We walked almost all day. I took my two-quart canteen, some apples, my compass and map, and my plant guide and put them all in my bag, leashed up Nick, and started out at about 6:30 this morning. We walked over to the area cut for power lines and started down it. It's pretty easy walking, really. It would have been easier if I hadn't had to hang on to Nick, but I didn't quite dare to let him go. If he left me, that would be the end.

I ate blueberries as we went, saw a snake, and just missed stepping into a yellow jacket nest. There was a well-worn path off to the side of the cut, and we walked down that to an old railroad bed, no longer used. We walked down that for a way, I picked some dandelions for Nick's collar and my hair, and I took some greens to eat tonight.

It was harder walking back, because it was all uphill. We stopped at the well and both took long drinks. Then we made a quick trip to the field for sorrel. I also found some thistles over in the far corner, so I'll eat well tonight.

11:00 P.M.   I don't know why I awoke, but I can't fall asleep again. The stars are very bright tonight. Stars are happy things — winking and dancing in the sky and getting tangled up in the trees. They're friendly companions, too, at times like this.

It's funny about the night — the darkness used to be a hiding place for strange, threatening sounds. My first night here was really frightening. But now the night is like a blanket of peace — even more silent than the day. But it's not a resting peace — I'm very much aware now that life continues at night, because I'm in the middle of it. Flying squirrels glide and play in the trees; white-footed mice scamper through the leaves looking for seeds; owls slip silently through the shadows, listening for the rustle of leaves that means dinner. The woods are alive and wonderful at night.

Tomorrow is it — my last day. I don't want it to end! I don't even want to think about it. I now have an awareness of myself and of my relationship to the world — and I want to live alone with that awareness for a while longer and expand it. That's impossible now, I suppose, but I'll be back.

FRIDAY, AUGUST 14

8:00 A.M.   I've packed everything up already, so I have the rest of the day free. Nick is whining longingly — he wants to go walking.

I'm going to live in the woods someday — build a house away from roads and people. I belong with trees and animals much more than I do with apartments and big crowds.

I've discovered and learned so much that I can't put into words! I have a new reverence and feeling and desire for life — and I have found out what peace is. Those are pretty big things — and you can't explain or describe them.

3:30 P.M.   I'm back at my camp. I fell asleep on Scout Hill, and when Nick woke me up, we went over to the field for a lunch of blackberries, clover, and sorrel. Then we sat in the sun, and I had a long talk with Nick. He looked sad, as though he knew it was ending.

It's time for us to go in now, I think, if my sun reading is any good. I'll be back — there's no way I could stay away. This is life.

Right, Nick?

DISCUSSION

1. Do you think you might like to try camping alone in the woods as Sarah did? Why or why not?
2. What ground rules were laid out for Sarah during her stay in the woods? Why was it important that she follow the rules?
3. Where did Sarah spend her survival week? Judging by Sarah's description, was the area well chosen for her experiment? Give reasons for your answer.

4. When did Sarah's experiment take place? Why would that be the best time of year in which to try living off the land?

5. According to Sarah's journal notes, what was her main reason for wanting to spend a week alone in the woods?

6. In your opinion, would you say Sarah was well prepared to face the challenge of living alone in the woods for five days? Give reasons to support your answer.

7. At the beginning of her journal, Sarah says, "I'm going to make it!" What does this statement tell you about her? What other characteristics did Sarah possess that enabled her to survive in the woods alone?

8. In what ways did Sarah feel that her stay in the woods was a valuable personal experience?

9. How did Sarah explain the change in her attitude toward night in her journal entry for August 13? To what did she compare each of the following things: night, stars?

10. Why do you think Sarah kept a daily journal? What are some of the advantages of keeping a journal or diary as Sarah did?

AUTHOR

Sarah Brown was a fifteen-year-old high school junior in Newton, Massachusetts, when she wrote *Five Days of Living with the Land,* a record of her survival experiences in the woods. Today she lives with her husband in Southington, Connecticut, on the family farm mentioned in the journal you have just read. She continues to write and spend time outdoors. Her hobbies also include cross-country skiing, reading, making and listening to music, and playing with her animals, a cat and a boa constrictor.

To Look at Any Thing

by JOHN MOFFITT

To look at any thing,
If you would know that thing,
You must look at it long:
To look at this green and say
"I have seen spring in these
Woods," will not do — you must
Be the thing you see:
You must be the dark snakes of
Stems and ferny plumes of leaves,
You must enter in
To the small silences between
The leaves,
You must take your time
And touch the very peace
They issue from.

Up
Close
and Personal

As the photo editor of a national magazine, I review thousands of photographs each week. I've noticed that as scientists learn more and more about everyday animal behavior, nature photographers, too, are focusing on the subtler aspects of life in the wild. These are quiet moments most of us are never privileged to see: two Kodiak bears in Alaska, languorously waiting for salmon to swim downstream; a female mallard duck in the split-second act of shaking water from her head; a bull caribou draped with underbrush. Although such photos may not be as sensational as action shots or as dramatic as close-ups, their impact is every bit as great. A number of these "up close" and personal moments are presented here together with the photographers' comments on how their photos came to be.

KAREN ALTPETER ZOGG

"For me the most exciting aspect of wildlife photography is the stalk, and I'd rather spend all my time moving in quietly toward some animal than sitting in a blind. To photograph this mallard, I spent an entire morning edging closer to her and her mate at their nesting site on Vancouver Island."

STEPHEN J. KRASEMANN

"Thanks to a record-breaking heat wave, these two Alaskan brown bears didn't seem bothered at all by my presence only forty feet behind them on the open ground next to this McNeil River tributary. Usually when the salmon are running, the bears are quite active catching and eating them. But these two-and-one-half-year-old cubs spent much of the day just lying low."

KATHY BUSHUE

"It may sound dull to spend seven hours a day in a burlap blind twenty feet from a hole in the ground in an Oregon farmer's field. But once these young burrowing owls began joining their parents outside the nest, it became one of the most fascinating field studies I've made. I photographed the birds, off and on, for two months."

DAN DAVIDSON

"No, this bull caribou wasn't trying to camouflage itself. It was using the underbrush to rub the velvet off its antlers just prior to the mating season. I spotted the animal from a road in McKinley National Park in late September and spent the next hour getting close enough to photograph it."

HELEN RHODE

SKILL

Tables

Many kinds of information can be logically organized and clearly presented in the form of a table. In social studies and in science, information that contains numerous facts and figures is easier to understand in a table than it would be in written form. Bus schedules and box scores are tables that enable readers to locate information quickly. Knowing how to read tables is not only helpful in your studies but also useful in your daily life.

The information in a table is arranged in columns and rows that make it easy to read. The caption, or title, gives the subject of the information, or data, being presented. The headings for the columns and rows give more specific information about the data shown. When a chapter or an article contains several tables, they are usually numbered for convenient reference.

Steps in Reading a Table

First read the caption to determine what the table is about. Table 1 on the next page presents information about some common metric measurements. Notice the headings at the top of the columns. The first column tells the types of metric measurements that are included. Each of the other columns has a heading that tells what information is included to help you understand the metric measures of length, volume, and mass. For example, the third column in the table gives the symbol for each of the metric units. The rows in the table give specific information about the units of measure listed under the heading *Unit.*

After you have looked at the table to find out how it is organized, you will be ready to use it to locate specific information. Suppose you were interested in learning the symbols for the metric volume units. You would look quickly down the first column until you found *Volume.* Then you would move to the second column to the word *milliliter.* By continuing across the row to the third column, headed *Symbol,* you would locate the symbol for a milliliter, *ml.* Follow the same procedure now to find the symbol for a liter.

TABLE 1. **Some Common Metric Measurements**				
Types	Unit	Symbol	Equals	About the same as
Length	millimeter	mm	$\frac{1}{1000}$ m	the thickness of a dime
	centimeter	cm	$\frac{1}{100}$ m	the thickness of a slice of bread
	meter	m		the height of a teacher's desk
	kilometer	km	1000m	the distance you can walk in about 12 minutes
Volume	milliliter	ml	$\frac{1}{1000}$ l	the volume of two nickels
	liter	l		the volume of four medium-sized glasses of water
Mass (weight)	gram	g		the mass of two raisins
	kilogram	kg	1000 g	the mass of a 500-page book

Reading a Table Showing Scientific Information

Tables are especially effective in presenting scientific information, which often contains many facts and figures for study and comparison. For example, as you can see from the caption, Table 2 on page 42 provides information about the solar system. Notice that the headings indicate exactly what information about the solar system is given in the table. In reading a table, you should be sure to note any terms, such as units of measure or time, given in the headings. In Table 2, it is important to note that time is given in Earth units and distance is in kilometers.

If you want information about a single planet, such as Earth, you simply locate the planet in the left column and read across the row. However, you can also use a table to compare and contrast information easily. Suppose you wanted to know which planet is the largest. You would locate the column headed *Diameter* and scan it to find the largest number. After locating 141,920, you would look to the left and see that it is in the row for Jupiter. Which planet is the smallest? Notice that the exact size of Pluto is uncertain, as indicated by the question mark following its diameter.

It is usually helpful to determine how the information in a table is arranged. For instance, the planets in Table 2 could have been arranged alphabetically or by size. In this table, however, they are arranged in order of their average distance from the sun, beginning with Mercury, which is nearest to the sun, and ending with Pluto.

TABLE 2. **The Solar System**					
Planet	Diameter (km)	Rotation period (Earth units)	Length of year (Earth units)	Average distance from sun (km)	Number of moons
Mercury	4,848	59 days (approx.)	88.0 days	57,572,800	0
Venus	12,080	249 days (approx.)	224.7 days	107,576,000	0
Earth	12,683	23.9 hours	365.3 days	148,729,600	1
Mars	6,752	24.6 hours	687.0 days	226,619,200	2
Jupiter	141,920	9.8 hours	11.9 years	773,944,000	13
Saturn	120,160	10.2 hours	29.5 years	1,424,963,200	10
Uranus	46,400	10.8 hours	84.0 years	2,843,233,600	5
Neptune	44,800	15 hours	164.8 years	4,479,096,000	2
Pluto	5,760?	6.4 days	248.4 years	5,847,051,200	0

Reading a Distance Table

Table 3 shows the airline distances between various cities of the world. Notice that in this type of table, the cities listed alphabetically as headings in the first column are also listed alphabetically as headings for the other columns. To find the distance between any two cities listed on the table, you must locate the name of one city in the first column and the name of the other city among the column headings. Then you read across the row and down the column and find the distance at the point where the row and the column for the two cities meet. It doesn't matter which of the two cities you work from in the first column as long as you locate the second city in the headings.

When you read a table, be sure to note any explanations that are given. In a distance table, for example, it is important to know whether the distances shown are in miles or kilometers. Notice in Table 3 that air distances are given in statute, or standard, miles.

Use Table 3 now to determine the distance by air between Chicago and Honolulu.

| TABLE 3. **Airline Distance Table** | | | | | | | | | |
| Airline Distances Between Selected Cities of the World | | | | | | | | | |
CITY	BANGKOK	BERLIN	CAIRO	CAPETOWN	CARACAS	CHICAGO	HONG KONG	HONOLULU	LONDON
BANGKOK	—	5,352	4,523	6,300	10,555	8,570	1,077	6,609	5,944
BERLIN	5,352	—	1,797	5,961	5,238	4,414	5,443	7,320	583
CAIRO	4,523	1,797	—	4,480	6,342	6,141	5,066	8,848	2,185
CAPETOWN	6,300	5,961	4,480	—	6,366	8,491	7,376	11,535	5,989
CARACAS	10,555	5,238	6,342	6,366	—	2,495	10,165	6,021	4,655
CHICAGO	8,570	4,414	6,141	8,491	2,495	—	7,797	4,256	3,958
HONG KONG	1,077	5,443	5,066	7,376	10,165	7,797	—	5,556	5,990
HONOLULU	6,609	7,320	8,848	11,535	6,021	4,256	5,556	—	7,240
LONDON	5,944	583	2,185	5,989	4,655	3,958	5,990	7,240	—

Source: Defense Mapping Agency Aerospace Center (statute miles)

Reading a Schedule

A schedule, like a distance table, usually appears without accompanying text. Schedules include lists of prices, programs of events, and bus and train timetables. Table 4 on page 44 is a schedule that shows the times of bus arrivals and departures between St. Louis, Missouri, and San Antonio, Texas.

TABLE 4. St. Louis—San Antonio Bus Service

READ DOWN			ST. LOUIS–SAN ANTONIO		READ UP		
6 20	**1 55**	**8 05**	Lv ▲ ST. LOUIS, MO. Ar	8 20	**12 10**	**7 30**
•**12 05**	•**8 35**	× 1 15	Ar ▲ SPRINGFIELD Lv	3 05	6 35	**1 45**
12 50	**10 00**	1 25	Lv SPRINGFIELD Ar	× 2 55	•5 50	•**12 50**
2 35	**11 35**	3 10	Lv Joplin Ar	1 20	↑	11 05
•**5 20**	× 1 55	•5 45	Ar ▲ TULSA, OKLA. Lv	**11 00**	2 25	8 15
6 00	2 05	6 20	Lv TULSA Ar	×**10 30**	× 1 55	•7 30
↓	↓	8 50	Lv Oklahoma City Ar	**7 40**	↑	↑
6 50	↓		Lv Okmulgee Ar	↑	1 05	6 40
11 00	6 15		Lv Denison, Tex. Ar		**9 35**	3 25
11 25	6 40	↓	Lv Sherman Ar		**9 10**	3 00
× 1 00	•8 30	•**12 50**	Ar DALLAS Lv	**3 40**	7 35	1 50
1 50	10 45	**2 05**	Lv DALLAS Ar	•**2 45**	•**6 35**	× 12 50
3 40	**12 50**	**4 00**	Lv ▲ Waco Ar	**12 35**	**5 15**	↑
↓	**1 55**	**4 55**	Lv Temple Ar	11 15	**4 00**	
↓	**2 15**	**5 20**	Lv Belton Ar	10 50	**3 40**	↑
6 05	**3 45**	**6 05**	Lv ▲ Austin Ar	9 10	**2 30**	**8 45**
7 55	**5 40**	**8 00**	Ar ▲ SAN ANTONIO Lv	7 15	**12 55**	**7 00**

REFERENCE MARKS
A.M. Lightface type   **P.M. Boldface type**
All buses run daily unless otherwise indicated.
▲ Full service agency handling tickets, baggage, and express
• Meal stop
× Rest stop

44

Abbreviations, varied type, and symbols are usually used in schedules to make it possible to include a large amount of information. Notice in the center column of Table 4 that the names of states are abbreviated and that each abbreviation appears only once. Look at the names in the first five rows of the column. You can see that the first and fourth cities listed, St. Louis and Tulsa, are followed by abbreviated state names. The fact that no abbreviation follows the names *Springfield* and *Joplin* tells you that those cities, like St. Louis, are in Missouri. How many different Texas cities and towns are listed?

Look at the information given in the section called *Reference Marks* at the bottom of the table. Are morning or afternoon times shown in lightface type in the table? In reading a timetable, it is important to remember that morning, or A.M., hours are the hours between midnight and noon and that afternoon, or P.M., hours are those between noon and midnight.

It is also important in reading a timetable to know whether to read up or down the columns. In Table 4, you can see that there are arrows as well as the column headings to guide you. If you wanted to check the schedule from Dallas to Tulsa, would you read up or down the table? Can you figure out the second purpose of the arrows? You're right if you said that the arrows show the cities and towns at which the buses do *not* stop. For instance, the 6:20 A.M. bus from St. Louis does not stop at Oklahoma City.

Look for the symbols for meal stops and rest stops on the table. Notice that wherever they occur, the name of the city in the center column is repeated. Suppose you were taking the 12:55 P.M. bus from San Antonio to St. Louis. You would have had lunch before boarding the bus. Between 6:35 and 7:35 P.M. you would have your evening meal in Dallas. At the time of the rest stop in Tulsa, 1:55 A.M., you would probably be fast asleep, but you would want to be awake for breakfast in Springfield between 5:50 and 6:35 A.M. You would have lunch in St. Louis sometime after the bus arrived there at 12:10 in the afternoon.

If you lived in Austin and needed to arrive in St. Louis on a Tuesday morning shortly before 9:00 A.M., at what time would your bus leave Austin? How long is the bus trip between Oklahoma City and Dallas? If you were going from Okmulgee to Austin, what time would you arrive in Austin?

TABLE 5. **Tides**				
		MORNING (A.M.)		AFTERNOON (P.M.)	
Nov.	High	Low	High	Low
Wednesday 1	7:30	1:15	7:53	1:44
Thursday 2	8:21	2:06	8:48	2:38
Friday 3	9:06	2:53	9:30	3:21
Saturday 4	9:43	3:34	10:11	4:04
Sunday 5	10:21	4:11	10:50	4:43
Monday 6	10:53	4:46	11:25	5:16
Tuesday 7	11:28	5:19	—	5:52
Wednesday 8	12:02	5:52	12:02	6:25
Thursday 9	12:37	6:27	12:37	7:06
Friday 10	1:15	7:06	1:19	7:45
Saturday 11	1:54	7:49	2:00	8:27
Sunday 12	2:41	8:34	2:49	9:18
Monday 13	3:31	9:31	3:40	10:09
Tuesday 14	4:26	10:27	4:35	11:00

Reading a Specialized Table

Table 5 above is another example of a table that would be used alone rather than with accompanying text. This table, like Table 4, has a specific and practical purpose.

Table 5 is a tide table that shows the times of high and low tides at a particular place for a two-week period in November. You can see that there are usually two high and two low tides each day. A tide table is especially useful to people planning recreational activities such as swimming, boating, and surfing and people who earn their living piloting ships, fishing, and digging clams. If you live or spend your vacation near a bay or a tidal river, you probably use a tide table frequently.

You can see in Table 5 that the high and low tides occurring between midnight and noon are shown in the third and fourth columns. The tides occurring between noon and midnight are shown in the last two columns.

Suppose you planned to dig clams on Saturday, November 11. You would want to do your digging in daylight around the time of low tide when there would be no water covering the clam flats. Use Table 5 to decide at what time the clam flats would be most exposed.

If you were going sailing, you would want to sail in daylight and at high tide, when there would be little danger of running aground on a sandbar. At what time on Sunday, November 12, would there be the least chance of running aground?

READING TABLES

On a sheet of paper, copy the number and letter of each question that follows, and then write your answer:
1. According to Table 1,
   a. what metric unit of length is about the same as the distance you can walk in about 12 minutes?
   b. what are the symbols for the two units of metric mass?
   c. what metric unit of volume is about the same as the volume of four medium-sized glasses of water?
2. According to Table 2,
   a. which planet has the longest rotation period in Earth units?
   b. what is the length of Saturn's year in Earth units?
   c. which planet has more moons, Jupiter or Saturn?
3. According to Table 3,
   a. what is the distance by air between London, England, and Berlin, Germany?
   b. which of the cities listed is farthest from Caracas?
   c. is Capetown or Honolulu closer to Bangkok?
4. According to Table 4,
   a. where would you have your first meal stop during the 7:00 P.M. bus trip from San Antonio to St. Louis?
   b. if you wanted to be in Austin early in the evening, at what time would you get a bus in Tulsa?
   c. how long is the bus ride from Sherman to Denison, Texas?
5. According to Table 5,
   a. when is the first low tide on November 9?
   b. what is the time difference between morning high tide and afternoon high tide on November 8?
   c. on how many days do afternoon low tides occur before 6:00 P.M.?

Raymond's Run

by TONI CADE BAMBARA

I don't have much work to do around the house like some girls. My mother does that. And I don't have to earn my pocket money; George runs errands for the big boys and sells Christmas cards. And anything else that's got to get done, my father does. All I have to do in life is mind my brother Raymond, which is enough.

Sometimes I slip and say my little brother Raymond. But as any fool can see, he's much bigger and he's older too. But a lot of people call him my little brother 'cause he needs looking after 'cause he's not quite right. And a lot of smart mouths got lots to say about that, too, especially when George was minding him. But now, if anybody has anything to say to Raymond, anything to say about his big head, they have to come by me. And I don't play the dozens[1] or believe in standing around with somebody in my face doing a lot of talking. I much rather just knock you down and take my chances even if I am a little girl with skinny arms and a squeaky voice, which is how I got the name Squeaky.

And if things get too rough, I run. And as anybody can tell you, I'm the fastest thing on two feet.

There is no track meet that I don't win the first-place medal. I use to win the twenty-yard dash when I was a little kid in kindergarten. Nowadays it's the fifty-yard dash. And tomorrow I am subject to run the quarter-mile relay all by myself and come in first, second, and third. The big kids call me Mercury 'cause I'm the swiftest thing in the neighborhood. Everybody knows that — except two people who know better, my father and me.

He can beat me to Amsterdam Avenue with me having a headstart of two fire hydrants and him running with his hands in his pockets, whistling. But that's private information. 'Cause can you imagine some thirty-five-year-old man stuffing himself into

---

[1] **play the dozens,** make rude remarks about the members of another person's family.

shorts to race little kids? So as far as everyone's concerned, I'm the fastest; and that goes for Gretchen too, who has put out the tale that she is going to win the first-place medal this year. Ridiculous. In the second place, she's got short legs. In the third place, she's got freckles. And in the first place, no one can beat me, and that's all there is to it.

I'm standing on the corner admiring the weather and about to take a stroll down Broadway so I can practice my breathing exercises, and I've got Raymond walking on the inside close to the buildings 'cause he's subject to fits of fantasy and starts thinking he's a circus performer and that the curb is a tightrope strung high in the air. And sometimes after a rain he likes to step down off his tightrope right into the gutter and slosh around getting his shoes and cuffs wet. Then I get hit when I get home. Or sometimes if you don't watch him, he'll dash across traffic to the island in the middle of Broadway and give the pigeons a fit. Then I have to go behind him apologizing to all the people sitting around trying to get some sun and getting all upset with the pigeons fluttering around them, scattering their newspapers and upsetting the wax-paper lunches in their laps. So I keep Raymond on the inside of me, and he plays like he's driving a stagecoach, which is okay by me so long as he doesn't run me over or interrupt my breathing exercises, which I have to do on ac-count of I'm serious about my running and don't care who knows it.

Now, some people like to act like things come easy to them, won't let on that they practice. Not me. I'll high prance down 34th Street like a rodeo pony to keep my knees strong even if it does get my mother uptight, so that she walks ahead like she's not with me, don't know me, is all by herself on a shopping trip, and I am somebody else's crazy child.

Now, you take Cynthia Procter for instance. She's just the opposite. If there's a test tomorrow, she'll say something like, "Oh, I guess I'll play handball this afternoon and watch television tonight," just to let you know she ain't thinking about the test. Or like last week when she won the spelling bee for the millionth time, "A good thing you got *receive*, Squeaky, 'cause I would have got it wrong. I completely forgot about the spelling bee." And she'll clutch the lace on her blouse like it was a narrow escape.

But of course when I pass her house on my early morning trots around the block, she is practicing the scales on the piano over and over and over and over. Then in music class, she always lets herself get bumped around so she falls accidentally on purpose onto the piano stool and is so surprised to find herself sitting there and so decides to try out the ole keys, and what do you know — Chopin's (shoh'pans') waltzes just spring out of her fingertips, and she's the most surprised thing in the world. A regular prodigy. I could kill people like that.

I stay up all night studying the words for the spelling bee. And you can see me any time of day practicing running. I never walk if I can trot, and shame on Raymond if he can't keep up. But of course he does, 'cause if he hangs back, someone's liable to walk up to him and get smart or take his allowance from him or ask him where he got that big head. People are so stupid sometimes.

So I'm strolling down Broadway, breathing out and breathing in on counts of seven, which is my lucky number, and here comes Gretchen and her sidekicks — Mary Louise, who used to be a friend of mine when she first moved to Harlem from Baltimore and got beat up by everybody till I took up for her on account of her mother and my mother used to sing in the same choir when they were young girls, but people ain't grateful, so now she hangs out with the new girl, Gretchen, and talks about me like a dog; and Rosie, who is as fat as I am skinny and has a big mouth where Raymond is concerned and is too stupid to know that there is not a big deal of difference between herself and Raymond and that she can't afford to throw stones. So they are steady coming up Broadway, and I see right away that it's going to be one of those Dodge City scenes 'cause the street ain't that big and they're close to the buildings just as we are. First I think

I'll step into the candy store and look over the new comics and let them pass. But that's chicken, and I've got a reputation to consider. So then I think I'll just walk straight on through them or over them if necessary. But as they get to me, they slow down. I'm ready to fight 'cause, like I said, I don't feature a whole lot of chitchat; I much prefer to just knock you down right from the jump and save everybody a lotta precious time.

"You signing up for the May Day races?" smiles Mary Louise, only it's not a smile at all.

A dumb question like that doesn't deserve an answer. Besides, there's just me and Gretchen standing there really, so no use wasting my breath talking to shadows.

"I don't think you're going to win this time," says Rosie, trying to signify with her hands on her hips, all salty, completely forgetting that I have whupped her many times for less salt than that.

"I always win 'cause I'm the best," I say straight at Gretchen, who is, as far as I'm concerned, the only one talking in this ventriloquist-dummy routine.

Gretchen smiles, but it's not a smile, and I'm thinking that girls never really smile at each other because they don't know how and don't want to know how, and there's probably no one to teach us how 'cause grown-up girls don't know either. Then they all look at Raymond, who

has just stopped his mule team, and they're about to see what kind of trouble they can get into through him.

"What grade you in now, Raymond?" asks Mary Louise.

"You got anything to say to him, say it to me, Mary Louise Williams of Raggedy Town, Baltimore."

"What are you, his mother?" sasses Rosie.

"That's right, Fatso. And the next word out of anybody and I'll be their mother too." So they just stand there, and Gretchen puts her hands on her hips and is about to say something with her freckle-face self but doesn't. Then she walks around me, looking me up and down, but keeps walking up Broadway, and her sidekicks follow her. So me and Raymond smile at each other, and he says "Gidyap" to his team, and I continue with my breathing exercises, strolling down Broadway toward 145th with not a care in the world 'cause I am Miss Quicksilver herself.

I take my time getting to the park on May Day because the track meet is the last thing on the program. The biggest thing on the program is the Maypole dancing, which I can do without, thank you, even if my mother thinks it's a shame I don't take part and act like a girl for a change. You'd think my mother'd be grateful not to have to make me a white organdy dress with a big satin sash and buy me new white baby-doll shoes that can't be taken out of the box till the big day. You'd think she'd be glad her daughter ain't out there prancing around a Maypole, getting the new clothes all dirty and sweaty and trying to act like a fairy or a flower or whatever you're supposed to be when you should be trying to be yourself, whatever that is, which is, as far as I am concerned, a poor black girl who really can't afford to buy shoes and a new dress you only wear once a lifetime 'cause it won't fit next year.

I was once a strawberry in a Hansel and Gretel pageant when I was in nursery school and didn't have no better sense than to dance on tiptoe with my arms in a circle over my head, doing umbrella steps and being a perfect fool just so my mother and father could come dressed up and clap. You'd think they'd know better than to en-courage that kind of nonsense. I am not a strawberry. I do not dance on my toes. I run. That is what I am all about. So I always come late to the May Day program, just in time to get my number pinned on, and I lay in the grass till they announce the fifty-yard dash.

I put Raymond in the little swings, which is a tight squeeze this year and will be impossible next year. Then I look around for Mr. Pearson, who pins the numbers on. I'm really looking for Gretchen, if you want to know the truth, but she's not around. The park is jam-packed. Parents in hats and corsages and breast-pocket handker-chiefs peeking up. Kids in white dresses and light-blue suits. The park-ees unfolding chairs and chasing the rowdy kids from Lenox as if they had no right to be there. The big guys with their caps on backwards, leaning against the fence, swirling the basket-balls on the tips of their fingers, wait-ing for all these crazy people to clear out the park so they can play. Most of the kids in my class are carrying bass drums and glockenspiels and flutes. You'd think they'd put in a few bongos or something for real like that.

Then here comes Mr. Pearson with his clipboard and his cards and pencils and whistles and safety pins and fifty million other things he's always drop-ping all over the place with his clumsy self. He sticks out in a crowd 'cause he's on stilts. We used to call him Jack and the Beanstalk to get him mad. But

I'm the only one that can outrun him and get away, and I'm too grown for that silliness now.

"Well, Squeaky," he says, checking my name off the list and handing me number seven and two pins. And I'm thinking he's got no right to call me Squeaky if I can't call him Beanstalk.

"Hazel Elizabeth Deborah Parker," I correct him and tell him to write it down on his board.

"Well, Hazel Elizabeth Deborah Parker, going to give someone else a break this year?" I squint at him real hard to see if he is seriously thinking I should lose the race on purpose just to give someone else a break.

"Only six girls running this time," he continues, shaking his head sadly like it's my fault all of New York didn't turn out in sneakers. "That new girl should give you a run for your money." He looks around the park for Gretchen like a periscope in a submarine movie. Then he says, "Wouldn't it be a nice gesture if you were . . . to ahhh . . ."

I give him such a look he couldn't finish putting that idea into words. Grownups got a lot of nerve sometimes. I pin number seven to myself and stomp away — I'm so burnt. And I go straight for the track and stretch out on the grass while the band winds up with "Oh, the Monkey Wrapped Its Tail Around the Flagpole," which my teacher calls by some other name. The man on the loudspeaker is calling everyone over to the track, and I'm on my back looking at the sky, trying to pretend I'm in the country, but I can't, because even grass in the city feels hard as sidewalk and there's just no pretending that you are anywhere but in a "concrete jungle."

The twenty-yard dash takes all of two minutes 'cause most of the little kids don't know no better than to run off the track or run the wrong way or run smack into the fence and fall down and cry. One little kid, though, has got the good sense to run straight for the white ribbon up ahead, so he wins. Then the second graders line up for the thirty-yard dash, and I don't even bother to turn my head to watch 'cause Raphael Perez always wins. He wins before he even begins by psyching the runners, telling them they're going to trip on their shoelaces and fall on their faces or lose their shorts or something, which he doesn't really have to do since he is very fast, almost as fast as I am. After that is the forty-yard dash, which I use to run when I was in first grade. Raymond is hollering from the swings 'cause he knows I'm about to do my thing 'cause the man on the loudspeaker has just announced the fifty-yard dash, although he might just as well be giving a recipe for angel food cake 'cause you can hardly make out what he's saying for the static. I get up and slip off my sweat pants, and then I see Gretchen standing at the starting line, kicking her legs out like a pro. Then, as I get into place, I see that ole Raymond is in line on the other side of the fence, bending down, with his fingers on the ground just like he knew what he was doing. I was going to yell at him, but then I didn't. It burns up your energy to holler.

Every time, just before I take off in a race, I always feel like I'm in a dream, the kind of dream you have when you're sick with fever and feel all hot and weightless. I dream I'm flying over a sandy beach in the early morning sun, kissing the leaves of the trees as I fly by. And there's always the smell of apples, just like in the country when I was little and use to think I was a choochoo train, running through the fields of corn and chugging up the hill to the orchard. And all the time I'm dreaming this, I get lighter and lighter until I'm flying over the beach again, getting blown through the sky like a feather that weighs nothing at all. But once I spread my fingers in the dirt and crouch over for "Get on your mark," the dream is gone, and I am solid again and am telling myself, "Squeaky, you must win, you must win; you are the fastest thing in the world; you can even beat your father up Amsterdam if you really try." And then I feel my weight coming back just behind my knees, then down to my feet, then into the earth, and the pistol shot explodes in my blood, and I am off and weightless again, flying past the other runners, my arms pumping up and down, and the whole world is quiet except for the crunch as I zoom over the gravel in the track. I glance to my left, and there

is no one. To the right a blurred Gretchen, who's got her chin jutting out as if it would win the race all by itself. And on the other side of the fence is Raymond with his arms down to his side and the palms tucked up behind him, running in his very own style, and the first time I ever saw that, and I almost stop to watch my brother Raymond on his first run. But the white ribbon is bouncing toward me, and I tear past it, racing into the distance till my feet with a mind of their own start digging up footfuls of dirt and brake me short. Then all the kids

"In second place — Miss Gretchen P. Lewis." And I look over at Gretchen, wondering what the *P* stands for. And I smile. 'Cause she's good, no doubt about it. Maybe she'd like to help me coach Raymond; she obviously is serious about running, as any fool can see. And she nods to congratulate me, and then she smiles. And I smile. We stand there with this big smile of respect between us. It's about as real a smile as girls can do for each other, considering we don't practice real smiling every day, 'cause maybe we are too busy being flowers or fairies or strawberries instead of something honest and worthy of respect . . . you know . . . like being people.

DISCUSSION

1. How do you think Squeaky felt about herself? Would you say that she had too high an opinion of herself? Why do you think as you do?
2. What responsibility did Squeaky's family assign to her? What made Squeaky's assignment difficult?
3. How did Squeaky get her nickname? How appropriate do you think the nickname was for her? What other nicknames can you suggest for her?
4. Squeaky referred to Rosie as standing "with her hands on her hips, all salty." What do you think she meant by *salty?*
5. How did Squeaky think girls usually treat each other? Do you agree with her? Why or why not?
6. Why was the annual May Day track meet so important to Squeaky? How did Squeaky get ready for it?
7. What suggestion do you think Mr. Pearson would have made if Squeaky's look had not stopped him? Why would such a suggestion have been unacceptable to Squeaky?
8. What surprising discovery did Squeaky make about Raymond? How did Raymond's run change Squeaky's attitude toward him?
9. How did Raymond's run change Squeaky's attitude toward herself?
10. After the race, what caused Squeaky's attitude toward Gretchen to change? Do you think that the two girls will become friends? Tell why you think as you do.

AUTHOR

Toni Cade Bambara has had an interesting and varied career since graduating from Queens College. She has been an investigator for the New York State Department of Welfare, a free-lance writer at the Ministry of Museums in Venice, Italy, a director of recreation in the psychiatry department of Metropolitan Hospital in New York City, an associate professor of English at Rutgers, a director of a settlement house, and an artist-in-residence at an arts center in Atlanta, Georgia. Her educational background is also varied. Since graduation from college she has studied at Katherine Dunham Dance Studio, Clark Center of Performing Arts, Studio Museum of Harlem Film Institute, a school of mime in Paris, and the University of Florence in Italy.

"Raymond's Run" is from a collection entitled *Tales and Stories for Black Folks,* which Toni Cade Bambara edited. Other stories and articles she has written have appeared in anthologies and various magazines.

SANCHO

by J. FRANK DOBIE

In the mesquite (mes-keet') and white-brush country southward from San Antonio, Kerr had a little ranch on Esperanza (es'puh-rahn'zuh) Creek. He owned several cow ponies and maybe forty cows and their offspring. Three or four acres of land, fenced in with brush and poles, grew corn, frijoles, watermelons, and calabazas[1] — except when a drought was on.

Kerr's wife was a Mexican named María. They had no children. She was thrifty, cheerful, always making pets of animals.

Late in the winter of 1877, while riding along San Miguel Creek, Kerr found one of his cows dead in a boghole. Beside the cow was a scrawny, mud-plastered, black-and-white paint bull calf less than a week old. It was too weak to trot; perhaps other cattle had saved it

from the coyotes. Kerr pitched his rope over its head, drew it up across the saddle in front of him, carried it home, and turned it over to María.

She had raised many dogie calves, also colts captured from mustang mares. The first thing she did now was to pour milk from a bottle down the orphan's throat. With warm water she washed the caked mud off its body. But hand-raising a calf is no end of trouble.

María called the dogie Sancho, or "Pet." She was especially fond of Sancho, and he grew to be especially fond of her.

She would give him the shucks wrapped around tamales (tah-mah'leez) to hold them together while they are being steamed. Then she began treating him to whole tamales, which are made of ground corn rolled around a core of chopped-up meat. Sancho seemed to like the meat as well as the corn.

---

[1] **calabazas** (kah-lah-bah'thas), squash.

As everybody who has eaten them knows, true Mexican tamales are well seasoned with pepper. Sancho seemed to like the seasoning.

In southern Texas the little *chiltipiquín* (cheel'tee-pee-keen') peppers, red when ripe, grow wild in low, shaded places. Cattle never eat them, leaving them for the wild turkeys, mockingbirds, and blue quail to pick off. In the early fall, wild turkeys used to gorge on them so avidly that their flesh became too peppery for most people to eat. The tamale diet gave Sancho not only a taste but a passion for the little red peppers growing under trees and bushes along Esperanza Creek; in fact, he became a kind of *chiltipiquín* addict. He would hunt for the peppers.

Furthermore, the tamales gave him a tooth for corn on the ear. The summer after he became a yearling, he began breaking through the brush fence that enclosed Kerr's corn patch. A forked stick had to be tied around his neck to prevent his getting through the fence. He had been branded and turned into a steer, but he was as strong as any young bull. Like many other pets, he was something of a nuisance. When he could not steal corn or was not humored with tamales, he was enormously contented with grass, mixed in summertime with the sweet mesquite beans. Now and then María gave him a lump of the brown *piloncillo* (pee-lohn-see'yoh) sugar, from Mexico, that was used throughout the border country.

Every night Sancho came to the ranch pen to sleep. His bed ground was near a certain mesquite tree just outside the gate. He spent hours every summer day in the shade of this mesquite. When it rained and other cattle drifted off, hunting fresh pasturage, Sancho stayed at home and drank at the well. Sancho was strictly domestic.

In the spring of 1880 Sancho was three years old and past, white of horn and as blocky in shape as any long-legged Texas steer ever grew. Kerr's ranch lay in a vast unfenced range grazed by the Shiner brothers, with headquarters on the Frio River. That spring they had a contract to deliver three herds of steers, each to number twenty-five hundred head, in Wyoming. Kerr was helping the Shiners gather cattle and, along with various other ranchers, sold them what steers he had.

Sancho was included. One day late in March the Shiners road-branded him **7 z** and put him in the first herd headed north. The other herds were to follow two or three days apart.

It was late afternoon before the herd got its final trimming and was shaped up for the long drive. It was watered and eased out on a prairie slope to bed down. But Sancho had no disposition to lie down — there.

He wanted to go back to that mesquite just outside the pen gate at the Kerr place on the Esperanza where he had without variation slept every night since he had been weaned. Perhaps his appetite called for an evening tamale. He stood and roamed about on the south side of the herd. A dozen times during the night the men on guard had to drive him back. As reliefs were changed, word passed to keep an eye on that paint steer on the lower side.

When the herd started on, next morning, Sancho was at the tail end of it, often stopping and looking back. It took constant attention from one of the drag drivers to keep him moving. By the time the second night arrived, every hand in the outfit knew Sancho by name and sight — the stubbornest and gentlest steer of the lot. About dark, one of the men pitched a loop over his horns and staked him to a bush. This saved bothering with his persistent efforts to walk off.

Daily, when the herd was halted to graze, spreading out like a fan, the other steers eating their way northward, Sancho invariably pointed himself south. In his lazy way he grabbed many a mouthful of grass while the herd was moving. Finally, in some brush up on the Llano (lan'oh), after ten days of trailing, he dodged into freedom. The next day one of the point men with the second Shiner herd saw a big paint steer walking south, rode out, read the 7 z road brand on his left side, rounded him in, and set him traveling north again. Sancho became the chief drag animal of this herd. Somewhere north of the Colorado there was a run one night, and when morning came, Sancho was missing. The other steers had held together; probably Sancho had not run at all. But he was picked up again, by the third Shiner herd, which was coming on behind.

He took his accustomed place in the drag and continued to require special driving. He picked up in weight. He chewed his cud peacefully and slept soundly, but whenever he looked southward, which was often, he raised his head as if memory and expectation were stirring. The men were all personally acquainted with him, and every night one of them would stake him. He never lunged against the rope as a wild cow brute would.

One day the cattle balked and milled at a bank-full river. "Rope old Sancho and lead him in," the boss ordered, "and we'll point the other cattle after him." Sancho led like a horse. The herd followed. As soon as he was released, he dropped back to the rear. After this, however, he was always led to the front when there was high water to cross.

The rains came right that spring, and grass came early. By the time the slow-traveling Shiner herds got into No Man's Land, beyond Red River, they were putting on tallow every day, and the sandhill plums were turning ripe. Pausing now and then to pick a little of the fruit, Sancho's driver saw the pet steer following his example. Learning to eat *chiltipiquíns* on the Esperanza had made Sancho experimental in foods.

Meantime the cattle were trailing, trailing, every day and Sunday too, in the direction of the North Star. For five hundred miles across Texas, counting the windings to find water and keep out of breaks, they had come. After getting into the Indian Territory, they snailed on across the Wichita, the South Canadian, the North Canadian, and the Cimarron. On into Kansas they trailed and across the Arkansas, around Dodge City, cowhand capital of the world, out of Kansas into Nebraska, over the wide, wide Platte, past the roaring cow town of Ogallala, up the North Platte, under the Black Hills, and then against the Big Horn Mountains. For two thousand miles, making ten or twelve miles a day, the Shiner herds trailed.

When, finally, the dogies reached their new home in Wyoming, Sancho was still halting every now and then to sniff southward for a whiff of the Mexican Gulf. The farther he got away from home, the less he seemed to like the change. He had never felt frost in September be-fore. The Mexican peppers on the Esperanza were red ripe now.

The Wyoming outfit received the cattle. Then for a week the Texans helped brand c r on their long sides before turning them loose on the new range. When Sancho's time came to be branded in the chute, one of the Texans yelled out, "There goes my pet. Stamp that c r brand on him good and deep."

Another drag driver said, "The line riders had better learn his tracks and watch for them."

And now the Shiner men turned south, taking back with them their saddle horses and chuck wagons — and leaving Sancho behind. They made good time, but a blue norther was flapping their slickers when they turned the remuda loose on the Frio River. After the Cowhands' Christmas Ball most of them settled down for a few weeks of winter sleep.

Spring comes early down on the Esperanza. The mesquites were all in new leaf with that green so fresh and tender that the color seems to emanate into the sky. Bluebonnets, pale pink Mexican primroses, and red phlox would soon sprinkle every open flat and draw. The prickly pear was ready to be studded with waxy blossoms and the white brush to be heavy with its own perfume. The windmill grass — "rooster's foot," as the vaqueros call it — was crowding the tallowweed out in

places. It was time for the spring cow hunts and the putting up of herds for the annual drive north. The Shiners were at work.

"We were close to Kerr's cabin on Esperanza Creek," John Rigby told me, "when I looked across a pear flat and saw something that made me rub my eyes. I was riding with Joe Shiner, and we both stopped our horses."

"Do you see what I see?" John Rigby asked.

"Yes, but before I say, I'm going to read the brand," Joe Shiner answered.

They rode over. "You can hang me for a horse thief," John Rigby used to tell, "if it wasn't that Sancho paint steer, four year old now, the Shiner 7 z road brand and the Wyoming c r range brand both showing on him as plain as boxcar letters."

The men rode on down to Kerr's.

"Yes," Kerr said, "old Sancho got in about six weeks ago. His hoofs were worn mighty nigh down to the hair, but he wasn't lame. I thought María was going out of her senses, she was so glad to see him. She actually hugged him, and she cried, and then she began feeding him hot tamales. She's made a batch of them nearly every day since, just to pet that steer. When she's not feeding him tamales, she's giving him *piloncillo*."

Sancho was slicking off and seemed mighty contented. He was coming up every night and sleeping at the gate, María said. She was nervous over the prospect of losing her pet, but Joe Shiner said that if that steer loved his home enough to walk back to it all the way from Wyoming, he wasn't going to drive him off again, even if he was putting up another herd for the c r owners.

As far as I can find out, old Sancho lived right there on the Esperanza, now and then getting a tamale, tickling his palate with chili peppers in season, and generally staying fat on mesquite grass, until he died a natural death. He was one of the walking Texas longhorns.

DISCUSSION

1. Do you think Sancho's taste for tamales and peppers was the main reason that he loved his home so much? What makes you think as you do?
2. How did Sancho happen to become a pet? For what foods did Sancho develop an unusual taste?
3. When did the Shiner men start the long drive? When did they reach Wyoming? Approximately when did they return home?

4. Why did Sancho become especially well known to the men in the cattle drive to Wyoming? How did Sancho help in the cattle drive?

5. Do you think the Shiner men had reason to be frustrated with Sancho? What makes you think as you do?

6. How do you think the Shiner men actually felt about Sancho? Why do you think that?

7. How long did Kerr say Sancho had been home? What reasons might have caused Sancho to reach home so much later than the drivers?

8. How did Maria react to Sancho's return? What do you think caused her to react as she did?

9. Have you ever felt strongly attached to a special pet? If so, what made it a favorite of yours?

10. Do you think Sancho was just an unusual animal, or would most animals behave as he did in a similar situation?

AUTHOR

Renowned as a collector of Texas folklore and an historian of the Southwest, J(ames) Frank Dobie was born in 1888 on a small ranch in Texas, not far from the Mexican border. He began writing as a summer reporter on Texas newspapers and was a professor of English at the University of Texas in Austin for many years.

In his early thirties, Mr. Dobie left teaching for a year to manage a half-million-acre ranch. Through this experience he became aware of the wealth of fascinating Southwest folktales and traditions of the range. After his return to teaching, Mr. Dobie began to edit the publications of the Texas Folklore Society, for which he was secretary and editor for over twenty years. As an author, he wrote hundreds of tales and anecdotes in a lively, informal style. His many books include *The Longhorns,* in which "Sancho" appeared.

Countless awards and honors went to Mr. Dobie. One of them, from England's Cambridge University, was accompanied by a citation written in Latin that read, in part, *"De bobus longicornibus quod ille non cognovit, inutile est alliis cognoscere"* — "What he doesn't know about longhorn cattle isn't worth knowing."

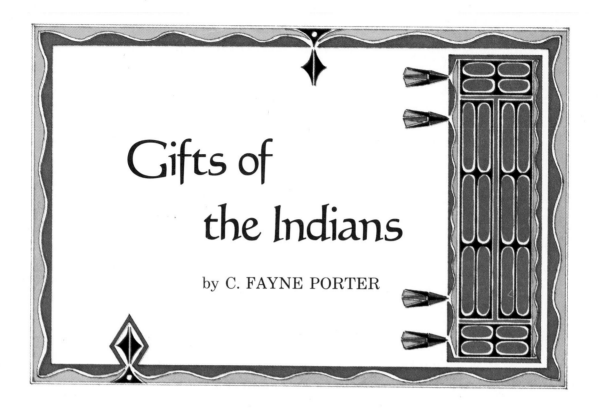

Gifts of the Indians

by C. FAYNE PORTER

Americans today have something of a reputation for being impressed by statistics concerning money, so try this one: The United States is, of course, the world's leading agricultural nation, but more than half of its cash farm crop comes from products the Indians developed! This makes them certainly the greatest of the Stone Age farmers.

Today's domestic farmers realize about three billion dollars annually from corn, the most valuable crop grown in the United States. Corn has been called the greatest natural resource of our country. A bumper corn crop will equal the total value of all wheat, potatoes, barley, rye, rice, tobacco, beans, and sweet potatoes grown yearly. Science is still puzzled as to how the Indians ever developed it in the first place, because no wild corn has ever been found. It is by now so thoroughly domesticated that it has lost the power to propagate itself in a wild state. It grows only where people plant it and is helpless without human care. Other cereal grains grow by themselves, but not corn; its origin is cloaked in mystery. Scientists have improved corn, true, *but all of the main types now grown were developed by the time of Columbus.* (This includes popcorn.)

And let's add the Irish potato, one of the world's most widely grown vegetables. Irish it is not; it came first from the high plateau country of Peru and Bolivia. The world took to it, and its total world production is now over eight billion bushels yearly. Its annual value is greater than that of all the gold and silver mined yearly throughout the world. While we're on the subject of potatoes, the sweet potato (not really a potato) and some types of yams can also be listed as American in origin.

This list is far from finished. Add tomatoes, the leading crop canned in the United States today. Include table beans, both the dry (kidney and lima) beans and the green beans, or string beans, as well as the castor bean, used for medicinal castor oil and a wide variety of commercial needs. List the peanut and its large range of by-products; pumpkins and the related squash families; the green or bell peppers and the red chili pepper (not black table pepper, however). Add pineapples, avocados, eggplant, wild rice, cassava (from which our tapioca comes), native grape strains, strawberries, blackberries, raspberries — on and on the list might go.

Then, too, quite an industry has been built around what the Indians of South America once called *cahuchi* (the weeping tree). The Indians would make cuts in the bark and gather the "tears" from this tree, which would be compressed into balls and used as toys and playthings. Today we know "the weeping tree" as the rubber tree, and the rubber industry is a giant one. In the United States alone, rubber and rubber-goods production is in the thirty-billion-dollar-a-year class.

Where would the scientific study of biology and medicine be without the ever-present guinea pig, domesticated by the South American Indians? In the field of medicine, make note of curare, quinine, cascara, arnica, petrolatum, ipecac, and wintergreen, only a few of the curative substances understood and used by the Indians. So skillful were the Indians in the knowledge of natural remedies that in 1952 a scholar could write ". . . in the four hundred years that the European physicians and botanists have been analyzing and examining the flora of America, they have not yet discovered a medicinal herb not known to the Indians."

In fact, the Indians whom the first settlers found had a far better idea of what good health is and how to maintain it than did the settlers themselves. The Indians were scrupulously clean, unlike the Europeans who first came to their shores. Columbus took back the news of how often the Indians bathed, and one of the first dictates set down by Queen Isabella of Spain was to the point, if misdirected: "They are not to bathe as frequently as hitherto."

Columbus took back another idea, which he got from the Arawaks —

BALL PLAY OF THE CHOCTAWS *by George Catlin*

one which would become synonymous with ships that sail the sea and those who sail them. That idea also concerned a tree, called the *hamaca*. Its bark was used to make a swinging bed, hung by vine ropes between two supports. This, of course, became the hammock, much loved by old sailors and do-it-yourself gardeners.

American soldiers who coursed over the world in World War II were greeted by small fry (and some fry not so small) in the farthest corners of the earth with the same classic question: "Got any gum, Yank?" Chewing gum, along with chocolate candy, became the wampum for Yanks everywhere. Chewing gum was of American Indian origin, as was chocolate. The Indians used many tree gums for chewing. One of them was the Central American chicle, which is the chewy base of all gum made today.

The white comers to the New World found themselves in a strange land almost completely unknown to them. There was only one way in which the white people could survive, and that was by emulating the Indians, who knew and understood the land and its ways. So the newcomers took nearly all that the Indians had to offer. They took the Indians' means of transportation, such as the canoe and the snowshoe, and the buckskin dress for life on the frontier. They took Indian foods, such as cornbread and persimmon bread and hominy

WHITE CLOUD *by George Catlin*

and succotash and the corn tortilla of the Southwestern Pueblo dwellers. As an interesting aside here, all the poor starving Pilgrims at Plymouth Rock, with centuries of supposedly superior learning behind them, refused to eat the plentiful clams of that area because they thought that clams were poisonous. We can thank the Wampanoags of Massachusetts for introducing the Pilgrims to the fine old Indian tradition of the clambake.

The newcomers took, too, the names the Indians had given to their rich and varied land. Probably in every county in the United States today (except in Hawaii) there is an Indian place-name — of a stream or a mountain or a city — whispering of the time when another people lived and worked and played there. The full, rich sound of the old Indian names is indelibly stamped into the fabric of the land — Mississippi and Monongahela, Narragansett and Natchez, Savannah and Seattle, Tishomingo and Taos, Winnemucca and Wichita. Half of our fifty states bear names which stem from Indian words.

All of these things we have talked about thus far have been tangible. Still unanswered is the question: What kind of people were those Indians? They came from many different backgrounds, and any statement would have to be a very general one. The Indians represented over two hundred and fifty different peoples in the United States alone, speaking a hodgepodge of languages and having widely divergent customs and cultures and habits.

Most revealing of the Indians' day-to-day life and attitude is a statement by one of the great early students of the plains peoples of this country. That man was George Catlin, who traveled among them and lived among them from 1830 to 1836. Catlin was a gifted artist. He captured on canvas many of the important leaders and many of the little-known ceremonies among better than two score of the plains peoples from the Canadian border southward into the territory then held by Mexico. Presenting the Indians as they were was his life's work. When he published his *Last Rambles Amongst the Indians of the Rocky Mountains and the Andes* in 1867, George Catlin could say of them:

I love a people who have always made me welcome to the best they had . . . who are honest without laws, who have no jails and no poorhouse . . . who never take the name of God in vain . . . who worship God without a Bible, and I believe that God loves them also . . . who are free from religious animosities . . . who have never raised a hand against me, or stolen my property, where there was no law to punish either . . . who never fought a battle with white men except on their own ground . . . and oh! how I love a people who don't live for the love of money.

DISCUSSION

1. Do you think that "Gifts of the Indians" is an appropriate title for this selection? Tell why or why not.

2. Why does the author say that American Indians are "the greatest of the Stone Age farmers"? What are some of the leading farm crops developed originally by the Indians?

3. What else besides foods did the settlers adopt from the Indians in order to survive in the New World?

4. In your opinion, is the author's claim that the Indians had a skilled knowledge of natural medicinal remedies well supported? Give reasons for your answer.

5. What product used by the South American Indians became the basis of a leading American industry?

6. Why is science still puzzled as to how the Indians ever developed corn in the first place?

7. What is meant by the opening words of the article, "Americans today have something of a reputation for being impressed by statistics concerning money"? Is the statement a fair one? Why or why not? Why, do you think, did the author begin with those words?

8. Why, do you think, did George Catlin devote much of his life to "the presentation of the Indians as they were"?

9. Look again at the quotation at the end of the article. In praising the Indians, Catlin was, by comparison, criticizing certain kinds of people. Of whom was he being critical and why?

10. Why is it appropriate that the author ended his article with Catlin's statement about "people who don't live for the love of money"? Can you think of any reasons why the Indians would not have valued money?

AUTHOR

With a background of social work and service in the United States Navy, C. Fayne Porter taught at Haskell Indian Junior College in Kansas, where the student body is made up of Native Americans from all over the country. Mr. Porter, a Californian, had a special interest in the culture and history of Native American peoples. He died in 1976.

Two Shivers

Homographs are words that have the same spelling but different meanings and completely different origins. The words may also differ in pronunciation and syllabication. Homographs are listed separately in dictionaries, and each entry is numbered.

Some familiar words may actually be homographs with second, third, and even fourth meanings that are totally unfamiliar. The sentence context usually gives clues to the meaning of such a word. One example is the word *shiver*. In "Blue Beach," Carlota explained in her narrative that she "had found that the best way to approach cold water was by small *shivers*, suffered one at a time." The word *shivers* in that sentence is a noun with the familiar meaning of "trembles from cold or a cold sensation." The word *shiver* is also a verb; the writer might have said that Carlota *shivered* from the effect of the cold water as she entered it. *Shiver* as it is used in these sentences comes from a Middle English word that refers to the chattering of teeth and is derived from an Old English word meaning "jaw."

A homograph of that common word *shiver* is used much less often in the language. The second word *shiver* might appear in a sentence such as "The next earthquake tremor shivered the window into a million glittering fragments." This second word *shiver* is a verb meaning "to cause to break into fragments." It is derived from a Middle English word meaning "fragment." Although both forms of the word *shiver* seem to suggest trembling and shaking, the homographs developed independently.

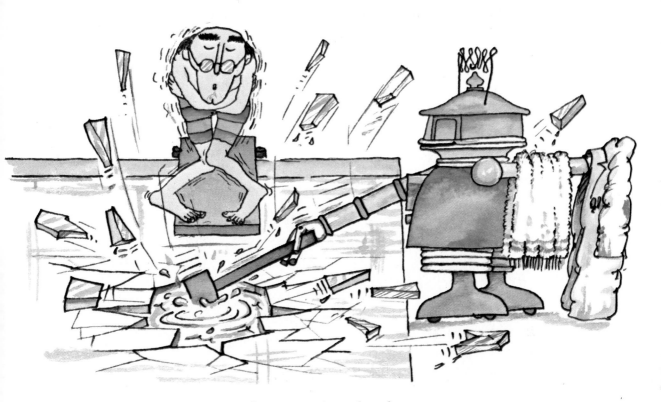

Other homographs may have meanings that do not seem even distantly related. In the sentence, "I will *pay* this telephone bill today," the meaning of the word *pay* is perfectly clear. The meaning of *pay* in the following sentence is less familiar: "'We have to *pay* the seams of the lower deck today,' groaned the new recruit." An experienced sailor would know that the word *pay* meant "to coat with tar or asphalt for the purpose of waterproofing." Almost anyone else would have to look the word up in a dictionary.

In each of the following sentences, the underlined word may be unfamiliar although its homograph is probably a familiar word to you. Using the context of each sentence, try to figure out the meaning of the word. Use a dictionary to check your answers.

1. When you travel through London, please stay at my <u>flat</u>.
2. We heard the cattle <u>low</u> their fear of the raging thunderstorm.
3. Police <u>scoured</u> the area in search of the missing locomotive.
4. The carpenter used a <u>plane</u> to smooth the birch surface.
5. The child <u>pines</u> for her older sister, who is at school.
6. I felt so strongly about the issue, I decided to join the <u>fray</u>.

Ordeal in Spring

by IRENE HUNT

The Civil War had been under way for nearly two years, and Jethro Creighton had sadly watched relatives and friends go off to fight — his brothers Tom and John; his cousin Eb, who had grown up with him; and the local schoolteacher, Shad Yale, who was almost like a brother. All were in their late teens or early twenties, but Jeth was Matt and Ellen Creighton's youngest son and not old enough to enlist. Besides, his father was too ill to work the southern Illinois farm, so it was up to Jeth and his older sister, Jenny, to raise crops to feed not only their parents and themselves but also their brother John's wife, Nancy, and her two small children. In the following excerpt from the book *Across Five Aprils,* young Jethro suddenly finds himself overtaken by the war — on a battlefield of his own.

The deserters came in droves. The Point Prospect campground was said to be swarming with soldiers who made forays on chicken coops, pigpens, and smokehouses where winter meat was hung. In the spring and summer, vegetable gardens, cornfields, and fruit orchards were robbed. No one dared to approach the camp. Even the U.S. agents from the cities upstate appeared to be in no hurry for a visit; it was known that the deserters carried their arms and that they were desperate. For a neighbor to have recognized a face among them might well have been sufficient reason for getting a bullet between the eyes; these men meant to take no chances with an informer.

The stories varied; some said there were a hundred men at Point Prospect; others put the number at nearer five hundred. In the early months of '63, the theft of food was their only crime against the community; by March, however, a killing took place.

There was a man known as Hig Phillips down in the southern part of the county, and the story came out that he had hired a substitute to go to war for him. That in itself was not uncommon; many others in the county had taken advantage of this method of dodging the draft, which in the spring of '63 included men from twenty up to the age of forty-five. Three hundred dollars was what it took. That was a lot of money, but once the substitute was found and the three hundred dollars paid, a man could sit back comfortably and yawn at the war news if he chose.

There were men who were forced to take advantage of this system of substitute-hiring because of serious illness in the home or the dependency of their motherless children. There was, however, no reason why Hig Phillips should have avoided the draft except that he was a lazy bachelor much favored by his mother, that he was fond of good food and a comfortable bed, and that he had been known to adhere to the opinion that fools could do the fighting while men of intelligence and property might take pleasure in the prospect of a long and easy life. He was not generally admired for these views, but that fact bothered him hardly at all.

Hardly at all, that is, until one moonless night a band of young men visited him — men who knew what gangrenous wounds were like, what marches through cold rain or blistering heat meant, while hunger gnawed at their stomachs or weakness from typhus or dysentery brought agony to every step; men who had seen the dead piled high on smoking battlefields and had come to believe that soldiers of two years had done their share, that the burden should now fall upon other shoulders.

Although there were many who held Hig Phillips in contempt, his murder was an act of lawlessness that terrorized the county. People realized that anything could be expected from a mob of undisciplined desperadoes. Nancy now heeded Ellen's advice and closed her house completely, bringing her stock up to Matt's barn and keeping her children in the comparative safety of their grandfather's home. Jenny was no longer allowed to drive alone to Hidalgo for the mail. No one ventured far away from home after nightfall, and no one ever went to bed with the full confidence of security. The fury of the abolitionists and the Copperheads was now taken over by the deserters.

One night in February of '63, as the family sat around the open fire, a wagon clattered down the road from the north and stopped in front of the house. Opening the door, Jethro saw three young men jump down from the wagon and stride up to the porch.

"Is this the home of Matthew Creighton?" one of them asked. Jethro noticed the crispness of the man's voice — an upstate voice, he thought.

"Yes, sir, my father's right here. Will you come indoors?"

They came inside with a great clatter of heavy boots. Jenny stood, wide-eyed, beside her father's chair; Nancy and Ellen held the small boys tightly in their arms. Matt tried to rise.

"Stay seated, sir. We're here to ask you a few questions." The young man who spoke threw back his coat to show his uniform and insignia. "We are representatives of the Federal Registrars; we are charged with hunting down deserters from the United States Army."

"Will you take chairs, gentlemen?" Matt said evenly, but Jethro noticed the sudden paleness of his father's face.

"Thank you, no. We are here to inquire if this is the home of Ebenezer Carron, Seventeenth Illinois Infantry, Army of Tennessee."

"It is. This has bin Eb's home since he was a lad of ten or so."

"Have you seen him lately?"

"Why, no. Him and my son Thomas left together for the Army in August of '61. My own boy was kilt at Pittsburg Landing; we ain't heered from Eb but once since then."

"You know the penalty for shielding a deserter from the United States Army?"

"I do. Air you tellin' me that Eb is a deserter?"

"His commanding officer has reason to believe that he is and that he has been making his way toward this part of the state — we assume toward his home."

Matt lifted a shaking hand and covered his eyes. Jenny glanced at him anxiously and then suddenly blazed out at the questioner.

"We haven't seen Eb. He's not here, and I'll thank you not to worry my father with more of this talk. If you want to look through this house —"

"We do, miss — this house and all other buildings around here."

Jenny grasped the kerosene lamp with a firm hand. "Jeth, you come with me. We'll show these soldiers through the house; they can hunt outside for themselves."

Her anger made Jenny a very grand lady, Jethro thought. He had never seen her more beautiful than she was that night, with her cheeks flaming and her eyes large and black with mixed anger and fear.

The soldiers grinned a little at one another and followed her and Jethro up to the sleeping rooms in the loft first and then down again to the kitchen and pantry where Jenny took down the big key to the smokehouse and handed it to one of the men.

"We lock the smokehouse these nights. It's true there are deserters in these parts, and there's thievin' around everywhere. But we're not shieldin' anyone. Go look in the smokehouse for yourselves; go through the barn, the grainery, everywhere you think someone might be hidin'. After that I would say you'd best go down to the Point Prospect campground. The talk is that there are plenty of deserters there."

The Federal Registrars looked uncomfortable.

"Yes, we've heard," one of them muttered.

Jenny nodded. "It is easier to come to a house and upset a sick old man and womenfolk. Nobody in this neighborhood thinks it's very healthy to go down to Point Prospect, but you sounded so brave just now — I thought you might want to do your duty down there."

The man who had done the questioning bowed mockingly before Jenny.

"We'll see to our duty, miss, and if we find Ebenezer Carron, we'll take him back with us — and you too maybe." He turned to Jethro. "Will you get a lantern, young man, and light us out back?"

Jethro took down the lantern that hung on the outside wall of the kitchen and started down the path toward the barn. The soldiers searched the place thoroughly and then walked back to their wagon. One of them spoke sternly to Jethro on the way.

"If this man Ebenezer Carron turns up, you know what to do?"

"No, sir."

"Then you'd better listen. You get word to the Office of the Federal Registrars in Chicago right away, telling them where the man is or expects to be. You fail to report him, and you

and your family will be up to your necks in trouble. Do you understand?"

Jethro nodded briefly. He was deeply antagonized by these men, but he knew they were simply carrying out a job assigned to them. Anyway, he was glad when the wagon carried them away — to the north. Evidently they were not going down to the deserters' camp at Point Prospect, not that night anyway.

There was an early spring that year. By the first of March the weather was warm, and the higher fields were dry enough for plowing. Jethro carried a rifle with him when he went down to John's place to work. It was always possible that he might bring down some kind of wild game for the table or that he would have need to defend himself against a desperate deserter.

The field he plowed that day in early March was bordered on the east by dense woods, and Jethro became conscious that each time he approached the woods side of the field, the sharp, harsh call of a wild turkey would sound out with a strange kind of insistence — almost as if some stupid bird demanded that he stop and listen. Once when he halted his team and walked a little distance toward the woods, the calls came furiously, one after the other; then when he returned to his team and moved toward the west, they stopped until he had made the round of the field.

After several repetitions of this pattern, Jethro tethered his team and, taking up his rifle, walked into the woods. His heart beat fast as he walked, and his slim, brown hand clutching the rifle was wet with sweat. A neighbor, Ed Turner, was giving him a day's help in the field across the road, but Jethro chose not to call him although he felt he was taking a dangerous chance.

He walked slowly and carefully, pausing now and then to listen. The calls stopped for a while, and he was half convinced that they had actually come from a wild bird. He made no move for a few minutes, and they began again, softer now and more certainly coming from the throat of a person.

Jethro stood quite still. "Hello," he called finally. "What is it you want of me?"

There was no answer. Then the call came again, softly, insistently, from a clump of trees, one of which was a tremendous old oak — long since hollowed out, first by lightning and then by decay.

Jethro walked closer, his gun raised, and after a minute the human voice which he had been half expecting to hear called out to him.

"Put yore gun down, Jeth; I ain't aimin' to hurt ye. I didn't dast take the chancet of Ed Turner hearin' me call to ye."

"Who is it?" Jethro asked. "Come out and let me see your face."

Then a skeleton came out from among the trees. It was the skeleton of a Union soldier, though the uniform it wore was so ragged and filthy it was difficult to identify. The sunken cheeks were covered with a thin scattering of fuzz; the hair was lank and matted. It fell over the skeleton's forehead and down into its eyes. The boy stared at it without speaking.

"Jeth, you've growed past all believin'. I've bin watchin' you from fur off, and I couldn't git over it — how you've growed."

Then Jethro realized who it was. "Eb," he exclaimed in a voice hardly above a whisper. "It's Eb, ain't it?"

There was utter despair in the soldier's voice.

"Yes," he said. "I reckon it's Eb — what there's left of him."

For a few seconds Jethro forgot the Federal Registrars and the fact that not only the word which preceded Eb but also his method of announcing himself gave credence to the suspicion that he was a deserter. But for those first few seconds Jethro could only remember that this was Eb, a part of the family, the boy who had been close to Tom, the soldier who would have more vivid stories to tell of the war than ever a newspaper would be able to publish. He held out his hand.

"Eb, it's good — it's so good to see you. Pa and Ma will be ——" he stopped suddenly. He noticed that Eb ignored his outstretched hand.

"Yore pa and ma will be scairt —

that's what you mean, ain't it? Scairt fer themselves and ashamed of me." He paused for a second and then added defiantly, "I deserted, you know; I up and left Ol' Abe's Army of the United States."

Jethro could only stare at his cousin; he could find no words.

"Desertin' ain't a purty word to you, is it? Well, I done it — I don't jest know why. We'd had another skirmish, and there was dead boys that we had to bury the next day — and we'd bin licked agin. All at oncet I knowed I couldn't stand it no longer,

and I jest up and left. Oncet soldiers have left, they're done fer. I've bin a long time gittin' home, and now that I'm here, it ain't no comfort."

"Eb, couldn't you just come up to the house and see them for a few hours or so? Couldn't you have a good meal and get cleaned up and tell the folks all you know about Tom?"

"I caint. I could git 'em into awful trouble. Besides, they would prob'ly jest as soon not set eyes on the likes of me agin."

"But, Eb, if you can't come up to the house, what *did* you come for?"

Eb's face showed quick anger. "I come because I couldn't help myself, that's why. *You* don't know what it's like. There be things that air too terr'ble to talk about — and you want to see the fields where you used to be happy, you want to smell the good air of old Illinois so much that you fergit — you go crazy fer an hour or so — and then you don't dare go back."

He shivered and leaned back against a tree trunk as if just talking had taken more strength than he had to spend.

"Have you been down to the Point Prospect camp, Eb?" Jethro asked after a while.

"A couple days. It's worse than the war down there, with fellers afraid and gittin' meaner as they git more afraid. I didn't come back to be with soldiers anyway. I'm sick of soldiers, livin' and dead; I'm sick of all of 'em." He threw himself down on a thick padding of dead leaves and motioned Jethro to do the same.

"I want ye to tell me about 'em, Jeth — Uncle Matt and Aunt Ellen, Jenny . . ."

"You knew Pa had a heart attack;

he's not been himself since. Ma's tolerable, and Jenny's fine. We do the work of the farm together, Jenny and me."

"And John and Shad — where air they? They jined up, didn't they?"

"Yes, John's in Tennessee under a general named Rosecrans. And Shad's in the East with the Army of the Potomac."

"How did you git the word about Tom?" Eb asked.

"Dan Lawrence was home on sick leave. His pa brought him over; he told us all about it."

"I was at Pittsburg Landing too, but I didn't know about Tom — not fer two or three days. I wanted to write, but somehow I couldn't do it. Tom and me had bin in swimmin' the day before the Rebs su'prised us; we was both of us in good spirits then, laughin' and carryin' on like we done in the old days back home. Somehow all the spirit in me has bin gone ever since. I could stand things as long as I had Tom along with me."

He ran his hand across his eyes as if to shut out a picture or a memory. "Tell me about Jenny; is she still in love with Shad Yale?"

"More than ever, I guess. She writes to him a lot; he sets great store by her letters."

"He ought to. People need nice letters when they're sufferin' with the homesick."

Jethro studied Eb's sunken cheeks and dull eyes.

"How do you manage to eat, Eb?"

"I don't do it reg'lar, that's shore. I live off the land — steal a little, shoot me a rabbit or squirrel and cook 'em over a low fire late at night. It ain't good eatin', but nothin's good these days like it used to be."

Jethro's insides twisted in sympathy. "Are you hungry now, Eb?"

"I'm allus hungry. Ye git used to it after a while."

"Nancy fixed me some grub to bring to the field with me; I'll go get it for you."

He ran to the fencerow where he had left two pieces of bread and the cuts from a particularly tender haunch of beef that Nancy had wrapped in a white cloth for him. Ordinarily he would have eaten the snack by midafternoon, but Eb's wild-turkey calls had made him forget it. He returned to Eb minutes later with the food and a jug of water.

They sat together in the shadows, while Eb ate with an appetite that was like a hungry animal's.

"Eb, I've got to tell you," Jethro said quietly after a while. "The soldiers that call themselves the Federal Registrars was at the house lookin' for you last month."

Eb seemed to shrink within himself. He looked at his hands carefully, as if he really cared about inspecting them, and his mouth worked in a strange, convulsive grimace. He wouldn't look at Jethro when he finally spoke.

"I was an awful fool — at least you got a chancet in battle — maybe it's one in a hunderd, but it's a chancet. This way, I got none. There's no place on this earth fer me to go. Even the camps of deserters don't want fellers as weak and sick as I am; they let me know that quick at Point Prospect. I'll either freeze or starve — or else be ketched. I'd give jest about anythin' if I could walk back to my old outfit and pitch into the fightin' agin. A soldier don't have to feel ashamed."

Jethro sat for a while trying to think of some way out of the situation; it appeared more hopeless the more he thought. He was frightened — for the despairing man in front of him, for himself, and for his family. When he finally spoke, he tried hard to sound reassuring, but the pounding of his heart made his voice shake.

"Well, you stay here till we can think of somethin', Eb. I'm goin' to get you some quilts and things from Nancy's place; I'll bring you what grub I can lay hands on — I can always get eggs and a chicken for you. I think you'd best eat all you can and rest for a spell; we'll think of what's to be done when once you get a little stronger."

Eb looked up then. "You all but fool me into believin' that somethin' *kin* be done, Jeth, but I know better. You ner no one else kin help me now — not even Ol' Abe hisself."

Ol' Abe. Mr. Lincoln. Mr. President.

"I ought to go back to work, Eb."

"I guess so." Eb looked at him with a suggestion of a smile. "I caint git used to it — you bein' big enough to handle a team alone. You seem almost a man these days, Jeth; even yore hair ain't quite as yaller and curly as it used to be."

Jethro turned away. "I'll bring you a quilt from Nancy's before I go in for the night," he said shortly.

He walked back to his waiting team; there was still time to plow a dozen furrows before sunset—and to think.

He had faced sorrow and fear; he had felt a terrible emptiness the day Shadrach and John went away. But he had never been faced with the responsibility of making a fearful decision like the one confronting him now.

The authority of the law loomed big in his mind; he remembered, "You and your family will be up to your necks in trouble." Loyalty to his brother Tom and the thousands who had fought to the last ditch at Pittsburg Landing, at Antietam, Fredericksburg, and all the other places that were adding length to the long list — how could loyalty to these soldiers be true if one were going to harbor and give comfort to a man who simply said, "I quit."

But, on the other hand, how would one feel at night to awake and remember, "I'm the one that sent my cousin to his death." Eb was not a hero, certainly — not now anyway. People scorned the likes of Eb; sure, so did Jethro himself, and yet ——

"How do I know what *I'd* be like if I was sick and scared and hopeless; how does *anyone* know that ain't been there? We got to remember that Eb has been in battles for two years; maybe he's been a hero in them battles, and maybe to go on bein' a hero in a war that has no end in sight is too much to ask. . . . Sure, deep down in me, I want Eb to get out, to leave me free of feelin' that I'm doin' wrong to give him grub, or takin' the risk of keepin' it a secret that he's here. Yes, it would leave me free if he'd just move on — but no, it wouldn't. I ain't goin' to be free even if he moves on; I can't set down to a table and forget that someone sick as Eb looks to be is livin' off the land, that he's livin' scared like a wild animal that's bein' hunted.

"But what's it goin' to be like if more and more soldiers quit and go into the woods and leave the fightin' to them that won't quit? What do you say to yourself when you remember that you fed and helped someone like Eb and maybe you get a letter from the East that Shad is killed and you see Jenny grievin', or that John is killed and Nancy and her little boys is left all alone — how do you feel when things like that come up?

"Of course, right now I could say to Pa, 'I leave it up to you' — and then what could he do? Why, he'd be caught in the same trap I'm in now; I'd wriggle out of it and leave the decidin' to a sick old man; I'd put him in the spot where any way he decided would be bad — hurtful to a person's conscience. No, there ain't an answer that's any plainer to an old man than it is to me."

Jethro lay awake in his room that night and wrestled with his problem. He wondered if, after all, it wouldn't be better to ask his father's advice, but he decided against that almost immediately and as firmly as he had rejected the idea that afternoon. What about Ed Turner, staunch and level-headed neighbor? No, Ed had two sons in the army; it wouldn't do to lay this responsibility upon Ed's shoulders. He thought of Eb's words, "You ner no one else kin help me now — not even Ol' Abe hisself."

Ol' Abe. Mr. Lincoln. Mr. President. Not even Mr. Lincoln himself!

Jethro turned restlessly in his bed. What if one put it up to Mr. Lincoln? What if one said, "I will abide by the word of him who is highest in this land"? But wasn't that word already known? Wasn't the word from the highest in the land just this: turn in deserters or there will be terrible trouble for you and your family?

But Mr. Lincoln was a man who looked at problems from all sides. Mr. Lincoln was not a faraway man like General McClellan or Senator Sumner or Secretary of State Seward. Mr. Lincoln had plowed fields in Illinois; he had thought of the problems people

came up against; he was not ready to say, "Everything on this side of the line is right, and everything on the other side is wrong."

But would one dare? A nobody, a boy on a southern Illinois farm — would he dare? Mr. Lincoln held the highest office in the land; what would he think? Would it vex him that a boy from southern Illinois could be so bold? And anyway, how could one say it? What manner of words could one use so as not to be too forward, too lacking in respect toward the President of the United States?

Jeth realized he was not going to be able to go to sleep. There was a candle in his room; there was some ink and an old pen. He got up in the quiet of the night, lighted his candle, and began to write on a piece of rough paper.

The next morning he hid sandwiches inside his coat, and at the barn he picked up a few eggs from the nests up in the loft. He dug an apple out of the straw in the apple-cave; no one would question that — a boy needed something to munch on in midmorning.

Eb was feeling a little better that morning. The quilts Jethro had taken from Nancy's house had made the long night more comfortable; he had washed himself in the creek and looked refreshed.

"You've brung me a feast, Jeth," he said gratefully.

They sat together for a while and talked in low voices.

"I'll be gittin' out in a day or so, Jeth. I caint hev you takin' all this risk."

"If you could go back to the army, you would, wouldn't you, Eb?"

"You're askin' a man if he had a chancet to live, would he take it. But I've told you, Jeth — a deserter caint go back. I'll be hunted the rest of my days — but the rest of my days ain't goin' to be too many."

Jethro said nothing, but as he plowed that morning, he made up his mind to send the letter. It was a frightening thing to do, but if one did nothing — well, that was frightening too. He knew Eb was not really planning to leave — Eb was a lost and frightened boy, and there was nowhere else to go. For Jethro there was nothing to do but send the letter.

The plowshares needed sharpening, Jethro told his father that noon. Hadn't he better drive over to Hidalgo and get that work done? He'd pick up the mail, too, for themselves and for Ed Turner. Was that all right with his father?

Matt seldom questioned Jethro's decisions. The boy was doing an adult's work; he was due the dignity accorded to an adult. Matt assented to the trip readily, and Jethro, with the letter in his pocket, drove off down the road, his heart pounding with excitement.

In Hidalgo the old man who took care of the mail glanced sharply at Jethro when he noticed the inscription on the envelope. But he was a silent man with problems of his own; as long as a letter was properly stamped and addressed, it was no affair of his. Privately he thought that some people were allowing their young ones to become a little forward, but that was their concern. He threw Jethro's letter in a big bag that would be taken by wagon down to Olney that evening.

The long wait for an answer was interminable. Jethro tossed at night and wondered: had he done an impudent thing, had he laid himself open to trouble, had he been a fool to think that a boy of his age might act without the advice of his elders? Sometimes he got up and walked about his narrow room.

Eb's often reiterated "I'll be goin' on soon, Jeth; I won't be a burden to you much longer" became like the whippoorwill's cry — always the same and never ending. Jethro closed his ears to it, but the tensions within him mounted, and the necessity of providing for Eb's needs in strictest secrecy became a task that seemed to grow in magnitude as the days went by.

"If I could be sure I'm doin' the right thing," he would say to himself, as he watched the dark earth fall away from his plowshares. "If I could feel really set up about doin' a fine thing, but I don't know. Maybe I'm doin' somethin' terrible wrong; maybe the next time they come, the Federal Registrars will take me."

The letter came one noon when they were all seated at dinner. As so often happened, it was Ed Turner who brought the mail out from town. Jenny ran to the door, eager for a letter from Shadrach; Nancy's eyes pleaded for word from John.

But Ed held only one large envelope, and that was addressed to Jethro in a small, cramped handwriting done in very black ink. The envelope was postmarked Washington, D.C.

"Looks like purty important mail you're gittin', Jethro," Ed said quietly. His eyes were full of puzzled concern.

Jethro's head swam. This was the showdown; now all the family, Ed Turner, and soon the neighborhood would know everything. In the few seconds that passed before he opened the envelope, he wished with all his heart that he had not meddled in the affairs of a country at war, that he had let Eb work out his own problems, that he, Jethro, were still a sheltered young boy who did the tasks his father set for him and shunned the idea that he dare think for himself. He looked at the faces around him, and they spun in a strange mist of color — black eyes and blue eyes, gray hair and gold and black, pink cheeks and pale ones and weather-beaten brown ones.

He read the letter through, word for word, and while he read, there wasn't a sound in the house beyond the slight rustle of the page in the shaking hand that held it. When he was through, he held the letter out to Jenny, with a long sigh.

"You can read it out loud, Jenny."

Jenny stared at him as if he were a stranger; then she shook her head.

"It's your letter, Jeth; you'd best do the readin'."

He didn't know whether he could or not — there was a great pounding in his ears, and his breath was short — but he ran his hand across his eyes and swallowed hard. After the first few words, his voice grew steady, and he read the letter through without faltering.

Washington, March 14 1863

To Master Jethro Creighton
Hidalgo, Illinois

Dear Jethro;

Mr. Hay has called my attention to your letter, knowing as he does the place in my affection for boys of your age and the interest I have in letters coming from my home state of Illinois.

The problem which you describe is one, among so many others, that has troubled both my waking thoughts and those that intrude upon my sleep. The gravity of that problem has become of far-reaching significance and is one in which the authority of military regulations, the decline of moral responsibility, and the question of ordinary human compassion are so involved as to present a situation in which a solution becomes agonizingly difficult.

I had, however, made a decision relative to this problem only a few days before receiving your letter. There will be much criticism of that decision, but you will understand when I say that if it be a wrong one, I have then erred on the side of mercy.

The conditions of that decision are as follows: all soldiers improperly absent from their posts, who will report at certain points designated by local recruit offices by April 1, will be restored to their respective regiments without punishment except for forfeiture of pay and allowances for the period of their absence.

This information you may relay to the young man in question, and I pray that the remorse and despair which he has known since the time of his desertion will bring his better self to the cause for which so many of his young compatriots have laid down their lives.

May God bless you for the earnestness with which you have tried to seek out what is right; may He guide both of us in that search during the days ahead of us.

Yours very sincerely and respectfully,

A. Lincoln

DISCUSSION

1. Have you ever been in a situation where you had to make a choice between solving a difficult problem by yourself or turning to another person for help? If you wish, tell how you handled the situation and what your feelings were.

2. What did Jenny's conversation with the Federal Registrars tell you about her?

3. Why had Eb deserted? How did he feel about his desertion? What did Eb think would eventually happen to him?

4. What conflicting feelings did Jethro have that made the situation in which he found himself seem so hopeless?

5. Why did Jethro decide not to tell his father about Eb? Why didn't Jethro go to Ed Turner for advice?

6. As you read this story, did you have greater sympathy for Jethro or for Eb? Why?

7. To whom did Jethro finally turn for help with his problem? Before seeking that help, what arguments for and against writing the letter did Jethro weigh in his mind?

8. What solution did Lincoln's letter provide to Jethro's problem?

9. Jethro worried that President Lincoln would think him bold and impudent for having written the letter. Judging from Lincoln's reply, what do you think his feelings about Jethro were?

10. President Lincoln expected that the decision he had made would be criticized. Why do you think some people would oppose his decision? Why would others favor it? How do you feel about his decision?

11. What qualities of character revealed in President Lincoln's letter have made him one of the most honored and beloved presidents in United States history?

AUTHOR

Irene Hunt was born near Newton, Illinois, was educated at the universities of Illinois, Minnesota, and Colorado, and was a teacher for a great many years. Good books have always held excitement for her, and she feels strongly that young people can gain important insights through reading well-written stories.

Miss Hunt's first book, published when she was in her fifties, was the widely acclaimed *Across Five Aprils,* which won numerous awards and was the sole Newbery Medal Honor book in 1965. For its setting, she used the southern Illinois farm on which she grew up. She did extensive research for the historical background of her novel, but many of the situations and episodes in the book were suggested by family records, letters, and by the stories told to her by her grandfather, who had been a boy of nine at the outbreak of the Civil War. Her second book, *Up a Road Slowly,* which is a present-day realistic story, received the Newbery Medal in 1967.

Miss Hunt now lives in St. Petersburg, Florida, where she spends most of her time writing. She lists among her hobbies gardening, music, and reading.

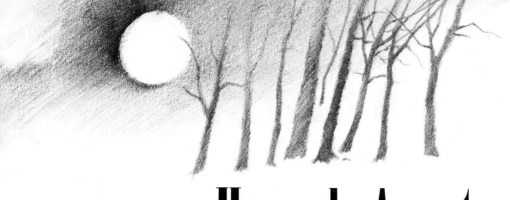

Hannah Armstrong

by EDGAR LEE MASTERS

I wrote him a letter asking him for old times' sake
To discharge my sick boy from the Army;
But maybe he couldn't read it.
Then I went to town and had James Garber,
Who wrote beautifully, write him a letter;
But maybe that was lost in the mails.
So I traveled all the way to Washington.
I was more than an hour finding the White House.
And when I found it they turned me away,
Hiding their smiles. Then I thought:
Oh, well, he ain't the same as when I boarded him
And he and my husband worked together
And all of us called him Abe, there in Menard.
As a last attempt I turned to a guard and said:
"Please say it's old Aunt Hannah Armstrong
From Illinois, come to see him about her sick boy
In the Army."
Well, just in a moment they let me in!
And when he saw me he broke in a laugh,
And dropped his business as President,
And wrote in his own hand Doug's discharge,
Talking the while of the early days,
And telling stories.

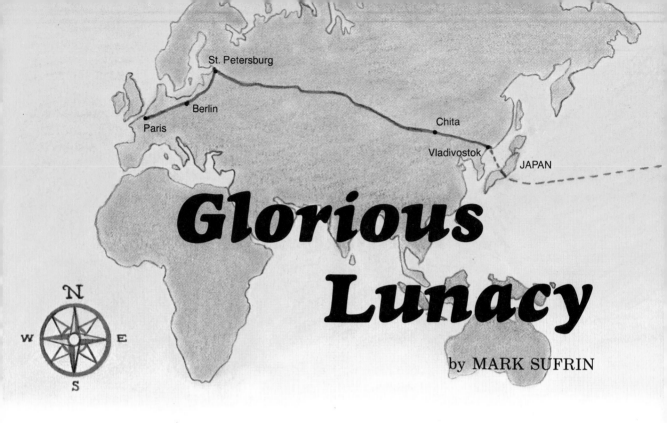

Glorious Lunacy

by MARK SUFRIN

On a bitter winter day, February 12, 1908, a quarter-million New Yorkers jammed Broadway north from Times Square, awaiting the start of the longest motor race in history. It was the 13,341-mile run from New York to Paris over a route that led west across America, by ship to Alaska and Asia, then overland across the frozen Siberian wilderness into Europe — a route that would take the winner 169 days to finish. Sponsored by a French newspaper for a $5,000 prize and a gold cup, it is still the most grueling motor-race course ever devised.

The six cars — an entry each from America, Germany, and Italy, and three from France — edged through a lane held open by mounted police. As the American Thomas Flyer moved up slowly, the great crowd went wild and tried to break through the police lines. It was an emotional, patriotic swarm, but few gave the Thomas the slimmest chance against the others. The European entries were crack machines with superbly trained crews.

Reprinted from the November/December issue of *Quest/77* by special permission. Copyright © 1977, Ambassador International Cultural Foundation. All rights reserved.

The Thomas looked like a lumbering Conestoga wagon, and perched high behind the wheel, driver George Schuster, thirty-five, chief road tester for the Thomas Company, was a contrast to the younger, dapper foreigners. With his spare frame, pleasant face, ordinary work clothes, and boxy high shoes, he was a caricature of the Yankee rube.

Schuster glanced at the German car, a Protos, the machine to beat. The driver was Lieutenant Hans Von Koeppen (hahns fahn kahp'pen), a stern, mustachioed Prussian wearing a dress uniform, leather greatcoat, and helmet. Schuster was a dogged man, an innocent, and for a time he underestimated Koeppen's slyness, his mania to win, and his brilliance as a driver. It was this striking difference between the two that gave their rivalry an epic quality.

At 11:15 A.M. a starter fired a pistol and the great adventure was on. Speeding toward the outskirts of the city, the Thomas and Protos set a fast pace, hanging close. Hitting open country, the Thomas shot into the lead. The Protos was a mile behind. Trailing were the Italian Zust (zoost) and the three French cars: a Motobloc, a Sizaire-Naudin (see-zayr'no-dahn') and a DeDion (duh-dee-ohn'), carrying the representative of the French sponsor. Crowds, bands, and flags lined the road into the Hudson Valley as the racers headed north for Albany on the first leg. The cars were rocking at a jaunty speed, and the race seemed a marvelous lark.

The original route was glorious lunacy. The cars would cross the continent to Seattle, push north through Canada and Alaska, cross the iced-over Bering Strait to Siberia, traverse the frozen tundras into Europe, and speed to Paris via St. Petersburg (now Leningrad) and Berlin. The race committee arranged for caravans to be dispatched through primitive country to deposit gasoline stores along the way, bringing news that "Insane men are coming in carts that move by magic." The distance was originally estimated at 19,200 miles, and to insure success, the start was in the dead of winter.

From the moment the plan was announced, it was ridiculed by experts. The Bering Strait was a wilderness of broken ice, crags, and crevasses that would break under the overloaded cars. Thousands of miles of trackless stretches in Alaska and Siberia were unexplored. In northern Siberia the mountains were sheer ice slopes, the first eleven hundred miles lacked human settlements, and it was almost four thousand miles to the first big town.

The race committee was forced to change the route. The cars would drive to San Francisco, ship to southern Alaska, cross overland to Nome, ship across the Bering Strait, and then follow the original route. Even this plan was further altered as the harrowing comedy unfolded.

Twenty miles outside New York City, the sky darkened and the snow began. A gentle flurry at first, it lashed into a bad blizzard. The road turned icy slick, and Schuster fought to keep the Thomas from skidding. Once the rear slued, and the car slipped out fast toward a ditch. He kept swinging the wheel and with a feather touch on the brakes was bringing it to a stop. Suddenly he saw headlamp beams prying through the snowfall. It was the Protos coming on at breakneck speed despite the treacherous conditions, and Schuster had to hang the Flyer on the edge of the embankment to avoid being hit. The Protos swept past and disappeared into the storm. Then Schuster knew he'd have to be wary of Koeppen and never give him a moment's advantage in the thousands of miles ahead.

Fifty miles from New York, the French Sizaire-Naudin quit the race with a broken differential. The second day, wind and snow still streaking in, the remaining cars were reduced to a crawl. A crew member waded ahead on foot to test the snow depth and guide the driver. The men tunneled through giant drifts that collapsed and almost buried them alive.

It was only a hint of the terrible rigors ahead. One motoring journal asked, "What will happen when the intrepid adventurers get outside civilization?" But the crews were undaunted. Extraordinary men in an age of unbounded optimism, they were confident their cars could meet the challenge.

The Protos was the product of German General Staff planning, an automobile that had great military potential. It weighed over six thousand pounds and was powered by a sturdy forty-horsepower, four-cylinder engine. Extra wide, it had crosswise sleeping space for the crew — Koeppen and two other army officers, who had trained for months. Six fuel tanks holding 176 gallons each were shaped around the Protos, enough for more than two thousand miles. It had been tested over the worst terrain in savage weather and repeatedly modified and improved.

The French DeDion, another hippo of a car, was insulated against Arctic cold with soft wood wrapped in felt and covered with rubber. It was the first car with a heater and had enormous gas capacity. A mast and sail rigged by crew member Hans Hansen, a Norwegian explorer, would be used for added speed across the tundras. Like most of the other European cars, it carried a complete mobile workshop.

There was no American entry until three days before the start. Then the Buffalo, New York, plant of the E. R. Thomas Company selected an ordinary production model — a four-cylinder, seventy-horsepower Flyer with a four-speed transmission and double-chain drive, capable of hitting seventy-five miles an hour — actually the fastest, lightest, most powerful car in the race. There were frantic preparations. The fenders were stripped and replaced with two rock-elm planks for tracking out of mud and snow. An extra gas tank was fitted behind the front seat and another strapped to the back under the spare tires. Holes were drilled in the floorboard to let engine heat through. A new axle to give the car higher road clearance was fitted when it passed through Buffalo.

The Thomas picked up a mechanic in Buffalo, George Miller, and eventually shuttled out front. The Protos was forty-four miles back. In Ohio, Koeppen made a sly move. He stripped the Protos, sent the extra equipment and supplies ahead by rail, and began gaining ground until almost within sight of the Thomas. But no matter what Koeppen tried, the heavy Protos lagged again as Schuster opened a tremendous lead.

The Thomas was first into Chicago on February 25 and left three days later. The Zust and DeDion trailed by a day. The Protos was nine days behind. West of Chicago, rain softened the frozen winter mud into a tideless sea of gumbo. The weather was maddening. One day frost turned the prairie into a hard speed track; the next, warming winds made it a nightmare of sucking mud that exhausted the crews as they pushed the dead weight of their stalled cars.

In Cheyenne, Wyoming, on March 8, Schuster took on another crew member: Hansen, the Norwegian from the DeDion. He had quarreled with the representative of the French sponsor in Chicago, caught a train west, and was waiting for the Americans. That same day the French Motobloc fell out of the race in Cedar Rapids, Iowa. Only four cars were left.

Between Rawlins and Rock Springs, Wyoming, there were no roads, and the Thomas rolled along the tracks of the Union Pacific. The railroad scheduled it as a special train. The flimsy tires kept blowing out as they bumped across the ties, and once while making repairs, still sitting in the track, the crew had to set out flares up the line to stop the San Francisco express.

Speeding for the Rockies, the Thomas was a thousand miles in front of the Zust and thirteen hundred ahead of the Protos. The Thomas and its half-frozen crew made it over the mountains through a howling, snow-filled pass eleven thousand feet up, headed south across the Nevada desert into California, and hit Death Valley. Flanked by dazzling, ridged sand dunes, they started across the crusted bottom of the vast depression. The heat was atrocious, as thick as vapor. There was no shelter anywhere, and the underside of the car was a furnace. But they finally gained the far mountain wall, rolled through sage and bleached grass into green country, and raced up the coast.

The Thomas reached San Francisco on March 24. It had covered thirty-eight hundred miles in forty-one days, the first car to cross the continent in winter. The city celebrated the American car's overwhelming lead despite Schuster's quiet protest that the race was far from over. There was no word of the Protos, which at last reckoning was three weeks behind.

On March 27 the Thomas sailed for Seattle, Washington, en route to Alaska. It reached Valdez, Alaska, on April 9 — the first car seen there. The next leg was cross-country north to Nome, where the Thomas was to be shipped across the Bering Strait. Schuster made a survey by dog sled and realized that the wild land was impassable. The snow was chest high, and massive drifts were softening fast. A car would not only be stopped, he thought — it would vanish. Conditions were similar on the Siberian side of the strait. The spring thaw that year was one of the earliest in history, after one of the coldest winters on record. The Thomas was loaded aboard the next steamer south for Seattle.

The route was again redrawn. The cars would start together across Asia from Vladivostok (vlad'uh-vahs-tahk') in southeast Russia. They could reach that point from Seattle by whatever means and direction they chose. From there they would cross Manchuria, skirt Mongolia, enter central Siberia, and eventually hit the original route to Paris.

The Protos had thrown two rods near Ogden, Utah, where Koeppen learned of the new route. He knew he'd never make up the time going overland, and now he had his excuse. He requested permission to ship by rail to Seattle. The committee refused, but Koeppen insisted that he couldn't be disqualified if he entrained for the coast. Brazenly he argued that the committee had "failed to provide passable roads," didn't wait for a ruling, and skipped a thousand miles of the worst country on the route.

Schuster reached Seattle April 18 and was told that the Zust and DeDion had sailed to Japan four days earlier. The Protos had just arrived, and Koeppen said he'd been disqualified but was shipping his car direct to Vladivostok. Factory mechanics and a new engine would be waiting. He was going to stick it out — if only as a lowly observer.

Schuster wasn't fooled. He'd already sized up the German as a man crazy to win by any means. Schuster was sure that the first car into Paris, whatever the circumstances, would reap the glory. At first he was going to stick close to Koeppen and ship to Vladivostok; then he decided to join the others in the first automobile crossing of Japan.

The committee meted out time penalties and bonuses. Koeppen's wily, constant intrigue paid off, and he was allowed to reenter the race at Vladivostok with a handicap of fifteen days against the Protos. The Thomas was given a bonus of fifteen days for its round-trip voyage to

Alaska. On May 17, after crossing Japan in two days, the Thomas regrouped with the other cars in Vladivostok. At this point the manufacturer of the DeDion, disgusted with the committee's incredible misjudgments and decisions, withdrew his car.

Schuster had welcomed the fresh start from Vladivostok, confident the Thomas could run its rivals into the ground. The German would have to reach Paris twenty-nine days ahead of the Thomas Flyer to cancel out handicaps and bonuses. But it wasn't impossible; anything could happen in the Siberian wilderness.

At dawn of May 22, Schuster was at the starting line — but Koeppen had slipped away two hours earlier. The American scrambled off in pursuit of the German car. The Zust met maddening delays and didn't get off until June 5. The Italians were out of the race, but the driver wanted to finish.

The Thomas's crew scanned the distance for bandits as they drove along the rim of northern Mongolia. Schuster refused relief at the wheel, pressing the Flyer to its limit. Soon he was close behind the Protos and finally drew even. The German car was sunk to its hubs in a mud bog, and Schuster felt that the sporting thing was to stop and help. No matter what Koeppen had done, his car was in trouble, and rules of the road demanded that the American offer aid. When the Protos was pulled out, Koeppen seemed to have a change of heart. He graciously thanked Schuster. The two men debated whether to stick to the official route or use the roadbed of the Trans-Siberian Railroad. They agreed to stay on the planned route and shook hands on it. The Thomas Flyer left first as the Germans pretended to scrape the mud from their car. The moment the Thomas was out of sight, Koeppen headed straight for the railroad, and he later won $1,000 for being first into Chita (chih-ta′), a prosperous Siberian city.

Still in Manchuria, the Thomas lost five days after breaking down in a swamp with a bad wheel and transmission (damaged when the Americans rescued the Protos). Hansen and Miller started on foot for a distant town but collapsed after struggling a few hundred yards in the mud. They kept lurching and stumbling, then rolled into the slime, trying to recoup their strength. Schuster thought everything was over when Hansen rose to his knees and pointed, trying to shout. Schuster saw a dark blur in the distance, heard a burst of sound, and was able to make out the shapes of horseback riders beating across the swamp — a company of Russian Cossacks.

The officer barked an order, and the riders tied ropes from the car to their saddle horns. Bursting into song, they spurred their mounts. Slowly the Thomas oozed out of the mud and was towed to the town, the Cossacks singing all the way. They cut the spattered ropes with sabers and left them lying in the road. The officer looked at the rusting, battered machine, laughed, and shook his head; then the cavalry galloped off in a fusillade of shots.

Repairs were made, but after seventy miles the road became impassable, so the Thomas doubled back to pick up the track of the Trans-Siberian Railroad. In the Lesser Khingan (shing'ahn') Mountains, though the weather improved, the Thomas barely escaped a head-on collision with a mail train at the entrance of a tunnel.

After abandoning the railroad, the Thomas met constant rain, cold, mosquitoes, and mud, and a track so overgrown that the crew had to chop a way through. In Siberia the rutted road ran through a flooded plain. Rivers had broken their banks, sweeping bridges away and swelling the fords. A black swamp stretched to the horizon. The Thomas kept sluing into ditches, hitting sunken rocks and logs that battered the vulnerable underside. A crew member wearing high boots, spelled every four hours, had to walk ahead and mark a path.

Soon the crew were attacked by thousands of gnats. They swathed themselves in netting and every shred of clothes they could find, but it was useless. Their only escape was to leap into the swamp and roll around, to suffer until the plague vanished with the darkness and the pinching cold. At last the flood receded, leaving a resinous bed of mud. They were able to keep the car rolling, but Schuster prayed for dry ground. The car was rusting and being jolted to pieces, and everyone was in bad shape. Snatches of sleep did the crew little good; they were used up, always tense, hungry, and thirsty. They froze by night and baked by day, and their exposed skin was cracking. Eyes were red and painfully strained from the wind and glare and from staring into the distance.

The water rose again with new storms. It came within an inch of the magneto and carburetor, and the springs were submerged. The lights were of little use, continually doused by mud and water thrown up by the wheels. Eventually the water was too high to keep the engine running. Schuster dismounted the magneto and carburetor and kept them dry in the folds of his mackinaw. Soon the running boards and the transmission were under water.

It was too much for Hansen. He had imagined the race as a glorious sweep with sails across a flat, glittering, frozen tundra. He leaped off the car into deep water and looked up at Schuster.

"I've had enough. I leave you now. I leave New York-to-Paris. I leave all this foolishness!"

Schuster pointed into the darkness. "Where do you figure on going?"

Hansen shook his head slowly and climbed aboard. By morning the water was topping the big wheels and the front seats were going under. The crew thought they should split up and search for help. Then the water level began to fall. In a few hours Schuster was able to start the engine, and they made good mileage before breaking down on June 14 near Shilka, a railroad town. He discovered that Koeppen had passed through a week earlier — using the railroad all the way across Manchuria. Schuster was still leading in terms of the penalties and bonuses and wanted to push on, but they needed rest. That night they slept on a billiard table and used cues to fend off rats.

Later in June, as the Thomas was crossing the Ob River on a one-car ferry, the flimsy craft sank ten yards off the far shore in shallow water. Hauled out by oxen, the Thomas continued on its way at a breakneck pace. The transmission failed twice more during the next two weeks, so more valuable time was lost.

Lagging behind the Protos by one day, the Thomas raced nonstop for eight days. Clinging to the rocketing car, no one could sleep. Schuster, who drove most of the time, kept pushing in a frantic effort to catch Koeppen. Nearing the end of their endurance, the crew could barely sit upright as the Thomas sped into St. Petersburg on July 23. At that moment Koeppen was nearing Berlin, almost a thousand miles in the lead.

During a celebration in Berlin, Koeppen heard that the Thomas had crossed the German border. He left immediately on the last leg to Paris, discarding anything that could cut his speed. He knew Schuster would be declared the winner but believed that the first car across the finish line would capture the attention of the world. He arrived on July 27 at 6:15 P.M. That same day Schuster entered Berlin and was told the bad news.

Koeppen's car sprinted down the Champs-Élysées[1] on a soft summer evening. There were few motorcars in the street, and only a small crowd remained. Koeppen drove to the office of the French newspaper sponsoring the race, where he received a cool reception. He left for Germany the next day, and there he received the victor's welcome denied him by the French.

On July 30 the crew hoisted a muddied Stars and Stripes over the sagging Thomas. Outside Paris they were met by hundreds of honking autos and huge crowds shouting *"Vive le car américain!"* [2] The convoy escorted them to Paris at 8 P.M., and the city poured out in tribute. At one point Schuster was flagged down by police for driving without

---

[1] **Champs-Élysées** (shons-eh-lee-zay′), a famous street in Paris.
[2] **Vive le car américain!** (veev luh kahr ah-meh′ree-cahn′), a cheer of congratulation meaning "Long live the American car!"

lights and was allowed to continue the triumphal parade only when a cyclist stuck a bicycle with its lantern in the Flyer's front seat.

There were parades in New York, Buffalo, and Washington, D.C., where the crew were received by President Theodore Roosevelt. Souvenir hunters almost tore the Thomas apart, but it was restored and is still on exhibition at an automotive museum in Reno, Nevada.

Koeppen died in World War I, but his Protos can be seen in a museum in Munich, Germany. The bad luck of the Zust persisted. It managed to limp into Paris only on September 17.

George Schuster, the unlikely hero, died in 1972 at the age of ninety-nine. For his victory, the Thomas Company raised his pay from $35 to $50 a week. After Thomas went out of business in 1912, Schuster was a representative in Asia and Africa for another automobile manufacturer. In the latter part of his life he was an automobile dealer. He gave up driving at ninety, when his eyesight failed — and he was no longer a contender in the speed, tension, and complexity of modern traffic.

DISCUSSION

1. What factors made the race of 1908 unique in the history of motor racing?
2. Judging by the author's descriptions, which episode in the race do you think would provide the most interesting photo and why?
3. Who sponsored the race? What was the prize? Which countries entered cars in the race?
4. Why was the original route of the race considered "glorious lunacy"?
5. Who was Lieutenant Hans Von Koeppen? Why, do you think, did Schuster at first underestimate Koeppen as a rival?
6. What do you think the author meant when he referred to the race as "the harrowing comedy"?
7. Why didn't most people give the American Thomas Flyer the slimmest chance of winning against the European entries?
8. What gave the Thomas an advantage over the other cars?
9. Before completing the race, what records did the Thomas set in San Francisco, California, and in Valdez, Alaska?
10. What happened in Manchuria to make the Thomas lose five days' time? Who came to its rescue there? What did the Cossack officer think of the Thomas Flyer as a means of transportation?
11. Why didn't Koeppen win the race, even though he crossed the finish line first?
12. Why, do you think, did the driver of the Zust want to finish the race even after learning that the Italians had no chance of winning it? Would you agree that finishing first is not necessarily the most important goal in a race? Why or why not?

AUTHOR

As a high school student in Brooklyn, New York, Mark Sufrin was an inter-scholastic swimming champion. After earning a master's degree at Columbia University, he became a free-lance writer. Among his credits are a prize-winning documentary film for which he wrote the script, numerous magazine articles, and several books.

Habits of the Hippopotamus

by ARTHUR GUITERMAN

The hippopotamus is strong
    And huge of head and broad of bustle;
The limbs on which it rolls along
    Are big with hippopotomuscle.

It does not greatly care for sweets
    Like ice cream, apple pie, or custard,
But takes to flavor what it eats
    A little hippopotomustard.

The hippopotamus is true
    To all its principles, and just;
It always tries its best to do
    The things one hippopotomust.

It never rides in trucks or trams,
    In taxicabs or omnibuses,
And so keeps out of traffic jams
    And other hippopotomusses.

SKILL

Graphs

Current studies indicate that there are many endangered species of animals in the world. Figures show that many birds suffer survival problems, with 67 species in danger. There are 33 endangered species of mammals. Among fish, of which there are more species than in the bird and mammal classes together, there are 29 endangered species. Eleven species of reptiles are endangered. Among amphibians 5 species are endangered.

Can you remember the facts in that paragraph well enough to compare or contrast the information it presents about endangered species of animals? Probably not, because written material containing many facts and figures is usually difficult to understand and remember when it is presented in paragraph form. Such information is often more meaningful if it is shown in graphic form. A graph is a drawing used to present numerical data or information clearly and simply. Graphs enable you to note likenesses and differences quickly and to make comparisons easily.

Reading a Bar Graph

Most of the information about animals in the opening paragraph is shown clearly in the graphs on the next page, which are called bar graphs. A bar graph uses bars to present numerical information. Graph 1 is called a horizontal bar graph because the bars run across the graph. The title tells you that the graph is about species of animals with backbones. Notice that each of the horizontal bars stands for a class of animal. The vertical lines help you find the number of species in each class. Each space between vertical lines represents 5,000 species. To find out the total number of species in a class, you need to determine the approximate point at which the bar for that class ends in relation to the figures at the top of the vertical lines. For example, the bar for amphibians ends about three-fifths of the way between 0 and 5,000, meaning that there are about 3,000 species of amphibians.

Notice that Graph 1 makes it easy for you to see not only the number of species in each class but also the differences between classes. For instance, you can see at a glance that there are more than twice as many species of fishes as there are of birds.

Graph 2, which provides information about endangered species, is called a vertical bar graph because the bars go up and down instead of across the graph. In this graph, each vertical bar represents a class of animal and each horizontal line represents a number of species. Each space between lines stands for 10 species. By looking at the bars, you can quickly see that the greatest number of endangered species are in the bird class, the least number in the amphibians class.

You can also use graphs 1 and 2 together to compare and relate information. For example, you can see from Graph 1 that there are more than twice as many species of fishes as there are of birds. However, if you compare the number of endangered species in each class, you can see from Graph 2 that there are more than twice as many *endangered* species of birds as there are of fishes.

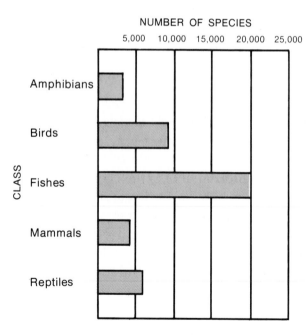

GRAPH 1. **Species of Animals with Backbones**

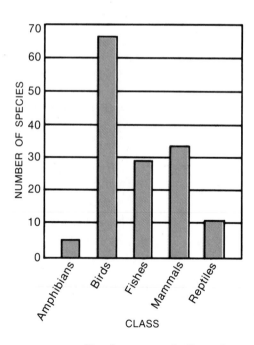

GRAPH 2. **Endangered Species**

Brazil	🐎🐎🐎🐎🐎🐎🐎🐎🐎🐎
United States	🐎🐎🐎🐎🐎🐎🐎🐎🐎🐎
China	🐎🐎🐎🐎🐎🐎🐎🐎
Russia	🐎🐎🐎🐎🐎🐎
Mexico	🐎🐎🐎🐎🐎
Argentina	🐎🐎🐎🐎
Mongolia	🐎🐎🐎
Poland	🐎🐎🐎
Ethiopia	🐎🐎
Yugoslavia	🐎

Each whole symbol represents 1 million horses.

GRAPH 3. **Leading Horse-Raising Countries, 1975**

Reading a Pictograph

The graph above is called a pictograph. Each symbol, or picture, in a pictograph stands for a particular quantity, as explained in the key. You can see from the caption that this pictograph is about leading horse-raising countries in 1975. The key at the bottom explains that each whole symbol represents 1 million (1,000,000) horses. From this information you know that half a symbol stands for half a million, or 500,000, horses. Like most graphs, Graph 3 is intended to give you approximate figures that are rounded off rather than exact numerical information.

To find out how many horses were raised in a given country in 1975, simply add the numbers represented by complete and partial symbols in that row on the pictograph. For instance, using the symbols in the row for Russia, you would add six whole symbols, meaning 6 million horses, and about three-quarters of a symbol, meaning 750,000 horses, to get a total of about 6,750,000 horses.

A pictograph, like other kinds of graphs, often can be used to help you make comparisons easily. For instance, a quick look at Graph 3 shows you that the leading horse-raising country, Brazil, raised only about half a million more horses than the United States. Now use the graph to find out whether Mexico or Argentina raised more horses in 1975.

Reading a Line Graph

Graph 4 is another type of graph used to present numerical information. It is a line graph, on which points that represent numbers are connected by a line. The caption tells you that the graph presents information about United States farm workers during a fifty-year period. The numbers at the left indicate that each space between horizontal lines stands for 2 million workers. The spaces between vertical lines represent intervals of ten years.

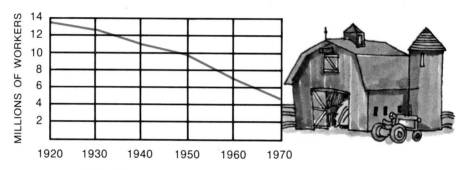

GRAPH 4. **U.S. Farm Workers, 1920–1970**

To find out how many workers there were on United States farms in 1960, first locate the vertical black line for that year. Then follow that line until you find the point at which the red line crosses it. Notice that the red line is about halfway between the horizontal lines that are numbered 6 and 8, meaning that in 1960 about 7 million people in the United States worked on farms.

Often you can use a line graph to observe a trend or change over a period of time. From Graph 4, you can see that there has been a downward trend in agricultural employment from 1920 through 1970, especially during the years from 1950 to 1970.

Now look at Graph 5 on page 111. Notice that it uses three colored lines to present information about the number of women who were in the United States labor force from 1948 through 1978. The key at the top of the graph tells what group is represented by each colored line. The numerals at the left tell you that each space between horizontal lines stands for 1 million women. The vertical lines represent intervals of five years.

110

To find out how many married women were in the U.S. labor force in 1953, first check the key to see which colored line represents that group. Then locate the point at which the green line meets the vertical line for 1953. You can see that those two lines meet at the horizontal line that represents 11 million, so you know that about 11 million married women were part of the labor force in 1953.

By reading the other colored lines that cross the vertical black line for 1953, you can see that in that year about 5½ million single women and about 3 million formerly married women were in the work force. If you want to know the total number of women employed in 1953, you add the figures 11, 5½, and 3, getting a total of 19½ million. Like a pictograph, a multilined graph enables you to make comparisons easily. For instance, Graph 5 makes it visually evident that of the three categories of women, married women in the labor force increased in number the most.

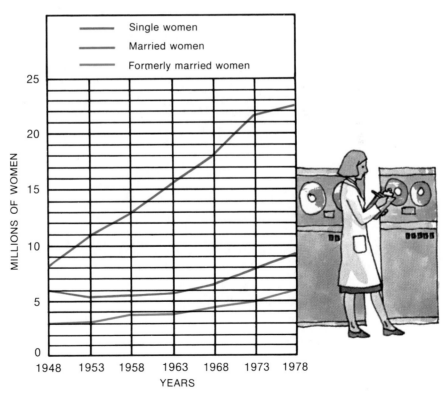

GRAPH 5. **Women in the U.S. Labor Force, 1948–1978**

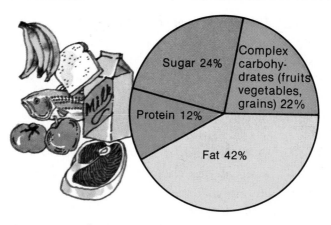

GRAPH 6. **Average U.S. Diet in 1977.**
SHOWS TOTAL DAILY CALORIE, OR ENERGY, INTAKE.

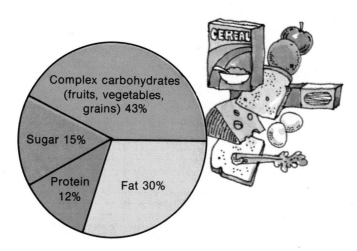

GRAPH 7. **Dietary Goals for the U.S.**
SHOWS RECOMMENDED TOTAL DAILY CALORIE INTAKE.

Source for graphs 6 and 7: 1977 report of the Committee on Nutrition and Human Needs of the U.S. Senate, *Dietary Goals for the United States.*

Reading a Circle Graph

A circle graph, which shows how parts are related to the whole, is another kind of graph used to present numerical information clearly. Circle graphs usually give information in percentages. The whole circle represents a total number, or 100%, of something, and each part represents a fraction, or percentage, of the whole.

112

Graphs 6 and 7 are circle graphs that deal in a special way with the diet, or eating habits, of people in the United States. The footnote tells you that the information for both graphs was taken from a report of the Committee on Nutrition and Human Needs of the U.S. Senate. Graphs are often accompanied by a footnote that gives the source of the figures. The footnote helps you to evaluate the information on a graph and may direct you to material that provides more details about the subject.

From reading the caption of Graph 6, you can see that it gives information about the average diet of people in the United States in 1977. The graph shows the sources of the total daily calorie, or energy, intake in the average person's diet. If you were reading an article or chapter on health and nutrition, you would be likely to find this kind of graph accompanying the text.

Look at the labels in the parts of Graph 6. Before interpreting a graph, you should be sure that you understand each term it contains. In the case of Graph 6, you are probably familiar with all of the terms except for *complex carbohydrates,* which has been explained in parentheses. By reading the explanation, you can tell which kinds of foods contain the calories known as complex carbohydrates.

A quick glance at Graph 6 shows that in 1977 the largest part of the average total daily calorie intake, or 42%, was made up of fat. By comparing the other parts of the graph, you can easily see that the smallest part, or 12%, of the total calorie intake was made up of protein. Interpreting the percentages given, you know that in 1977 a major portion of the average daily calorie intake of people in the United States came from foods containing fat.

Now look at Graph 7. From the caption you can tell that the graph presents the dietary goals, or balance, that people in the United States should *try* to achieve. In contrast to Graph 6, Graph 7 shows suggested, not actual, percentages. Therefore, you can conclude that the graph is intended to represent a healthier diet than is shown for 1977 in Graph 6.

If you compare graphs 6 and 7, you can see what changes in eating habits are suggested. According to Graph 7, how great a decrease should there be in the percentage of fat consumed?

When you are using graphs, you should remember two things. One is that graphs often present more information than you sometimes want. When you are using a graph, look only for the information that you need. Another thing to remember is that graphs usually present approximate figures, which are rounded off because most graphs are not designed to show specific amounts. If you need more exact information, you should use another source.

If you keep these two points in mind, you will find that graphs are a useful study tool.

READING GRAPHS

Use the graphs you have read in this lesson to answer the following questions. On a piece of paper, write the numeral of each question and then write your answer.

1. According to Graph 1, about how many species of reptiles exist?
2. About how many more species of reptiles are there than species of amphibians?
3. According to Graph 2, about how many species of mammals are endangered?
4. According to Graph 2, about how many more species of reptiles than amphibians are endangered?
5. In Graph 3, how many horses were raised in Argentina?
6. Which country raised about twice the number of horses raised in Argentina?
7. According to Graph 4, approximately how many farm workers were there in 1940?
8. How many fewer farm workers were there in 1960 than in 1940?
9. According to Graph 5, which category of working women increased the most in number between 1973 and 1978?
10. How many more single women were in the labor force in 1978 than in 1973?
11. According to graphs 6 and 7, what percentage of decrease is recommended for sugar consumption?
12. According to graphs 6 and 7, how great an increase would be desirable in the percentage of complex carbohydrates consumed?

Margaret Mead

by KATHLEEN BOWMAN

In October, 1925, a young woman named Margaret Mead stood on the deck of a ship bound for Samoa. As the vessel pulled away from the Hawaiian shore, Margaret and the other passengers festively tossed flower leis into the ocean and watched the bright petals float on the ship's wake.

But as she sailed toward the tiny island in the Pacific, some seventy-five hundred miles from home, Margaret became increasingly consumed by a sense of urgency. It was her first field trip, and it had become so important to her that it felt more like a mission. Margaret knew that it was only a matter of time before modern civilization would bring new ideas and technology to remote parts of the world, changing forever the old ways of those societies. She had been taught that a major role of anthropologists was to try to record every facet of remote cultures before the traditional ways had vanished. They must study people's dress, what they ate, how they worked, and how they played. Important too were their family life, their child-rearing habits, and the work considered appropriate for women and for men.

Many people had preceded Margaret Mead to Samoa: missionaries, government officials, and tourists. Because the culture as a whole was quite well-known, Margaret planned to focus her energies on a single area of investigation: the life of adolescent girls in Samoan society. She was curious to see if their experiences were different from those of teen-age girls in our own society. Margaret wanted to find out how the Samoan girls spent their days and how they made friends. She also wanted to know if the teen-age years in Samoa were a period of "storm and stress," as they generally were in American society.

The day the ship was to arrive in Samoa, Margaret was up at dawn. She had never seen a South Sea island, and she watched with fascination as it came into view.

When Margaret stepped off the boat in Pago Pago (pahng'go pahng'go) that October, her only companions were a camera, a portable typewriter, several fat notebooks, and six cotton dresses. No one was waiting for her. She found no one eager to help her learn or ready to share her enthusiasm and anxieties. For the first time, Margaret was confronted with the loneliness of field work.

For six discouraging weeks, Margaret lived in a hotel room in Pago Pago. Each day she walked around the port town, trying out her new Samoan phrases on the children. But she remained apart from the community she wanted to understand. Finally, a woman Margaret had met in Honolulu came to her aid. She found a family that would adopt Margaret, the family of a chief in the village of Vaitogi (vie-toh'nyee).

For ten days, Margaret lived as an adopted family member in the chief's household, gaining firsthand experience in Samoan culture. She slept on a pile of mats, learned the rules of Samoan eating etiquette, and had her first dancing lessons. Though her legs ached from learning to sit correctly on the ground, the physical pain was a welcome change from the pain of isolation she had previously felt.

The chief's daughter, Fa' amotu (fah'ah-moh'too), was Margaret's constant companion. She taught Margaret everything from how to identify high-ranking officials to the names of special leaves used to weave mats. She also provided Margaret with her first contacts with young girls in Samoan society.

The bonds of friendship Margaret had established with the chief's family made leaving Vaitogi difficult. But the village was too modern for her study of adolescence. Margaret would do her research on the island of Tau (tah-oo'), "island of the turtle and the shark."

On Tau, Margaret's living quarters were on the back veranda of a medical dispensary. These living conditions allowed her to be visited by adolescent and preadolescent girls for simple examinations. She utilized the opportunity to find out about each girl's background. Her research was interrupted on one dramatic occasion by a hurricane that damaged the dispensary and destroyed the house Margaret was to have as a workroom. More importantly, village ceremonies were halted as everyone's energies went into rebuilding the village. But nine months after she began, Margaret Mead completed her research.

In June, 1926, Margaret returned home and began recording her experiences and insights in a book that was to become a best seller— Coming of Age in Samoa. Among her findings was the conclusion that adolescence in Samoa was *not* a period of stress. For the young in that society, life was easygoing and casual, with conflict being very rare. These conditions seemed possible in Samoa partly because the pace of life was slow, the population small,

and the threat of poverty minimal. Moreover, the choices presented to a Samoan teen-ager were few. By contrast, American youth face an overwhelming number of choices.

Coming of Age in Samoa was published in 1928. Margaret received her Ph.D. from Columbia University in 1929. The book continues to sell over one hundred thousand copies a year. The reason for its popularity seems to be that it is written "in English," as Dr. Mead said, rather than in academic jargon filled with statistics. She called the book a "tale of another way of life," and, indeed, it has many attributes of a story filled with interesting characters and behavior. She disguised the names so that actual Samoans could not be identified.

Coming of Age in Samoa set the pattern that persisted throughout Dr. Mead's life of "studying the lives of other peoples . . . so that Americans might better understand themselves." She also studied American culture to gain an understanding of its features and changes.

The career of the world's most famous anthropologist spanned more than fifty years. Until her death in 1978, Dr. Mead ran an office at the American Museum of Natural History with many assistants who did research, wrote bibliographies, and made arrangements for her writing and speaking engagements. She lectured over sixty

times a year, wrote for a national magazine, and made frequent radio and television appearances. In 1975 she received the Woman of Conscience award made by the National Council of Women of the United States. Predictably, she used the award money to help finance a trip to Samoa the following summer.

On the stage, Dr. Mead was a distinctive figure. She often wore a long, flowing cape and always carried a tall, black varnished walking stick. The shoulder-high staff was acquired in 1966 after Dr. Mead broke her ankle and the doctor told her to use a cane. She rejected the idea of "looking old" by using a cane and walking with stooped shoulders, so she got a tall English "thumb stick." She was frequently seen at meetings, waving her stick or pounding it on the floor to gain attention. Her ankle healed, but the stick was never discarded.

In her lifetime of world travel and study, Dr. Mead saw both the space age and the Stone Age. Her experience awakened her to hundreds of concerns, many of which became speeches. Her topics included many major issues of the times.

Margaret Mead turned her attention increasingly to problems of the future. She was concerned with the new pressure that twentieth-century human beings face — the necessity of adapting to an ever-changing world. Change is so rapid that decisions must be made quickly and correctly. "Twentieth-century life," she said, "is like a parachute jump. You have to get it right the first time."

Dr. Mead was not alone in recognizing these problems, but she *was* one of the few experts who offered a solution. She believed that we must unite the generations, allowing grandparent, parent, child, and grandchild each to contribute the perspective of his or her life to that of the others. When generations of a family are combined, any member can understand his or her place in the passage of time. It is a way of anchoring oneself in an otherwise overwhelming flood of change.

This theory was the product of Dr. Mead's own experience. She considered her grandmother to have been the most decisive influence in her life. Dr. Mead vividly remembered her grandmother's accounts of her own childhood experiences. Those tales, Dr. Mead claimed, gave her "an extra century of life."

But Dr. Mead was quick to point out that equal emphasis must be placed on the younger generation. In a world constantly overturned by change, it is the younger population that remains closest to that change. If the world is to survive, it must pay heed to the youth culture, for in Dr. Mead's opinion "there are no elders anywhere who know what the young people know."

Dr. Mead offered her solution with an optimistic spirit because she had personally experienced humanity's ability to be—and become—almost anything. To American youth who cry out that adolescence is an inevitable period of strain and nervousness, she could answer that she had seen differently. The Samoans she studied in 1925 arrived at adulthood with little pain or conflict. To American men and women who feel forced into behavior patterns solely on the basis of their sex, Dr. Mead could offer her experiences with the Tchambuli (chahm'-buh-lee) culture of New Guinea (gin'ee). There the women dress modestly and are strong and hearty in their management of life's business affairs. The men, on the other hand, content themselves with gossiping and strutting about the village in fashionable clothes. Life is flexible, she said, because "human nature is infinitely plastic. That is what anthropology teaches us."

In the course of her lifetime, Margaret Mead saw Samoa change so drastically that the grandchildren of Fa'amotu would not recognize the anthropologist's description of their island. Dr. Mead was in the rare position of having lived long enough to see successful adaptation, to see "what few people have ever seen . . . people who have moved from the Stone Age into the present in thirty years."

DISCUSSION

1. Judging by this article, what was Margaret Mead's view of the younger generation? Give reasons for your answer.

2. What was Margaret Mead's area of investigation in Samoa? Why did she choose that area of investigation?

3. What important conclusion did Margaret Mead reach in comparing the lives of adolescents in Samoa and America? How did she account for the lack of conflict in the lives of Samoans during adolescence?

4. According to Margaret Mead, why is adolescence a period of conflict for American youth? Do you think that facing many choices may cause conflict during adolescence? Why or why not?

5. What do you think Margaret Mead meant by saying that her grandmother gave her "an extra century of life"? Would you agree with Margaret Mead's view that within families the members of each generation can make an important contribution to the others? Why do you think that?

6. Why did Margaret Mead believe it is possible for people to adapt successfully to the rapid changes in our space-age society? Do you agree with her optimistic view of human nature? Tell why you think as you do.

AUTHOR

Kathleen Bowman was born and grew up in Minneapolis, Minnesota, and received B.S., M.A., and Ph.D. degrees from the University of Minnesota. She has taught at both the secondary school and college levels and has been program consultant for the Minnesota Department of Education. Since 1977 she has served as research associate of the Legislative Advisory Council on the Economic Status of Women.

Dr. Bowman's books for young people include the "New Women" series, which she both wrote and edited, including *New Women in Social Sciences,* from which the selection about Margaret Mead was taken. Kathleen Bowman is married to an archeologist, has three children, and lives in Minneapolis. Among her special interests are weaving and classical piano.

The Coming of the Corn

by CYRUS MACMILLAN

In old times there dwelt on the shores of a great lake a mighty warrior. His people had all been driven far away inland by hostile tribes, but he remained behind to roam over the islands in the lake and to send his people word of any approaching attack. His wife was dead; she had been killed by treacherous foes. He had two little boys, and he kept them with him in his wanderings by the lake. He was a great magician as well as a man of great strength, and he had no fear in his heart. The islands in the lake were haunted by spirits, or manitous (man'ih-tooz'), but the man was not afraid of them, and with his boys he paddled his canoe up and down, watching for signs of his foes. Each night he landed in a cove, pulled his canoe far up among the trees, and slept in the woods out of sight of travelers. But he found it very hard to get game and fish, and often his boys were very hungry.

One morning at dawn of day, he rose and went to find food for breakfast. He left his little boys asleep under the trees. He walked through the forest until he came suddenly upon a wide and open red plain. There was not a tree or a rock or a blade of grass upon it. He set out across the plain, and when he reached the middle of it, he met a small man with a red feather in his cap.

"Where are you going?" said the little man.

"I am going across the plain to the woods on the other side," said the man. "My boys are hungry, without food, and I am looking for game."

"How strong are you?" said the little man.

"I am as strong as the human race," said the man, "but no stronger."

"My name is Red Plume," said the little man. "We must wrestle. If you should make me fall, say to me, 'I have thrown you.' If you should overcome me, you will never want for food, for you will have other nourishment than fish and game."

They wrestled for a long time. The warrior was growing weak, for the little man was very strong, but at last he threw Red Plume down and cried, "I have thrown you." At once the little man disappeared.

When the warrior looked on the ground where his opponent

had fallen, he saw only a crooked thing like an acorn with a red tassel on it. He picked it up and looked at it, and as he looked, a voice from it said, "Take off my outside covering; split me into many parts, and throw the parts over the plain; scatter every bit of me; throw my spine near the woods. Then, in a month, come back to the plain." The warrior did as he was told and then went back to his boys. On the way he killed a rabbit and cooked it for breakfast. He did not tell his boys what he had seen.

At the end of a month, he went alone again to the plain. In the place where he had scattered the pieces of the strange object, he found blades of strange grass peeping green about the ground. And where he had thrown the pieces of the spine near the wood, little pumpkins were growing.

He did not tell his boys what he had found. All summer he watched for his foes, and in the autumn he went again to the place where he had thrown down the man of the Red Plume. The plain was covered with Indian corn in the ear, and there were

123

also pumpkins of great size near the woods. The corn was golden yellow, and red tassels grew from the top of the ears. He plucked some ears of corn, gathered some of the pumpkins, and set out to find his boys. Then a voice spoke from the corn. He knew it at once to be the voice of the man of the Red Plume. It said, "You have conquered me. If you had failed, you would still have lived, but often you would have hungered as before. Henceforth you shall never want for food, for when game and fish are scarce, you will have bread. And I will never let the human race lack food if they keep me near them." So corn came to the Indians in olden times, and never afterwards did they want for food.

When the man came to his boys, he told them what he had found. He ground some of the corn between stones and made bread from the meal, and he cooked a pumpkin and ate it. Then he thought of his poor old father and mother far away beyond the hills, perhaps without food. So that night he took his boys and traveled far through the forest until he found his parents. He told them of his meeting with the man of the Red Plume and of the coming of the corn. He brought them back with him to the manitou islands near the shores of the great lake. And ever afterwards the fields were fruitful, and corn was abundant and never failed in the land where Red Plume fell.

DISCUSSION

1. In "Gifts of the Indians" the author stated that the origin of corn is "cloaked in mystery." How do you think this Indian legend seems to reflect the same view?
2. Why did the mighty warrior remain behind after his people had been driven inland by hostile tribes?
3. What kind of person was the mighty warrior? Which of his characteristics, do you think, were of greatest value to his people? Why do you think that?
4. Why were the warrior's boys often hungry? What made him leave the boys at dawn one morning?

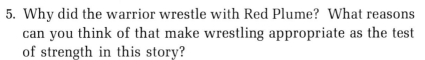

5. Why did the warrior wrestle with Red Plume? What reasons can you think of that make wrestling appropriate as the test of strength in this story?
6. What clues in the story indicate that Red Plume represents corn, or the spirit of corn?
7. Whom do you think the mighty warrior represents? Tell why you think as you do.
8. At the end of a month, what did the warrior find growing on the red plain? When did he find the full-grown corn and pumpkins?
9. What staple food did the warrior make from corn? How did he make it?
10. Even though the story is imaginary, can you suggest a real geographic location in which it might have occurred? Use one or more details in the story to support your choice.

AUTHOR

Cyrus Macmillan, a native of Prince Edward Island, Canada, held various positions in the Canadian government, among them Minister of Fisheries and member of parliament. He was also head of the English department at McGill University in Montreal. His published works include collections of Canadian Indian myths. Mr. Macmillan died in 1953.

Thirteen-year-old Miyax (mie'yaks), an Inuit, or Eskimo, girl living in northern Alaska, had reached a turning point in her life. Rebelling against a forced marriage, she decided to run away from home and seek help from a friend in San Francisco. She acted on the remembered advice of her long-missing father: "When fear seizes, change what you are doing." Determined to make her way to a seaport and eventually to the home of her pen pal in San Francisco, Miyax set off alone across the Arctic wilderness. Now she finds herself in a desperate predicament that tests her endurance and courage.

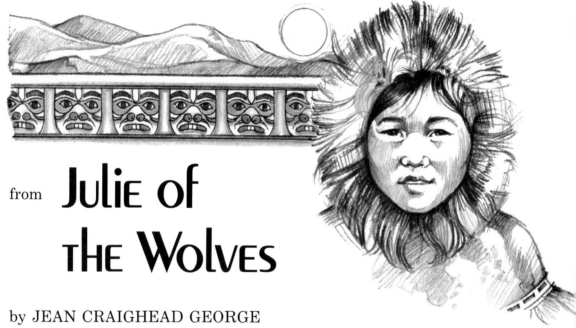

from # Julie of the Wolves

by JEAN CRAIGHEAD GEORGE

Miyax pushed back the hood of her sealskin parka and looked at the Arctic sun. It was a yellow disc in a lime-green sky, the colors of six o'clock in the evening and the time when the wolves awoke. Quietly she put down her cooking pot and crept to the top of a dome-shaped frost heave, one of the many earth buckles that rise and fall in the crackling cold of the Arctic winter. Lying on her stomach, she looked across a vast lawn of grass and moss and focused her attention on the wolves she had come upon two sleeps ago. They were wagging their tails as they awoke and saw one another.

Her hands trembled, and her heartbeat quickened, for she was frightened, not so much of the wolves, which were shy and many harpoonshots away, but because of her desperate predicament. Miyax was lost. She had been lost without food for many sleeps on the North Slope of Alaska. The barren slope stretches for three hundred miles from the Brooks Range to the Arctic Ocean, and for more than eight hundred miles from the Chukchi (chook′chee) Sea to the Beaufort (boh′fert) Sea. No roads cross it; ponds and lakes freckle its immensity. Winds scream across it, and the view in every direction is exactly the same. Somewhere in this cosmos was Miyax; and the very life in her body, its spark and warmth, depended upon these wolves for survival. And she was not so sure they would help.

Miyax stared hard at the regal black wolf, hoping to catch his eye. She must somehow tell him that she was starving and ask him for food. This could be done she knew, for her father, an Eskimo hunter, had done so. Once he had camped near a wolf den while on a hunt. When a month had passed and he had seen no game, he told the wolves' leader that he was hungry and needed food. The next night the wolf called him from afar, and her father went to him and found a freshly killed caribou. Unfortunately, Miyax's father never explained to her how he had told the wolf of his needs. And not long afterward, he paddled his kayak into the Bering Sea to hunt, and he never returned.

She had been watching the wolves for two days, trying to discern which of their sounds and movements expressed goodwill and friendship. Most animals had such signals. The little Arctic ground squirrels flicked their tails sideways to notify others of their kind that they were friendly. By imitating this signal with her forefinger, Miyax had lured many a squirrel to her hand. If she could discover such a gesture for the wolves, she would be able to make friends with them and share their food, like a bird or a fox.

Propped on her elbows with her chin in her fists, she stared at the black wolf, trying to catch his eye. She had chosen him because he was much larger than the others and because he walked like her father, Kapugen (ka-poo′jen), with his head high and his chest out. The black wolf also possessed wisdom, she had observed. The pack looked to him when the wind carried strange scents or the birds cried nervously. If he was alarmed, they were alarmed. If he was calm, they were calm.

Long minutes passed, and the black wolf did not look at Miyax. He had ignored her since she first came upon them two sleeps ago. True, she moved slowly and quietly, so as not to alarm him; yet she did wish he would see the kindness in her eyes. Many animals could tell the difference between hostile hunters and friendly people by merely looking at them. But the big black wolf would not even glance her way.

A bird stretched in the grass. The wolf looked at it. A flower twisted in the wind. He glanced at that. Then the breeze rippled the wolverine ruff on Miyax's parka, and it glistened in the light. He did not look at that. She waited. Patience with the ways of nature had been instilled in her by her father, so she knew better than to move or shout, yet she must get food or die. Her hands shook slightly, and she swallowed hard to keep calm.

Miyax was a classic Eskimo beauty, small of bone and delicately wired with strong muscles. Her face was pearl-round, and her nose was flat. Her black eyes, which slanted gracefully, were moist and sparkling. Like the beautifuly formed polar bears and foxes of the north, she was slightly short-limbed. The frigid environment of the Arctic has sculptured life into compact shapes. Unlike the long-limbed, long-bodied animals of the south that are cooled by dispensing heat on extended surfaces, all live things in the Arctic tend toward compactness, to conserve heat.

She spoke half in Eskimo and half in English, as if the instincts of her father and the science of the *gussaks* (guhs′uhks), the white-faced, might evoke some magical combination that would help her get her message through to the wolf.

Amaroq glanced at his paw and slowly turned his head her way without lifting his eyes. He licked his shoulder. A few matted hairs sprang apart and twinkled individually. Then his eyes sped to each of the three adult wolves that made up his pack and finally to the five pups that were sleeping in a fuzzy mass near the den entrance. The great wolf's eyes softened at the sight of the little wolves, then hardened into brittle yellow jewels as he scanned the flat tundra.

Not a tree grew anywhere to break the monotony of the gold-green plain, for the soils of the tundra are permanently frozen. Only moss, grass, lichens, and a few hardy flowers take root in the thin upper layer that thaws briefly in summer. Nor do many species of animals live in this rigorous land, but those creatures that do dwell here exist in bountiful numbers. Amaroq was watching a large cloud of Lapland longspurs wheel up into the sky, then alight in the grasses. Swarms of crane flies, one of the few insects that can survive the cold, darkened the tips of the mosses. Birds wheeled, turned, and called. Thousands sprang up from the ground like leaves in a wind.

The length of her limbs and the beauty of her face were of no use to Miyax as she lay there on the lichen-speckled frost heave in the midst of the bleak tundra. Her stomach ached, and the royal black wolf was carefully ignoring her.

"*Amaroq* (am′uh-rok), *ilaya* (ih-lay′-yuh), wolf, my friend," she finally called. "Look at me. Look at me."

The wolf's ears cupped forward and tuned in on some distant message from the tundra. Miyax tensed and listened too. Did he hear some brewing storm, some approaching enemy? Apparently not. His ears relaxed, and he rolled to his side. She sighed, glanced at the vaulting sky, and was painfully aware of her predicament.

Here she was, watching wolves — she, Miyax, daughter of Kapugen, adopted child of Martha, citizen of the United States, pupil at the Bureau of Indian Affairs School in Barrow, Alaska, and thirteen-year-old wife of the boy Daniel. She shivered at the thought of Daniel, for it was he who had driven her to this fate. She had run away from him exactly seven sleeps ago.

The wolf rolled to his belly.

"Amaroq," she whispered. "I am lost, and the sun will not set for a month. There is no North Star to guide me."

Amaroq did not stir.

"And there are no berry bushes here to bend under the polar wind and point to the south. Nor are there any birds I can follow." She looked up. "Here the birds are buntings and longspurs. They do not fly to the sea twice a day like the puffins and sandpipers that my father followed."

The wolf groomed his chest with his tongue.

"I never dreamed I could get lost, Amaroq," she went on, talking out loud to ease her fear. "At home on Nunivak Island, where I was born, the plants and birds pointed the way for wanderers. I thought they did so everywhere . . . and so, great black Amaroq, I'm without a compass."

It had been a frightening moment when two days ago she realized that the tundra was an ocean of grass on which she was circling around and around. Now as that fear overcame her again, she closed her eyes. When she opened them, her heart skipped excitedly. Amaroq was looking at her!

"Ee-lie," she called, and scrambled to her feet. The wolf arched his neck and narrowed his eyes. He pressed his ears forward. She waved. He drew back his lips and showed his teeth. Frightened by what seemed a snarl, she lay down again. When she was flat on her stomach, Amaroq flattened his ears and wagged his tail once. Then he tossed his head and looked away.

Discouraged, she wriggled backward down the frost heave and arrived at her camp feet first. The heave was between herself and the wolf pack, so she relaxed, stood up, and took stock of her home. It was a simple affair, for she had not been able to carry much when she ran away; she took just those things she would need for the journey — a backpack, food for a week or so, needles to mend clothes, matches, her sleeping skin and ground cloth to go under it, two knives, and a pot.

She had intended to walk to Point

Hope. There she would meet the *North Star*, the ship that brings supplies from the States to the towns on the Arctic Ocean in August when the ice pack breaks up. The ship could always use dishwashers or laundry workers, she had heard, and so she would work her way to San Francisco where Amy, her pen pal, lived. At the end of every letter Amy always wrote, "When are you coming to San Francisco?" Seven days ago she had been on her way — on her way to the glittering, white, postcard city that sat on a hill among trees, those enormous plants she had never seen. She had been on her way to see the television and carpeting in Amy's school, the glass buildings, traffic lights, and stores full of fruits; on her way to the harbor that never froze and the Golden Gate Bridge. But primarily she was on her way to be rid of Daniel.

She kicked the sod at the thought of her marriage; then shaking her head to forget, she surveyed her camp. It was nice. Upon discovering the wolves, she had settled down to live near them in the hope of sharing their food until the sun set and the stars came out to guide her. She had built a house of sod, like the summer homes of the old Eskimos. Each brick had been cut with her half-moon-shaped *ulo* (oo'loh), the woman's knife, so versatile it can trim a baby's hair, slice a tough bear, or chip an iceberg.

Her house was not well built, for she had never made one before, but it was cozy inside. She had made it windproof by sealing the sod bricks with mud from the pond at her door, and she had made it beautiful by spreading her caribou ground cloth on the floor. On this she had placed her sleeping skin, a moose-hide bag lined with soft white rabbit skins. Next to her bed she had built a low table of sod on which to put her clothes when she slept. To decorate the house, she had made three flowers of bird feathers and stuck them in the top of the table. Then she had built a fireplace outdoors and placed her pot beside it. The pot was empty, for she had not found even a lemming to eat.

Last winter, when she had walked to school in Barrow, these micelike rodents were so numerous that they ran out from under her feet wherever she stepped. There were thousands and thousands of them until December, when they suddenly vanished. Her teacher said that the lemmings had a chemical similar to antifreeze in their blood, which kept them active all winter when other little mammals were hibernating. "They eat grass and multiply all winter," Mrs. Franklin had said in her singsong voice. "When there are too many, they grow nervous at the sight of one another. Somehow this shoots too much antifreeze into their bloodstreams, and it begins to poison them. They become restless, then crazy. They run in a frenzy until they die."

Of this phenomenon Miyax's father

had simply said, "The hour of the lemming is over for four years."

Unfortunately for Miyax, the hour of the animals that prey on the lemmings was also over. The white fox, the snowy owl, the weasel, the jaeger, and the siskin had virtually disappeared. They had no food to eat and bore few or no young. Those that lived preyed on one another. With the passing of the lemmings, however, the grasses had grown high again, and the hour of the caribou was upon the land. Healthy, fat caribou cows gave birth to many calves. The caribou population increased, and this in turn increased the number of wolves, which prey on the caribou. The abundance of the big deer of the north did Miyax no good, for she had not brought a gun on her trip. It had never occurred to her that she would not reach Point Hope before her food ran out.

A dull pain seized her stomach. She pulled blades of grass from their sheaths and ate the sweet ends. They were not very satisfying, so she picked a handful of caribou moss, a lichen. If the deer could survive in winter on this food, why not she? She munched, decided the plant might taste better if cooked, and went to the pond for water.

As she dipped her pot in, she thought about Amaroq. Why had he bared his teeth at her? Because she was young, and he knew she couldn't hurt him? No, she said to herself, it was because he was speaking to her!

He had told her to lie down. She had even understood and obeyed him. He had talked to her, not with his voice, but with his ears, eyes, and lips; and he had even commended her with a wag of his tail.

She dropped her pot, scrambled up the frost heave, and stretched out on her stomach.

"Amaroq," she called softly, "I understand what you said. Can you understand me? I'm hungry — very, very hungry. Please bring me some meat."

The great wolf did not look her way, and she began to doubt her reasoning. After all, flattened ears and a tail wag were scarcely a conversation. She dropped her forehead against the lichens and rethought what had gone between them.

"Then why did I lie down?" she asked, lifting her head and looking at Amaroq. "Why did I?" she called to the yawning wolves. Not one turned her way.

Amaroq got to his feet, and as he slowly arose, he seemed to fill the sky and blot out the sun. He was enormous. He could swallow her without even chewing.

"But he won't," she reminded herself. "Wolves do not eat people. That's *gussak* talk. Kapugen said that wolves are gentle brothers and sisters."

The black puppy was looking at her and wagging his tail. Hopefully, Miyax held out a pleading hand to

him. His tail wagged harder. The mother rushed to him and stood above him sternly. When he licked her cheek apologetically, she pulled back her lips from her fine white teeth. They flashed as she smiled and forgave her cub.

"But don't let it happen again," said Miyax sarcastically, mimicking her own elders. The mother walked toward Amaroq.

"I should call you Martha after my stepmother," Miyax whispered. "But you're much too beautiful. I shall call you Silver instead."

Silver moved in a halo of light, for the sun sparkled on the guard hairs that grew out over the dense under-fur, and she seemed to glow.

The reprimanded pup snapped at a crane fly and shook himself. Bits of lichen and grass spun off his fur. He reeled unsteadily, took a wider stance, and looked down at his sleeping sister. With a yap, he jumped on her and rolled her to her feet. She whined. He barked and picked up a bone. When he was sure she was watching, he ran down the slope with it. The sister tagged after him. He stopped, and she grabbed the bone too. She pulled; he pulled; then he pulled and she yanked.

Miyax could not help laughing. The puppies played with bones as Eskimo children played with leather ropes.

"I understand *that*," she said to the pups. "That's tug of war. Now how do you say 'I'm hungry'?"

Amaroq was pacing restlessly along the crest of the frost heave as if something were about to happen. His eyes shot to Silver, then to the gray wolf Miyax had named Nails. These glances seemed to be a summons, for Silver and Nails glided to him, spanked the ground with their forepaws, and bit him gently under the chin. He wagged his tail furiously and took Silver's slender nose in his mouth. She crouched before him, licked his cheek, and lovingly bit his lower jaw. Amaroq's tail flashed high as her mouthing charged him with vitality. He nosed her affectionately. Unlike the fox who met his mate only in the breeding season, Amaroq lived with his mate all year.

Next, Nails took Amaroq's jaw in his mouth, and the leader bit the top of his nose. A third adult, a small male, came slinking up. He got down on his belly before Amaroq, rolled trembling to his back, and wriggled.

"Hello, Jello," Miyax whispered, for he reminded her of the quivering dessert her mother-in-law made.

She had seen the wolves mouth Amaroq's chin twice before, and she concluded that it was a ceremony, a sort of "Hail to the Chief." He must indeed be their leader for he was clearly the wealthy wolf; that is, wealthy as she had known the meaning of the word on Nunivak Island. There the old Eskimo hunters she had known in her childhood thought the riches of life were intelligence, fearlessness, and love. Someone with these gifts was rich and was a great spirit who was admired in the same way that the *gussaks* admired a person with money and goods.

The three adults paid tribute to Amaroq until he was almost smothered with love; then he bayed a wild note that sounded like the wind on the frozen sea. With that, the others sat around him, the puppies scattered among them. Jello hunched forward, and Silver shot a fierce glance at him. Intimidated, Jello pulled his ears together and back. He drew himself down until he looked smaller than ever.

Amaroq wailed again, stretching his neck until his head was high above the others. They gazed at him affectionately, and it was plain to see that he was their great spirit, a royal leader who held his group together with love and wisdom.

Any fear Miyax had of the wolves was dispelled by their affection for one another. They were friendly animals and so devoted to Amaroq that she needed only to be accepted by him to be accepted by all. She even knew how to achieve this — bite him under the chin. But how was she going to do that?

She studied the pups, hoping they had a simpler way of expressing their love for him. The black puppy approached the leader, sat, then lay down and wagged his tail vigorously. He gazed up at Amaroq in pure adoration, and the royal eyes softened.

"Well, that's what I'm doing!" Miyax thought. She called to Amaroq. "I'm lying down gazing at you, too, but you don't look at *me* that way!"

When all the puppies were wagging his praises, Amaroq yipped, hit a high note, and crooned. As his voice rose and fell, the other adults sang out, and the puppies yipped and bounced.

But the song ended abruptly. Amaroq arose and trotted swiftly down the slope. Nails followed, and behind him ran Silver, then Jello. But Jello did not run far. Silver turned and looked him straight in the eye. She pressed her ears forward aggressively and lifted her tail. With that, Jello went back to the puppies, and the three sped away like dark birds.

Miyax hunched forward on her elbows, the better to see and learn. She now knew how to be a good puppy, pay tribute to the leader, and even to be a leader by biting others on the top of the nose. She also knew how to tell Jello to baby-sit. If only she had big ears and a tail, she could lecture and talk to them all.

Flapping her hands on her head for ears, she flattened her fingers to make friends, pulled them together and back to express fear, and shot them forward to display her aggression and dominance. Then she folded her arms and studied the puppies again.

The black one greeted Jello by tackling his feet. Another jumped on his tail, and before he could discipline either, all five were upon him. Jello rolled and tumbled with them for almost an hour; then he ran down the slope, turned, and stopped. The pursuing pups plowed into him, tumbled, fell, and lay still. During a minute of surprised recovery, there was no action. Then the black pup flashed his tail like a semaphore signal, and they all jumped on Jello again.

Miyax rolled over and laughed aloud. "That's funny. They're really like kids."

When she looked back, Jello's tongue was hanging from his mouth, and his sides were heaving. Four of the puppies had collapsed at his feet and were asleep. Jello flopped down, too, but the black pup still looked around. He was not the least bit tired. Miyax watched him, for there was something special about him.

He ran to the top of the den and barked. The smallest pup, whom

Miyax called Sister, lifted her head, saw her favorite brother in action, and struggling to her feet, followed him devotedly. While they romped, Jello took a short rest behind a clump of sedge, a moisture-loving plant of the tundra. But hardly was he settled when a pup tracked him to his hide-out and pounced on him. Jello narrowed his eyes, pressed his ears forward, and showed his teeth.

"I know what you're saying," she called to him. "You're saying, 'Lie down.'" The puppy lay down, and Miyax got on all fours and looked for the nearest pup to speak to. It was Sister.

"*Ummmm,*" she whined, and when Sister turned around, Miyax narrowed her eyes and showed her white teeth. Obediently, Sister lay down.

"I'm talking wolf! I'm talking wolf!" Miyax clapped and, tossing her head like a pup, crawled in a happy circle. As she was coming back, she saw all five puppies sitting in a row watching her, their heads cocked in curiosity. Boldly the black pup came toward her, his fat backside swinging as he trotted to the bottom of her frost heave and barked.

"You are *very* fearless and *very* smart," she said. "Now I know why you are special. You are wealthy and the leader of the puppies. There is no doubt what you'll grow up to be. So I shall name you after my father, Kapugen, and I shall call you Kapu (ka′poo) for short."

Kapu wrinkled his brow and turned an ear to tune in more acutely on her voice.

"You don't understand, do you?" Hardly had she spoken when his tail went up, his mouth opened slightly, and he fairly grinned.

"*Ee-lie!*" she gasped. "You do understand. And that scares me." She perched on her heels. Jello whined an undulating note, and Kapu turned back to the den.

Miyax imitated the call to come home. Kapu looked back over his shoulder in surprise. She giggled. He wagged his tail and jumped on Jello.

She clapped her hands and settled down to watch this language of jumps and tumbles, elated that she was at last breaking the wolf code. After a long time, she decided they were not talking but roughhousing, so she started home. Later she changed her mind. Roughhousing was very important to wolves. It occupied almost the entire night for the pups.

"*Ee-lie,* okay," she said. "I'll learn to roughhouse. Maybe then you'll accept me and feed me." She pranced, jumped, and whimpered; she growled, snarled, and rolled. But nobody came to roughhouse.

Sliding back to her camp, she heard the grass swish and looked up to see Amaroq and his hunters sweep around her frost heave and stop about five feet away. She could smell the sweet scent of their fur.

The hairs on her neck rose, and her

eyes widened. Amaroq's ears went forward aggressively, and she remembered that wide eyes meant fear to him. It was not good to show him she was afraid. Animals attacked the fearful. She tried to narrow them but remembered that was not right, either. Narrowed eyes were mean. In desperation, she recalled that Kapu had moved forward when challenged. She pranced right up to Amaroq. Her heart beat furiously as she grunt-whined the sound of the puppy begging adoringly for attention. Then she got down on her belly and gazed at him with fondness.

The great wolf backed up and avoided her eyes. She had said something wrong, perhaps even offended him! Some slight gesture that meant nothing to her had apparently meant something to the wolf. His ears shot forward angrily, and it seemed all was lost. She wanted to get up and run, but she gathered her courage and pranced closer to him. Swiftly she patted him under the chin.

The signal went off. It sped through his body and triggered emotions of love. Amaroq's ears flattened, and his tail wagged in a sign of friendship.

After accepting Miyax into the pack, the wolves provided her with food and protection. But during the rest of her journey across the tundra, she faced many dangers, including the rigorous Arctic winter, on her own. At the end of the journey, she had to come to terms with the conflicts between her Eskimo heritage and a new, changing way of life.

Like other Eskimos, Miyax has an English name as well as an Eskimo name. Her English name is Julie, and you can read the rest of her story in the book **Julie of the Wolves.**

DISCUSSION

1. Why, do you think, did the old Eskimo hunters consider the riches of life to be intelligence, fearlessness, and love rather than money and goods?
2. What outstanding qualities of character did Miyax show as she studied the wolves and gained their friendship?
3. How did Miyax know that it was possible to communicate with wolves? Why did she have to try to communicate with them?
4. Why did Miyax strive to win the black wolf's attention and approval? What was the first evidence Miyax had that she and Amaroq were communicating?
5. What caused Miyax to lose her sense of direction on the tundra?
6. Why did Miyax choose San Francisco as her destination?
7. Why did Miyax have to remain on the tundra for a month? What preparations did she make for her month-long stay there?
8. How did the wolves communicate with one another? What are some of the different ways in which human beings communicate with one another besides talking? Which do you think communicate more effectively with one another, human beings or animals? Support your answer.
9. How did Miyax first succeed in "talking wolf"?
10. What made Miyax sure that Kapu had understood what she said to him? Do you think that the wolf pup really understood what she said? Why do you think as you do?

11. What action of Miyax's brought her Amaroq's friendship and acceptance into the pack?

12. After being accepted into the pack, how do you suppose Miyax expected to get food from the wolves?

AUTHOR

As you might suspect, a sensitive book like *Julie of the Wolves* could come only from Jean Craighead George's own personal commitment and her first-hand observation. In 1970 the author and one of her teen-age sons spent several weeks in Alaska studying wolves and the Arctic tundra. She filled notebooks with material from generous scientists and with two definite sources of inspiration. As they stepped off the plane upon their arrival in Barrow, Mrs. George had spied a small fur-clad girl walking toward the lonesome wilderness of the tundra. The girl was, of course, to become Julie in the book. Later in the visit, the sight of a magnificent wolf — leader of a pack — and the wolves' apparent communication with each other impressed Mrs. George. A year and a half later she finished the story of Julie. The book was awarded the Newbery Medal and received many other honors.

Jean George says that she grew up in the wild edges of Washington, D.C. Her father, an entomologist, and her twin brothers, now wildlife ecologists, often took her with them on camping trips in search of birds, trees, fish, wildflowers, salamanders, and mammals. She says, "My childhood in retrospect seems like one leaping, laughing adventure into the mysteries and joys of the earth."

In the third grade, she began writing, and after two college degrees, she went on to become a reporter for several Washington newspapers. She also worked as a magazine artist, reporter-artist, and an author and illustrator of magazine articles and books. After she married John George, a conservationist, they wrote six books together, all of which she illustrated.

In all, Jean George has written over thirty books, all of them related to nature. Many have received acclaim. Mrs. George says, "I wrote about the natural things I had loved since childhood: the stars above the roof, the wolves I saw on the tundra of Alaska, and all 173 wild pets that my three children and I have raised about the house here in Chappaqua, New York."

Inuit Song

And I think over again
My small adventures
When with a shore wind I drifted out
In my kayak
And thought I was in danger.
My fears,
Those I thought so big,
For all the vital things
I had to get and to reach.

And yet, there is only
One great thing,
The only thing:
To live to see in huts and on journeys
The great day that dawns,
And the light that fills the world.

Eye This

Have you ever wondered why a writer chose a particular verb? Well-chosen verbs are the heart of good writing. Sometimes a verb comes to mind that seems to fit the context perfectly; other verbs must be chosen with great care. One example is the verb *ventured* as it appears in "Ordeal in Spring": "No one ventured far away from home after nightfall . . ."

A number of other verbs could have been used in place of *ventured* (*went, walked, traveled, wandered,* and so on), but none of them would have conveyed a sense of danger as the word *ventured* did. That element of danger is part of the definition of the word *venture,* "to take a risk; to dare." Sometimes a word carries a mood or implication that goes beyond its dictionary definition.

Each of the following sentences contains a verb that describes a particular way of seeing. The verb *looked* (or the words *looked at*) could be substituted for the underlined verb in any of these sentences. Notice that the underlined verb in each sentence is more specific and effective than the verb *looked* would be.

1. My cousin <u>scrutinized</u> the car before buying it.
2. She <u>glanced</u> at the secret documents before shredding them.
3. The shipwrecked sailor <u>spied</u> a tanker in the distance.
4. My sister <u>stared</u> at the screen in disbelief.
5. The mayor <u>scowled</u> at the mob of noisy demonstrators.
6. He quickly <u>scanned</u> the front page of the evening newspaper.
7. The child <u>peeked</u> at me through pudgy fingers.
8. The watchmaker lovingly <u>inspected</u> his masterpiece.
9. She <u>peered</u> through a rusted gate at the old manor house.
10. A scientist <u>examined</u> the precious chip of moon rock.
11. She <u>glared</u> at the noisy popcorn-eater seated beside her.

How many of these verbs do you use frequently? There are many other verbs you might use instead of the verb *look*. You might use *pry, peep, squint, regard, behold, view, eye, sight, contemplate, admire,* or *gape, yawp, gaze, ogle, goggle,* or *leer.*

The following sentences include particularly effective verbs. For each, think about some words that have similar meanings and decide if any would give the sentence exactly the same meaning. Then look up the meanings of any verbs you don't know in a dictionary.

12. The famous cellist <u>radiated</u> joy, humanity, and good will.
13. My confession will <u>assuage</u> my guilt about the murder.
14. The ancient river <u>meandered</u> lazily across the barren plain.
15. We <u>abhor</u> the suffering of these innocent people.
16. Two Mayan temples <u>towered</u> above the dense rain forest.
17. We were <u>appalled</u> by the rowdy behavior of the hockey fans.

Books to Enjoy

Year Walk by Ann Nolan Clark
A Spanish Basque boy, learning to herd sheep across the Northwest frontier of America in 1910, encounters cattle rustlers, floods, and wild animals on a four-hundred-mile trail through the wilderness.

Janet Guthrie: First Woman Driver at Indianapolis
    by Edward F. Dolan and Richard B. Lyttle
This is a biography of the physicist who broke into the all-male world of sports car racing.

Wild Animals, Gentle Women by Margery Facklam
The challenging and sometimes dangerous careers of ten women who work with wild creatures are dramatically presented here.

The Mark of Conte by Sonia Levitin
After the computer at school mistakenly registers Conte Mark under two names, he decides that he can go through two sets of classes as two people — all with complicated, funny results.

Native American Testimony: An Anthology of
    Indian and White Relations edited by Peter Nabakov
Spoken or written accounts by Native Americans constitute a significant record of tragic times in American history.

Wild Foods by Laurence Pringle
This beginner's guide to identifying, harvesting, and cooking edible wild foods contains recipes, photos, and detailed drawings.

Awards

MAGAZINE TWO

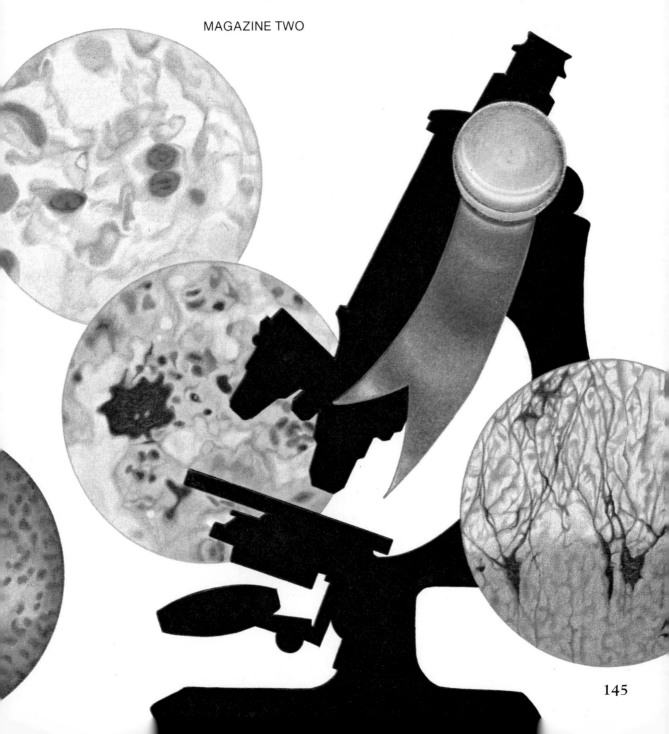

Contents

Prairie Winter

by ROSE WILDER LANE

Caroline and Charles were young newlyweds who had come by team and wagon across the plains to the South Dakota frontier of the 1850's. Their first home was a dugout hollowed out of the bank of a creek. There, on Caroline's seventeenth birthday, their baby was born. After a grasshopper plague destroyed their wheat crop, Charles was forced to go east to find work until they could plant again in the spring. Caroline stayed behind in order to keep possession of the farm. Charles was confident that the Svensons, their only neighbors, would keep an eye on Caroline and the baby in his absence; but soon after he departed, the Svensons gave up and went back east. Now Caroline faces winter alone, miles from any neighbor.

Three days and nights the winds did not cease to howl, and when Caroline opened the door, she could not see the door ledge through swirling snow. How cold it was she could not guess. At the sight of clouds earlier, she had hurriedly crammed every spare inch of the dugout with hay. Twisted hard, it burned with a brief, hot flame. Her palms were soon raw and bleeding from handling the sharp, harsh stuff, but she kept on twisting it. She kept the dugout warm.

In the long dark hours — for she was frugal with kerosene, and only a wavering light came from the drafts and the broken lid of the stove — she began to fight a vague and monstrous dread. It lay beneath her thoughts; she could not grasp it as a whole; she was always aware of it and never able to defeat it. It lay shapeless and dark in the depths of her. From time to time it flung up a question:

What if the baby gets sick?

"He won't be sick!" she retorted. "He's a strong, healthy baby. If he's sick, I'll take care of him. I'd take care of him anyway; there's no doctor in town."

Suppose something has happened to Charles? Suppose he never comes back?

"Be still! I won't listen."

That was like a wolf's howl in the wind. Wolves?

"Nonsense, I have the gun. How could a wolf get through the door?"

When you go out —— If a wolf sprang suddenly —— What of the baby, alone in the dugout?

"Why am I scaring myself with horrible fancies? Nothing like that will happen."

She could never conquer the shapeless, nameless dread itself. Silenced, it did not leave her. It would begin again.

What if the baby gets sick?

"Oh, stop, stop! I can't stand this!" her spirit cried out in anguish. And she asked herself angrily, "What is the matter with you? Brace up and show a little decent spunk! It's only a storm; there'll be lots of them before spring." She tried to conquer the shapeless, dark thing by ignoring it.

The wind howled; gray darkness pressed against the paper pane; a little hard snow, dry as sand, was forced through the crack beneath the door.

On the fourth morning, Caroline was awakened by an immense, profound silence. The frosty air stung her nostrils; the blanket was edged with rime from her breath. Snug in the hollow of her body, the baby slept cozily. The window was a vague gray in the dark. She lighted the lamp and started a fire in the cold stove.

She was not perturbed until she tried to open the door. Something outside held it against her confident push. And suddenly wild terror possessed her. She felt a Thing outside, pressed against the door.

It was only snow. She said to herself that it was only snow. There was no danger; the ledge was narrow. She flung all her strength and weight against the door. The stout planks quivered, and from top to bottom of them ran a sound like a scratch of claws. Then snow fell down the abrupt slope below the ledge, and sunlight pierced Caroline's eyes.

Taking the shovel, she forced her body through the narrow aperture she had gained. For an instant the pain in her eyes blinded her. Then she saw the immensity of whiteness and dazzling blue. She confronted space.

Under the immeasurably vast sky, a limitless expanse of snow refracted the cold glitter of the sun. She drew a deep breath, and with her shovel she attacked the snow. The winds had packed it hard as ice against the door and the creek bank. The path was buried under a slanting drift. Inch by inch, pounding, digging, scraping, lifting, she made a way on which she could safely walk, and that scratch on the measureless waste of trackless snow was a triumph.

A blizzard of such severity so early in October seemed to predict an unusually hard winter. She could not know when the next storm might strike, and her first care was fuel. She dug into the snow-covered stacks by the barn, and tying a rope around big bundles of hay, she dragged them one by one down the path and into the dugout.

When she threw out the water in which she washed her hands, she noticed that its drops tinkled on the ice crust. They had frozen in the air. Startled, she looked into her mirror. Her nose and ears were white, and she had to rub them with snow till they painfully thawed.

Then for three weeks the weather was mild; the snow was melting. There were days when the door stood open and the air was like spring. From above the dugout she could see the town; she could, indeed, see fifty miles beyond it.

In early November the winter settled down. Blizzard followed blizzard out of the northwest. Sometimes there was a clear day between them, sometimes only a few hours. As soon as the winds ceased their howling and the snow thinned so that she could see, she went out with the shovel.

The wind would be steadily blowing, driving a low scud of snow before it. She worked sometimes waist-deep in blown snow so thick that she could not see her feet. The whole world seemed covered with white spray flying under the cold sunshine. Her eyes were bloodshot, and her skin burned red and blistered, and she never came into the dugout without looking to see if her face and ears were frozen.

On the dark days of the blizzards, she twisted hay; she lighted the lamp for cleaning and cooking and washing. And she played with the baby.

He was older now; he watched the gleams of firelight and clapped his hands, and his soft little palms hardly ever missed each other. His blue eyes looked into Caroline's; his firm little body had a will of its own. He could hold up his own head proudly; he could straighten his backbone; all by himself he could sit up, and he could crawl. Kicking and crowing, he burbled sounds almost like words.

Then came the seven days' blizzard. There had been only a few hours of clear weather, but Caroline had worked desperately; she had enough hay for three days, and she had never known a blizzard to last longer. On the third day, she burned the hay sparingly, but she was not alarmed. On the fourth day, she broke up and burned a box, keeping the stove barely warm. On the fifth day, she burned the remaining box. The heavy benches and table were left, and the cradle; but in her folly she had left the ax in the barn.

If she and the baby lay close together under blankets, they could exist for some time in the warmth of their own bodies. If this were to go on forever —— It could not, of course. She finally had to give up on the heavy benches, which she could not break up with her hands. It must be the cradle. But she feared to burn it so soon.

During the seventh day, she smashed and frugally burned the cradle. The birds that Charles had carved on it helped to boil tea and potatoes. She mashed a potato in a little hot water and fed it with a spoon to the baby. Then she put out the lamp and lay down with him under all the bedding.

A change in the sound of the wind awakened her. She did not know whether it was night or day, but when she forced the door open, she saw a whiteness of driven snow. A fierce north wind was driving the flakes steadily before it, and Caroline's relief

was like a shout of joy. The snow was not swirling; the blizzard was over!

When next she opened the door, the storm had diminished so that she could see vaguely into it. She was able to clear the path, and when she reached its top, she could see dim shapes of barn and haystacks. The wind almost took her off her feet, and when she had a bundle of hay and was dragging it through the soft drifts, she had to fight it as though it were a live thing struggling to get away. After she had filled the dugout with hay, she stretched a rope from the barn to the top of the path so that she could fetch fuel, if necessary, during a blizzard.

Vaguely through the storm she seemed to see a dark patch on the opposite bank of the creek. It troubled her, for she could not imagine what it might be. She shut the door against it hurriedly and gave herself to the marvel of warmth and rest.

In the morning, in a dazzling glitter of sun on snow, she saw across the creek a herd of cattle. Huddled together, heads toward the south and noses drooping to their knees, they stood patiently enduring the cold. In terror she thought of the haystacks. The creek bank hid them from the cattle now, but if the herd moved southeast, across the slough, and saw that food, would all the strength of the wind prevent them from turning and destroying her fuel?

She put on her wraps and took the pistol. Not with pitchfork or ax, she knew, could she keep starving cattle from food. Nor did she dare risk facing the stampede. She could only try to turn it with shots, and failing, take refuge in the barn. If the fuel was lost ——

The cattle did not move. It came to her, while she watched, that for a long time they had not moved. She stared at them — gaunt sides and ridged backbones, dropped necks and lax tails, motionless as if carved. Were they dead — frozen? No; breath came white from their nostrils. The thought that they might be dead had brought a vision of meat.

Her courage quailed. There was something monstrous, something that gave her an unreasoning terror, like a breath of the supernatural, in this herd of motionless cattle. Her jaw clenched against the cold, she went slowly, knee-deep in drifts, down the bank and across the frozen creek. Was this too great a risk? Leaving the baby in the dugout and venturing into she knew not what? She went within ten yards of the cattle, five, two. They did not even lift their heads.

Over their eyes — thick over their eyes and hollowed temples — were cakes of ice. When she saw this, she understood. Their own breath, steaming upward while they plodded before the storm, had frozen and blinded them.

In a rage of pity, she plunged through the snow to the nearest patiently dying creature, and she wrenched the ice from its eyes. The steer snorted; it flung up its head in terror and ran, staggering. The herd quivered.

Caroline knew what she must do. She thought of the baby, drawing his strength from hers. She held all thought, all feeling, firmly to the baby, and walking to the nearest young steer, she put the pistol to its temple, shut her eyes, and fired. The report crashed through her.

She felt the shudder of all the beasts. When she opened her eyes, they had not moved. The steer lay dead with only a little blood trickling, freezing, from the wound. And perhaps it had been merciful to kill it.

Then, like an inspiration, a revival of all hope, she thought of a cow. A cow! Why not? In the herd there were many cows. Alas, they belonged to somebody. To whom? She did not know; that might never be known; impossible to guess how many miles — hundreds, perhaps — they had been driven by the storm. But they were branded. She could not steal. Yet, if she did not take one of these cows, would it not die? The whole blinded herd was helpless and dying. To kill for food was permissible, but to steal? Was she a cattle thief? But a cow — to have a cow!

Milk for the baby. To surprise Charles, when he came home, with a cow!

She thought that perhaps there might be a yearling that was not branded. In her excitement, she was almost laughing. Clumsy in boots and coat and shawls, she pushed into the harmless herd. The heifers, she knew, would be in the center. The old bull grumbled in his throat, shaking his blind head, but he did not move; he did not even paw the snow. There was a young heifer, unbranded, almost plump, a clear red all over. Caroline marked it for her own, for their own cow.

This incredible marvel of good fortune filled her with laughing joy. What a triumph, what a joke — to take a cow from the blizzard, to take it from the very midst of a dangerous herd! And to have a cow — after so many calamities, in spite of calamities, to have a cow — this was a vindication of all confidence and hope.

She struggled through the drifts, across the creek, up the bank, to the dugout. She fed the stove with hay; she fed the baby, dressed him warmly, wrapped him in blankets like a cocoon. Then she went to the barn for a rope.

The short winter day gave her not too much time. The sun was overhead before she had succeeded in prodding and tugging the terrified, wild, blinded heifer out of the herd. It was near sunset before she got the heifer into the barn. She put hay into the manger and tore the ice from the heifer's eyes. With the rope and ax she went back to the herd. She cut the best parts of meat from the half-frozen carcass and tied the pieces together. Then, trembling in her weariness, she went from animal to animal, tearing off the blinding ice. The cattle snorted and plunged; each one staggered a little way and waited, bawling. Slowly the herd drifted before the wind. The sun sank in coldness, the glow faded from the snow, and in the dusk she released the old bull. He lifted his head, bellowed weakly, and plunged, staggering, after the herd.

In the dark they would not see her hay. The wind was blowing toward the town site; let the townspeople deal with the survivors that reached it. Caroline had given the cattle a chance for their lives, and she felt she had earned her cow.

The blizzard that came that night lasted only a day. Caroline lay cozily in bed. The baby gurgled and kicked in exuberance of spirits; a great beef stew simmered on the stove, filling the air with its fragrance. The snowy hay in the manger would suffice the heifer for both food and water. The howling of the blizzard no longer disturbed Caroline.

If only Charles could know that they had a cow! But now she was confident that Charles would come home strong and well; this winter would end; they would be together in the spring.

She had left two haunches of the beef outside the door, to freeze on the snow. The blizzard had buried them, and she did not touch that drift when she dug the path again. Snow was still falling thickly enough to fill the air as with a mist, through which she saw the barn and haystacks.

The heifer was still safely tied to the manger. It snorted and plunged, wild-eyed, while she brought in hay and set two pails of snow within its reach. She spoke to it soothingly but did not touch it. In time, it would learn her kindness and be gentle. It had all the marks of a good milch cow.

She closed the barn door and snapped the padlock, feeling a proud sense of property to be taken care of. There was no wind, and all around her she could hear the soft rustle of the falling snow. Carrying the shovel and rope, Caroline went toward the haystack.

Afterward she always said she did not know what made her stop and turn around. By the corner of the barn stood a wolf.

If you went out —— If a wolf sprang —— What would become of the baby, alone in the dugout? *It's come,* her frozen heart knew.

She had only the shovel.

The wolf's haunches quivered, not quite crouching. The hair stood rough along its back. Fangs showed beneath the curling lip. It was a big, gaunt timber wolf. Its mate could not be far. Its mate was perhaps creeping up somewhere behind her. It shifted a paw. Caroline did not move. Swiftly the wolf turned and vanished, a shadow, in the falling snow. The snow at once became a menace, hiding the lurking danger.

Caroline walked steadily through the white blindness toward the dugout. She did not run; she knew that if she ran, her inmost self would yield to shattering terror. As long as the wolf could not be seen anywhere, she was safe; the wolf would not spring unless it could see her. But while she was going down the path in the creek bank, it might spring on her from above. She knew it was following her.

She reached the path and ran. There was no measure in time for the length of that distance from the edge of the prairie to the door's slamming behind her. A long wolf howl rose from the ceiling above her head. Another answered it from the frozen creek below.

That evening she heard snarling and crunching at the door. The wolves had found the fresh meat. They must have been following the cattle, and the carcass of the steer she had killed had kept them near her. She heard a scratch of claws on the door.

She kept the lamp lighted and sat all night watching the paper pane. The window space was too small to let a wolf through easily. If paw or head appeared, she was ready to shoot. The ax was in the dugout, and she decided rather than go out in the storm again, to chop up the table and benches and burn them. But she made the hay last two days, and then a sliver of light above the snow piled against the window told her that the sun was shining.

Little by little she forced the door open. The pistol was in her hand. She found no trace of the wolves anywhere, and in the barn the heifer was safe. After that, she often heard wolves howling and found their tracks at the door and around the barn. She never left the dugout without the pistol. She was constantly reminded of Charles's warning about wolves — and outlaws. When she stirred the fire, she thought of the smoke ascending from the chimney. For seventy miles around, on clear days, it could be seen that the dugout was inhabited. Claim jumpers would probably not come. But outlaws?

She felt within herself a certainty that at any human threat of danger she would kill. She said to herself that no stranger should enter that dugout — not under any circumstances, not with any fair words. This she determined upon, sure of herself. But she did not yet know herself.

Blizzard followed blizzard, with

clear hours or days between. She had lost reckoning of time and was not quite sure whether December had ended and January begun. But each day brought nearer the end of this winter. The baby was healthy, the heifer was safe in the barn, and she was holding out pretty well. More and more often she dreamed of springtime and Charles.

February had come, though she did not know it. Three clear days of terrible cold were ending, near nightfall, in the rising of the blizzard winds. That day Caroline had filled half the barn with hay; the heifer was now so gentle that she could turn it loose with that abundance of feed, and the washtub full of water provided for it if this blizzard lasted a week. The baby slept. The box was full of twisted hay, and the supper dishes were washed. By the faint light of the dying fire, Caroline combed her hair for the night.

A blow struck the door, and all at once the forces of the air gave tongue. Caroline thought how like demon riders they sounded, racing and circling overhead with unearthly, inhuman shriek and scream and wild halloo. A little snow, fine and hard as sand, was driven through the crack beneath the door. She shook her hair back and put up her hands to braid it, and in the gleam of light from the broken stove lid, she saw a joint of the stovepipe suddenly bend. The two ends of pipe slid upon each other; a crack opened between them. Petrified, she heard a human cry and a groaned exclamation.

A man was on top of the dugout. Blind in the storm, he had stumbled against the chimney. No honest man, no lost homesteader. Not for miles around was there an undeserted homestead. All afternoon the blizzard had been threatening; no honest man would have gone far from shelter. Only a rider out of the northwest might have fled before the storm — a rider out of the northwestern refuges of the outlaws. "Wolves and outlaws will be moving back to settled country," Charles had said.

The man had struck the chimney on the eastern side; he was going toward the creek. Only a few steps and he would fall down the creek bank, down into the deep drifts below. He would be gone, lost, buried somewhere by the storm. Only his bones would be found after the snow melted in the spring. "Keep still!" she said to herself. "Don't move. It isn't your business. Don't let him in. Who knows what he is, what he would do? Think of the baby. *What are you doing?*"

Her mouth close to the stovepipe, she shouted, "Stand still! Don't move!" The soot dislodged from the open joint of the pipe fell on her face, so quickly had she acted. "You hear me?" she called.

A vague shout replied. He seemed to have fallen or to have wandered a

step or two toward the creek. She knew how the winds were swirling, beating and tugging at him from every side, how the sandlike snow was flaying his face; she saw him blinded, deafened, lost. An outlaw, but human, fighting the storm.

"Lie down! Crawl!" she shouted. "Creek bank ahead! Follow it to the right! The right! Find a rope! You hear?"

His shout was dull through the shriller winds. Then she hesitated. But the barn was padlocked. "There is a path!" she called. "Path! Down! To the left!"

159

If he shouted again, she did not hear him. She twisted her hair and thrust pins into it, buttoned her basque, and lighted the lamp. She got her pistol and made sure it was loaded. Some instinct, hardly reasonable — for who would harm a baby? — made her lift Charles John, wrap him in a blanket, and lay him on the hay in the woodbox. She felt better with the baby behind her. Then she lifted the bar on the door, retreated behind the table, and waited.

She had time to regret what she had done and to know that she could not have done otherwise.

The wind suddenly tore open the door. Snow whirled in and cold. The lamp flared smokily, and as she started forward, the man appeared in the white blizzard. He was tall and shapeless in fur coat and cap and ear-muffs caked with snow. He was muffled to reddened slits of eyes and snow-matted eyebrows. It was an instant before she knew him and screamed. The wild scream was dizzily circling in her head when his arms closed around her, hard and cold as ice.

"Oh, how — how — how did you get here?" she gasped after a while, unable still to believe it. Her hands kept clutching, clutching up and down the snowy fur, as if her hands were separate things, frantic too, to make sure this was Charles.

"Gosh, I'm freezing you to death! I've got to shut the door," he said.

They were together; everything was all right. She heard the clamor of the storm, all the demons shrieking. But now it was simply a blizzard, simply the winter weather on their farm.

DISCUSSION

1. In your opinion, which of the two things Caroline faced throughout the story would be harder to fight — fear or the blizzard itself? Why do you think as you do?
2. From the severe early blizzard at the beginning of the story, what prediction did Caroline make?
3. Why, do you think, did Caroline burn hay instead of wood? Why did she twist the hay into tight strands?
4. When the seven-day blizzard came, in what way was Caroline unprepared? How did she make it possible for the baby and herself to survive the cold?

5. When Caroline saw the herd of cattle, what was she afraid would happen?
6. Why did Caroline kill the young steer? In what other way did Caroline benefit from the appearance of the cattle?
7. Why did it seem unlikely that claim jumpers would come to the dugout but likely that outlaws would come?
8. How did Caroline deal with her encounter with the wolf?
9. What had Caroline vowed she would never do if a stranger came to the dugout? What did she actually do when she thought that a stranger had stumbled upon her roof?
10. Why, do you think, did Caroline go back on her vow so quickly even though she thought the stranger was an outlaw? Would you provide shelter for a stranger under similar circumstances? Why or why not?
11. What qualities of character did Caroline show in the episodes involving the cattle, the wolf, and the arrival of the "stranger"?
12. What part did good luck play in Caroline's survival? Did good luck alone account for her triumph over hardships? Why do you think as you do?

AUTHOR

Rose Wilder Lane was born in 1887 in the part of Dakota Territory that is now South Dakota. Her mother, Laura Ingalls Wilder, was the author of the "Little House" books that were based on her own experiences growing up in the pioneer Midwest. The family lived in Dakota for seven years after Rose was born, but after a succession of crop failures, sicknesses, and disastrous weather conditions, they moved to the Ozark Mountains in Missouri. The trip by horse and wagon took three months. The family later moved to Louisiana.

After graduating from high school, Rose went to San Francisco to become a newspaper reporter. She later worked as an office clerk, a telegrapher, and an agent selling farmland before becoming a writer. She lived in nearly every state in the United States and also traveled extensively in Europe, the Near East, and parts of Russia.

Rose Wilder Lane wrote many books and frequently had stories published in magazines, but she once claimed that her favorite occupations were learning a new language and building a house. She died in 1968.

Thunder

by BARBARA KUNZ LOOTS

Thunder
is so heavy.
It shoves itself
through the crowded air
and
  lumbers
    down
      the world
with all the sullen weight
of summer.

The Gulls of
Smuttynose Island

by JACK DENTON SCOTT

Rising from the wind-foamed water off the Maine and New Hampshire coasts are the famous Isles of Shoals. At the turn of the century some of them were exclusive summer resorts; now they are mainly a natural paradise for gulls and other sea birds.

Two of the islands, Smuttynose and Appledore, are the ranking gull rookeries along the New England coast. They are part of Kittery, Maine, but the gulls virtually own Smuttynose and Appledore. Perhaps one reason for the birds' supremacy is that they are protected by federal law. Killing any gull is punishable by a fine of five hundred dollars and six months in jail.

It wasn't always so. Less than a century ago the herring gull (now the most numerous) was almost wiped out along the North Atlantic coast. Gulls' eggs were sold by the barrelful; hunters shot gulls by the thousands for milliners who used the birds' snowy feathers and black-trimmed wings to spruce up ladies' hats.

That slaughter was finally stopped when intelligent observers noted that the herring gull seemed to prefer the debris of civilization to anything else. Here was an effective sanitation department that worked without wages. Eventually the herring gull's appetite actually saved it and the other gulls in the United States. The herring gull took all the other species along with it when the law was passed protecting gulls.

The Social System

The two species of gulls that dominate Smuttynose, although closely related, have one dissimilarity. The herring gull (so called because it gathers in flocks to dive and feed upon schools of tiny herring, often driven to the surface by savage bluefish), with its mantle of pearl-gray, is often seen near populated areas. The black-back (the great black-backed gull), with the ebony saddle that gave it the name, prefers solitude.

But both come to Smuttynose in the early spring for the same purpose: to mate in a natural, protected breeding ground used by themselves and their gull ancestors for many years.

Territorial imperative — claiming a certain area of space and defending it against others — is the law at Smuttynose. The black-backs are larger (28 to 31 inches in length, with a 5½-foot wingspread, compared with the herring gull's 22½- to 26-inch length and 4½-foot wingspread) and therefore select the higher reaches of the island, the pinnacles of rock and the knolls. This forces the herring gulls to keep to the lower areas closer to the water. Black-back guards patrol their territories, both land and air, and fiercely drive off the herring gulls that try to trespass.

But the rights of trespass are not the only rules of order. Each gull is a member of an exclusive club system that dates back more than a million years.

Each spring when the gulls return to Smuttynose, the black-backs and the herring gulls re-form into private clubs by species and by status. A small gullery of about two hundred birds would have as many as four clubs. The huge population at Smuttynose probably has one hundred such clubs, formed for the social life and preservation of the species. The bringing together of the clubs each spring begins with a gigantic parade, with all of the birds joining in a walk around the rookery. Next comes a concerted flight, swooping and circling over Smuttynose and nearby Appledore, where most of the gulls were born.

The signal for the re-formation of the clubs begins when one old, aggressive bird glides from the parade in the sky, lands, and stands alone, head raised. At this signal, all birds descend to land, and what seemed a formless collection of gulls is converted into a series of close social circles ruled by class distinction. Each club has its leader, an old, aggressive gull, with several associates just a step lower in the status-by-age-and-aggression scale. The clubs claim their own territory, where the birds gather in groups when they are not mating, breeding, nesting, flying, or on food forays. Once these clubs are formed, the birds belong to them for life.

Like all clubs, these have their newcomers, brought in by other club members. Most of the older birds returning to Smuttynose are mated, but the younger ones reaching their fourth summer eagerly search for mates. Once that mating is accomplished, it is for life; but while they are gone from their summer place, wintering in the south, the pairs separate.

Although gulls may migrate in flocks to the same areas of the south and even live together in colonies as they do on Smutty-nose in the spring and summer, their winter lives are drastically different. They migrate along the seacoasts, where food is more accessible. Some stop longer than others. Each bird appears to go more or less its own way.

Niko Tinbergen, the world's foremost herring-gull expert, says that in the winter the gulls never show any behavior indicating personal attachment. "A winter flock," he claims, "seems to be made up of individuals, not pairs."

Once they return to Smuttynose, it is as if the mates had never parted. As Tinbergen observed, "The pair keep strictly together, and when they move from one area to another, they are attached to each other as if by a string." This ornithologist saw one pair in flight instantly recognize each other at the summer breeding place at a distance of thirty yards. He later observed many more proofs of this amazing power of recognition, with mates identifying one another at great distances.

Incubating the Eggs

Both birds begin collecting twigs, moss, discarded feathers, seaweed, and grass for the nest. When the nest has been partially formed, they take turns sitting in it, picking up and rearranging material while in the nest, and restlessly turning in all directions — with a purpose. The constant adding and rearranging, and the movement while in the nest, results in a well-rounded, well-lined nest-cup about eighteen inches in diameter and four inches thick.

When the female lays the first egg, there is an abrupt change in the daily rhythm of the pair. Prior to this, the birds were together continually, at their club, in the air, on the flights for food. Now, although the first egg is rarely incubated, it is always guarded by one of the pair because other gulls will eat the egg if given the chance. At intervals of two, often three, days the other eggs are laid. The normal clutch is three greenish or bluish eggs about the size of chicken eggs, speckled with brown, black, or purple spots. The spots break up the contours of the eggs, helping camouflage them against the neutral background of the nest.

Now the incubation begins in earnest. Both gulls take turns sitting on the eggs. A bird may occasionally leave the nest for a period but rarely for more than ten minutes and only if its nest-relief is late, which seldom happens. Gulls are serious incubators, so much so that if the female arrives early to spell the male, often he will not leave the eggs until his incubation clock tells him to do so.

If another gull invades the nest territory while one of the pair has incubation duties, the bird will use restraint and not fly off the nest and attack — until its mate returns. One observer watched a big male herring gull boldly cross the no-trespassing line of a nesting territory while a male was incubating eggs. The bird on the nest completely ignored the intruder. But when its mate arrived, ready for her nest chores, the male hopped off the eggs and fiercely attacked the other bird. The invader probably would have been killed if it hadn't managed to get into the air and escape to a nearby club.

The eggs are warmed constantly by one parent or the other and turned daily about seven times for even heating and incubation. The embryos will develop properly in twenty-four to twenty-eight days, with the average twenty-six days, when the first egg that was laid is hatched.

Mere hours before that first egg hatches, a rock-hard calcium deposit grows on the tip of the tiny beak of the chick in the egg — its life-giving egg tooth. Using that hard tip, the chick strikes the wall of the shell. Tiny cracks first appear near the large end. After trying all day, the chick manages to break a small hole, but the struggle is only beginning.

For twenty-four arduous hours the chick continues to use its egg tooth to break out of its prison — meanwhile squirming to tear the membrane that encases it like a net — cracking, then chipping off more of that hard eggshell. Finally the chick falls out of the egg — wet, exhausted, and helpless. Even brooded by a parent, the bedraggled little gull will take six hours to dry out.

Brooding the Chicks

Each chick is fluffy and handsome, its head and back light brown to buff, with dark brown and black spots much like those on the egg from which it fought its way to life. These spots blend the chick into its surroundings, helping to protect it from any predators.

The first few days of their lives the chicks spend their time eating and sleeping. They awaken, see their parents, beg food, then fall asleep. As the young grow, they become more active. Two weeks after hatching, the young gulls begin to grow flight feathers and become restless. Born wanderers, they start to move around the rocky isle, always watched by one parent. If they do not cross into another gull's territory, they are safe, for their main enemies on Smuttynose are other gulls.

At less than a month of age, still unable to fly, young gulls are vulnerable to storms. If they move too far down on the rocks, they can be smashed against them by sudden strong wind and surf. But they are curious and stand for long periods near the edge of a cliff, watching the surging sea, which one day soon they will conquer.

Surviving to eight weeks means that the young gulls will probably live to adulthood, which in itself is an accomplishment. Patricia McGill, a graduate student studying the herring and the black-back gulls at the marine laboratory on nearby Appledore, banded four hundred chicks so she could identify them from nest to nest. She concluded that of all gulls banded, only one third survived.

Survivor is an apt word to describe gulls, for not only do they have the ability to eat almost anything, alive or dead, but they can also walk, fly, and swim extremely well, a combination of assets most birds do not have. But survival is a constant concern in gull life. Even after the immature bird learns to fly well, it

must obey territorial regulations. If, while flying, it lands on claimed ground, it is immediately attacked and driven away.

For the young on Smuttynose, the learning process goes on throughout the summer. Watched by adults, the fledglings look for food in the water, get some swimming lessons, and practice landing and taking off from the surface of the sea. Actually, few swimming instructions are necessary, for gulls are born with that instinct. But the diving, the spearing of fish, and the polishing of takeoffs and landings continue for many weeks. Even while swimming, supposedly in an area where there are no territorial rights, a young gull must watch where it is going. If a young herring gull swims too close to a black-back and its offspring, the intruder may be killed immediately.

Built for Flight

The gulls of Smuttynose are superb in flight. They lift off from land, drifting through the air with the ease and grace of fish gliding through water. Long, flexible, tapered wings lazily flap until they catch those invisible currents that lift the birds one above another in perfect symmetry. They sail higher and higher, wings stretched without motion, the flight under total control.

That spectacular flight depends upon feathers, and one of the main occupations at the various Smuttynose clubs is the preening of that lustrous covering that also offers protection. Preening, oiling, bathing, and dusting are all part of the daily feather-care routine.

Gulls preen by nibbling certain feathers with their bills. The construction of the feathers shields the body from water and also controls body temperature. At the base of the tail is a gland that produces the oil that the birds move from tail to feathers with their bills. The oil not only waterproofs their bodies but also conditions the feathers, preventing them from drying and splitting, which would hinder flying. To discard feathers that have become worn or broken, gulls molt in the fall and spring, losing just a few damaged ones at a time, which doesn't affect their flight.

In addition to those well-tended feathers, the gull has a light skeleton of hollow bones. With its long tapered wings and a body that literally floats, it has only to spread its wings and give a slight push, and it is airborne. Often, just before taking off, the birds preen the top feathers of their wings to give them a smooth surface and reduce friction. The feathers must be perfectly arranged under the wings, and much time is spent at this task.

The gulls' skill in flight is so great that daily food-finding flights of one hundred miles can be mere routine. When winds are strong in rising currents over sand dunes, gulls soar for hours without moving a wing. Updrafts around rocky islands and high ridges near the ocean keep them gliding and circling for long periods, seemingly not looking for food but just interested in flying.

Gulls revel in dark, stormy days with a sea raging beneath them and clouds boiling around them. Then they simply ride into and on the winds, turning the elements to their advantage. They also hitchhike rides behind ships by riding without beating their wings on the air currents that result when wind strikes the sides of boats and rises in updrafts.

High in the sky, the gull seems invulnerable. But, below on Smuttynose, it is a member of a society so rigid and fierce that many a gull lies dead among the rocks because it broke the rules of territory or social order. Here the view of a gull society is not a romantic one. Observers have seen a herring gull struck dead in the air by a black-back whose territory it had invaded.

With the fading of summer, however, life among the gulls at Smuttynose seems more relaxed, more blissful, if such a state is possible in a gull rookery. Territory is no longer too important: The young are self-sufficient; the noisy mating and breeding are over for the year. Mated gulls are beginning to part, to take solitary walks to the sea. Soon their flight south will begin, the flight that will make these remarkable birds individuals again and Smuttynose a deserted island.

DISCUSSION

1. Do you think laws to protect endangered species of birds are necessary? Why do you think that?
2. How did the herring gull's appetite cause gulls in the United States to be protected?
3. Where are New England's two most important gull rookeries located?
4. What are the chief differences in the appearance of black-back gulls and herring gulls? Which of the species prefers solitude? Which one is usually seen in populated areas?
5. Why do the gulls re-form into private clubs when they return to Smuttynose each spring? Can you think of any similarities in people's clubs and those formed by gulls? If so, what are they?

6. Why, do you think, is the leader of each club an old and aggressive gull?

7. What details in the article indicate that pairs of mated gulls are remarkably loyal and attached to each other? How seriously do they accept their duties as parents? Give reasons for your answer.

8. Judging by this account, what do you think the author admires most about gulls? Why do you think that?

9. When do gulls seem to be flying just for the fun of it?

10. Have you ever watched any birds closely enough to observe their habits? If so, what are some of the interesting things you learned about them?

11. Gulls are useful to people because they help clear the seas and shores of debris. Do you know of other ways in which birds are beneficial?

12. What are some of the places besides refuges or bird sanctuaries where you might go to observe birds? How can you attract them into your own yard?

AUTHOR and PHOTOGRAPHER

Jack Denton Scott is a naturalist and world traveler who has written books on a variety of subjects. A former war correspondent, he also wrote an adventure column for the *New York Herald Tribune* that took him to such places as Ceylon (now Sri Lanka), where he looked for giant lizards, and India, where he studied leopards and tigers. He and his wife, Maria Luisa, have traveled around the world fourteen times, and he has written over a dozen books and over two thousand articles for leading magazines.

Besides being interested in nature and travel, Mr. Scott is a gourmet cook and has written several cookbooks, some in collaboration with his wife.

Ozzie Sweet is a well-known photographer who has shot over 1,700 covers for leading magazines and photographed many eminent people. In recent years he has been official photographer for the spring training camps of the major league baseball clubs in Florida. Mr. Sweet's main interest, however, is photographing wildlife.

SKILL

The Main Idea of a Group of Paragraphs

Did you ever read an article and say to yourself when you finished, "What was the point of that?" As you advance in school, you will be reading more and more informative material of increasing difficulty. Rather than reading such material several times to determine what it is about, you need to learn to read it efficiently. Once you have learned to do this, you should have no trouble in getting the point of an article or identifying the main idea that is being emphasized. Then, even if you have to reread the material for details, you will already have a basic understanding of it.

The Topic and the Main Idea

Good writers try to present informative material in well-organized paragraphs that make it easy to understand. For example, in a single well-written paragraph, all or nearly all of the sentences tell about the same thing. As you already know, that one thing is called the topic of the paragraph. Usually the topic can be expressed in a word or a phrase. The most important idea that the paragraph gives about the topic is called the main idea. You can usually express the main idea in a full sentence.

The main idea of a paragraph is what the author most wants you to know. It is often a summary of the contents of a paragraph. Most facts and details in a paragraph are presented to illustrate the main idea or make it clearer. The main idea is sometimes, but not always, stated directly somewhere in the paragraph. Being able to identify the main idea, whether it is stated or not, will help you to understand and remember the contents of the paragraph.

Getting the Main Idea of a Group of Paragraphs

Most of the material you read involves more than a single paragraph. Frequently an author writes a group of paragraphs that all relate to one subject, or topic. As in the case of a single paragraph, the most important idea given about the topic of a group of paragraphs is known as the main idea. Often you may need to study carefully an article that is made up of several informative paragraphs. If you can identify the main idea by putting together ideas that the different paragraphs give about the topic, you will be better able to understand the material.

To identify the main idea of a group of paragraphs, first you need to decide what the topic of the group of paragraphs is. Try to think of a word or phrase that expresses the one thing that each of the paragraphs relates to or tells about. Once you have decided what the topic of the paragraphs is, try to determine the most important idea about the topic expressed in the group of paragraphs. Sometimes you may find a statement in the group of paragraphs that summarizes the contents. That statement is the main idea of the group of paragraphs.

In the group of paragraphs that follows, the main idea is expressed directly. Read the paragraphs to decide on the topic and find the statement of the main idea.

Mighty wolves once roamed freely over North America. But their days were numbered. Just ten years after the Pilgrims landed, the first wolf bounty was posted in America.

Offering a bounty, or reward, for each wolf killed proved effective. The last wolf in Massachusetts was killed in 1850, and by 1900 all the wolves in New York and Pennsylvania had been killed. At the request of western sheep and cattle ranchers, the United States Congress set aside money for wolf control in 1915. Over twenty-four thousand wolves were killed in the next twenty-five years.

Among the most beautiful and intelligent of all the animals, wolves today are plentiful only in the subarctic regions of Canada and Alaska. In just three hundred and fifty years, wolves have been eliminated from nearly all of North America, including most wilderness areas.

What is the topic of the group of paragraphs you just read? You are right if you said something like *The killing off of wolves in North America.* Did you find the main idea of the paragraphs? It is stated in the last sentence of the last paragraph: *In just three hundred and fifty years, wolves have been eliminated from nearly all of North America, including most wilderness areas.*

In the next group of paragraphs the main idea is not directly stated. Read the paragraphs carefully to decide what the main idea is.

> The bright orange-and-black markings of the monarch butterfly are a familiar sight in many parts of North America. Surprisingly, the brilliant colors serve as a warning to insect-eating birds and animals — monarchs taste terrible. A bird that has tasted a monarch will recognize and avoid eating monarchs from then on. The viceroy, another butterfly, profits from the reputation of the monarch. It is protected from harm by its strong resemblance to the monarch, a condition that is known as mimicry. Although the viceroy doesn't taste bad, its black-and-orange markings are so similar to the monarch's that birds that have tasted monarchs avoid viceroys as well.

> Other insects are protected from enemies in the same way as the viceroy. For instance, there are flies and moths that look like bees and wasps. The tiger beetle is another insect that insect-eating birds and animals avoid. Insects that closely resemble tiger beetles are protected by mimicry.

Which sentence best expresses the main idea of that group of paragraphs?

1. The viceroy butterfly strongly resembles the monarch.
2. Insect-eating birds and animals avoid insects that taste bad.
3. Some insects are protected from insect-eating birds and animals by a condition known as mimicry.

In order to choose the best statement of the main idea from the three sentences given, you first needed to identify the topic, *Mimicry.* Since the main idea was not directly stated in the paragraphs, you then had to think of a sentence that would

express it. You might have asked yourself, "What is the most important thing these paragraphs say about mimicry?" You should have recognized that the main idea of the group of paragraphs is expressed in sentence 3: *Some insects are protected from insect-eating birds and animals by a condition known as mimicry.*

The Importance of Getting the Main Idea

In organizing informative material in a clear and meaningful way, good writers generally place special emphasis on a topic and main idea. The topic is usually clear; the main idea is also usually clear if you know how to look for it. Remember that the main idea of a group of paragraphs may be stated somewhere directly in the passage itself. If it is not, you can make up your own statement of the main idea by putting together ideas that the different paragraphs give about the topic. The important thing is that by determining the main idea, you are much more likely to understand and remember what you read.

DETERMINING MAIN IDEAS OF PARAGRAPHS

Read each of the following groups of paragraphs, which are typical passages you might have to read in two different books. From the three numbered sentences that follow each passage, choose the one that best expresses the main idea of that group of paragraphs and write the number of it on a sheet of paper.

Book A

Since the early 1970's the energy crisis has been a matter of growing concern in the United States. The major fuels used to produce energy — coal, oil, and natural gas — cannot be replaced once they are used up, and they are being used up at an alarming rate. More and more energy is being used in homes, in industry, and in transportation.

Homes in the United States are full of appliances that are supposed to make life easier or more pleasant — radios, televisions, vacuum cleaners, dishwashers. Each of these appliances runs on electricity, which is a form of energy. In order to produce enough electrical energy to run houses with many appliances — not to mention the factories that make those appliances and other products — power plants must use tremendous amounts of fuel.

The growing demand for transportation also increases the need for energy. The number of registered motor vehicles has doubled in the past twenty years. Airplane travel has increased enormously. Most of the energy for transportation comes from a single fuel — oil.

Unfortunately, another cause of the energy crisis is waste. In some homes, lights and appliances are left on when they are not being used. Such appliances as televisions that turn on instantly use power even when they appear to be off. Because often a car carries only one passenger, more cars than necessary are using fuel.

The yearly growth in the population also increases the need

for energy. In fact, energy and the fuels that supply energy are being used at a dangerous pace. Since the common fuels are not replaceable, the result is an energy crisis.

1. A great deal of energy is wasted.
2. The common energy-producing fuels — coal, oil, and natural gas — are not replaceable.
3. The energy crisis in the United States has several causes.

Book B

Sunlight is free and abundant. In fact, if it could be efficiently controlled and directed, the sunlight that reaches earth would supply more than enough energy — solar energy — for the whole planet.

Scientists are finding ways to harness the sun's rays to generate electricity, heat and air-condition homes, cook food, and purify water. They have even developed solar furnaces hot enough to melt steel. Not all the problems involved in capturing solar energy have been solved, but scientists are certain that in the future they will be able to devise efficient ways to collect and store energy from the sun.

1. Solar energy is difficult to control and direct.
2. Solar energy may be a good source of energy in the future.
3. Solar energy can be used to melt steel as well as cook food.

The Greenwood Boys

by WILLIE MORRIS

Where did boys growing up in the 1940's find fun and excitement in a small Southern town? Here Willie Morris recalls a comical incident from his happy childhood in Yazoo City, Mississippi.

There was something in the very air of a small town in the Deep South, something spooked-up and romantic that did funny things to the imagination of its bright and resourceful young. It had something to do with long and heavy afternoons with nothing doing, with rich slow evenings when the crickets scratched their legs and the frogs made delta music, with plain boredom, perhaps with an inherited tradition of making plots or playing practical jokes. I believe this hidden influence has something to do also with the Southern sense of fantasy and the absurd. We had to work our imaginations out on *something*, and the less austere it was, the better.

People rarely believe that a boy we knew ran all the way around a very large block in thirty seconds, hence breaking every track record in the world. Well, there is some truth to this story, but sometimes one has to lie to tell the truth, and I had better describe this event in a little more detail.

There was a pair of twins who lived in the town; their names were Paul and Pinky Posey. They looked so much alike that at times even their parents could not tell them apart. They both had long red hair, they were identically bowlegged, they had the same floppy ears and squeaky voices, and they wore the same clothes, which usually consisted of blue jeans and white T-shirts, minus shoes. They even got warts in the same places at the same time. Paul was slightly more intelligent than Pinky, but that was not saying too much. The only way we could tell them apart was that Pinky had four toes on his left foot, but seldom did anyone want to get close enough to make a thorough examination.

One summer a group of five or six boys from Greenwood, a town about fifty miles up the river, came to Yazoo for a two-week visit with their rich relatives. They were extremely obnoxious visitors, and since Greenwood was a somewhat larger town, they lorded it over us, calling us country bumpkins and the like, and acting for all the world as if they were from Paris or London or Constantinople or the lost underwater island of Atlantis. I have met many snobs in my lifetime, but to date, these boys from Greenwood, Mississippi, still rank as the biggest.

One afternoon Spit McGee, Bubba Barrier, Billy Rhodes, and I were playing marbles in front of the Yazoo high school, just minding our own business, when the visitors from Greenwood walked by and decided to show us how superior they were. "Here come them Yankees from Greenwood," Spit said.

"Wonder what they're gonna tell us *now?*"

They proceeded to tell us how wide the main street was in their town and how big the houses were. "Why, the Yazoo River up there," one of them said, "is a lot cleaner than it is by the time it gets down here. Up there it's blue as can be. You can even see the gars wigglin' at the bottom. Down here it's all mud. You're gettin' all our dirt." They went on like this for a few minutes. Bubba and Spit and Billy Rhodes and I ignored them and concentrated on our marbles. Finally one of the Greenwood boys said, "And you see this big fellow right here? He can outrun anybody in this hick town." The object of this superlative was a tall hatchet-faced individual named Marsh.

"That's true," Marsh said. "I can outrun anybody in town, and I can do it runnin' backwards!"

"Well, can you now?" Spit McGee suddenly exclaimed, jumping up from his game of marbles with such vengeance in his eye that I wondered what had gotten into him to break our icy silence in the face of the visitors' provocations. "Here's bettin' you five dollars and ten moonpies that we know somebody who can run around this-here block in thirty seconds, and it'll take your man at least three minutes to do it by Bubba Barrier's daddy's stop-watch."

"Thirty seconds to run around *this* block?" The leader of the Greenwood gang laughed. "That's impossible. Let's just walk around this-here block and see how big it is." So we all started from the front of the high school building, turned left on College Street, left on Calhoun, left again on Jackson, and a final left on Canal, arriving after a good eight or ten minutes' walk in front of the school again. It was not only a long block; it was the longest in town.

"Your man can't do it in thirty seconds," the Greenwood leader said. "Ol' Marsh can do it in three minutes, though, and your man can't do it in five."

"Meet us right here in front of the school this time tomorrow," Spit McGee said, "and bring your five dollars and enough extra spendin' money for the moonpies."

"We'll be here," the boy said, "and we'll make you look mighty silly."

After they had left, we all turned on Spit. "Are you crazy?" Billy Rhodes shouted.

"Shut up!" Spit exclaimed. "Just leave it up to me. It's three-thirty now. Y'all meet me right here at three tomorrow afternoon. Bubba, be sure and bring your daddy's stopwatch."

At three the next day, after a night of considerable worry, Bubba and Billy Rhodes and I showed up in front of the high school. There, on the front steps, was Spit McGee, and with him were Paul and Pinky Posey.

Spit was at fever pitch. "Bubba, you'll run the stopwatch. Paul, this here's the place you'll start runnin'. Pinky, you come with me. The rest of you don't do nothin' till I get back. And remember, Paul, once you turn the corner out of sight, you stay hid behind Mr. Frady's house till we come for you." With that, he and Pinky Posey started walking down the sidewalk, in the opposite direction from the finish line for the race, and soon disappeared. Two or three minutes later Spit returned alone.

"Where's Pinky?" Billy Rhodes asked.

"He's hidin' in the shrubs in front of Miz Williams's house, just before he turns the corner for the homestretch," Spit said mysteriously. It was just beginning to dawn on us what Spit was up to, but before we could question him as to particulars, we caught sight of the Greenwood boys coming our way.

"You mean this is the little twerp that can outrun Marsh?" The leader laughed when he saw Paul Posey, floppy ears and all, sitting on the steps of the school.

"Why, I could whip him *crawlin'*," Marsh said.

"We'll see about that," Spit said. "You run first," he added, pointing to the incorrigible Marsh. "Pick somebody from your side to run the stopwatch with Bubba Barrier so you'll know we ain't cheatin'."

Marsh lined up at the starting point, and when Spit shouted "Go!" he took off at a lightning pace. Soon he was out of sight and around the corner. We all sat nervously and waited. Billy Rhodes and I exchanged glances, while Paul Posey limbered up his bowlegs and did some exercises.

Finally, about two and a half minutes later, the Greenwood runner came into sight at the opposite end of the block. "There he is!" our antagonists yelled gleefully. "He sure can run!" Marsh approached the finish line, and as he did so, Bubba posted his time at three minutes, six seconds.

"Okay, Paul," Spit said. "Line up." Paul Posey went to the line, and with the shout "Go!" he started out, legs churning, and disappeared around the first turn.

"That little twerp's so bowlegged he won't even finish," Marsh said.

"His bowlegs pick up steam after the first turn," Spit replied.

Now the Greenwood slickers sat down to wait for Paul's appearance around the final turn in the opposite direction three or four minutes hence. To their horror, in a mere ten seconds he appeared around that corner and headed toward the finish line.

"Faster!" Spit shouted. "Speed it up!" Billy Rhodes yelled. The red-head, his features contorted and weary, his hair waving in the breeze, raced in our direction and crossed the finish line. I counted four toes on the left foot.

"Thirty seconds even," Bubba judged, and the boy from Greenwood who had been checking the stopwatch, by now wordless and in a state of shock, agreed. As we all patted our man on the back, the Greenwood boys stood off by themselves, shaking their heads and whispering in astonishment.

"That'll be five dollars, plus fifty cents for ten moonpies," Spit said, extending his hand. Our enemies counted out the money and then departed, too defeated to offer their congratulations. They never had the gall to face us again.

When they were out of sight, Spit said, "Let's go." Considerably more respectful of Spit McGee than we had ever been, we turned the corner where Paul Posey had originally disappeared and walked to the back of Mr. Frady's house. Paul Posey was sitting nonchalantly on the back steps of the house. "Come on, Paul," Spit said. "Let's go eat some moonpies."

Spit kept three dollars for himself and gave a dollar apiece to Paul and Pinky Posey.

DISCUSSION

1. Do you feel that the Greenwood boys deserved the treatment they received? Why do you feel as you do?
2. How does the opening paragraph of the story help to explain Spit McGee's thinking of his clever scheme?
3. Why were the boys from Greenwood unpopular?
4. What does the term "country bumpkin" mean? Who were called "country bumpkins" in this story?
5. What does the term "city slicker" mean? Who could have been called "city slickers" in the story?
6. Why, do you think, were the Greenwood boys' taunts usually received by the Yazoo boys with "icy silence"? What do you suppose prompted Spit McGee to break the silence and propose the bet?
7. What bet did Spit McGee make with the Greenwood boys? Since it was Spit McGee who had made the bet and was responsible for trying to win it, why did the other Yazoo boys have "a night of considerable worry" before the race?
8. How did Spit manage to win the bet?
9. How would you explain the popularity of stories in which the "country bumpkin" or the underdog wins out?

AUTHOR

When Willie Morris was seventeen, he left Yazoo City, Mississippi, to attend the University of Texas. Following graduation, he was a Rhodes scholar at Oxford University in England. He returned to Texas and became the editor of a well-known newspaper, *The Texas Observer.* Several years later, he moved with his wife and young son to New York City, where he was the youngest editor in chief in the history of *Harper's,* the oldest magazine in the United States.

Now a full-time writer, Mr. Morris is the author of several books about the South as well as of various magazine articles and stories. "The Greenwood Boys" is an excerpt from his book *Good Old Boy.*

Harriet Quimby Flies the Channel

by SHERWOOD HARRIS

By 1911, just eight years after the Wright brothers' first flight, the new field of aviation was booming. Flying schools flourished in the United States, Britain, and continental Europe. The first air races were drawing enormous crowds and large numbers of pilots. New speed, altitude, and endurance records were being set almost every month as better and better flying machines appeared on the scene.

The first men who took to the air were thought of as death-defying, daredevil heroes. But a woman who wanted to fly was considered slightly disreputable. Women were expected to stay at home and "behave themselves." The strait-laced Wright brothers refused to enroll any women at all in their flying school in Dayton. Claude Grahame-White, one of Britain's most famous fliers, declared, "I have taught many women to fly, and I regret it. My experience has taught me that the air is no place for a woman. The truth is that women lack qualities which make for safety in aviation. They are temperamentally unfitted for the sport."

Even as Grahame-White was saying this, he was being proved wrong by a small but determined group of female pilots in France and the United States. Two French women, Hélène Dutrieu (eh-len' doo'tree-uh) and Marie Marvingt (ma-ree' mar-vahn'), were among the first pilots in Europe and had been setting records as early as 1909.

The American women got a later start but caught up fast. By the end of 1911, three American women — Harriet Quimby, Matilde Moisant (mwuh-zant'), and Blanche Scott — had earned their licenses and were flying regularly in the United States. "Flying seems easier than voting," said Harriet Quimby, and in fact it was. The Constitutional amendment guaranteeing women the right to vote was not ratified until 1920.

Harriet Quimby, while still in her twenties, was drama critic and editor of the woman's page for *Leslie's Weekly*, a fashionable New York magazine. One evening, as she was working on an assignment for the magazine, she met some pilots who were in town for a big air show. From then on, she was determined to become a pilot too.

In the summer of 1911, Harriet Quimby passed her tests and received the first official pilot's license issued to a woman in the

United States. Hélène Dutrieu was the only other woman in the world who had an official license. Harriet Quimby flew in the New York area for a while and made a barnstorming trip to Mexico with Matilde Moisant. But women aviators still weren't taken seriously — most newspaper write-ups devoted as much space to their flying suits as to their flying skill. So Harriet Quimby planned a flight that would earn the respect of other pilots and show the world what women fliers could really do. She decided to fly across the English Channel.

It's hard for us today to imagine that a flight across the English Channel could ever have been considered a daring and impressive feat. The distance from Dover, on the English side, to the French port of Calais (ka-lay') is only twenty-two miles. Most modern jets take only about two minutes to make the trip, and hundreds of people do so daily with less trouble than driving to the supermarket.

But it was a different story in Harriet Quimby's time. Those twenty-two watery miles looked like one great, wet graveyard to most early pilots. On a clear, calm day it might not be so bad. But the Channel is hardly ever clear enough of fog and mist to see from one coast to the other. Calm days are likewise very few. The Channel's water is notoriously rough, choppy, and cold. To a generation of pilots who had learned from experience that their engines could easily quit every time they made a flight, the Channel was the worst place to be over in case of a forced landing.

The first flight across the Channel had been made in 1909 by French pilot Louis Blériot (lwee blay'ryo'), who said he didn't think he'd care to try it again. Two other French pilots set out to cross the Channel at the same time as Blériot. One was fished out of the water, uninjured but very agitated, shortly after he took off. The other decided his plane wasn't up to the trip and returned to Paris. By the time Harriet Quimby decided to try the flight, several men pilots had managed it successfully; but one very competent English aviator had disappeared without a trace on a Channel flight in 1910, and many more had simply decided there were better places to fly.

In early March 1912, Harriet Quimby went to Paris to arrange a plane for her flight. She picked out a new Blériot monoplane — the same type that Louis Blériot had used for his Channel flight. It was one of the finest aircraft of its day but far from ideal for a flight out to sea. The cockpit was open and not even protected by a windshield. The engine had so little power that the plane couldn't take off if the wind was more than five miles per hour. In the air, the controls were so ineffective that it often took several tries before a pilot could get a turn started.

The new plane was sent on to a little seaside resort on the French coast about thirty miles south of Calais. Since the Blériot was so tricky to fly, Harriet Quimby tried to get in some practice before setting out across the water. Each day she arose before dawn and went to the field where the plane was kept. But day after day, high winds prevented her from flying. So she shipped the plane to Dover, hoping that the weather would be better for practice on the other side of the Channel.

Sunday, April 14, was a perfect day for flying. The wind was calm, and from the airfield near Dover Castle, the young American could make out the hazy outline of the French coast in the distance. Her friends urged her to take off at once, but she made it a rule never to fly on Sunday. Bad weather set in again on Monday, but at three-thirty on Tuesday morning it seemed to the crew at the field that conditions were improving. They put in a call to Harriet Quimby at her hotel. She quickly gulped a cup of hot tea and raced to the field. It was just getting light when the plane was rolled from its hangar and warmed up. The wind was calm and the sky was clear, although patches of fog still drifted in from the sea.

Experienced pilots advised that it would be cold crossing the Channel in the open cockpit of the Blériot, so the pilot dressed accordingly: two suits of long underwear under her satin flying suit, two overcoats over the suit, and a wide sealskin stole over her shoulders. At the last minute, someone handed her a hot-water bottle, which she tied to her waist like an enormous gurgling locket.

These were the *only* preparations she made for flying the Channel. At 5:30 A.M. Harriet Quimby took off for a coast she couldn't see through the fog in a plane she had never had a

chance to try out. She had no maps, no instruments, and no life jacket or other survival equipment in case she came down in the water.

She climbed to about fifteen hundred feet, then circled back over Dover Castle so that a movie crew could film her departure. The fog was thicker now; only the top battlements of the old fortress loomed above the swirling gray blanket. In an instant the cliffs of Dover were behind. The fog was thinner over the water, and Harriet Quimby spotted a tugboat that had been sent out by a London newspaper to follow her flight and help her if she was forced down. But up ahead, the French coast was hidden by another wall of fog that stretched as far as she could see in either direction.

With no hesitation, she plowed right into it. Moisture from the cloud bank drenched her plane and dripped from every surface in the open cockpit. Her goggles fogged up, and she had to remove them. The warmth of the hot-water bottle soon disappeared in the damp, penetrating cold. Unable to see anything, she flew on by instinct alone.

All great pilots seem to have a powerful inner feeling about flying. When the odds turn against them, their intuition takes over, and they make the right moves without even thinking about them. So when the Channel fog closed around Harriet Quimby in her primitive monoplane, she simply flew on, guiding the plane as best she could until something told her she was near the coast of France.

Then she nosed over and began her landing descent. With the ground covered by fog and with no altimeter aboard, she had no way of knowing how close she was getting to the ground. Down, down she went. Then suddenly the fog parted, and she saw a sandy beach below! She had arrived in France.

She flew back and forth for a while to find the best place to land, then alighted on the beach. For a few moments she was all alone. Then an excited crowd from a fishing village rushed up. One of the women miraculously produced a mug of hot tea and some bread and cheese, and some of the people pushed the plane beyond the reach of the rising tide. In crossing the Channel in a flight that lasted a little over thirty minutes, Harriet Quimby had become the most famous woman pilot in the world.

Harriet Quimby's fame was short-lived, unfortunately. The same year she crossed the Channel, she died in a bizarre accident while flying at an air meet in Boston. Coming in over Boston Harbor for a landing, her plane unaccountably flipped over while still several hundred feet up. Harriet Quimby fell out — pilots didn't wear seat belts in those days — and plunged to her death in the harbor.

DISCUSSION

1. Do you think that the risks Harriet Quimby took in her flight across the Channel were necessary and justifiable? Why do you think as you do?
2. In the early days of aviation, what was the common attitude toward women who wanted to fly?
3. Why did Harriet Quimby decide to fly across the English Channel?
4. What is your opinion of the famous British flier's statement that women "lack qualities which make for safety in aviation" and are "temperamentally unfitted for the sport"?
5. The article mentions that Harriet Quimby made a barnstorming trip to Mexico. What does the word *barnstorming* suggest to you about where early air shows were held?
6. What were the dangers of flying the Channel in Harriet Quimby's time?
7. How was Harriet Quimby prepared against the cold on the flight? For what dangers was she unprepared?
8. Approximately how fast did Harriet Quimby's plane fly in the trip across the Channel?
9. If she were alive today, which branch of aviation do you think Harriet Quimby would prefer? Give reasons for your choice.

AUTHOR

Sherwood Harris has written two books about aviation, *Great Flying Adventures,* in which "Harriet Quimby Flies the Channel" appears, and *The First to Fly*. Mr. Harris has been a pilot for many years. He learned to fly in the United States Navy, where he flew combat planes from aircraft carriers. Mr. Harris works as an editor and lives in Bedford, New York. In his spare time he teaches flying, and he is also an enthusiastic scuba diver.

Winter Morning

by CHARLES REZNIKOFF

This smoky winter morning —
do not despise the green jewel shining among the twigs
because it is a traffic light.

In a former gold-mining area in Australia, three teen-
agers are trapped by a cave-in at the mouth of an abandoned mine: solid, dependable Johnathan; spoiled, passive
Bruce; and independent Louise. They have partially explored the two tunnels leading off the dead-end passage in
which they now are huddled. One is another dead end. A
tiny spot of light in the darkness of the other indicates a
small opening, possibly another entrance to the mine, but
Johnathan believes the passage to be too narrow for them
to negotiate to the end. Moreover, he tells Louise and
Bruce that he has heard the rock in the tunnel "talk," or
creak. Obviously there are cracks in the rock there, and
any undue movement or pressure could bring the top down
on them. They wait in the darkness, hoping that rescuers
will come to dig them out.

A
DISTANT
EYE

by MAVIS THORPE CLARK

194

Louise began to feel detached, as though she weren't one of the three. Although it was dark, she could see quite plainly all of them sitting there, sitting waiting. Bruce was staring at his feet, irritated because they weren't carrying him out of this hole as they carried him out of most holes; Johnathan was staring at the rock face opposite, having the patience to wait, like the waiting for the growing of a tree. And the girl — who was herself — was irritated as well as patient, but grateful for these pictures that her mind plucked, like sound waves, out of the darkness. It occurred to her that she should write down what she saw and felt — write down this experience. Though they might be going to die, this was an experience of living.

"It's getting very stuffy," said Bruce, and he coughed.

"Strike a match, Johnathan," said Louise. "We've been here a long time — and I can't hear anything yet. Strike a match. Give us a look at ourselves — so that we know we're not just turned into voices."

Johnathan tried hard to strike a match. He struck three . . . four . . . five. . . . But while they flickered into life, they died instantly, as though an invisible hand snuffed out the flare.

"That's funny," said Johnathan.

But they all knew what it meant. They were the youth of a gold-mining district, and even if there was scarcely any mining done today, they had listened through the years to stories of the mines. They knew that foul air — or gas — was extinguishing the matches.

In the darkness, Louise felt Bruce quiver at her side, while Johnathan went taut.

"Gas is seeping in from somewhere," Johnathan said stiffly. "The fall of earth has moved something — shut us in — but opened a pocket of bad air."

"How long . . . can we last? . . ." whispered Bruce.

"It's hard to say. We don't know for how long, or how fast, the gas has been coming through."

"When it puts out a match, . . ." Louise began, scarcely believing.

"I know, it's pretty thick," Johnathan finished for her. "There certainly won't be enough time now for anyone to find us and dig us out."

"Carbon dioxide, . . ." said Bruce, and his voice, somehow, was lazy and as unbelieving as the girl's.

"Stand up — get on your feet!" Johnathan suddenly ordered. "I know we can't stand upright . . . but the gas is heavier than air and is thickest at ground level. It pushes the air upward. Stand up!"

There were awkward movements as the three got to their feet but no quick stretching for the purer air at the roof of the tunnel, as though they were already listless.

They stood quietly, half-crouched or bent according to height, no one willing, it seemed, to voice the alternative they had to not being dug out — in time.

It was Louise who deliberately shook her body as though she would wake it and said, "That leaves only the other tunnel — we'll have to try it."

At once Bruce jumped, as though a string had pulled him back from that simmer of laziness, and his arm shot out. "No, no!" He gripped Louise's shoulder so hard that he twisted her and slammed her into the rock wall. "Johnathan tested part of it . . . remember! He found that it got almost too narrow for his body . . . and that the roof would fall. I'm broader than Johnathan. I'd rather the gas."

Now it was Louise who caught hold of Bruce's hand, while consciously forcing her feet to feel the rock floor, above which she seemed to be floating, and deliberately pushing from her mind the fuzzy mixed-up pictures of the three of them waiting. "It *is* a chance! If we stay here, there's *no* chance."

"You go, I'll stay. Gas is painless — just going to sleep."

"*We're all going.* You have to make a bid to live — as long as there's a chance."

"You will only get caught in there — jammed in there. Jammed! Think of it!"

"We have to try it." Louise sounded quite calm. She felt quite calm, and her mind was very clear now. There was this chance — their only chance — to get out of here alive. "I'll start off. But I'll stop — and not move an inch, Bruce — if you don't follow."

She didn't know whether she meant it — whether she really could stay back with this boy in the foul air while there was still a thread of a chance to escape. But she did know that to go without him, to leave him to certain death, would haunt her forever if she herself escaped. And when Johnathan said, "We won't move without you, Bruce," she knew that Johnathan felt the same.

She felt Bruce tremble and realized the magnitude of the decision they had forced upon him — the decision for their three lives — the terrible choice they were offering. It would be so much easier to yield to the gas — to drift into the darkness of the mind as well as darkness of surroundings — to let go, to wait for it to happen — painlessly. In his body, close to her, trembling, cold, she felt the battle that was in his mind.

She waited. She touched his hand again. "Now," she said. "We can't waste any more time."

"You'd never give up, would you, Louise?" Bruce said very quietly. "You'd do what you felt you had to do."

Louise could see nothing in the darkness, but she felt she was staring at the voice. "I suppose so."

"It would be so much easier if you would just go . . . and leave me. I wouldn't mind . . . you leaving me," Bruce said, his voice tired.

Louise cried out then. "I'm waiting for you! We're both *waiting for you!*" There was so little time.

Waiting for him! Waiting for him to decide between the gas — which was so much easier for him to face, but which would certainly take his two companions with him — or the chance in the tunnel, fraught with a possibility horrifying beyond contemplation. Nonetheless, it was a chance that these other two were eager to take. With his face screwed wryly in the dark, Bruce knew he couldn't deny Louise and Johnathan this chance.

"Then . . . start, . . ." he said.

Louise began to crawl forward, trying to make no noise so that she could hear that Bruce was following. And presently she heard him behind her . . . breathing in jerks . . . but following, and Johnathan behind him.

They crawled into thick darkness, but there were no more matches struck. To see another match die would surely destroy what was left of their morale.

If Louise and the two boys had had a torch, they could have moved fairly quickly along the main tunnel to the offshoot that might lead them to safety. They would not have been able to walk erect, for it was not high

enough for even Louise to stand upright; but they would not have had to
go practically on all fours, feeling
along the wall for the opening — the
second opening — as they went.

Louise continued to lead, with
Bruce directly behind her, and then
Johnathan. Louise had never thought
of herself as a leader and certainly had
never been a leader among the girls at
school; but when confronted with a
choice that appeared to her to be no
choice at all, then she was a leader. So
she led forward, feeling a good deal of
admiration for Bruce, whose decision
had been so difficult, and aware now
that it was she herself who may have
condemned all three of them to a slow,
cruel death.

Bruce kept very close behind her,
bumping her now and again. Even
while they were sitting in the thick
darkness, he had touched her at intervals, as though reassuring himself that
she was still there. She wished he
wouldn't. He was expecting too
much, a strength that she might not
possess. She dared not think how she

might react if she did come to that point where there was not room enough to go on ... if she was jammed. She only knew that she had to go on as long as she could and that the boys would follow.

This second crawl along the dark, wet passage, however, was quicker than the first. It helped to have been in the tunnel before, to know that there were several deep holes that could be skirted only by pressing into the craggy wall and that the second tunnel came rather quickly after that first dead end. Behind them, urging them on, was the carbon dioxide.

Or was it with them all the way? Were they already breathing it in, poisoning their blood, filling their lungs, dulling their brains with fumes they could neither see nor smell, until they slept and died, without knowing they were doing either?

Louise wouldn't let herself think of the gas or whether her eyes were getting heavy and her limbs leaden. She crawled on, heartening herself with the thought that some fresh air must be coming in the hole through which they hoped to escape and praying that Bruce and Johnathan were still following. She passed one lead-off and came to the second.

"I am turning, . . ." Louise said over her shoulder to Bruce. "After three or four more twists — four at the most — we should see the opening ahead.

"D'ye think . . . it will be wide enough . . . for me to go through?" There was already the beginning of hysteria in Bruce's voice.

Louise was trying not to make her own fears real and was tempted to snap back, "How should I know!" But she managed to say, "I'll be ahead of you. I'll be able to tell you."

She crawled on over more and more stretches of wet, feeling the mud beginning to cake on her, and once a small frog leaped into her face. That was when her own hysteria came close to matching Bruce's. She kept going only because she was certain that when they rounded the next bend, the speck of distant light would welcome them and beckon them and lead them — light that was not only light but air — the clean, free air of sunlight and warmth and blue of sky.

But when she turned the corner, she cried out in disappointment and fear. "It's gone! It's not there! The opening — it's not there!"

And from far behind Bruce — very far, it seemed, for there was not much space for even a voice to travel — Johnathan spoke for the first time since they had set out. "That means it's night, Louise. The sun's gone."

For a moment Louise stopped crawling. Her disappointment hurt like a wound. During the hours she and Bruce and Johnathan had sat waiting in the darkness, she had been buoyed up by the thought of that eye of light. It had helped her hold on to the fact that there was still an outside world, an outside world that filtered into this narrow, crouched cavern.

When they had started to crawl toward it, crawling away from the poisonous air behind, she had had an almost uncontrollable desire to get up and run toward it — to scream toward it. But her own practical sense had held her, soothed her, saved her, and in the darkness still led her.

Now it was not there. There was only darkness ahead; a darkness that grew narrower and narrower — she could feel it pushing on her shoulders, on the arms that elbowed her along, on her thighs where her jeans kept catching on sharp edges. Once the seam on a side pocket ripped, and she was thankful for the layer of material that protected the flesh beneath it.

Now she stopped. The will to go forward left her. She smelled the smell of damp, buried rock. A drop of moisture fell from the close ceiling onto the back of her neck, which was stretched almost horizontal. Louise wondered if there was any other living thing in this tunnel except the frog. She recalled that most forms of life need light. Near the entrance there might be some spiders perhaps, or even bats, but not here.

She was very cold, and Bruce's hand that reached out and touched her ankle was cold too. Bruce had said nothing since he had asked his question in that high-pitched voice.

His touch moved her forward again. There was death behind, but a faint hope of life ahead.

Although she couldn't see it happening, she knew almost at once that the tunnel grew narrower. This narrowing was what had driven Johnathan back before. She was able to crawl still, but she was crouching more. In the heavy darkness she felt the walls moving in, beginning to clasp her. She wondered how soon they would begin to "talk." She began to crawl faster, and faster, losing her caution for what she might meet. Somewhere ahead, even if she couldn't see it, there was that slit of light.

From behind her she heard Bruce's harsh breathing and then a cry, "Louise . . . Louise . . . where are you — I can't reach you!"

She didn't want him to touch her ankle. She didn't want to feel his trembling fingers.

"Louise . . . I . . . I want to push at this rock all around me. . . . I want to push it out of the way. You do understand! My shoulders are . . . sort of . . . swelling into it."

"The roof, . . ." she thought. "It'll fall!"

"Keep crawling," she said. "Catch up to me. . . . I'm not far ahead."

She stopped, hating to stop, and she felt his hand grasp her ankle. It was a tight, tight grip, a clamp around her foot; as she tried to press forward again, she felt his weight chaining her to him.

"Let go, . . ." she said, trying to keep her voice steady. "You know I'm here . . . just ahead of you. Let go. . . . I can't move if you don't let go."

He let go suddenly, and she knew he was ashamed. "I'm sorry."

Funny, she thought, how darkness and nothingness all around could give you a glimpse of yourself.

The way became narrower. Louise was crawling flat now, elbowing her way along on her stomach — going forward into darkness, into she knew not what. Surely there must be some variation in the depth of dark ahead to show that there was an opening. It had been there earlier — that shining eye. Now there was nothing — surely there should have been a star. Was it possible that somehow they had taken the wrong turning, the wrong tunnel — that this didn't lead to that opening but just went farther into the middle of the earth? The track certainly seemed to be going down now — down — and she felt it should go up! Whatever it was, it still led onward and still pressed in farther and farther until the rocks were wrapping around her. She realized then that even if they wanted, it would be a physical impossibility to go back.

Louise knew that the boys must be in severe straits. Their wider shoulders, especially Bruce's, must now feel the actual clutch of the rock. Their elbows must find it hard to have freedom enough to propel them forward. The weight of the earth must be resting on them — and pressure, just light pressure, might start the rock "talking" again.

She heard the boys' grunts and uneven breathing. She heard the dislodgment of stones, and she thought, in cold sequence: "It's coming down. The roof's coming down. We're disturbing it — and it's going to fall. This is where we die."

She struggled harder and faster, and she wanted to scream when Bruce clutched her foot again.

"Keep going!" she called back. "Keep going! Don't hold me — just let me go — and follow."

If he hung on now, if he prevented her from going any farther, if this sense of being jammed in on all sides finally took hold of him and he yielded to it — and hung on to her — then they were trapped just as if the roof did fall in. Johnathan at the rear, working in such a confined space,

would not be able to drag Bruce back or break his hold on her. Without leverage, even his tough muscles would be helpless. And even if he could, to where would he draw back? To the foul air in the wider tunnel? That would be preferable, though, to this kind of death. Bruce had been right.

"Let go, Bruce," she said quietly.

"If it gets any narrower . . . I won't be able to get through — my shoulders are scraping!" he gasped. "I thought I was wedged tight!"

She tried to turn his thought. "Bruce, how is Johnathan? Is he still coming?"

Johnathan answered, "I'm right behind Bruce. My shoulders are scraping too."

It was a somber voice, and she realized it was scarcely any easier for him than for Bruce — except Johnathan knew that if Bruce got through, there was room enough for him to follow.

"It can't be much farther," she said. "We've been crawling for hours . . . it seems."

"The wrong tunnel perhaps . . . and no opening!" Bruce shuddered.

"No! No!" Johnathan roused himself to shout. "No — this is the right tunnel — there was no other. Go on, Louise."

It helped to have Johnathan give a directive like that — calm still, even if somber, not giving up — helping her to do what she had to do.

Louise kicked her foot out of Bruce's grasp, risking striking his face, and elbowed her way on. She wormed through damp and cold, and at times her long hair caught in a crevice or on some rough spike of overhead rock.

Now there was a dreadful smell in the tunnel coming from somewhere ahead as though the earth were a creature with a bad breath. Or else some animal, a fox perhaps, had crept into the tunnel to die, and she would have to pull herself over its decomposing body.

She was nearly sick. And then the thought leaped at her. If it was an animal, that must mean they were almost at the entrance. An animal — even one coming in to die — would never retreat too far into darkness. They must be near the entrance — they *must* be near. The earth and rock pressed down closer; her arms barely had room to move. With their wider shoulders, could the boys make it?

And then the floor fell away from her probing, grasping hands; her shoulders eased out into a space that allowed their full expansion; her body wriggled and jostled forward, propelled now by her feet. She slipped into a kind of shallow basin, and there, straight in front of her, was an oval slit of darkness that was gray compared to the inky darkness immediately behind her. The entrance! And big enough to allow them through.

But Bruce wasn't following! She felt around for the hole that had just disgorged her. "Bruce . . . Bruce . . . come on! I've made it. I'm here — at the entrance."

"You've made it!" There was surprise and disbelief in the words. "You've made it!"

"Yes. Yes! Come on!"

Then he said, "I'm stuck — I can't move an inch!"

Louise trembled to control her panic. "Shrink, Bruce, shrink your shoulders! Don't press into the walls — press into yourself. Shrink yourself. Bruce — I'm free! D'ye hear? I'm free — you can be free too!"

She leaned forward as far as she could into the narrow passage. "Give me your hand — I'll try to pull. Push with your feet."

She groped, but no hand came to meet hers. She screamed, "Your hand, Bruce — give me your hand! It isn't just you — it's Johnathan — behind you. If you don't get out — he can't get out either!"

"I can't! I can't move! I'm wedged in."

"Johnathan!" the girl shouted. "If you can hear me — push him from your end. Start him forward. Johnathan — I'm out. Try to help him forward!"

Now a kind of moan came from Bruce as though he were someone coming out of an anesthetic. "You mean . . . you're out, Louise . . . you're free!"

"I'm free of the tunnel, Bruce . . . and I can see the outside night light. Try to reach my hand — try hard."

She was partly back in the tunnel herself now, reaching in as far as she could, and Bruce's fingers found hers. They clung hard, and Louise eased backward. At first it seemed that the boy could not follow, that the walls were deliberately holding him. "Bruce, shrink yourself!" she cried.

And somehow Bruce's bones stopped pushing against the rock walls and yielded and contracted and dissolved into the flesh. Louise pulled hard; Johnathan pushed as best he could from the rear. Presently the boy's head and then his shoulders — his broad shoulders — emerged into the saucer of cave whose entrance was that oval of lighter dark.

Soon he was crouched beside Louise, still not able to stand upright in the shallow hole, and extending his

arm toward Johnathan. Johnathan wasn't quite as broad as Bruce and followed slowly but surely into safety.

And when he, too, was crouched in the cave, Louise stepped toward the oval opening, knowing that she was stepping over the remains of the animal that she had smelled back in the tunnel, and felt the webs of spiders that caught the insects that blundered through the entrance. It was not a big opening, but by flattening herself, she was able to thrust head and shoulders and arms through and to feel with her hands whether there was any kind of ledge out onto which they could crawl. To her relief, she found that the ground seemed to slope gently downward and that they need not fear crawling out into the nothingness of space.

Once out of the cave she stood upright, stretching her muddied limbs and feeling the joyousness of the free flow of her blood. The night was not moonlit but bright with stars and the wash of the Milky Way — the River of the Sky; a night that was not all darkness but patterned with the light and shade of ochre-tinted earth and green bush and red rock; a night of sweet smells, even the burning of wood.

DISCUSSION

1. Louise had never thought of herself as a leader. Do you think that she had judged herself fairly? Why do you think that?
2. Why did the three young people become frightened when the matches Johnathan lit kept going out? Why did Johnathan tell Louise and Bruce to stand up?
3. When the young people realized that rescuers could not reach them in time, what two choices did they have? What did Bruce want to do?
4. How did Louise and Johnathan finally convince Bruce, despite his feelings, to go along with them? Why was the choice they made the more difficult of the two to carry out?
5. Do you think that Louise and Johnathan would have stayed with Bruce in the passage in which they had been trapped if he had refused to leave? Why do you think that?
6. What traits of character did Louise and Bruce show while making the decision about trying to go through the tunnel?
7. What advantages were there to Louise's going first in the tunnel? Why was it a good thing that Bruce was between her and Johnathan?

8. What bitter disappointment did Louise experience when she turned the last bend in the tunnel? What did Johnathan say to try to reassure her?

9. After Louise freed herself from the narrow tunnel, what problem did the group still face? How did Louise help to solve this problem?

10. Why, do you think, did Louise want to write down what she saw and felt when she and her friends sat waiting after the cave-in? Did she perhaps write about it later? Why do you think that?

AUTHOR

At one time Mavis Thorpe Clark was afraid of closed-in places and felt panic whenever she was inside a cave. This feeling is what she recalls in *If the Earth Falls In,* the book from which "A Distant Eye" is taken.

Ms. Clark was born and raised in Melbourne, Australia, and has been writing since her school days. When only fourteen, she wrote a full-length children's book that appeared in serial form in a weekly Australian newspaper. After she married Harold Latham, she continued to use her maiden name as her pen name. She produced many short stories and articles for magazines, and she wrote and adapted scripts for children's radio programs. Since her two daughters became old enough to attend school, she has written many novels, mostly for teen-agers. Most of her novels are set in Australia.

The books of Mavis Thorpe Clark have won many awards and have been translated into several languages. Among them are *The Min-Min, The Sky Is Free,* and *Wildfire.*

How Romantic

What could be more American than a story about boys in blue jeans looking for excitement in the "spooked-up and romantic" Deep South of the 1940's? "The Greenwood Boys" is pure Americana, yet the very words the author uses can be traced back to origins outside the United States. Our language, like our population and culture, springs from many different sources. In American literature the South is often portrayed in romantic tones, yet the very word *romantic* comes to us from across the Atlantic Ocean, from Rome, of course. *Romantic* is a variation of the word *romance.*

Romance derives from a Latin word that originally meant "Roman; made in Rome." The word has evolved and expanded its meaning. Today the word *romantic* conveys the adventure and mystery that Willie Morris remembered in the Deep South.

The blue jeans that Willie and his friends wore seem American, but they weren't originally. *Jeans* are named after the heavy cotton fabric of which they are made, *jean.* This fabric is named after the place where it was first made, Genoa, Italy. *Denim,* a similar fabric used to make blue jeans, is also named for its place of origin, the words *de Nîmes* (duh neem) meaning "from Nîmes," France.

Consider some other things that seem truly American. What could be more American than the *hamburger* or the *frankfurter?* Actually, there is nothing American about the origin of their names, which come from Hamburg and Frankfort, two German cities. We eat fruits with foreign names, such as the *tangerine*, named by the French for Tangier, Morocco, from which this fruit was first imported. Another such fruit is the *peach*, named by the Romans for Persia, the land from which it came. *Mayonnaise* was named for Mahon on Minorca, a Mediterranean island. The *turkey* was confused with a similar fowl first imported by the Portuguese from Africa by way of Turkey.

Products from many different countries bear the names of their places of origin, though many of them are less obvious than *china* from China. Fabrics like silk are good examples. The word *silk* relates to a Greek word that originally meant "the Chinese," or "the silk people." Other names of fabrics are similar: *Calico* is named for Calicut, India; *muslin* for Mosul, Iraq; *angora* for Angora, now called Ankara, Turkey; and *gauze* probably for Gaza in the Middle East. British woolens bear place names too: *Worsteds* originated in Worstead, England; *tweed* was originally a trade name influenced by the name of the Tweed River in Scotland.

You probably use a surprising number of words that are derived from place names every day. If you pay attention to them, you'll find that American English comes from all over the world.

Each of the following sentences contains a word derived from its place of origin. You should be able to guess the places of origin of some of the underlined words. Use a dictionary to check them and to find out the origins of the others.

1. The French official slipped into a <u>limousine</u> and disappeared.
2. That author's new story is called "The <u>Rhinestone</u> Caper."
3. Succotash is made with corn and <u>lima</u> beans.
4. A blue <u>afghan</u> was draped over the sleeping figure.
5. How many <u>manila</u> folders do you need for your stories?
6. The child held two subway tokens and five <u>copper</u> pennies.
7. The detective grabbed his <u>mackinaw</u> and darted outside.
8. All team members wore blue <u>jerseys</u> bearing the team insignia.

Chino's Tale

by MARY STOLZ

Like Miss Mixter, the woman he lives with, Chino is old. If for every human year a cat ages seven years, Chino is one hundred and five. Getting on.

This is his story.

Fifteen years ago, Athena, the beautiful Siamese cat that Miss Mixter had had for not quite five years, took sick from something and died. Miss Mixter grieved for her. She made up her mind never to have another pet.

Several months passed.

On an evening in winter, Miss Mixter came home from seeing a show in town. As she reached her porch, she heard a furious muted mewing in the bushes.

She paused, listened, then said aloud, "This is not my affair," and let herself into the house. "A stray. A neighbor's pet just passing by. Nothing to do with me."

She put the kettle on for tea.

It was a windy night, and snug inside, she could not hear anything outside. In her mind, though, she *could* hear. The cry

had been that of a kitten, not a cat. To her expert ear, it had been the angry complaint of hunger.

"Well, by now it's gone, I'm sure," she said. "It wouldn't linger at a stranger's house on a night like this."

Miss Mixter, over the years, had got in the way of talking aloud to her cats and, now that she had no audience or companion, could not teach herself to think thoughts silently.

"Still, I suppose I shall have to check. Though I'm sure," she repeated, "that by now it's gone."

The night air had gotten colder, and a sprinkle of snowflakes had begun to toss in the wind.

"As I thought," said Miss Mixter. "Gone. Quite gone."

A tiny yowl greeted this comment. The light from the porch revealed a skinny, big-eyed kitten wobbling and grumbling onto the pathway.

"Well," said Miss Mixter, "I've had a lot of experience with cats, but I've never seen one quite as homely as you, and that's a fact."

"Yaaah!" said the kitten, trying to climb the steps.

"The voice is the voice of Siamese," said Miss Mixter, "but the shape is the shape of alley."

She realized, however, that the battle was lost, so she went down the steps, picked up the victor, carried him into the house, and closed the door.

"You'll be wanting to eat," she informed him, and the thought crossed her mind that it was pleasant to have someone to talk to again.

She offered the kitten a saucer of warm milk and corn flakes. "This dish was a favorite of Athena's," she told him. "See what you think."

The kitten clearly agreed with Athena.

After supper he fell asleep in front of the fire; Miss Mixter, dreamily content, sat on the sofa and read.

After a very short time, the kitten woke up, looked around suspiciously, then set about investigating. He padded from room to room, eyes wide and wild, legs uncertain. He poked behind books, studied the undersides of chairs and sofas, climbed the draperies and hung at the top, giving his demon's cry. Miss Mixter had to lift him down, as he seemed to have no idea how to descend.

All this time, he talked. He screamed and muttered and wailed and now and then seemed to sing. For an animal not much larger than a teacup, he had a voice like the kettle at the boil.

Miss Mixter, who'd accompanied him for a while as he rummaged and reconnoitered, had gone upstairs to get ready for bed.

"Chino!" she called. "Chino, stop that noise and come up here."

She had no idea where the name had come from. It had simply slid into her mind as she stood at the top of the stairs wondering how to quiet him.

Beneath her in the hallway, the kitten skidded to a stop and looked up at her curiously.

"That's right," she said softly, "that's to be your name: Chino. So — come along, Chino, Chino, *Chee*-no. . . ."

He mounted the stairs, clinging to the rug and calling as he came. In the bedroom he clawed his way up the dust ruffle and settled at the foot of the bed.

And so it happened that at well past midnight, with the wind whining in the dark and snow drifting up the panes, Chino and Miss Mixter established their first habit. He would come when she called him, and he would sleep at the foot of her bed.

Looked ahead to, the years seemed endless. Looked back on, Miss Mixter thought they'd gone before she could get a grip on them. When she looked in the mirror, she could scarcely believe what she saw.

"How odd," she said to her cat. "How odd of us, Chino, to turn out to be so old. Chino!"

Chino, curled on a cushion on a chair, looking like a battered, much-used cushion himself, did not stir. His kittenhood and his roving, hardy young cathood were gone, long gone, leaving a slow, calm, sleepy old gentleman who, of late, had not bothered to talk with Miss Mixter or even to come when called. Miss Mixter's heart was heavy; she feared that she was losing Chino's affection.

"It can't be," she said aloud, but to herself now. "He's just tired. But he must be hungry. He hasn't had a bite since breakfast. Chino!" she called louder. "Chino, my dear friend, dinner is ready. And just think, I have *shrimp* for you."

But the cushion on the cushion did not stir. Not a whisker.

Miss Mixter walked to the chair and picked up her cat, who opened his faded blue eyes and looked into hers. He murmured as she carried him to the kitchen and set him before his dish. He ate all the chopped shrimp with relish.

After dinner he retired to a corner near the bookcase, and when she called him to bed, he remained motionless. Miss Mixter had to carry him upstairs.

The next day Miss Mixter took her old friend to a veterinarian.

"You see," she explained anxiously, "something is wrong, very wrong. That is, Chino still eats and doesn't seem sick. He's never been sick. But he won't come anymore when I call. He has *always* come to me when I called. He doesn't talk anymore, either. Chino has always been a great one for talking. And when I tell him it's bedtime, he pays no attention. He doesn't come when I turn the key in the lock or when I call him for dinner, even if it's shrimp."

She wrung her lean hands. "Oh, Doctor, what is wrong? What is wrong with him?"

The doctor felt Chino's bones, looked in Chino's eyes. "This is a very old cat," said the doctor, who was very young.

"Yes, yes, we know that."

"Most cats don't live to be this old."

"I know," said Miss Mixter proudly.

"Well, Miss Mixter, it seems to me that it would be a kindness to have him put away."

"Put away?"

"Put to sleep."

"Killed?" said Miss Mixter. "Put to death? For what reason?"

"Well, he's so old."

"So am I so old. Do you suggest that it would be a kindness to have me put away too?"

"Oh, now, Miss Mixter," said the young doctor, shocked. "How can you say such a thing?"

"How can *you* say such a thing?"

Miss Mixter rose, took Chino in her arms, held him against her. "He is old, and so am I, and we are just about alone. But we

relish the things of life, Doctor. We care about the world, and I don't think either of us is ready to be put out of it."

"Please, please," said the doctor, rising too. He was upset and ashamed. "Please, Miss Mixter, sit down again. I apologize. I am sorry. You see, not all people get so attached to cats. That is, I didn't think —"

"At all," Miss Mixter interrupted.

"But surely you'll agree," he said, "that most — I mean, many — people feel that when animals get this old, the kindest thing to do is to put them out of their —"

"Misery," she snapped. "Get them out of the way is more like it. Well, Doctor, Chino is not in misery. It would be no kindness to take from him his hours in the sun on the windowsill, his pleasure in food, his happiness when I stroke his head, just behind his ears.

"And no kindness to me, Doctor, to leave me in a world empty of his friendship, where there would never again be someone in the room who cared about me."

She started out, holding Chino closely. He was purring.

"Miss Mixter? Miss Mixter, please."

She turned. "Yes, young man?"

"Come back. You have taught me something, and I just want to say — to say thank you. You have, truly, taught me something."

"Well," said Miss Mixter as she sat down. "Well, well. That's an unusual admission."

"It's an unusual occurrence," he said.

With an air of intentness, he got up, circled behind Miss Mixter's chair, and clapped his hands loudly, just behind Chino's ears. Miss Mixter jumped, but Chino lay peacefully purring.

"I do believe," said the doctor, "that we've got the answer."

"I see," said Miss Mixter thoughtfully. "I see what you have in mind."

"Chino is deaf."

"Deaf," said Miss Mixter. "Deaf, poor thing. And I never thought of it." She sighed. "Well, there's nothing to do about that, of course. We shall have to make the best of it."

"Veterinary science, Miss Mixter, has made some marvelous advances. It is possible — *if* the animal cooperates — to fit a pet with contact lenses these days or even a hearing aid."

"A hearing aid? For a cat?"

He nodded. "Of course," he added quickly, "it's pretty expensive, and most people don't think it worthwhile —"

Miss Mixter held up a hand. She was thinking, not whether she should pay for a hearing aid for Chino, but *how* she would pay for it. She was not a rich woman, not at all.

"How much, Doctor?"

"Well, I —"

"Doctor, what would it cost for Chino to be fitted with a hearing aid? If *I* needed one, we'd get it. Now, how much for Chino's?"

"Ah, I fear it would run in the neighborhood of one hundred and fifty dollars — about that." He sat back.

"So," thought Miss Mixter, "there goes my winter coat *and* the new bedspread that was to replace the one that was thoroughly clawed." Well, the present bedspread and coat would probably last her time, and what were things like that compared to the joy of having Chino lift his head and come to her call, of having Chino talk again?

"He doesn't talk because he can't hear, is that right?" she asked.

"That's probably it," he agreed.

"When shall we fit him for the hearing aid?"

The doctor blinked, recovered himself, and said, "It will take a little time to order one. And we don't know if Chino will accept it. We must be prepared for that."

"We can only try," said Miss Mixter. "We must try."

One week later, Chino and Miss Mixter were back in the young veterinarian's office.

On the examining table was a very small plastic hearing aid, a little battery, and a small blue collar. On either side of the table stood the doctor and Miss Mixter, tense, nervous, hovering over Chino, who lay beside his hearing aid, peaceful and uninterested.

"Well," said the doctor, "shall we get on with it?"

Carefully he fitted the collar around Chino's neck and stood back.

Chino stirred, yawned, and went back to sleep.

"Encouraging," said the doctor, "most encouraging."

Miss Mixter looked doubtful.

"Now — for the real test," he said, and with delicate fingers he gently inserted the hearing aid and attached the battery to the collar.

Again, he stood back. They watched as Chino's left hind leg reached forward and expertly flipped the offending object from his ear.

"Oh, dear," said Miss Mixter.

"We'll try again," said the doctor.

They tried again. And again. And again. Each time the hearing aid was put in place, Chino, with no sign of resentment, calmly flicked it out.

"Well," said the doctor after what seemed a long, long time, "I'm afraid he is not going to cooperate."

Miss Mixter, who'd been watching all this in brooding silence, suddenly said, "How foolish we are. How ridiculous. Doctor — try again."

This time Miss Mixter firmly held Chino's legs so that he could not move.

"Chino," she said clearly as the hearing aid was adjusted, "Chino! Look at me."

With an air of surprise, the old cat looked up at his friend. He struggled, lay still, then listened intently as she talked, explaining to him all about the function of the hearing aid.

The veterinarian appeared to be torn between tenderness and laughter as he observed the two of them.

"There," said Miss Mixter at length. "Now he understands."

She released the cat's legs, and Chino stood up. He made no further attempt to dislodge his new appendage.

"Amazing," said the doctor. "Simply astonishing."

"Oh, I don't know," said Miss Mixter. "It was merely a matter of letting him hear my voice and having him *realize* that he was hearing it. After all, it's been a long time. See how pleased he looks."

And indeed, thought the doctor, the ancient cat appeared awake and interested for the very first time.

"Amazing," he said again.

"We're deeply grateful," Miss Mixter said, picking up Chino, who gazed about with a keen and curious eye. "Yes, deeply grateful."

She and her cat went home to talk it over.

The veterinarian sat at his desk to think it over.

Now, after Chino is settled at the foot of the bed each evening, Miss Mixter removes his hearing aid and puts it on the bureau in an old Spode[1] saucer.

In the morning she carefully fits it back in his ear. Then she goes to the kitchen and calls, "Chino! *Chee*-no! It's breakfast time."

As he walks sedately to breakfast, Chino gives a yodel to let her know he's on his way. Miss Mixter sips her tea and watches as Chino tucks away his corn flakes and milk.

"Just like the old days," Miss Mixter says, her voice silky with contentment.

"Yaaah," says Chino.

---

[1] **Spode** (spohd), porcelain or china of fine quality.

DISCUSSION

1. Imagine yourself in Miss Mixter's place. Would you have bought a hearing aid for Chino? Why or why not?
2. Why, do you think, did Miss Mixter make up her mind not to have another pet after her cat named Athena died?
3. How did Miss Mixter and Chino first find each other? What made Miss Mixter change her mind about having another pet?
4. Miss Mixter's first meeting with Chino is referred to as a "battle" in which Chino was the "victor." Do you think that these words accurately describe what happened? Why do you think as you do?

5. How did Chino's behavior change when he got old? What did Miss Mixter think that change might mean?

6. What comparison does the author use to help you picture the changes in Chino's appearance and behavior when he got old?

7. What did the veterinarian advise when Miss Mixter first told him of Chino's behavior? How did Miss Mixter respond to this advice?

8. How did Chino react to the hearing aid at first? How was Miss Mixter able to help him accept it?

9. What do you think the author meant when she said that the veterinarian was "torn between tenderness and laughter" as Miss Mixter explained the hearing aid to Chino?

10. Why did Miss Mixter refer to Chino as "my dear friend"? Would you agree that many people come to regard their pets as friends? Why or why not?

AUTHOR

As a child, Mary Stolz loved to read and write, and in school her favorite exercise was to choose one sentence from the chalkboard and write a story around it. Even with this early interest in writing, she did not begin serious writing as an adult until she was hospitalized for several months. During that time, she wrote a novel and sent it to a publisher, who accepted it for publication. Since then she has written more than thirty popular books, including *Land's End, Leap Before You Look,* and *The Edge of Next Year,* a National Book Award finalist.

Mary Stolz lives in Connecticut with her husband, a doctor.

No Turning Back

by RICHARD DEMING

It's all over now but the shouting, because the battle has been won. The United States is already so far along the road to metrication, or conversion to the metric system, that there is no chance of turning back. Opposition from industry has not stopped altogether, but a recent survey by the United States National Bureau of Standards showed that 70 per cent of American manufacturers favor metrication. Many industries are already well along in the process of converting to metrics. In the educational field, national associations are on record as wholeheartedly supporting conversion. Engineering and technological associations and societies are also almost unanimously in favor of conversion.

In some areas the United States has already quietly converted to metrics. The favorite film size for still cameras is 35 mm. Movie film comes in 8 mm and 16 mm sizes. The pharmaceutical industry has been metric for some time. Prescriptions are filled in centigrams and centiliters instead of in ounces of weight and ounces of liquid. Most scientific and engineering laboratories have used the metric system for years. Large automotive repair garages, and even many of the smaller ones, have had to buy metric tools as well as conventional ones in order to repair foreign-made cars. Some highway signs now give distances both in miles and in kilometers.

In 1875, the United States was one of eighteen nations that signed the Treaty of the Meter at Paris, but only in recent years has the drive to go metric gained ground in America. The turning point was when England decided in 1965 to go metric. By the mid-1970's, the United States was the only major industrial nation in the world that was not using the metric system.

The result has been to place American industry at a competitive disadvantage in trading with other nations. Metric nations would rather buy products made to metric measurements. American industries have had to tool some of their plant space to metrics in order to sell to foreign markets while still keeping inch-pound machines in order to turn out products for the domestic market. One auto company was turning out 30 per cent of its product to metric standards even before it decided on complete conversion.

For this reason alone, there can be no turning back. The United States has no choice but to get in step with the rest of the world.

Chances are that within the next few years the metric system will be the only measurement system taught in public schools anywhere in the United States.

Organized opposition to the adoption of the metric system in the United States has all but disappeared. That does not mean, however, that there are no longer any objections to the system. It still has critics.

One criticism that sounds good until you look at it closely is that with the metric base of 10 you lose the considerable advantage of being able to divide units, such as feet, by 2 over and over again. Ten can be divided by 2 only once, because that gives you 5, which is not divisible by 2.

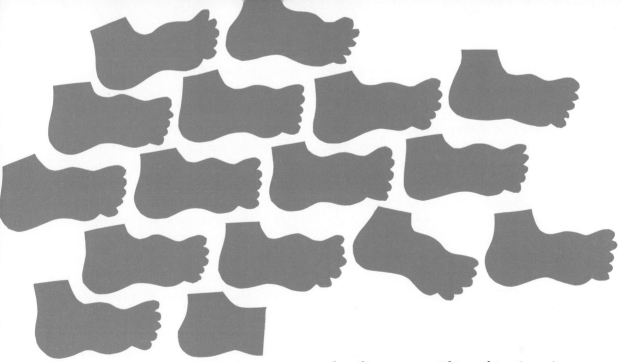

People who favor this argument ask how anyone is going to slice a pie into ten pieces or fold a piece of paper into ten equal parts. The answer is that no one should try. Such operations do not involve measurement; they involve only division. Nothing in the metric system says that you can't go right on using such convenient customs as cutting a pie into equal pieces by first slicing it in half, then into quarters, and finally into eighths, or that you will be kept from folding a piece of paper into eight equal parts.

An even more common objection to adopting the metric system is that Americans will not only have to learn an entirely new system but will also have to unlearn the old familiar one. This objection is based on the assumption that all Americans "know" the present system. But do they really?

The three basic quantities needing measurement in day-to-day living are length, capacity, and weight. Of course everyone knows the common units of length and could mark off fairly accurate approximations of an inch, a foot, or a yard without a measuring rule. But how many people know that a rod is 16½ feet and that a furlong is 40 rods? And how many remember that a league is 3 miles?

Most people have a fair idea of how much a pint by volume is, or a quart, or a gallon. But how many can define a gill or a hogshead? You can probably imagine the weight of an ounce, a pound, and a ton, but can you define a scruple or a dram?

When you add the specialized measurement units used within certain trades — such as the surveyor's link (7.92 inches) and the English ell used in measuring cloth (45 inches) — there are well over a hundred units of measure in the customary system. Even excluding specialized units, there are more than sixty separate units for general measurement. Since few people have more than a vague idea of what most of them mean, it is hardly accurate to say that Americans really "know" the customary system.

Some common units, even some you may think you know, have different meanings in different places. When you say *mile*, do you mean the statute mile of 5,280 feet or the Admiralty mile of 6,080 feet or the United States nautical mile of 6,080.20 feet or the international nautical mile of 6,076.11549 feet? When you say *ton*, do you mean the United States short ton of 2,000 pounds, the United States long ton of 2,240 pounds, the nautical ton of 100 cubic feet used to measure cargo capacity, the displacement ton of 35 cubic feet used to figure a ship's displacement of water, or the freight ton of 40 cubic feet used in shipment by rail?

In the metric system there is no such confusion in meaning. When you say *kilometer*, you always mean exactly 1,000 meters, no matter where you are in the world. When you say *gram*, you always mean the same unit of mass. The customary ton can be either a unit of mass of varying size or a unit of capacity of varying size. The *megagram* (sometimes called a *metric ton*) is always a unit of mass and is always exactly 1,000 kilograms, no matter what you are weighing or where you are in the world. The *liter* is always the same measure of capacity, whether you are measuring gasoline or maple syrup.

The biggest advantage of the metric system over the customary one is that it is simple. Everything is in multiples or divisions of 10. In the metric system you have to learn only a single progression for *all* units of length, capacity, and weight. For multiples, you multiply by 10 and for subdivisions you divide by 10, no matter what you are measuring. This means that decimals can be used instead of fractions in most cases.

People who are apprehensive about metrication seem to think that on some given date the use of the inch, the quart, and the pound will suddenly cease and from that day on they will have to wrestle with the unfamiliar units of the meter, the liter, and the kilogram. No such sudden change is going to take place, of course. But on the other hand, the United States is no longer going to drift slowly into metrication as it has been doing for over a hundred years. No one has said that metrication can take place in less than several years, and it is accepted as a matter of course that in a few areas there will never be conversion. These special areas may be roughly divided into two categories: (1) traditional matters in which the customary system of measurement is such an important part that there would almost certainly be widespread resistance to change and (2) areas where it would be economic idiocy to try metrication.

Football is an example in the first category. The length of a football field will no doubt remain 100 yards instead of changing to 91.44 meters, and you are unlikely ever to hear a sports announcer say, "Third down, one and eight-tenths meters to go." Baseball diamonds and basketball courts will probably continue to be laid out in customary units also, at least in the near future. In track and field and swimming, however, distances that haven't already been metricized probably will be rather quickly, because Olympic measurements in these sports are all in metric terms. Broad jumps, high jumps, pole vaults, and distance throws are already measured in metric terms in many schools in order to make it easier to prepare for the Olympics.

There would probably not be a great deal of opposition to adopting complete metrication in track-and-field competition.

In the second category a good example is railroad lines. Certainly it would be foolish to suggest that all the railroad track in the country be torn up and replaced with the metric-gauge track used in Europe. Metrication will never take place, even as track wears out and has to be replaced, because two different gauges of track would require two different sets of wheels and axles for every locomotive and car that passed over the track. The United States will keep its railroads nonmetric because that is the only sensible thing to do.

The goal of the federal metrication program will be to upset everyday life as little as possible during the changeover but to convert as quickly as possible in those areas that count the most. Areas that are thought to count most are those where metrication will either make computations easier or transactions between individuals simpler.

The metric system is the only measurement system ever to come close to worldwide adoption. Thousands of years after the dawn of civilization, we are finally going to have a universal language of measurement.

DISCUSSION

1. Do you agree with the author that the same standards of measurement should be in use throughout the world? Why or why not?
2. What does the term "metrication" mean?
3. What are some areas in which metric measurement has been in use for some time in the United States?
4. By the mid-1970's, how many major industrial nations in the world were *not* using the metric system?
5. Why, do you think, was England's decision to go metric "the turning point" in the drive to convert the United States to the metric system?
6. What does the author mean by saying, "The United States has no choice but to get in step with the rest of the world"?
7. What are some of the advantages of the metric system?
8. Into what two categories does the author divide the special areas in which there may never be conversion? What examples does the author give for the two categories?
9. What other examples can you think of in which conversion may never take place or may not take place for a long time?
10. What examples, other than those given in the article, can you think of where gradual conversion is now being made to the metric system?

AUTHOR

Even while earning his living by doing something else, Richard Deming has always considered himself a writer. He has had such different occupations as social worker, short-order cook, teacher, and soldier. Since the early 1950's he has been a full-time writer and has over fifty books, many of them mysteries, and about seven hundred short stories to his credit. Much of his writing has been published under pseudonyms rather than under his real name. "No Turning Back" is taken from his book *Metric Power: Why and How We Are Going Metric.*

The Season of Light

by JEAN LITTLE

Anna Solden and her family had come to Canada from Germany in 1934. Five years later, her new country and her old country were at war. Rudi, Anna's older brother, enlisted in the Canadian navy. While his ship was in Halifax harbor, there was an accident, and cleaning fluid splashed into his eyes, causing him to go blind. Anna understood Rudi's problem better than anyone else in the family because five years earlier it had been discovered that, even with thick glasses, her eyesight was very poor. In her determination to help Rudi, she turned to Mrs. Schumacher, the person who had taught Anna how to live with her own visual disability.

As Anna neared the Schumachers' house, she felt apprehensive. What if she could not make Mrs. Schumacher understand? Yet she was the most understanding person, except for Papa, that Anna knew. She had, after all, understood Anna herself when nobody else could get past the sullen, stubborn, uncaring face she had turned

227

toward the world, the wall of pride she had built around herself. Now she was sure Rudi was behind a wall, too, and Anna longed to find a way to get him out.

Mrs. Schumacher opened the door before Anna had time to ring the bell and led the way into the living room. She seemed to know from the beginning that this was not one of Anna's customary visits, that she had come about something serious.

Anna told Eileen Schumacher everything, all the small things and the big ones that were worrying her.

A man from the Canadian National Institute for the Blind had come to see Rudi soon after Papa brought him home. Anna had just come in from school, so she stayed to listen.

"Rudi was perfectly polite," she told Mrs. Schumacher, "but at the end he said, 'I don't think I'm quite ready, yet, for the things you're suggesting, sir. I just want to rest at the moment. I'll have my father telephone your office when I think you can help me.'"

"That sounds good," Mrs. Schumacher said. "It sounds as though he realizes he has to give himself awhile to adjust, and then he'll ask for help."

"It does sound like that," agreed Anna, struggling to put her anxiety into words. "His words always sound all right, but there's nothing underneath what he says. It's as though he's not really there — just politeness and words but not Rudi himself. I'm sure he only listens enough so he can make the right answers. Otherwise he doesn't care. And nothing he says really means anything."

She paused and took a deep breath. Mrs. Schumacher waited for her to go on.

Anna's story came spilling out. "It's hard for me to know how to say it. To me, the worst part is that he is going further and further away from us. He's disappearing, escaping maybe, into some safe secret place where nobody can reach him or hurt him anymore. What's wrong is you can't live in that place. I've been somewhere like it. A little like it, anyway. It's like being shut up inside a shell, with no way out. I remember. I still dream about it sometimes."

"Oh, Anna," Eileen Schumacher said.

Anna paid no attention. She was not sorry for that little girl now; she was worried about Rudi.

"When I was small and everything seemed so hard and Rudi was mean, I went there, but I couldn't love anybody from inside that place. You and my friends and Papa all rescued me. You just broke the shell, a little at a time, until you could come in, and I couldn't stop you. You could come in, and I could come out."

Mrs. Schumacher smiled at that. She even laughed softly.

"You were extremely prickly at first, I must admit," she said. "I thought of you, I remember, as a little porcupine with all its quills sticking out. And I can see why you are concerned now. But what do you want to do?"

"I want to rescue Rudi," Anna said simply. "I think — I don't know why — that we could wait too long. He might go so far in we'd never be able to bring him back."

"I think you have a plan, don't you, Anna?" said Mrs. Schumacher. "I can see it in your face. Tell me. That's what you really came for, isn't it?"

229

Anna nodded, not surprised that Mrs. Schumacher had guessed. She had always been good at reading the minds of the children she taught. But Anna wanted this plan to be a secret. It had to be, or it wouldn't work. This was going to be the tricky part. She had no choice but to trust her old teacher.

"It's like this," she said, and explained. She did not confide her whole idea, not the last part, which she would play by herself, if she had to. She would do it only if the first part wasn't enough, and whatever happened, it would be between Rudi and her, no one else.

"Can you help?" Anna asked. "Will you?"

"That's a tall order, Anna, but I think perhaps I can. I can try anyway," Mrs. Schumacher said slowly.

Anna felt giddy with relief. There had been the chance that Mrs. Schumacher would not go along with the idea.

"Maybe, very likely in fact, we're going about this all wrong, and we should leave it to the professionals," Mrs. Schumacher said, hesitating for one moment.

"I know Rudi better than anyone," Anna said, surprised to realize this was true. "I know how he can put people off. I think . . . you see, he was so mean to me once, not just one time but often, back a few years before I knew you even. We don't speak of it now, but he feels sorry when he thinks of it. Or he did, before he went away. Then last year we got to be a sort of team. Maybe, because of those things, I can get through to him. I do want to try. If I fail, and it doesn't help, then someone else, some grown-up, can still do the professional things."

Getting ready to put Anna's plan into operation took nearly a month. She had to go over to the Schumachers' almost every day after school.

Finally it was too late to back down. The night came when she had to try it, good or bad, right or wrong. She went up to Rudi's room and got things ready in an out-of-the-way corner, where he would be sure not to trip over anything. She went back down, waited the long, long hours till bedtime, and tried not to grow so afraid, while she was waiting, that she would be unable, in the end, to carry her plan through. She also had to keep all of this inner turmoil hidden from her family. She had never in her life been more grateful than she was that night when Mama said, as usual, "Off to bed, Anna. Sleep well."

The time had almost come.

Anna had worried about falling asleep, but she was far too tied up in knots even to doze. She heard all the noises of the household settling down: water running in the bathroom, Papa and Mama talking downstairs, light switches being clicked off, the last news broadcast signing off, beds creaking. Papa began to snore. After an endless stretch of time, she heard Rudi start to walk back and forth, as though he were locked in a cage.

She took a small flashlight, eased out of bed without making a sound, inched her way cautiously to Rudi's bedroom, opened the door soundlessly and slid her body around it, beamed the thin line of light down at the talking book machine, and reached for the knob that turned it on. She waited till Rudi was on the far side of the room. He was talking to himself. She couldn't hear the words, only muttering, but they made him miss the one little click. She had worried about that click ahead of time and never dreamed it would be so simple.

Breathing shallowly, doing her level best to keep her hand steady, she moved the phonograph needle into place.

"*A Tale of Two Cities*," a man's voice read out, startling even Anna, who had known what was coming, "by Charles Dickens. Read by Stanley Wellman."

Having practiced at the Schumachers' over and over, Anna then moved the needle a little farther on in order to miss all the part about it being a talking book to be used exclusively by blind people and to reach the story itself. It caught the tail end of the last word of what she wanted to skip and then went on, the deep voice speaking the words with love, with respect, exactly the way they should be read.

> "It was the best of times, it was the worst of times, it was the age of wisdom, it was the age of foolishness, it was the epoch of belief . . ."

"What is it? Turn it off. Stop it! Who's there?" Rudi cried out.

She had been amazed he had let the record play that long. She switched it off.

"It's only me, Anna," she said. "That was the first record of a talking book. I picked it because I knew you liked it, even though you had read it before. I thought . . ."

"Anna, please, I told you, leave me alone," Rudi said.

"I will in a minute," she answered, keeping on even though she could hear her voice starting to shake. "But first I have to do one more thing. Listen, just this once. I want to read you something."

Rudi said nothing, but she could feel his mind set against her. If anything, the wall was stronger.

Slowly, painstakingly slowly, she began to read. She had marked off the breaks in the first paragraph with bits of paper glued to the page. Since she had been following, she knew how to pick up exactly where the reader on the record had been cut off.

"It . . . was . . . the . . . epoch . . . of . . . in . . . cre . . . du . . . li . . . ty . . . it . . . was the . . . sea . . . son . . . of . . . Light . . ."

"Anna," he stopped her.

"Yes?" she said.

"Why are you reading like that, so slowly?"

"It's very fast for me. I only know the basic alphabet, none of the abbreviations. If I didn't have it practically memorized, I'd have been slower still," she said, not giving him a direct answer, trying to make him go on talking.

"Anna," he said again.

"Yes?" Anna said, her heart lifting a fraction, for his voice sounded alive — not warm, nor understanding, nor welcoming, but curious and really Rudi's.

"How are you reading?"

"In Braille," Anna said.

"Were you looking at it?"

"No. How could I be? I didn't turn on the light."

There was a long silence. Then she began to talk to him in a quiet, level, almost angry voice.

"Rudi, stop being the way you are. You're not you at all. If I can read Braille after only a few lessons from Mrs. Schumacher, you can too. You can listen to this book all night here in the darkness, instead of pacing up and down, up and down."

"So you did hear me other nights," he said softly, bitterly.

"Yes. I've always heard you. But I'm talking about something else. You're going away inside. Mama says you're getting better. You have even Papa nearly fooled. . . ."

"But not smart little Anna," he mocked.

"No, not me," she said, "because I know how it is."

"You know!" he jeered again.

But once more she was glad, for he sounded ready to fight. She had not heard him ready to fight for weeks. Now she would have to use her last weapon, the one she had withheld till now.

"I couldn't see much till I was nine," she said, "and you — you called me Awkward Anna and made fun of me and kept saying I was stupid. Do you remember that? I was more afraid of you than of anyone."

"But I didn't know," he said, taken off guard by her sudden attack.

"Oh, it's all over long ago, that hurting. And I wasn't like you, because I didn't know, either, that I couldn't see properly. I believed you were right, that I was stupid and clumsy and no good. I believed you so much that I went away inside myself, where you couldn't reach me to keep hurting. Like you, now."

"Where's the phonograph?" he asked suddenly.

Anna knew when to stop.

"Let me turn on the light for myself," she said, "and I can get you to it. I used a tiny flashlight to help me find it before, so you wouldn't hear me and I could surprise you."

"You're just lucky I didn't have a heart attack," her brother said, as she pulled his hand into the crook of her elbow and led him to the talking book machine. Showing him how to operate it was simple. "The records go around much more slowly than on our own phonograph," she explained, "and here are all the other records that make up the rest of the book."

He picked them up and carefully put them back down.

"I can teach you the Braille alphabet, which is how everybody begins, after school — if you help me with my math, that is."

She held her breath while she waited. Had she gone too far?

Then he laughed, a cracked little laugh that sounded something like a sob. But Anna knew it was laughter.

"Go back to bed, Little Stupid, little Awkward Anna," he said. "We'll see what tomorrow brings when we get there. Turn out the light when you go."

She got up and left him, without another word, because she couldn't speak with such a lump in her throat. She ran to her alcove, fell onto her bed, and lay there, listening.

Would the pacing begin again?

What had she done?

He hadn't promised anything.

"It was the best of times, it was the worst of times . . ." the voice began again.

Then it said, ". . . it was the season of Light, it was the season of Darkness, it was the spring of hope . . ."

Anna hugged her pillow to her and let the tears of joy come any old way they wanted to.

DISCUSSION

1. Do you think that the title of this story is appropriate? Why or why not?
2. What was Anna's reason for going to Mrs. Schumacher? Why was Anna worried about her brother Rudi?
3. Why did Anna call upon Mrs. Schumacher for help with her plan? How did Mrs. Schumacher feel about Anna's plan?

4. What advantage did Anna believe she had that an adult professional would lack in dealing with Rudi's problem? Do you think someone who has overcome a problem is often able to help another with the same problem? Why or why not?

5. What do you think Anna meant when she spoke of the safe, secret place into which Rudi was escaping in this way: "What's wrong is you can't live in that place"?

6. What was Anna's purpose in going to the Schumachers' every day for nearly a month? Why, do you think, did Anna feel that her plan must be kept secret in order to work?

7. After first hearing the talking book, Rudi told Anna that he wanted to be left alone. How did Anna finally succeed in arousing Rudi's curiosity? Why, do you think, was Anna glad to find out that Rudi sounded ready to fight with her?

8. What was the "last weapon" Anna used to draw Rudi out of his shell? Considering the circumstances, do you think it was a fair weapon to use? Why or why not?

9. Judging by the story ending, would you say that Anna's plan is likely to work with Rudi? Give reasons for your answer.

10. Do you think the words of the talking book from *A Tale of Two Cities* had special significance for Rudi? Tell why you think as you do. If you wish, tell how something you have read either influenced or changed your way of thinking.

AUTHOR

Jean Little, a popular Canadian author, was born on the island of Formosa (now Taiwan), where both her parents were missionary doctors. She grew up in Guelph, Ontario. Blind at birth, Miss Little gained limited sight in one eye and was able to graduate from the University of Toronto. Before becoming a writer, she taught children with physical disabilities, an experience that is reflected in several of her books.

Miss Little has a zest for life. She takes frequent and often extended trips. Once she lived in Japan, where she studied Japanese and tutored teen-agers in English. While in Japan she was notified that she had received the Vicky Metcalf Award, given for excellence in writing that is inspirational to Canadian youth. The 1978 Canada Council Award for Children's Literature in the English Language was presented to Miss Little for her book *Listen for the Singing,* from which "The Season of Light" is taken.

from # Music

by AMY LOWELL

The neighbor sits in his window and plays the flute.
From my bed I can hear him,
And the round notes flutter and tap about the room,
And hit against each other,
Blurring to unexpected chords.
It is very beautiful,
With the little flute-notes all about me,
In the darkness.

SKILL

Outlining: Taking and Organizing Notes

Thelma sat at her desk, a stack of books in front of her. She sighed in despair. "I'll never get my report about the energy crisis written. There's so much information that I don't know where to begin."

Have you ever felt as discouraged as Thelma when you had a report, either written or oral, to do? Finding materials about your subject can be fairly easy, but selecting and organizing information from those materials into a good report can seem very difficult. Learning to take notes from more than one source and to organize those notes into an outline will help you whenever you have to prepare a report.

Planning for Note Taking

You already know that taking brief notes as you are reading will help you to understand and remember the material. In general, if that is your purpose, you take notes on whatever is important. When your purpose in taking notes is to prepare for presenting a report, however, the notes you take will be more selective. You will not take notes on everything that is important in the material but only on those things you will include in your report. You can see, then, that before you take notes for a report, you must first decide what you are going to include in the report.

Most subjects are simply so large that they can't be covered in a report of only a few pages. Obviously, if you have several books about your general subject, you must choose some part of that subject and find information in the books about that part of it. There are a couple of ways to do this.

One way to narrow down the subject of your report is to ask questions. This is a particularly good plan if you know very little about the subject. For instance, Thelma is writing a report on the energy crisis. She could begin by asking herself questions like these: *What are the causes of the energy crisis? How does the energy crisis affect our daily lives?* As Thelma read, she would take notes on information that answered those questions.

Another way to narrow down your subject is to make a working outline. This is particularly easy to do if you already know something about the subject. You can often make a working outline after you have read something fairly general about your subject, such as an encyclopedia article. The working outline indicates main topics and subtopics that you think you will want to cover in your report. It is not the final outline for your report, and it may be changed as you go along. Thelma might make a working outline similar to the following:

I. **Causes of the energy crisis**
   A. **More energy used**
   B. **Waste of energy**
   C. **Fuels running out**
II. **Effects of the energy crisis**
   A. **Power shortages**
   B. **Gasoline more expensive**

As Thelma read, she would take notes on information that would fit into the outline. Some of the notes would be details for the subtopics.

Whether Thelma chose to start with questions or with a working outline, she would avoid taking notes on anything that wasn't important to her. For instance, she would not take notes about how coal is mined or about water pollution caused by oil spills even if those subjects were explained in one or more of her books.

Preparing to Take Notes

Once you have narrowed down your subject and planned your report enough to know what notes to take, you are ready to start taking the notes. The best way to take notes for a report is to use index cards. The size most often used is three inches by five inches, but you may use larger ones if you like. The important thing is to use cards that are all the same size. The information in the books you use is not likely to be organized in the same way in each book or in the way you wish to organize your report. If you take your notes on index cards, you can easily rearrange your notes, putting notes about the same topic from different books together and organizing the notes in logical order.

You should first make an index card for each book you use. Write on it the author's name, the title, the publisher, and the place and date the book was published. These cards form your working bibliography. A bibliography is the list of books and other sources used by an author. When you finish your report, you will write your final bibliography, listing all the sources you used. You can add to your working bibliography or drop parts of it as you go along, depending on whether you find additional sources or discover that one you have is not useful after all. You may wish to number your bibliography cards. Then, as you take notes from a particular book, you need only write the number of the bibliography card on each note card. If you don't number the bibliography cards, simply write the author's name at the top of each note card. The important thing is to keep track of the book each note is from. An example of a bibliography card for a book Thelma might use follows:

Bibliography card 1
Halacy, D.S., Jr. *The Energy Trap*, Four Winds Press, New York, 1975

As you take notes, remember to look for main ideas that help answer the questions you've asked or that provide information on the topics and subtopics of your working outline. Look also for details that support or illustrate the main ideas.

Here are some other suggestions to keep in mind as you take notes.

1. Use a separate note card for each fact or idea. Include the bibliography-card number or the author's name and the number of the page on which the information appears. It is also

helpful to write in the top right-hand corner a word or phrase that tells the subject of the note. Such a word or phrase is called a slug. The slug may be a topic or subtopic from your working outline. This will help you to group your notes later.

2. Use as many shortcuts as you can. Your notes should be clear and brief. Leave out unimportant words and use abbreviations where possible. You may want to use your own symbols or abbreviations for terms that you expect to use often. Just be sure that you don't use so many that you can't understand your notes when you reread them.

3. Use your own words most of the time as you take notes rather than copying from your source. This helps you to remember the material. It also assures that your report will be in your own words.

4. Copy from the source, using quotation marks, only if you are planning to quote the author's exact words in your report. You may wish to use a quote if the author has stated something especially well or if the information given is so important that you don't want to change it even by rewording it.

5. Jot down your own reactions and thoughts about the material as you take notes. You may do this on separate note cards or on the cards your thoughts apply to. Use a star or another symbol to indicate the notes that give your thoughts and reactions to help you remember that they are your own and did not come from the material.

The first of the following note cards shows notes Thelma took from the book listed on the bibliography card illustrated on page 239. The rest show notes that she took from the first three paragraphs of the passage headed Book A beginning on page 178 of this reader. Notice the many abbreviations Thelma used. What symbol on note card 4 shows Thelma's thoughts? Thelma used several different slugs on her cards. Notice that her slugs show she is already thinking about how to organize her notes, since she has a slug for *Energy use* and others for specific uses of energy — for instance, *Energy use — homes.*

Practice note taking now by taking notes on the rest of the passage headed Book A. Show what slug you would use for each note card.

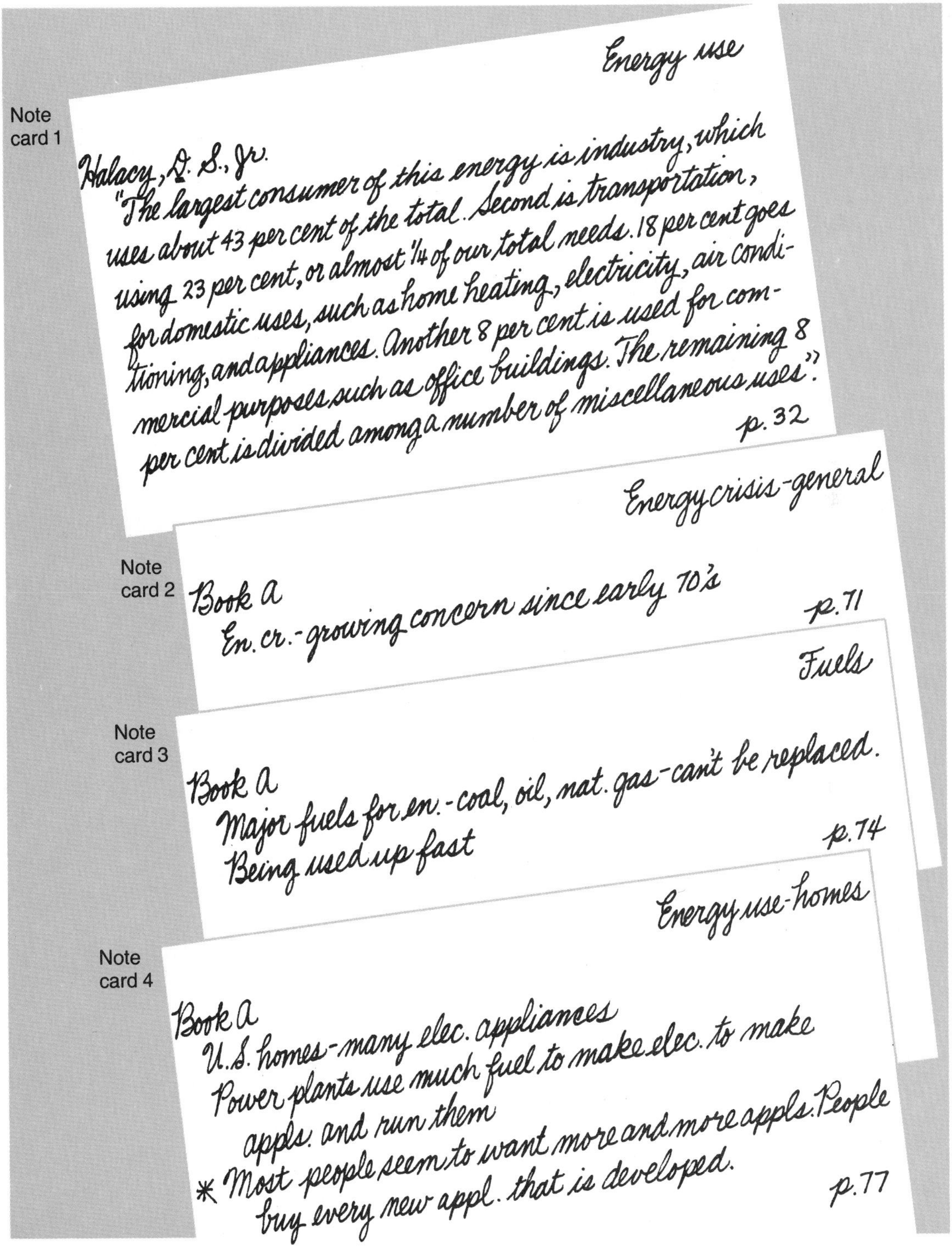

Note card 1

Energy use

Halacy, D. S., Jr.
"The largest consumer of this energy is industry, which uses about 43 per cent of the total. Second is transportation, using 23 per cent, or almost ¼ of our total needs. 18 per cent goes for domestic uses, such as home heating, electricity, air conditioning, and appliances. Another 8 per cent is used for commercial purposes, such as office buildings. The remaining 8 per cent is divided among a number of miscellaneous uses."

p. 32

Note card 2

Energy crisis-general

Book A
En. cr. - growing concern since early 70's

p. 71

Note card 3

Fuels

Book A
Major fuels for en. - coal, oil, nat. gas - can't be replaced.
Being used up fast

p. 74

Note card 4

Energy use-homes

Book A
U.S. homes - many elec. appliances
Power plants use much fuel to make elec. to make appls. and run them
* Most people seem to want more and more appls. People buy every new appl. that is developed.

p. 77

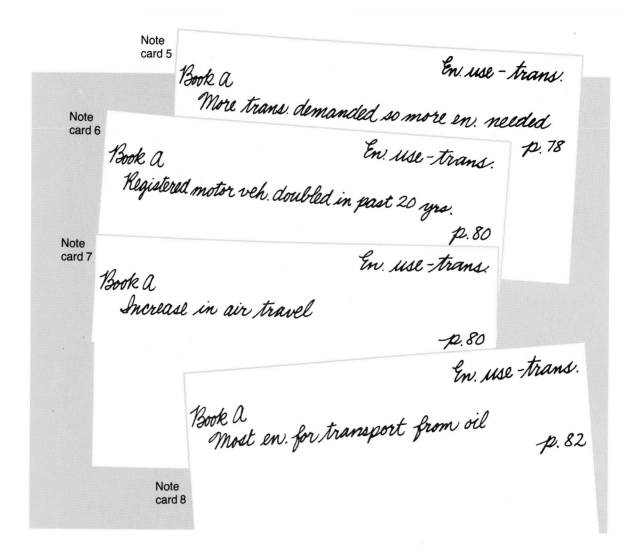

Note card 5

Book A
En. use - trans.
More trans. demanded so more en. needed
p. 78

Note card 6

Book A
En. use - trans.
Registered motor veh. doubled in past 20 yrs.
p. 80

Note card 7

Book A
En. use - trans.
Increase in air travel
p. 80

Note card 8

Book A
En. use - trans.
Most en. for transport from oil
p. 82

How many note cards did you plan to use? You would probably want at least three — one with your notes about energy waste, one that noted the growing population, and one that used the information in the last paragraph as part of a summary. You may have decided to list the examples of energy waste on separate note cards. How many different slugs did you need? Did you use new ones or did you repeat some of Thelma's. You might have used all new ones if you used three — *Energy waste, Energy needs,* and *Energy crisis — causes.* Be ready to explain why you chose the slugs you did.

Organizing Notes into an Outline

You have now looked closely at the notes Thelma took from the Halacy book and Book A and have taken a few notes yourself. Thelma also took notes from Book AA. Study the note cards below and on page 244. Think about how they fit together with Thelma's other notes and the ones you took.

You can see that Thelma's notes, with yours added, are not yet in logical order. Having notes on cards, of course, makes rearranging them very simple. For instance, note card 15 is the only

Note card 9

En. shortages

Book AA
Demand for power may be more than system can supply.
Result is blackout or brownout.   p. 214

Note card 10

En. shortages

Book AA
Blackouts - temporary cut-off of power
May be limited to a specific area by power company
May cover wide area if demand is sudden   p. 216

Note card 11

En. shortages

Book AA
Brownouts - temporary decrease in voltage by power company
Small decrease isn't noticed.
Larger decrease - lights dim somewhat, appls. give off less heat
Largest decrease - TV pics become smaller, lights dim more,
some motor driven appls. run slower or burn out   p. 216

Note card 12

En. shortages

Book AA
General shortages of power
Public buildings (schools, etc.) forced to keep
thermostats turned down
Some businesses (restaurants) forced to close temporarily
          p. 216

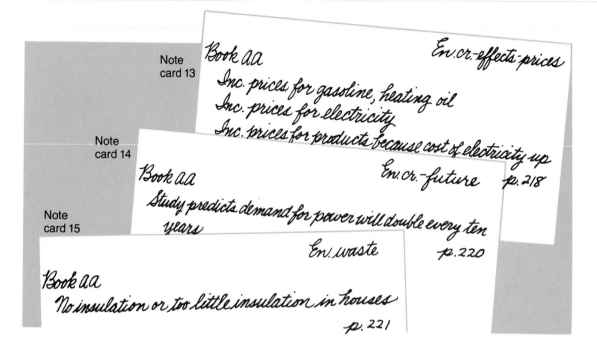

Note card 13

Book aa

En. cr.-effects-prices

Inc. prices for gasoline, heating oil

Inc. prices for electricity

Inc. prices for products because cost of electricity up

p. 218

Note card 14

Book aa

En. cr.-future

Study predicts demand for power will double every ten years

p. 220

Note card 15

Book aa

En. waste

No insulation or too little insulation in houses

p. 221

note from Book AA on energy waste. Logically, that note should go with those from Book A on energy waste, which are among the notes you took. Note card 1 contains notes on energy use. Where would be a logical place to put it?

Putting the note cards in logical order is the first step in using them to prepare a report. The next step is to make an outline from the notes. Making an outline from notes helps you to see how the information you have fits together. As you make the outline, you pick out main topics, subtopics, and details and consider how they should be organized. The process can be shown using Thelma's notes and the ones you took.

First look back at Thelma's working outline on page 238. What are the main topics? Now check the notes. Are there notes on the causes and effects of the energy crisis? *Causes of the energy crisis* and *Effects of the energy crisis* become two main topics for the outline. However, you know that reports usually begin with some kind of introduction. In this case, Thelma would want to make some general comments on the energy crisis before explaining the causes and effects. She could use *Energy crisis* as the first main topic in her outline. The notes on note cards 2 and 14 would fit into an introduction well. Therefore, they would become subtopics under the main topic *Energy crisis*.

Thelma may also want to use the term *Energy Crisis* in the title of her outline and the working title of her report. When she prepares the final report, she may want to use a livelier title.

Causes of the energy crisis would be the second main topic. Check the working outline and all the notes again to decide on subtopics. The notes provide four subtopics for that main topic.

Repeat the process for the third main topic, *Effects of the energy crisis*. There are two logical subtopics.

Study the following outline made from all the notes and compare it with the notes. Do you agree with the subtopics that go under each main topic?

The Energy Crisis

I. Energy crisis
   A. Growing concern since early 1970's
   B. Demand for energy to double every ten years
II. Causes of the energy crisis
   A. Increased use of energy
       1. More electrical appliances in homes
       2. Electrical energy needed to make appliances
       3. More transportation used
   B. Waste of energy
       1. Lights and appliances left on
       2. Instant-on appliances
       3. One person in each car
       4. Too little insulation in homes
   C. Growing population requires more energy
   D. Shortage of common fuels: coal, oil, natural gas
       1. Being used up rapidly
       2. Can't be replaced
III. Effects of the energy crisis
   A. Power shortages
       1. General shortages
       2. Blackouts
       3. Brownouts
   B. Price increases
       1. For fuels
       2. For electricity
       3. For products

Now look at the details that have been placed under each subtopic. You can see that not every detail from the notes has been included as a detail on the outline. As you prepare a report, you expand the information from your outline by adding figures and examples. For instance, the figures on energy use from note card 1 do not appear on Thelma's outline. However, Thelma may include them in her report as she writes or speaks about the details of energy use. The same is true for the notes on note cards 6 and 7. She may include the facts from them in her report, but they don't have to appear on the outline.

The outline on page 245 is logical and well organized. However, it is not the only way to outline the information. Someone else might arrange the information in a different order so as to stress different information. When working with notes you have taken yourself, you must organize them in a way that makes sense to you. If you start by rearranging your note cards and then go on to making an outline of your notes, you will find that you have finished the hardest part of preparing your report.

TAKING AND ORGANIZING NOTES

In order to practice taking and organizing notes, assume that you are preparing a report. Your working title is *Solutions to the Energy Crisis*. Write down two or three questions about that topic. Then read and take notes on the passage headed Book B on page 179 and on the following passage headed Book BB. Use note cards or sheets of paper cut into equal-sized pieces. Be sure to indicate which book each note is from and to write the appropriate slug on each note card. When you have completed your note taking, organize the note cards into an outline. Be ready to explain why you took the notes you did and how you decided on the main topics, subtopics, and details of your outline.

Book BB

The demand for energy is increasing so rapidly that the energy supply cannot keep up. The need to find solutions to the resulting energy crisis is critical and immediate. Conserving energy, using it more efficiently, may be a partial solution.

There are many ways to conserve energy. Developing mass transportation systems, which many cities already have, is one way. People who now commute by car could use mass transportation instead and save much of the fuel used by individual cars.

Poorly insulated homes require large amounts of energy for heating and cooling. With that in mind, the government encourages homeowners to insulate their houses. Taxpayers who insulate save money on their taxes as well as energy.

There are many ways in which citizens can help to conserve energy. Realizing this, various groups are trying to educate the public about energy conservation. Gas, oil, and electric companies send information about conserving energy to their customers. Public-service shows on radio and television suggest ways to use energy more efficiently.

Recycling is another means of conserving energy. Some communities, community organizations, and even companies have run recycling centers. People are asked to save and bring to the recycling centers newspapers, cans, and bottles. These products or the materials they are made of can be reused, and the recycling process takes less energy than does making new products.

Conservation, however, remains only a partial solution to the energy crisis. New sources of energy are needed and are being developed. Although nuclear power plants generate a great deal of electricity, serious questions of safety are involved. Unless those questions can be resolved, nuclear energy will be of limited use.

Solar energy is another source of power being developed. Solar energy is now being used to heat and cool buildings and for other small-scale projects. One scientist suggests that orbiting solar power stations could convert solar energy into electricity that would be beamed back to Earth. Such power stations could supply large amounts of electricity.

Other sources of energy are beginning to be developed. The wind and the tides are used to produce power in some places. Even the heat deep beneath the earth's surface — thermal energy — is being used on a limited scale.

Dr. Dan

by LOUIS HABER

"SEWED UP HIS HEART" shouted the headline of the Chicago *Daily Inter-Ocean.* History had just been made. In a time when few surgeons dared to operate on the abdomen, let alone on the heart, Dr. Daniel Hale Williams had successfully operated on a dying man who had been stabbed in the heart. The man not only survived but lived for fifty years afterward. It was the first time in the history of medicine that this kind of surgery was attempted, and it was performed successfully! Who was this great pioneering surgeon?

Born in Hollidaysburg, Pennsylvania, on January 18, 1856, Dan was the fifth of a family of seven children. His father, . . . very active in the abolitionist cause, was a prominent member of the Equal Rights League. . . .

At the age of forty-seven Dan's father died of consumption, leaving his wife and seven children in financial difficulties. Dan, who was ten years old at the time, was apprenticed to a shoemaker in Baltimore, and his mother left Pennsylvania and went to Rockford, Illinois. Unhappy with his lot, Dan managed to run away and rejoin his mother in Illinois. A few months later, however, his mother returned east without him. Left on his own, Dan worked on lake steamers and learned the barber's trade. When his oldest sister, Sally, wrote asking him to join her in Edgerton, Wisconsin, Dan jumped at the chance. Opportunities for the black were greater in the West than in the South, and he soon opened his own barbershop in Edgerton at the age of seventeen. But Janesville, a few miles away, had schools, an opera house, and flourishing industries, so Sally and Dan moved there, and Dan got a job in the barbershop of Harry Anderson. After Dan's sister married and left Janesville, Anderson took Dan into his home and treated him as one of the family.

Dan began to attend Haire's Classical Academy, which was the equivalent of a present-day high school.

After graduating, he clerked and read the law in a lawyer's office for about one year, no doubt influenced by his older brother, who was already a successful practicing lawyer. However, Dan soon realized that the law was not for him.

In Janesville everybody stood in awe of Dr. Henry Palmer, a local physician. Dr. Palmer was an excellent surgeon who had been the director of the largest military hospital during the Civil War and Surgeon General of Wisconsin for ten years. News of Dr. Palmer's exciting work was often in the local newspaper, and when Dan read of it, he was determined that medicine was going to be his life's work. At the age of twenty-two he became an apprentice in Dr. Palmer's office. He stayed there for two years, reading medicine, learning to practice, and scrubbing up the office at the end of the day.

In those days it was customary for people to open their own private medical practices at the end of two years of apprenticeship in a doctor's office. Few physicians at that time had gone to medical college. Dan, however, under Dr. Palmer's influence, was determined to obtain the best medical training available. In 1880, with a one-hundred-dollar bank loan in his pocket, Dan went off to Chicago Medical College (later to become Northwestern University Medical School). At that time, Chicago Medical College, one of the best medical schools in the country, maintained the "heroically high standard" of an eighteen-month course. Although standards were very high, laboratory work was virtually nonexistent, and the staff lectured, and operated also, in stiff collars and swallow-tailed coats. Dan graduated from medical school in 1883 and opened an office at Thirty-first Street and Michigan Avenue in Chicago.

Dan Williams's true place in medicine must be measured against the background of his times. A new era in surgery began in the eighties. As a graduate in 1883, he belonged to a group of doctors not bound by the prejudices of the previous generation and receptive to new thoughts and practices in surgery. A revolution was taking place in this field because of the work of Louis Pasteur in France and Joseph Lister in England. In the late seventies, Pasteur had laid the foundations of bacteriology. He had proven the relationship between certain microorganisms and specific diseases. He set forth his "Germ Theory of Disease" that was to sweep the medical world. Lister applied Pasteur's theory and revolutionized surgery by demonstrating the effectiveness of antiseptics (germ-killing chemicals) in the treatment of wounds. A furor was created, although it was difficult for the doctrine of antisepsis to gain acceptance among the older doctors of that day.

Many explanations of disease were offered before Pasteur. It was thought that illness was caused by demons inhabiting the body. The art of healing was dominated by superstition, witchcraft, and misinformation. Surgery was practiced by barbers. It was held that a sick person was filled with bad blood and for a cure should be bled. In many cases, patients who should have been given blood had blood taken from them instead. More patients died from the treatment than from the disease.

It remained for Pasteur to prove that disease was caused by harmful microorganisms, or germs, within the body. His work was to result in the virtual elimination of many diseases caused by germs. This knowledge was just beginning to be known in Williams's day. Abdominal and chest surgery was rarely if ever attempted because, even if successful, the infection that invariably followed caused the death of the patient.

When Williams began to practice medicine, Pasteur's germ theory of disease, Lister's antiseptic surgery, and the availability of anesthetics opened new vistas for the surgeon, and Williams was in a position to take advantage of these advances. Operations could be attempted now that were previously out of the question.

In his practice of medicine, "Dr. Dan," as his patients and friends came to call him, turned more and more to surgery. In those days operations in private homes were common. Not only did people distrust hospitals but

Joseph Lister

Louis Pasteur

251

blacks could not gain admission except in the city's charity wards, where they were either neglected or used for experimentation. Furthermore, black doctors could not get hospital appointments because of racial prejudice and, therefore, could not get their patients into hospitals. It was even impossible for black people to get training as nurses, since training schools would not accept them.

Most of Williams's first operations took place in the kitchens and dining rooms of patients' homes. In each case he applied Lister's principles of antiseptic surgery conscientiously and meticulously. He scrubbed the entire room with soap and water. He then sprayed carbolic acid, a strong germ killer, all over the room and followed that by sterilizing all the instruments to be used in the operation in a washboiler filled with steam. Hands and clothing were also included in the cleaning and sterilizing process. His results were excellent. Infection, the feared and dangerous aftermath of surgery, was avoided.

Soon Dr. Dan's reputation as a successful surgeon spread, and he was appointed to the surgical staff of the South Side Dispensary in Chicago. He also became clinical instructor and demonstrator in anatomy at the Chicago Medical College, where one of his students was Charlie Mayo of the famous Mayo brothers. Later still, he became surgeon to the City Railway

Company, a position never previously held by a black physician. His appointment to the Illinois State Board of Health in 1889 was indicative of the kind of recognition he was shown. While the position carried no salary, it carried tremendous prestige.

It was a cold, wintry day in 1890. Dr. Dan was sitting in the warm, comfortable parlor of his friend, the Reverend Louis Reynolds, pastor of St. Stephen's African Methodist Church. The Reverend Mr. Reynolds had just asked him to use his influence to have Reynolds's sister admitted to a training course for nurses in one of the Chicago hospitals normally closed to all black applicants. Williams thought for a moment and then said, "No, I don't think I'll try to get your sister into one of these training courses. We'll do something better. We'll start a hospital of our own, and we'll train dozens and dozens of nurses." He went on, "There must be a hospital for blacks but not a black hospital." Williams had been thinking of it for some time. He was well established in private practice by 1890 and was famed for his surgical skill, but still, as a black, he lacked a hospital appointment. This lack, and his indignation that all black patients were thrown into the city's charity wards, made him determined to start a new kind of hospital — one to be owned, staffed, and managed by blacks and whites together. Here black sick and poor would receive the best of care; ambitious young black doctors would have their chance; and young black people, not admitted to white schools, would be trained for the nursing the times demanded.

Williams threw himself into this new effort with enthusiasm. He formed committees of black and white people. He spoke at churches, street corners, club meetings, and anywhere else he was permitted to speak. He got the cooperation of many people, rich and poor, black and white. The idea of a hospital run by blacks, where blacks would be received on an equal basis, was very appealing to the black community.

On January 23, 1891, medical history was made. The first interracial hospital in the United States was founded. Articles of incorporation were drawn up in the name of the Provident Hospital and Training School Association. The trustees, executive committee, and finance committee were all black. The hospital itself opened its doors in May, 1891 — a three-story building at Twenty-ninth Street and Dearborn, with room for twelve beds. The first year, out of 175 applicants for nurse training, Dr. Dan accepted seven, the sister of the Reverend Mr. Reynolds among them. All were high-school graduates. The training period was for eighteen months.

The staff of Provident Hospital was made up of black and white doctors carefully selected for their qualifications. At the end of the first year, of 189 sick and injured treated at the Provident Hospital, twenty-three had improved, three had not, twenty-two had died, and 141 had recovered entirely — a remarkable record when only desperate cases were taken to a hospital. However, the economic depression of 1893 began to threaten Provident's existence. At that time help came in the form of Frederick Douglass, one of the most important black leaders in the country. It was the year of the Chicago World's Fair, and Douglass came as the Haitian commissioner. At the Fair he urged blacks to contribute to Provident Hospital, the type of interracial organization of which he highly approved. Money began to come in, and things became easier for the hospital.

July 9, 1893, was a hot and humid day in Chicago, and tempers were short. A fight in a saloon ended in the stabbing of a young black messenger, James Cornish. He was rushed to Provident Hospital with a one-inch knife wound in the chest near the heart. The call went out for Dr. Dan. By the time he arrived, Cornish had collapsed from loss of blood and shock, and it was obvious that he would soon die if nothing was done. But what could be done? Opening the chest

253

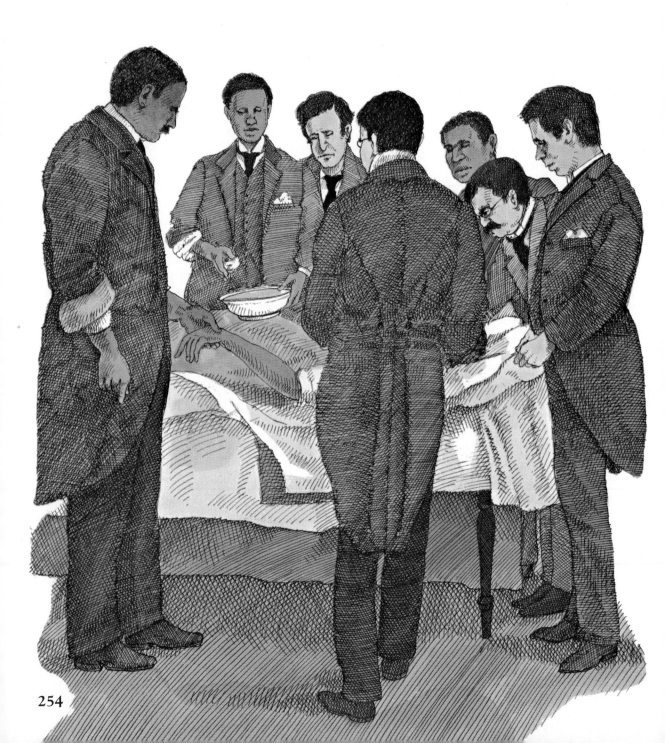

cavity in those days was an invitation to death. Nobody would have criticized Williams for following the standard treatment in this case of "absolute rest, cold, and opium," after which the patient invariably died. Why should he risk his surgical reputation? If he did not operate and the patient died, nobody would blame him. If he did operate and the patient died, he would be condemned by the medical profession. X-rays had not as yet been discovered to help him, blood transfusions were unknown at that time, sulfa drugs and antibiotics to fight infection were also unknown. What to do? The patient was sinking. Dr. Dan decided to operate.

Six physicians — four white and two black — witnessed the operation. Dr. Dan worked swiftly. He opened the chest cavity and saw that the knife used in the stabbing had penetrated the heart about one tenth of an inch and had made a cut in the pericardium, or sac surrounding the heart, one and one-quarter inches in length. He decided that the heart muscle did not need any suturing, or sewing up, but he did suture the pericardium. The atmosphere was tense as he worked and continued to be so until he finally closed up the wound. It was a daring operation — the first time a surgeon had entered the chest cavity. Would it work? Would the dread infection set in and kill the patient? On August 30, fifty-one days after Cornish had entered the hospital a dying man, he was discharged completely recovered. He lived for fifty years afterward and died in 1943, having outlived his surgeon by twelve years!

Although Dr. Dan did not make an official report of this operation until three and a half years later, the newspaper headlines sent the news around the world. Williams was hailed as the first person in the world to "sew up the heart." Of course his great contribution was successful entrance of the chest and surgical exploration of the heart. His aseptic surgery was so perfect that no sign of infection appeared in the patient after the operation. The results were miraculous when one considers that Williams had very few of the advantages that modern surgeons have today in performing their open-heart surgery and heart transplants.

The world will long remember Dr. Williams as a great American surgeon accorded top rank by his contemporary colleagues, white and black; as the founder of Provident Hospital, the first interracial hospital in the United States and forerunner of a hundred such institutions; as the first surgeon in the world to enter the chest cavity successfully; as the one who introduced the training of black nurses and interns in the United States; as a charter member of the American College of Surgeons; and, finally, as a founder and first vice-president of the National Medical Association.

DISCUSSION

1. Reread the final paragraph in which the author lists six of Dr. Dan's accomplishments. Which do you think was the greatest? Why?

2. How did Daniel Hale Williams begin his medical training? Why didn't he follow the custom of his time and start to practice medicine as soon as he had finished his apprenticeship?

3. How would you compare Dr. Dan's medical training with a doctor's training today?

4. What two men were chiefly responsible for the revolution in medicine that took place a few years before Dr. Dan became a surgeon? What contribution did each of them make?

5. What effect did the work of Pasteur and Lister have on Dr. Dan's methods and success as a surgeon?

6. Although it was unjust and unfortunate that Dr. Dan was denied the use of hospitals in his early practice of surgery, what advantages may there have been in his performing operations in patients' homes?

7. Why, do you think, was Dr. Dan determined that the hospital he founded should be owned, staffed, and managed by blacks and whites together?

8. Why was the founding of Provident Hospital a milestone in medical history? In what ways did the hospital benefit blacks?

9. Why, do you think, were only desperate cases taken to a hospital in the early 1890's?

10. What personal qualities did Dr. Dan exhibit in deciding to perform the first surgery that involved opening the chest cavity?

AUTHOR

Louis Haber has had a long and distinguished career in the teaching of science and holds degrees in both science and education. He has been a college science professor, the head of a high-school science department, and a director of teacher education. His work has also included research for the United States Office of Education.

Dr. Haber has contributed articles to numerous science magazines and has collaborated on college textbooks. Now retired from teaching, he devotes his time to writing about the history of science. "Dr. Dan" is an excerpt from his book *Black Pioneers of Science and Invention*.

How the Educated Bulldog Said Too Much

by CARL CARMER

Indiana corn is said by those who know (and *who* should know as well as Indianians?) to grow faster and have a better flavor than any other kind. I don't quite know whether or not to believe a farmer of French descent who lived near Vincennes who said that he almost laughed himself to death when he was sowing corn because the sprouts came up from the seeds so fast that they tickled his feet. He said he went to the house to call his hired man, and when he came out, the corn had already eared at a height of about thirty feet. He sent the hired man climbing up a stalk after the ears, and by the time he'd got up thirty feet, the corn was growing so fast the ear was thirty feet higher. The hired man climbed on up and finally got so high he was out of sight. The farmer said he hollered to him to start back, and he said he'd been trying to, but the corn was growing faster than he could come down, and he was getting higher all the time. He never did get down, and the farmer never saw him again. This particular stalk, the farmer said, happened to be popcorn, and when the ears got up so close to the sun, the heat was so great that all the kernels popped and fell all over his hay-field. He said a mule that was standing hitched to a hayrake in that field mistook all those white popcorn kernels for a June snowstorm and just naturally lay down and froze to death.

This same farmer had a son of whose ability he was very proud, and the son had a bulldog. When the boy was eighteen years old, the farmer sent him way across the state to Earlham College to get an education. The boy took the bulldog along for company. After the boy and the dog had been at Earlham a month or so, the old man received a letter from his son.

This is what the boy wrote:

"Father, an astonishing thing has happened. The bulldog has begun to talk. Moreover, he seems to have a fairly good mind. I'd like to make a suggestion to you. If we educated the bulldog along with me here at Earlham, we'd have at the end of four years not only the one talking bulldog in the world but the one and only talking bulldog with a college education. We could exhibit him then all over Indiana, charge admission, and make a lot of money. If you agree with me, Father, just send me double the usual amount of money for books, laboratory fees, incidentals, and miscellaneous. It will be a mighty good investment."

So for four years the farmer sent his son double the usual amount for the usual items, and finally the day came when his son and the remarkable bulldog were to return home with their college degrees. The boy wrote that the bulldog had made an outstanding record at Earlham and had taken honors in two subjects. He said that he and the dog would travel by train to Vincennes and then hire a boat to take them downriver to the farm.

The old man got very excited on the day they were due to arrive, and he waited anxiously on the bank as the little boat approached. When the boy jumped ashore, his father clasped him in his arms — and then he looked about and said, "And where's our educated bulldog?"

"Well, Father," said the boy, "it was as I said. The bulldog graduated with honors, and then we both took the train for Vincennes. When we got there, I hired a boat to bring us here. And on the way down I said to the bulldog, 'Isn't it wonderful! In less than an hour, now, we'll be back with my father.'

"'What, that stupid, uneducated old ignoramus?' said the bulldog, and, Father, it made me so angry to hear him speak so insultingly of you that I kicked him overboard. He couldn't swim a stroke, and so he was drowned."

Well, that's the story — sworn to as gospel truth by a lot of respectable Indianians — so I guess it must be so. They say that the father was convinced it was true, praised his son for being so loyal to his old dad, and gave him a homecoming party that night at the farmhouse that folks remember to this day.

AUTHOR

Carl Carmer, noted as a folklorist and historian of up-state New York, was a professor of English before he turned to full-time writing and editing. Besides his many books for young people, Mr. Carmer's best-known books are probably the Rivers of America series, written for adults. He died in 1976.

from

Bert Breen's Barn

by WALTER D. EDMONDS

TREASURE

The sturdy barn that Bert Breen built in the late 1800's became, more than a generation later, a symbol of all the things young Tom Dolan wanted out of life. Tom's shiftless father had deserted the family. His mother, Polly Ann, did laundry and housework to provide for Tom and his two sisters on their run-down farm in upper New York State. Tom scrimped and saved from his wages at the feed mill, sensing that if he could buy the barn from the Widow Breen and move it to the Dolan farm, their hard life would take a turn for the better. Tom and Polly Ann took pride and pleasure in finally being able to buy the barn, and Tom began to dismantle and move it.

After the Widow Breen's death, however, the Dolans' pleasure was marred when rumors started to circulate that Bert Breen had hidden all his money somewhere on the property and that it was still there. Dangerously evil Yantis Flancher and his brothers established themselves at the Breen place to search it. Although the Dolans, as owners of the barn, would be entitled to anything found there, they knew that the Flanchers would not hesitate to attack them and rob them of any money they might find.

By the time Tom had moved all but the floor of the barn, he had an idea that Bert Breen's money might really be buried beneath it. He planned to delay taking up the floor until some cold, dark night in late fall when the Flanchers might have gotten tired of searching and keeping watch. Polly Ann knew of a roundabout route to the Breen place that Tom could take with the horse and wagon so that suspicion would not be aroused. As the following selection begins, the Dolans are happily tired after holding a joyous barn-raising celebration at their farm.

Polly Ann drew a deep breath.

"We got just about enough left over for our supper," she said. "We'll milk, and eat, and go to bed. It's been a long day. A wonderful day, though. I never thought to see so good a barn standing here."

But when they had milked, Tom said he had to grease the wheels on the wagon. Polly Ann stared at him.

"Why tonight," she asked, "after all there's been to do?"

"I want to go up to the Breen place tonight," he said.

"*Tonight!*" Polly Ann exclaimed. "*That's* why you want to grease the wagon wheels?"

He nodded. Ellie and Cissie-Mae just looked bewildered. Polly Ann explained to them that Tom thought he had figured out where the Breens had kept their money and that she was going to go with him to look for it.

"But I don't see why tonight," she protested, "when we are practically wore out."

"That's why," he answered. "The Flancher brothers were here nosing around. Yantis begun asking why we hadn't brought down the floor for the stable. Yantis may get a notion why I left it. But he wouldn't think of our going up there tonight any more than you did."

He paused a minute.

"It ought to be a good night for us to go. Moon's already set. We won't get more than starlight, and it looks as if it might cloud over too. You think you'd feel able to come with me?" he asked. "After all the work you've been doing all day?"

"Yes, I will," Polly Ann said. "You couldn't keep me from going, no matter if you tried. Besides, you wouldn't ever find your way in from the Irish Settlement road by yourself."

"Then we'll go," Tom said. "We'll wait until half past six, to let it get a little darker."

Twilight was beginning to give way to darkness as they topped the slope up to the canal. Tom turned their old horse, Drew, to the left onto the towpath and glanced at his mother. He could see her profile against the last streak of light along the top of Tug Hill, but only as a silhouette. She had on a thick sweater with a collar that rolled up around her neck under her small, determined chin. He was glad she was coming with him.

Cissie-Mae and Ellie had come out of the house to see them off. He had told them that if anybody came asking for him and Polly Ann, they were to say she had been taken sick and he was driving her up to Boonville to see the doctor. No telling when they'd be home. Tom could have hung one of the lanterns he had brought on the dashboard hook, but the light might be

seen from a canalside farm, and he didn't want people speculating who might be traveling the towpath that night.

Now he looked back down the valley. It was too dark to see the road from Port Leyden. No lights shone in all the valley except the windows on the Quarry place, and a hundred feet farther along, a fold in the ground shut them away. From then on, the wagon moved through the dark with only the reflections of a few early stars on the water of the canal beside the towpath to mark their course.

Drew plodded on at his own pace, halfway between a trot and a walk, and Tom let him have his head. The old horse had always been clever at finding his way along a road in the dark.

They made very little sound; the wheels hardly whispered as they tracked along the double path beaten by the canal teams. It came as a shock when the thump of Drew's hoofs and the grating of the wheels over sandy gravel echoed suddenly from planking overhead — they had not seen the shadow of the bridge ahead of them. Now for a moment the stars were blotted out. Then they left the bridge behind and were again moving in almost total silence.

There were three more bridges to pass under before they reached the one that carried the Dutch Hill road down into Forestport. The first of these, at Hawkinsville, was the only one that troubled Tom. Unlike the first bridge, it showed up well ahead as they approached, its white timbers picked out against the sky by the dim glow from the village windows on the hill below it. Anyone crossing it was bound to see the wagon coming along underneath on the towpath. It all depended on luck; but luck was with them, and not a rig passed over. Drew hauled the wagon underneath and out on the other side. They passed the village without hearing anything at all, not even a dog's bark.

A heavy mist was lifting off the water. It thickened and kept rising as they went on. By the time they reached Forestport about an hour later, it had risen high enough to blot out the towpath and canal.

They crept ahead in a silence broken only by the sound of the river rapids forty feet below and occasional anxious snorts from the old horse. He seemed to push his way into the mist, cautiously and very slowly, his forefeet feeling for the towpath. Tom felt they must be getting close to the Dutch Hill bridge. He put a little pressure on the left rein to warn Drew to look for the turn off the towpath down to the river. The horse seemed able to make it out in some way a human would not comprehend. The wagon pitched downhill, and they went on a step at a time with the mist much heavier against their faces, carrying the cold of river water. Suddenly the wheels rumbled out onto bridge planking. They heard the rush of water underneath. Then the road sloped up, and presently the mist began to thin out. They moved along a street with houses on each side.

"The road forks a piece ahead," Polly Ann said. "The one to the left goes down to the Armond place, but we take the one straight ahead. It's the Irish Settlement road."

It began with a steep hill. At times the wheels grated on gravel and then bumped with the roughness of the road. Drew heaved against the tugs, uttering grunts of self-pity, but eventually the road leveled off, and though they were traveling through woodland, Tom judged they had reached the beginning of the sand-flat country. They passed house lights here and there.

Tom slapped the reins on Drew's rump, persuading the old horse into a shuffling trot. The road cleared the settlement and went on across a natural meadow. The sky was speckled bright with stars, framed by the outlines of trees on either side. He could dimly make out the wheel tracks leading on, with the path beaten by a single horse between them.

"There's nobody but Nelson Farr uses it," Polly Ann said.

Tom had heard about Farr, a thin, middle-aged, silent man who lived by himself in a weathered house above Wingert's pond. He always had at least one bird dog living with him in his house, and a hound for running deer. It was the hound, mainly, Tom had on his mind now. The dog slept outside in an old kerosene barrel, Polly Ann said, and if it noticed the wagon going by, it would bark. It had a voice you could hear half across the township.

A faint stir of air came out of the southwest, moving from the house toward the road. They went along with no more sound than the faint plop of Drew's hoofs on the dusty track. Imperceptibly the roof of Farr's house took shape against the stars. Then they could see the corner of one wall against a yellow glow so dim it hardly showed. Farr's kitchen window faced out toward the pond, and the lamplight showed he must still be up. As they moved softly along, the glow vanished and, with it, the shape of the house. They heard the faint clink of the hound's chain and a low whimpering whine; whether it had heard them or caught their scent, there was no way of knowing. But they were now by, and the flat land that marked the end of the Breen place began to open out ahead. The track turned right for fifty feet and then left.

"That's the corner of Armond's land," Polly Ann said. "There used to be good blackberries in there."

What made her think of blackberries now was more than Tom could figure out. He was trying to get his bearings. He thought that Breen's Hill

ought to show up just ahead, but he couldn't make it out. And he knew they would have to get across Cold Brook yet, to reach the barn.

He felt Polly Ann's hand on his arm.

"We better get down and lead Drew."

She pointed to a line of scattered trees barely visible against the stars.

"We want to get near them, Tom. There's a farm track goes along them to Cold Brook. That's where the ford is."

They led Drew ahead. He didn't like it much now he was off the road, poor as it had been, but as they were walking beside him, he made no objection. He turned instinctively as his hoofs felt the track she had mentioned, before they themselves were aware of it. They followed it toward the brook until the land sloped down.

"This ought to be Cold Brook," Polly Ann said, just above a whisper; and sure enough, now that they were stopped, Tom could hear the gurgle of moving water.

He looked around for something to tie Drew to. The old horse wouldn't wander far, but Tom didn't want him moving at all if it could be helped. A little way off, a dark shadow stood on the land about eight feet high; it was a young white pine. He led Drew over to it and tied him to it with a hitching rope. His silhouette and that of the pine would make one shape, supposing anybody would be able to see that far from where the house was. Then he felt in the wagon for one of the lanterns he had brought and his pinch bar. He didn't intend to light the lantern unless he had to.

"I'm going over there now," he said in a low voice. "You stay here, Ma."

"I will not. I'm coming with you, Tom."

Her voice was so determined it was as good as seeing her cocked chin and set jaw. When she sounded that way, there wasn't much use trying to change her mind.

The wheel tracks deepened as they generally did on each bank at a brook crossing, and Tom felt his way down, trying to keep between them. When he stepped into the water, it was so cold he was glad he hadn't put off coming until November. His legs were numbed from the knees down, even though the brook was less than eight feet across. He heard Polly Ann draw her breath sharply just behind him. Then they were both going up the other bank.

The floor of the barn was no more than two hundred feet ahead. They approached it slowly, finding their way by the wagon track until what was left of the Breen house showed up on their left, a gloomy smudge against the stars. There was no light, no sign of a person anywhere, but they stood still together, straining to hear any sound. Behind them a barred owl started hooting in the Armond woods. The bird repeated itself twice and then fell silent. Presently from the big swamp east of the Breen place, another answered. Then they began a dialogue, punctuated by silences of varying lengths as if what each said in turn was of variable importance.

Listening, Tom fell into a sort of trance until Polly Ann took his arm.

"Just two fool birds calling," she said. "We hadn't ought to waste more time."

Tom gave himself a shake. He didn't know what had got into him, but his head became clear. He led the way to where the barn had stood, and all at once, under their feet, they felt the floor timbers of the cow run.

Tom set the lantern down close to where the sill had been.

"I don't want to light it unless I've got to," he said quietly. "Anyways until I've found where the money is. If it's there."

"It's there, Tom," Polly Ann said, almost in a murmur. "Don't you doubt it."

But now that he was really about to look for it, all his confidence seemed to have gone. His idea had been that Bert Breen would have had his loose flooring not too near his box of sand and chaff but halfway down the length of the barn; but it seemed best to begin at one end and work straight on until he did or didn't find something loose. He was sure that it wouldn't be right inside the door, but he began there anyway.

He was right. All the timbers were

spiked solid to the three stringers underneath them. He kept on giving one
after another a pry with his pinch bar
until he was well past where the box
was. They continued to be spiked fast
all the way past the middle, and a cold
doubt about his being dead wrong in
his ideas took hold of his mind. Then
he thought maybe the natural place to
look would have been the far end. He
was tempted to go down and try, but
it seemed better to keep on the way
he was going.

He heard the sound of Polly Ann's
feet moving quietly down the run behind him. She said softly, "Tom."

But he had the pinch bar prying
against the end of the next timber, and
it lifted.

"What is it, Ma?"

"The owls have stopped hollering,"
she said. "If they *was* owls."

"They're owls all right. They've
just said everything they had to say."

"Perhaps. But the second one has
come up out of the swamp, and now

it's near the road, opposite us," she said. "It was the one quit first."

"Well, I've got a loose piece here," Tom said. "I better try the next."

He lifted the loose timber out and laid it to one side. He took hold of the next one with his hand, and it was loose also. Then the next and a fourth. As he took the loose timbers out, he put them down in order so he could put them back the way they'd been. Polly Ann was kneeling at the edge of the uncovered space.

"Tom," she whispered. "They made a hole here, and there's a couple of trunks in it."

He touched her arm and felt her trembling — or maybe it was himself. He listened against the dark but heard only the crickets.

He had to struggle to control his voice, even to whisper. "Are they heavy, Ma?"

She tugged. "Yes. Kind of. But I guess we can carry them all right."

He moved over to kneel beside her

and felt for the first trunk. It was small, maybe three feet by two on top, he judged. It oughtn't to be too heavy.

He got a grip on the handles and heaved it up. It was a good deal heavier than he'd expected, but he got it out without much trouble. The second was a bit smaller but seemed to weigh even more. He heaved it out also.

"We've got to get them over to the wagon," he said.

She whispered, "Yes."

Each of them took hold of a handle of the second trunk and started back toward Cold Brook. It was harder to make their way in the dark carrying the trunk. The weight interfered with their balance, and it was necessary to move very slowly. They made a good deal more noise, also, crossing the brook. But finally they got the trunk up the far bank and located Drew and the wagon and heaved the trunk onto the wagon bed.

Polly Ann was breathing quite hard, but she wouldn't hear of resting, and they went straight back for the other trunk. Its larger size made it clumsier to handle, but it wasn't quite so heavy, and that made the second trip seem easier. They got it onto the wagon with no trouble, and Tom said, "I want you to take Drew back to the corner of the Armond land. If anybody shows up, they won't see you that far off, and if there's any kind of a commotion here, you start going home. I'll walk back."

"What do you aim to do, Tom?"

"I want to get those floor timbers back where they were," he told her. "And scatter some of that sand and chaff over them."

"All right. I'll go to the corner, but I won't leave without you, Tom."

She watched him turn back toward the barn.

"Tom," she said quietly. "Don't forget to bring the lantern."

Tom had forgotten all about it, never having had to use it. He raised his hand, not thinking that she couldn't see him at all. After he crossed the brook, he could hear her taking Drew away across the open land toward Armond's corner.

He had no trouble finding the loose timbers, and it didn't take long to fit them back in place, even in the dark, for he had laid them down in proper order. He felt his way back along the flooring to the box of chaff and sand, and it was then he realized he hadn't brought anything to carry the sand in. He tried to remember if there was an old shovel lying about, but he couldn't recall having seen any such thing. There would probably be a saucepan or something in the house, but to find one, he would have to light his lantern, and he didn't want to do that. He scratched his head, wondering what to do. His hat tilted over his eyes, and suddenly it came to him that it would do as well as a saucepan. He set it down in the box, filled it with handfuls of sand, and carried it back to the loose timbers.

He would have liked some lantern light now. Scattering sand evenly in the dark wasn't easy. Besides, from having been out in the weather, it was damp. He had to hope that a night's dew would make it appear more natural, but that was only a guess. He went back for another hatful, wondering how long they had spent at Breen's — too long, he thought. And all at once he felt a trickle of sweat between his shoulders run down to the small of his back. He went back to the loose timbers and scattered the second hatful as well as he could.

He was going to get a third, but before he reached the box, a light appeared on the road. It came along smoothly, so he knew it was on a wagon; a lantern carried by hand always has a kind of bob to it. It could be coming only to Breen's.

There wasn't time for any more sand. He felt around for his own lantern, which he had put in one corner of the box of sand, and picked it up. It was time to vamoose. He went down to Cold Brook and waded through just as the wagon lantern turned the corner to come into the Breen place. He moved up the bank to where they had left the wagon and stood close beside the pine tree. He could see the wagon come up to the barn floor. A man got down; then two more. To his mind, they couldn't be anybody but the Flanchers.

He drew back behind the pine, and when it was between him and the men, set off across the open land to find Drew and Polly Ann. He kept himself from hurrying. Rapid motion could attract attention no matter how dark it was. He moved evenly and slowly, making as little noise and disturbance as he knew how, his legs brushing easily through blueberry bushes, and in about five minutes he was nearing the corner of Armond's back line.

With the woods and underbrush beyond, Tom could see absolutely nothing of the wagon or Polly Ann, but presently he heard Drew blowing deep, soft breaths in his direction. When Tom reached out his hand, it met a rear wheel.

"Ma," he said quietly. "It's me."

"I know," she said. "Drew heard you first, and then I did. Coming so quiet, I knowed it was you."

He said, "There's three men back at the barn. It's the Flanchers probably. I'm going to lead Drew until we get around the bend and up past Farr's."

He felt his way along the wagon and stroked Drew's shoulder. The old horse blubbered his lips on the back of Tom's hand as he reached for the chin strap, and the wagon started forward with hardly a sound. Tom was glad, now, he had greased the wheels.

They moved on, feeling for the track, turned the corner, and in a minute or two were behind Farr's house once more. Tom couldn't see any light from the kitchen window this time. The hound was quiet too; there was no sound of a chain. Tom continued leading Drew, though, till they crossed the bridge over Crystal Creek. He felt it was safe to stop for a few minutes then, and he went back along the wagon, telling Polly Ann to hold the lines.

"I want to tie those trunks down," he told her.

He had brought a length of light rope, which he passed through the trunk handles, securing the ends to rings on the sides of the wagon bed, and then at last he lit a lantern.

"You think it's safe going with a light?" Polly Ann asked.

"I want to make better time," he said. He hung the lantern on the dashboard hook, and for a minute it blinded them, as if the night had suddenly become a room with solid walls around them. But in a moment their eyes became accustomed to the light, and then they could see a bit of the road reaching forward from Drew's front hoofs. Drew plainly liked the change, for he started ahead without a word from Tom or a hitch of the lines. They could see each other now, too.

"Why don't you put your hat on?" Polly Ann asked him.

"I used it to carry sand in," he told her. "I shook it, but there's still some left in it."

She gave a sniff. "I'd have thought a boy your age would have sense to turn his hat inside out if he was going to put dirt into it."

"I know, Ma," he said sheepishly, "but there wasn't anything else to carry it in, and I wanted to get away from there."

"Yes," she said, and he could see she was smiling a little. Then she asked what was in both their minds. "Why do you suppose those Flanchers came up to Breen's tonight, Tom?"

"I don't know. I thought they'd started back home, thinking that after the raising we was too tired to do anything but go to bed."

"Maybe they came back just to check up. And when they saw the wagon and Drew was gone, they asked the girls."

"We told them to say I'd taken you to the doctor," Tom said.

Polly Ann nodded. "But they didn't believe it. They came to Breen's instead. Likely, when they don't find anything, they'll go back to our place."

"I was thinking that too," Tom said. "I don't think we should take the money back home."

Polly Ann agreed. "But where could we take it?"

"I was wondering if Lawyer Baxter would still be up."

"I don't know," Polly Ann said, "but I've heard he sits up most of the night sometimes."

"It'll be way past midnight when we get to Boonville," he said.

"Never mind," Polly Ann said.

"We'll go to Mr. Baxter's, and if it shows no lights, we'll knock until he comes to his door."

Tom had to agree, for he couldn't think of anything else for them to do.

The mist had left the river. After they crossed the bridge, he turned Drew into the Dutch Hill road, and they went up the steep pitch to the canal. They got past the house beside the towpath before anybody came out. But a man yelled after them, wanting to know where they thought they were going this late.

Tom didn't answer. He hoped they had got far enough away so they could not be recognized.

Misgivings seized Tom as Drew turned the corner into Leyden Street, his hoofs thumping a loud tattoo on the packed dry dirt. Boonville had gone to bed. The only lighted window they had seen since coming off the towpath opposite the depot was in the front of Dr. Grover's house, no doubt left on for his return from some back farm.

Calling on anybody so late at night didn't seem a proper thing to do, but as they rolled up the street, Tom was reassured to see a light reach out toward the street from a window of the lawyer's little house. Billy-Bob Baxter was undoubtedly still up, working his mind over whatever case he had in hand at the moment. Tom turned Drew into the drive beside the house, so that the wagon was hardly noticea-

ble from the street, and gave Polly Ann the lines to hold while he went up on the front porch and knocked gently on a pane of the office window. He couldn't see Billy-Bob from where he stood, but heard the scrape of his desk chair being shoved back, and presently the lawyer came into view in his worn, shiny jacket. He had taken his watch from his waistcoat pocket, and now he was putting it back. When Billy-Bob saw Tom standing outside the window, he nodded and a moment later opened the front door.

"Well, Tom," he said, "must be something on your mind to bring you here this late. I heard you had a barn raising on your place today."

Tom said yes, they had had one.

"Should have thought that would be enough for one day, even for a strapper like you. But come in and tell me what you want."

Tom didn't go in. He told how he and Polly Ann had decided to go up to the Breen place and why. And then how the Flanchers had showed up. They'd been lucky to get away.

Billy-Bob looked at him a minute.

"You mean you found something, Tom?"

Tom told him. "Two trunks, not big ones."

"With money in them?"

"We didn't want to stop to look."

"You've got them outside in the wagon? Where anybody can see them?"

"Yes, but it's around the side of the house, and Ma's sitting in it."

"Well," Billy-Bob said almost fussily, "we can't have them out there. You go and lead your horse around to the back, and we'll bring the trunks and Polly Ann in through the kitchen. Then put your horse in my barn and come inside yourself."

It took only a few minutes to get the trunks into the kitchen, where Billy-Bob made a jerky little bow toward Polly Ann.

Tom went out to lead Drew into the barn. Billy-Bob no longer kept a horse. Tom found some oats in a bin, but they smelled stale and sour, so the old horse would have to go hungry until he got home. Tom told him he was sorry and left him standing there, probably philosophizing on the unreasonableness of people.

Polly Ann and Billy-Bob had moved the trunks into his office, and the shades had been pulled down over the windows.

"Let's get them up on my desk," Billy-Bob said.

They showed they had been in the ground. There was some mildew on the leather sides, but they still looked sturdy, and the smaller one had wood slats reinforcing it. Both of them were locked.

"Seems a shame to break them," said the lawyer. He pulled open a

Tom obeyed. A piece of muslin cloth covered the top, and Polly Ann lifted it. Underneath were bundles and bundles of money, each tied with fine string.

Billy-Bob Baxter broke the silence with a kind of chortling noise in the back of his nose and said, "Looks like there's quite a pile of money there, if old Bert Breen didn't keep his underwear underneath it."

Tom lifted out a bundle. It seemed to be all ten-dollar bills.

Polly Ann said, "I think we ought to open up the other trunk and then count all the money at once."

"I agree," Billy-Bob said. So they went to trying keys, and the eighteenth or twentieth fitted the second trunk. When Tom heaved up the lid, they saw it was loaded full of money like the first one.

"Well," Billy-Bob said, "let's start counting it."

It took them quite a while. The square clock with a brass horse on top of it, which stood on the shelf behind the small chunk stove, struck one and then it struck one again for the half hour before they had finished counting the money.

"Well, Tom," Billy-Bob said. "By this count you're eight thousand seven hundred seventy-nine dollars richer than you were yesterday when you and Polly Ann went up to Bert Breen's. That doesn't include the loose silver in the bottom of the little trunk, but I don't expect it will

drawer in his desk and took out a flat box filled with keys. "Ought to be something in this lot to open them up. Here. Try that one, Tom."

It didn't fit the lock of the first trunk at all. It entered the keyhole of the second lock, but Tom couldn't turn it either way.

"Put it to the side," Billy-Bob said, "and try this one."

None of the first eight keys worked. But with the ninth, Tom gave a twist and saw the hasp move a bit. He got out his jackknife and pried with the blade. The hasp came free, but he hesitated about lifting the lid.

"Open it up," Billy-Bob said a bit impatiently.

amount to any big amount more. The question is, what are you going to do with it?"

Tom couldn't find words to answer. In all the thinking he had done about the Breen money, he hadn't thought of what it might amount to. If he had, he would never have thought of it coming to anything as big as half that amount. He just didn't know how to answer Billy-Bob.

"Well," the lawyer said, "you can't keep it around here. I'm not going to sit on what will come to maybe nine thousand dollars cash money in my house. You've got to get it into the bank."

"I wouldn't want to take it home," Tom answered. "On account of Yantis Flancher."

"I agree. I'll keep it here tonight, but tomorrow I'll take it to the bank. I'll hire a rig and deliver it at nine o'clock, sharp. You be there too."

They packed it back in the trunks. Tom locked them and put the keys in his pocket and helped Billy-Bob carry the trunks into a closet off the office, the door of which Billy-Bob locked also. Then Tom and Polly Ann went out, got Drew out of the barn, and started home. They hardly spoke all the way, except that Polly Ann drew a deep breath after they crossed Fisk Bridge and said, "Oh, Tom, it's going to be so different for us now!"

DISCUSSION

1. Why did Tom decide that the night of the barn raising was the time to look for Bert Breen's money?
2. Why were Polly Ann and Tom worried about passing by Nelson Farr's house? What did they hear as they passed it the first time? The second time?
3. Why, do you think, was Tom sure that he would not find the money near where the barn door had been?
4. How did Tom conduct his search for the money?
5. While Tom was searching, Polly Ann pointed out to him that the owls had stopped making any noise and said, "If they *was* owls." What do you think she meant by that statement?

6. What precautions did Tom take when he found the loose timbers and started lifting them out?

7. After Polly Ann and Tom had put the trunks in the wagon, why did Tom tell his mother to take the horse and wagon back to the corner of the Armond land? If you had been Polly Ann or Tom, would you have looked in the trunks as soon as they had been put in the wagon to see what was in them? Why or why not?

8. Why did Tom bother to replace the timbers? Why did he then scatter sand and chaff over them?

9. Why did the Dolans go to Lawyer Baxter's with the trunks?

10. About how much money was in the trunks? Why do you think it took so long to count the money?

11. Tom and Polly worked very well together as a team. What qualities did they have that enabled them to do so?

12. The money they had found seemed an enormous amount to the Dolans. What do you think they may have done with it? If you suddenly came into a large sum of money, what would you do with it?

AUTHOR

Walter D. Edmonds was born and grew up on a farm near Boonville, New York, a small town in upstate New York located near the old Erie Canal. This region of the Mohawk Valley is the setting for most of his books, including *Bert Breen's Barn.*

Mr. Edmonds spent most of his youth from the age of thirteen in New England schools and graduated from Harvard University in 1926. While he was at Harvard, he began writing, and his first story appeared in serial form in *Scribner's* magazine. Since then he has written many stories for leading magazines and has had approximately thirty books published, some for adults and many for young people. One of his distinguished works is *Drums Along the Mohawk,* a book that is regarded as a classic and that established him as an outstanding American writer. This and several of his other books have been made into motion pictures or plays. He has been the recipient of many awards and honors, including the Newbery Medal, the Boys' Clubs of America Award, and honorary degrees from several universities.

The book *Bert Breen's Barn* brought new acclaim to Mr. Edmonds, for in 1975 it received a National Book Award as "the most distinguished children's book by an American citizen published in the United States." It also won a Christopher book award as being "representative of the highest level of human and spiritual values."

Some of Mr. Edmonds's other books that you may enjoy are *Cadmus Henry,* a historical story about the Civil War, and *Seven American Stories,* a collection of his short stories.

Walter D. Edmonds lives during the winter months in Concord, Massachusetts, where he continues to write. He says, "I still spend summers on the place in Boonville. I sleep in the room in which I was born."

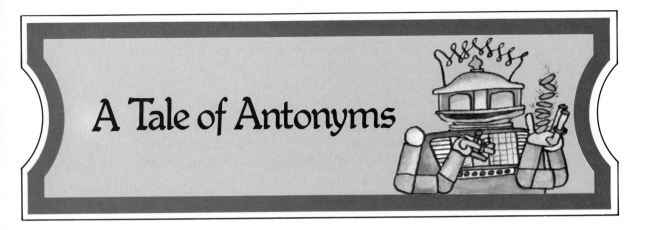

A Tale of Antonyms

The proper use of antonyms can give great impact to writing. Antonyms, because they are opposites, show the strongest contrast between two ideas. The impact of antonyms can be illustrated by a pair of cymbals. The farther apart a percussionist holds a pair of cymbals, the greater the sound when they are struck together. Writers use many kinds of comparisons and contrasts, some very subtle, others very strong. Antonyms are, of course, the strongest.

In "The Season of Light" you read part of a classic use of antonyms from the beginning of *A Tale of Two Cities* by Charles Dickens. It describes the many conflicting forces that existed at once at a particular time in history. Notice how this skillful author used antonyms to convey the turmoil of the times in which the story took place.

> "It was the best of times, it was the worst of times, it was the age of wisdom, it was the age of foolishness, it was the epoch of belief, it was the epoch of incredulity, it was the season of Light, it was the season of Darkness, it was the spring of hope, it was the winter of despair, we had everything before us, we had nothing before us . . ."

The contrast between *the best* and *the worst* sets a pattern that is repeated almost rhythmically. Because of that pattern, the placement of the word *incredulity* clearly indicates that it means the opposite of *belief*. *Despair* is clearly the antonym of *hope*.

As you read the following sentences, notice the pair of antonyms in each.

> I was anything but jubilant; I was crestfallen.
> He was not belligerent after all; he was friendly.
> Neither dawdle nor hurry; but take enough time to do it well.
> Usually she treated me to a long description, but this time her remarks were terse.

If you do not know the meaning of one of the words in a pair, you can get a good idea of its meaning by knowing its opposite. To make sure of the meaning of the less familiar word, consult a dictionary. Notice how a pair of antonyms can express the difference between what is expected and what actually happens or can help someone define exactly what they mean.

Each of the following sentences contains a pair of antonyms. The underlined antonym is probably the less familiar word of the pair. Use the meaning of its antonym to figure out the meaning of the underlined word. Then find the word at the bottom of the page that is closest in meaning to the underlined word. Check your answers in a dictionary.

1. That cannot be a serious remark; it is ludicrous.
2. Her cheerful attitude offset his morose mood.
3. She may be my friend, but today she is my adversary.
4. His remark was obvious, but hers was enigmatic.
5. For such a timid soul, he makes audacious remarks.
6. To a silent person like me, he seems to be a garrulous man.
7. The level hike was easy, but the uphill climb was arduous.
8. Her flushed cheeks suddenly became pallid with fear.
9. We had an abundance of corn but a paucity of other food.
10. Was that comment inspired by kindness or by malice?
11. He is as excitable as his sister is placid.
12. I try to maintain order, but you prefer chaos.

scarcity	calm	enemy	gloomy
puzzling	bold	difficult	pale
talkative	spite	laughable	confusion

Books to Enjoy

Annerton Pit by Peter Dickinson
In this gripping story, two brothers, one blind, are held captive in an abandoned coal mine in northern England.

Window into a Nest
by Geraldine Lux Flanagan and Sean Morris
Remarkable close-up photographs enhance this study of three months in the life of a family of birds.

Notes on the Hauter Experiment by Bernice Grohskopf
When Evelyn suddenly finds herself locked in a timeless world of perfect order with other teen-agers, she keeps a record of the experience, realizes something is missing, and wants to escape.

Nine Black American Doctors
by Robert Hayden and Jacqueline Harris
This collection of profiles includes, among others, Dr. Angella Ferguson, a sickle-cell anemia researcher; Dr. Samuel Fuller, a psychiatrist; and Dr. Jane Wright, a cancer researcher.

Louie's Ransom by E. W. Hildick
Louie manages to keep his sense of humor when he and his friends fly from England to America and fall into the hands of kidnappers.

The Perilous Gard by Elizabeth Marie Pope
In this mystical historical fantasy, Kate Sutton, lady-in-waiting to Princess Elizabeth, is exiled to the Perilous Gard, a mysterious castle with a strange secret.

Awards

MAGAZINE THREE

Contents

The Horsecatcher

by MARI SANDOZ

Young Elk slipped along just under the crest of the ridges. He moved as the wolf travels, where he would not be silhouetted against the sky and yet where he could search the wide slopes of prairie on both sides and vanish quickly in either direction if need be.

The young Cheyenne was dressed to fade into the drying summer prairie, in a gray-figured calico trader's shirt, his braids wrapped in the calico too, his leggings and breechclout of deerskin, with sturdy moccasins and an extra pair tied to his back. He carried only a light bow and quiver, for around his waist was a thick coil of rope.

Cautiously the Cheyenne youth crept over a ridge to look at the small herds of wild horses dotting all the wide plain below him and as far westward as he could see. The closer ones grazed or stomped flies, the colts down sleeping or running in play, the far-off only small dark specks on the hazy summer prairie. As Young Elk looked from one herd to another, searching, the horses suddenly swept together like dark leaves in a gust of wind and then spread over the plain, moving, running. They could not have seen him, he knew. It must have been a wolf, perhaps, or a dry-weather whirl-wind or a rolling tumbleweed that frightened one horse to running, and so all went.

It must have been something small, perhaps only a rattlesnake's angry whirring, for the horses didn't run far. But they kept moving now, and Elk followed, edging in closer, creeping to one knoll after another, from weed to bush to washout, until he found the little herd he sought —

mostly mares, gray and bay, with a black and a sorrel, and their colts. He was very careful now and swung around down a draw and ran to head them, so if he must follow a long time, he would not be in some far enemy country.

The young Cheyenne kept well hidden, but in the excitement of this first chase afoot and alone, he ran too hard, without the judgment of a trained runner or the horse stalker's patience. Instead, his moccasins sang on the grass as though he could hope to outdistance any mustang before the next ridge. He ran until he was winded, and his side ached as from the hot thrust of a Kiowa lance. Torn with the pain, he recalled an old Cheyenne remedy. Stooping far over to his left side without bending a knee, he picked up a pebble, spit under it, and replaced the little white stone in its exact nest. He smiled to himself as the pain eased off.

With his side relieved a little, he decided to take a look over the next ridge. He wasn't far enough ahead of the little herd, his circling entirely too short, but he was pleased actually to see the colt that he had noticed two days ago on the way home with a party from a ceremonial. The colt was a very late one, just born then, and staggering to his feet; the mare, old and not worth a chase, Elk's father had said — not even the short chase required to capture such a poor one. But the wobbly black foal had fine long legs and on one side a white patch shaped like a bear reaching from the rump forward to the shoulder, a big white patch like a bear running, flat paws lifted in its hurry up the withers.

Now Elk had found the colt again, but already much stronger, playfully jumping and shying around the restless mares. He wished he had his brother Two Wolves along, and fast horses. They could easily catch the whole little bunch and be much safer than Elk alone, afoot. It was true that the horses were not worth the chase and the taming, particularly so far in dangerous country, yet Young Elk had been drawn to the new foal by something beyond the value for use or trade. Watching Bear Colt the day before yesterday, he had wanted, not to catch him, but to run beside him over prairie and hilltop in sun and in rain. There seemed something like a calling on the summer wind from the colt, a calling that made a gaiety and a softness within the breast of the young Cheyenne.

Overimpatient now that the colt was there before him, Elk started to crawl toward the resting horses. He moved carefully up along a low place, the grass as unstirred by his passing as from a snake's cautious glide. But he had no plan, even if he got close enough for an arrow. Either he had to tire the horses out or shoot the mare, if he could. Then the little foal would be easy to wear down by cutting across on him, as a wolf does a rabbit. But while Elk was trying to overcome his deep reluctance to any killing, a bird flew up from among the mares. It was the shining black bird that rides on horses and picks insects and nits out of the long, ensnaring manes. In return it was a good watcher, as good a scout as any guarding a Cheyenne village.

The bird burst into the air with a sharp cry of alarm, and the horses were off again, past the young Indian, the mares with their heads up, manes and tails flying in a windy cloud about them, their colts running at their flanks. Behind them the stallion hurried the lagging old mare, threatening to nip her rump if the chase got hot. Her colt tried hard to keep up, the clean white side like a galloping bear.

Young Elk was angered by his foolish impatience. But there was nothing to do now except follow out upon the open prairie, where he could be detected by enemies from very far off, with nowhere to run.

For a while Elk made himself remember these enemies as he followed the little herd, slipping through draws and gullies whenever he could. But he must keep the horses moving, for therein lay his vague hope of catching Bear Colt. He must give them no rest and no time to eat or to water night or day. It would be hard, for humans also liked sleep, and Elk could sleep as soundly as the badger in its winter

burrow. Unfortunately too, an Indian needed to eat and drink as much as the horses did, and the little waterskin now bobbing at Elk's belt and the bladder of pemmican that he had taken from his mother's store would not last long.

Several times he tried to get the little herd headed back toward his home region, but the long runs around them always gave the horses a little rest. When he reappeared, the wily lead mare just swung out past him, and Young Elk had to run even harder to keep the herd from edging eastward to lower ground, where the creeks were not yet dry and where no lone pursuer could hope to keep them from watering.

By now, Elk was more than two sleeps of regular travel from where he had first found Bear Colt again, better than forty of the white people's miles. Surely the lead mare would circle back northward soon, to her usual range. But, instead, she headed straight on, and all that Young Elk could do was to try to stay close enough to keep the horses moving, keep them from feed or rest and particularly from water.

Around dusk the herd began to lag, and an excitement rose in Elk as he got his rope out to catch the little colt. But as he hurried to cut the distance, the rise of the late moon seemed to strengthen the horses, or perhaps it was the howling of the coyotes and wolves that echoed from ridge to ridge. Slowly the herd drew farther away, until they were only darkish blurs in the dusky moon. If they struck water, they could drink their fill before Elk could get there.

Elk was tired, too, worn as a coyote that had been fleeing all day before a prairie fire; but as the moon hazed in a thin clouding, the hoofs ahead hurried faster, drawn by some far smell of water. Once more Elk had to run to scatter a cluster of dark shadows from a drying pond and do it without whoop or noise for enemy ears. But this time the herd did not start away, just watched a short distance off. Elk walked around the muddy bank to leave a disturbing human smell, yet the mares still tried to sneak in around him. He snatched the calico strips from his braids and tied them to rosebushes on the bank. But the horses still hung around in uneasy clots of darkness, always just out of reach of the Indian's rope; one trying to run around him on this side, one on the other, until he was driven to take the chance of a little fire. He threw together a narrow smudging row of twigs and leaves for a slow burning, one that would make little flame until he was well back in a dark draw, in case enemies were around.

Reluctantly, the mares started their faltering colts away from the smell of smoke, and once more Elk had to start, too, stiff and worn out, when he could have been home asleep. He could have been deep in the soft bed robes instead of dozing as he ran over the dark, cactus-patched prairie, feeling ready to go down like a horse with a foot in a badger hole.

But the bear-marked colt drew Young Elk on, and he hoped that he was still following the right horses. As Elk hurried to keep the horses moving, he tried to detect the small dragging steps of a young colt; yet any would be worn and sleepy now, so he could only follow into the light of dawn. To keep himself awake as his worn moccasins felt out the rough ground, he began to talk softly to Bear Colt, speaking the words to himself as in a dreaming.

"Let me catch you, tame you, care well for you," he murmured in his coaxing, gentling way. "We will have a softness in our breasts for each other. I will warm to the sight of you on the hillsides, and you will come to my call. If I am hurt, you will not leave me, and I shall pursue anyone who steals you to the ends of the horizon. We shall harm no living thing, but together we shall be one, a tall man-horse, or, better, a horse-man, for there will be much more of you, Bear Colt, than of me."

When the warm dawn cleared, the young Cheyenne found himself close to Bear Colt, the old mare a good whooping distance behind the straggling herd. The stallion, weary too, let her go to the failing colt, stumbling, but still too fast for the worn Elk. Once he took his rope down, but as though smelling the danger, the colt staggered on, growing stronger with the increasing day.

The sun rose and spread a shimmer of heat dance along the western horizon, crossed overhead, and still the young Indian plodded on, his legs really broken with fatigue, his feet bleeding from the cactus and brush and rock of the long chase. He was in strange country now: dry and gray, with little except snakes, lizards, and scrubby sagebrush. No sign of buffalo, not even an antelope running its curious semicircle or a rabbit hopping. By midafternoon Elk was still following the slow dust of the horses but more to be led out to water than to turn their direction or to do any capturing. There was little weight left in the water pouch, and since yesterday, he had been saving it for the suffering colt. For his own burning thirst he tried to work a pebble around in his mouth, but his stubborn tongue remained dry and swelling.

Then suddenly Young Elk had to realize that he was being trailed. Perhaps he had suspected it since he followed the faltering colt out on the bare, empty plain, with no draws, no gullies, that might offer escape if enemies came. It was reckless, but the gaunted little foal had been going down every few steps, although still brave, springing up at every approach, still trying to overtake the old mare. Worn as the colt seemed, and taming, Young Elk was stumbling, too, with shimmering heat burning his back and his eyes, his feet swollen and as awkward as stumps of wood.

There seemed to be no birds to fly up in warning, but Elk watched the sky for the eagle or the buzzard making a sudden turn. He finally saw something of the enemy himself — three Indians leading extra horses, coming along a far draw, very cautiously, perhaps unwilling to believe that one youth could be out here alone, afoot. He must be a decoy, a bait for an ambush.

Young Elk could not run now or even hope to hide. Besides, the colt was staggering and falling again, his legs crumpling; and this time Elk stood still and made his soft, gentling song in his parched throat. The gaunted colt clambered to his forelegs and then up; but instead of stumbling after the mare, he turned and came toward Elk, spraddle-legged, head down and swaying, the poor swollen tongue far out. He came to Elk as to one he had known a long time, as he had for two of his four days of life, his poor nose groping at the youth's clothing, trying to suck at the ragged shirttail. The young Indian laid his arm over the thin, bony neck and held the colt to him a moment, looking off the way the herd was straggling, knowing they must be following a smell of water somewhere in the breaks standing bluish against the southwest. But behind him and his colt were the stalking men, and although the sun was lowering fast, the enemy would be upon them before dark, and by then the colt might die if he got no milk or even water. So Elk slipped his rope in a hackamore about the bony head and helped the colt into a little washout and dribbled the bit of water left in the skin pouch into his eager, uplifted mouth. Then he tied the sticks of legs together and laid the struggling colt out carefully, so he could not get his back downhill. Even the strongest horse can die in a few hours that way, Elk knew. Afterward, he looked carefully back over the empty plain before he slipped out to try to catch the loitering mare, plodding slowly after the rest now. He hurried almost to dropping and considered trying to halt her with an arrow; but he was not close enough for a sure shot with his little bow, and he would not wound her foolishly.

Then suddenly the three Indians were there but ahead of him, rising out of a canyon, riding for him across the sun-yellowed evening plain. Elk ran back toward the washout, for he must not let the Bear Colt die tied with a rope, die with his legs shamefully tied. It was a good white person's mile away, and only the thought of the colt got Elk there ahead of his enemies. He fell into the hole with tearing breath and red streaks before his eyes. The colt was alive and kicking feebly. Young Elk dug in under the bank, hacking at the soft earth with his knife as his pursuers stopped short of the washout, apparently still fearing a trap. They kept back and shot arrows into the hole, Kiowa and Comanche war arrows; and Elk returned several of them to hold the men away while he pushed the leg-tied colt into the hole and then backed in, too, as far as he could get.

By now the entire washout was in deep shadow, the arrow points glistening in the slanted sun as they came from both sides; and Elk knew that the warriors would certainly be in upon him with war clubs and knives before he could try to get away in the coming dusk. They would kill him; and then the colt, brave as the bear of courage on his side, would die, for no one would trouble with such a poor creature.

Angered by this thought, Young Elk set another of the arrows sticking around him to the bowstring, and then another and another, arcing them to fall near the washout, shooting fast, trying to make it seem there were several warriors here. At least the men up there wouldn't find him with their arrows like a porcupine's risen quills sticking foolishly unused all around him.

One arrow surely hit, for a man roared out an angry word, an angry Cheyenne word. It seemed they crept up around him in earnest now, for the arrows came in straighter. He squeezed in tight against the colt, the poor little creature sucking at his braid, at the torn cloth of his shirt, at his ear. It was so pitiful that the young Indian wanted to leap out, defy these enemies with his naked knife, kill them all to save the poor little spotted horse.

Then he heard more words from the fading light above him, awkward Kiowa words for "Give up!" and something perhaps intended as the same in Comanche and finally in clear Cheyenne. The sudden hope for Bear Colt made Young Elk reckless, made him forget that Cheyennes sometimes became part of the enemy both by capture and by marriage.

"I am Cheyenne!" Elk called out. "Of the Cut-finger People!"

There was a brief silence as of whispering and then a roar of laughter. "So you are a Cut-finger? More truly a crooked-tongue Kiowa son of a captive! Where is your party?"

"There is no party. I am alone — Young Elk, son of Elk River."

There was a snort of disbelief. "Elk River is, then, truly the father of a foolish one, to stray so far——"

"I was chasing a colt."

"Alone? Why should one not yet a warrior be permitted so far in enemy country?"

"It is our country too," Elk replied angrily; then he realized the danger of his hasty tongue. "It is true that the enemy — that others — are more often here," he had to admit in his fear for Bear Colt.

There was a mumbling in the dusk above to this, and finally one man crept nearer in the thickening dark before the moon's rise. He asked and answered many questions. He talked like a good Cheyenne, and because Young Elk had to get quick help for his colt, he finally let himself be coaxed out into the light of a little fire that the men shielded from the prairie with their blankets. He saw their faces, their accouterments. Plainly they were Cheyennes — three young men who had gone down southward afoot from Bent's Fort to locate some good horses, not mustangs but the larger ones, the Spanish horses of the Texas settlements.

"Our young friend is impatient with your long tongue," one of the men interrupted the speaker. "It seems he would say something."

Young Elk was hurt by the words that were spoken as of a boy; but he could not protest, not with the colt tied in the washout, perhaps already dead. They jumped down with a twist of burning sagebrush for light. The tough Bear Colt was alive, sucking at Elk's shirt as he untied the cramped legs. "It is this bear upon his side that I have been following," he tried to explain.

"The colt is a very poor and starving one to risk a life among enemies," the oldest Cheyenne said as he poured a little water over the blackened tongue and into the sucking mouth.

Young Elk made the sign of agreement as he drank sparingly and began to chew a little pemmican for the colt to suck, as he had heard could be done. And while he chewed, he moved his weary hand over the white bear patch, rubbing the sand away slowly, and more slowly, until he was asleep, bent over the colt. The three Cheyennes squatting around the tiny coals laughed a little, but gently.

DISCUSSION

1. Do you think Elk will care well for the colt? What passages or incidents in the story support your answer?
2. Why did Young Elk follow one particular herd?
3. What had Young Elk named the colt? Do you think he wanted the colt for practical uses? Why do you think that?
4. Why did Elk keep circling the herd? What was Elk's purpose in keeping the herd moving?
5. Why was it dangerous for Elk to be so far out on the plain?
6. In what ways did Elk show his inexperience as a horsecatcher?
7. Do you think Elk was cruel to keep the horses from resting, eating, and drinking? Why do you think that?
8. What did Elk do between the time he first sighted the warriors and the time they arrived near the washout? What does your answer suggest about the vastness and flatness of the plain?
9. Had Elk originally intended to go so far from home to capture the colt? How do you know?
10. If Elk had been asked why he eventually went so far, what explanation might he have given? Have you ever been in a situation where you felt driven to accomplish a certain goal? If you wish to do so, tell about it.
11. Why did the three warriors stop short of the washout instead of attacking immediately? Why did Elk shoot back the warriors' arrows as quickly as possible?
12. Do you think Elk was foolish to risk his life in order to capture the colt? Why do you think as you do?

AUTHOR

Mari Sandoz was born of Swiss immigrant parents in the cattle country of northwest Nebraska in 1901. She began writing almost as soon as she learned to read, and a number of her early stories were published on the junior page of the Omaha *Daily News.* At sixteen she passed a teachers' certification examination and found a job in a rural school. She later attended the University of Nebraska. She worked for the Nebraska State Historical Society, at various times as a proofreader, an editor, a researcher, and eventually as the director of research. After 1935 writing became her principal occupation, and her stories and articles appeared in national magazines. Her first book, a biography of her father, was awarded a five-thousand-dollar prize by the Atlantic Monthly Press.

A painstaking researcher and a colorful writer, Miss Sandoz became one of America's leading regional historians, and her books rank among the best ever written about the West. The selection you have just read is an excerpt from *The Horsecatcher,* a runner-up for the Newbery Medal.

A Blessing

by JAMES WRIGHT

Just off the highway to Rochester, Minnesota,
Twilight bounds softly forth on the grass.
And the eyes of those two Indian ponies
Darken with kindness.
They have come gladly out of the willows
To welcome my friend and me.
We step over the barbed wire into the pasture
Where they have been grazing all day, alone.
They ripple tensely, they can hardly contain their happiness
That we have come.
They bow shyly as wet swans. They love each other.
There is no loneliness like theirs.
At home once more,
They begin munching the young tufts of spring in the darkness.
I would like to hold the slenderer one in my arms,
For she has walked over to me
And nuzzled my left hand.
She is black and white,
Her mane falls wild on her forehead,
And the light breeze moves me to caress her long ear
That is delicate as the skin over a girl's wrist.
Suddenly I realize
That if I stepped out of my body I would break
Into blossom.

The Boy Who Predicted Earthquakes

by MARGARET ST. CLAIR

"Naturally, you're skeptical," Wellman said. He poured water from a carafe, put a pill on his tongue, washed the pill down. "Naturally, understandably. I don't blame you, wouldn't dream of blaming you. A good many of us here at the studio had your attitude, I'm afraid, when we started programming this boy Herbert. I don't mind telling you, just between ourselves, that I myself was pretty doubtful that a show of that sort would be good television."

Wellman scratched behind an ear while Read looked on with scientific interest. "Well, I was wrong," Wellman said, putting the hand down again. "I'm pleased to say that I was a thousand per cent wrong.

The kid's first, unannounced, unadvertised show brought nearly fourteen hundred pieces of mail. And his rating nowadays . . ." He leaned toward Read and whispered a figure.

"Oh," Read said.

"We haven't given it out yet, because those buzzards at Purple simply wouldn't believe us. But it's the plain simple truth. There isn't another TV personality today who has the following the kid has. He's on short wave, too, and people tune him in all over the globe. Every time he has a show, the post office has to send two special trucks with his mail. I can't tell you how happy I am, Read, that you scientists are thinking about making a study of

him at last. I'm terrifically sincere about this."

"What's he like personally?" Read asked.

"The kid? Oh, very simple, very quiet, very, very sincere. I like him tremendously. His father — well, he's a real character."

"How does the program work?"

"You mean how does Herbert do it? Frankly, Read, that's something for you researchers to find out. We haven't the faintest idea what happens, really.

"I can tell you the program details, of course. The kid has a show twice a week, Mondays and Fridays. He won't use a script"— Wellman grimaced — "which is pretty much a headache for us. He says a script dries him up. He's on the air for twelve minutes. Most of that time he just talks, telling the viewers about what he's been doing in school, the books he's been reading, and so on. The kind of stuff you'd hear from any nice, quiet boy. But he always makes one or two predictions, always at least one, and never more than three. They are always things that will happen within forty-eight hours. Herbert says he can't see any farther ahead than that."

"And they do happen?" Read said. It was less a question than a statement.

"They do," Wellman replied, somewhat heavily. He puffed out his lips. "Herbert predicted the stratosphere-liner wreck off Guam last April, the Gulf States hurricane, the election results. He predicted the submarine disaster in the Tortugas. Do you realize that the FBI has an agent sitting in the studio with him during every show, out of range of the scanners? That's so he can be taken off the air immediately if he says anything that might be contrary to public policy. They take him that seriously.

"I went over the kid's record yesterday when I heard the university was thinking of studying him. His show has been going out now for a year and a half, twice a week. He's made two hundred six predictions during that time. And every one of them, every single one of them, has come true. By now the general public has such confidence in him that" — Wellman licked his lips and hunted for a comparison — "that they'd believe him if he predicted the end of the world or the winner of the Irish Sweepstakes.

"I'm sincere about this, Read, terrifically sincere. Herbert is the biggest thing in TV since the invention of the selenium cell. You can't overestimate him or his importance. And now, shall we go take in his show? It's just about time for him to go on."

Wellman got up from his desk chair, smoothing into place the design of pink and purple penguins on his necktie. He led Read through the corridors of the station to the observation room of studio 8G, where Herbert Pinner was.

Herbert looked, Read thought, like a nice, quiet boy. He was about fifteen, tall for his age, with a pleasant, intelligent, somewhat careworn face. He went about the preparation for his show with perfect composure, which might hide a touch of distaste.

". . . I have been reading a very interesting book," Herbert said to the TV audience. "Its name is *The Count of Monte Cristo*. I think almost anybody might enjoy it." He held up the book for the viewers to see. "I have also begun a book on astronomy by a man named Duncan. Reading that book has made me want a telescope. My father says that if I work hard and get good grades in school, I can have a small telescope at the end of the term. I will tell you what I can see with the telescope after we buy it.

"There will be an earthquake, not a bad one, in the North Atlantic States tonight. There will be considerable property damage, but no one will be killed. Tomorrow morning about ten o'clock they will find Gwendolyn Box, who has been lost in the Sierras since Thursday. Her leg is broken, but she will still be alive.

"After I get the telescope, I hope to become a member of the Society of Variable Star Observers. Variable stars are stars whose brightness varies because of internal changes or because of external causes. . . ."

At the end of the program Read was introduced to young Pinner. He found the boy polite and cooperative but a little remote.

"I don't know just how I do do it, Mr. Read," Herbert said when a number of preliminary questions had been put. "It isn't pictures, as you suggested, and it isn't words. It just comes into my mind.

"One thing I've noticed is that I can't predict anything unless I more or less know what it is. I could predict about the earthquake because everybody knows what a quake is, pretty much. But I couldn't have predicted about Gwendolyn Box if I hadn't known she was missing. I'd just have had a feeling that somebody or something was going to be found."

"You mean you can't make predictions about anything unless it's in your consciousness previously?" Read asked intently.

Herbert hesitated. "I guess so," he said. "It makes a . . . a spot in my mind, but I can't identify it. It's like looking at a light with your eyes shut. You know a light is there, but that's all you know about it. That's the reason why I read so many books. The more things I know about, the more things I can predict.

"Sometimes I miss important things too. I don't know why that is. There was the time the atomic pile exploded and so many people were killed. All I had for that day was an increase in employment.

"I don't know how it works, really, Mr. Read. I just know it does."

Herbert's father came up. He was a small, bouncing man with the extrovert's persuasive personality. "So you're going to investigate Herbie, hum?" he said when the introductions had been performed. "Well, that's fine. It's time he was investigated."

"I believe we are," Read answered with a touch of caution. "I'll have to have the appropriation for the project approved first."

Mr. Pinner looked at him shrewdly. "You want to see whether there's an earthquake first, isn't that it? It's different when you hear him saying it himself. Well, there will be. It's a terrible thing, an earthquake." He clicked his tongue deprecatingly. "But nobody will be killed, that's one good thing. And they'll find that Miss Box the way Herbie says they will."

The earthquake arrived about nine fifteen, when Read was sitting under the bridge lamp reading a report from the Society for Psychical Research. There was an ominous muttering rumble and then a long, swaying, seasick roll.

Next morning Read had his secretary put through a call to Haffner, a seismologist with whom he had a casual acquaintanceship. Haffner, over the phone, was definite and brusque.

"Certainly there's no way of foretelling a quake," he snapped. "Not even an hour in advance. If there were, we'd issue warnings and get people out in time. There'd never be any loss of life. We can tell in a general way where a quake is likely, yes. We've known for years that this area was in for one. But as for setting the exact time — you might as well ask astronomers to predict a supernova for you. They don't know, and neither do we. What brought this up, anyway? The prediction made by that Pinner kid?"

"Yes. We're thinking of observing him."

"Thinking of it? You mean you're only just now getting around to him? What ivory towers you research psychologists must live in!"

"You think he's genuine?"

"The answer is an unqualified yes."

Read hung up. When he went out to lunch, he saw by the headlines that Gwendolyn Box had been found just as Herbert had predicted on his television program.

Still he hesitated. It was not until Thursday that he realized that he was hesitating, not because he was afraid of wasting the university's money on a fake, but because he was all too sure that Herbert Pinner was genuine. He didn't want to start this study. He was afraid.

The realization shocked him. He

got the dean on the phone at once, asked for his appropriation, and was told there would be no difficulty about it. Friday morning he selected his two assistants for the project, and by the time Herbert's program was nearly due to go out, they were at the station.

They found Herbert sitting tensely on a chair in studio 8G with Wellman and five or six other station executives clustered around him. His father was dancing about excitedly, wringing his hands. Even the FBI agent, who usually remained detached, was joining warmly in the argument. And Herbert, in the middle, was shaking his head and saying, "No, no, I can't," over and over again doggedly.

"But why not, Herbie?" his father wailed. "Please tell me why not. Why won't you give your show?"

"I can't," Herbert said. "Please don't ask me. I just can't." Read noticed how white the boy was around the mouth.

"But, Herbie, you can have anything you want, anything, if you only will! That telescope you'd like — I'll buy it for you tomorrow. I'll buy it tonight!"

303

"I don't want a telescope," young Pinner said wanly. "I don't want to look through it."

"I'll get you a pony, a motorboat, a swimming pool! Herbie, I'll get you anything!"

"No," Herbert said.

Mr. Pinner looked around him desperately. His eyes fell on Read, standing in the corner, and he hurried over to him. "Please see what you can do with him, Mr. Read," he panted.

Read chewed his lower lip. In a sense it was his business. He pushed his way through the crowd to Herbert and put his hand on his shoulder. "What's this I hear about you not wanting to give your show today, Herbert?" he asked.

Herbert looked up at him. The harassed expression in his eyes made Read feel guilty and contrite. "I just can't," he said. "Don't you start asking me too, Mr. Read."

Once more Read chewed his lip. Part of the technique of parapsychology lies in getting subjects to cooperate. "If you don't go on the air," he said, "a lot of people are going to be disappointed."

Herbert's face took on a tinge of sullenness. "I can't help it," he said.

"More than that, a lot of people are going to be frightened. They won't know why you aren't going on the air, and they'll imagine things. All sorts of things. If they don't view you, an awful lot of people are going to be scared."

"I —" Herbert said. He rubbed his cheek. "Maybe that's right," he answered slowly. "Only . . ."

"You've got to go on with your show."

Herbert capitulated suddenly. "All right," he said, "I'll try."

Everyone in the studio sighed deeply. There was a general motion toward the door of the observation room. Voices were raised in high-pitched, rather nervous chatter. The crisis was over; the worst would not occur.

The first part of Herbert's show was much like the others had been. The boy's voice was a trifle unsteady, and his hands had a tendency to shake, but these small abnormalities would have passed the average viewer unnoticed. When perhaps five minutes of the show had gone, Herbert put aside the books and drawings he had been showing his audience (he had been discussing mechanical drawing) and began to speak with great seriousness.

"I want to tell you about tomorrow," he said. "Tomorrow" — he stopped and swallowed — "tomorrow is going to be different from what anything in the past has been. Tomorrow is going to be the start of a new and better world for all of us."

Read, listening in the glass-enclosed room, felt an incredulous thrill race over him at the words. He glanced around at the faces of the others and saw that they were listening intently, their faces strained and rapt. Wellman's lower jaw dropped a little, and he absently fingered the unicorns on his tie.

"In the past," young Pinner said, "we've had a pretty bad time. We've had wars — so many wars — and famines and pestilences. We've had depressions and haven't known what caused them; we've had people starving when there was food and dying of diseases for which we knew the cure. We've seen the wealth of the world wasted shamelessly, the rivers running black with the washed-off soil, while hunger for all of us got surer and nearer every day. We've suffered; we've had a hard time.

"Beginning tomorrow" — his voice grew louder and more deep — "all that is going to be changed. There won't be any more wars. We're going to live side by side like brothers and sisters. We're going to forget about killing and bombs. From pole to pole the world will be one great garden, full of richness and fruit, and it will be for all of us to have and use and enjoy. People will live a long time and live happily, and when they die, it will be from old age. Nobody will be afraid anymore. For the first time since human beings have lived on earth, we're going to live the way human beings should.

"The cities will be full of the richness of culture, full of art and music and books. And every race on earth will contribute to that culture, each in its degree. We're going to be wiser and happier and richer than any people have ever been. And pretty soon" — he hesitated for a moment, as if his thought had stumbled — "pretty soon we're going to send out rocket ships to Venus and Jupiter. We'll go to the limits of our solar system to see what Uranus and Pluto are like. And maybe from there — it's possible — we'll go on and visit the stars.

"Tomorrow is going to be the beginning of all that. That's all for now. Good-by. Good night."

For a moment after he had ceased, no one moved or spoke. Then voices began to babble deliriously. Read, glancing around him, noticed how white the people's faces were and how dilated their eyes.

"Wonder what effect the new setup will have on TV?" Wellman said, as if to himself. His tie was flopping wildly about. "There'll be TV, that's certain — it's part of the good life." And then, to Pinner, who was blowing his nose and wiping his eyes, "Get him out of here, Pinner, right away. He'll be mobbed if he stays here."

Herbert's father nodded. He dashed into the studio after Herbert, who was already surrounded, and came back with him. With Read running interference, they fought their way through the corridor and down to the street level at the back of the station.

Read got into the taxicab uninvited and sat down next to Herbert. The boy looked quite exhausted, but his lips wore a faint smile. "You'd better have the cab driver take you to some quiet hotel," Read said to the senior Pinner. "You'd be besieged if you went to your usual place."

Pinner nodded. "Hotel Triller," he said to the driver of the car. "Go slow, cabby. We want to think."

He slipped his arm around his son and hugged him. His eyes were shining. "I'm proud of you, Herbie," he declared solemnly, "as proud as can be. What you said — those were wonderful, wonderful things."

The driver had made no move to start the cab. Now he turned round and spoke. "It's young Mr. Pinner, isn't it? I was watching you just now. Could I shake your hand?"

After a moment Herbert leaned forward and extended it. The driver accepted it almost reverently. "I just want to thank you — just want to thank you — excuse me, Mr. Herbert. But what you said meant a lot to me. I was in the last war."

The cab slid away from the curb. As it moved downtown, Read saw that Pinner's injunction to the driver to go slow had been unnecessary. People were thronging the streets already. The sidewalks were choked. People began to spill over onto the pavements. The cab slowed to a walk, to a crawl, and still they poured out. Read was afraid Herbert would be recognized.

News dealers were screaming on corners in raucous hysteria. As the cab came to a halt, Pinner opened the door and slipped out. He came scrambling back with an armload of papers he had bought.

"NEW WORLD COMING!" one read, another "MILLENNIUM TOMORROW!" and another quite simply, "JOY TO THE WORLD!" Read spread the papers out and began to read the story in one of them.

"A fifteen-year-old boy told the world that its troubles were over beginning tomorrow, and the world went wild with joy. The boy, Herbert Pinner, whose uncannily accurate predictions have won him a worldwide following, predicted an era of peace, abundance, and prosperity such as the world has never known before. . . ."

"Isn't it wonderful, Herbert?"

Pinner panted. His eyes were blazing. He shook Herbert's arm. "Isn't it wonderful? Aren't you glad?"

"Yes," Herbert said.

They got to the hotel at last and registered. They were given a suite on the sixteenth floor. Even at this height they could faintly hear the excitement of the crowd below.

"Lie down and rest, Herbert," Mr. Pinner said. "You look worn out. Telling all that — it was hard on you." He bounced around the room for a moment and then turned to Herbert apologetically. "You'll excuse me if I go out, son, won't you? I'm too excited to be quiet. I want to see what's going on outside."

"Yes, go ahead," Herbert answered. He had sunk down in a chair.

Read and Herbert were alone in the room. There was silence for a moment. Herbert laced his fingers over his forehead and sighed.

"Herbert," Read said softly, "I thought you couldn't see into the future for more than forty-eight hours ahead."

"That's right," Herbert replied without looking up.

"Then how could you foresee all the things you predicted tonight?"

The question seemed to sink into the silence of the room like a stone dropped into a pond. Ripples spread out from it. Herbert said, "Do you really want to know?"

For a moment Read had to hunt for the name of the emotion he felt. It was fear. He answered, "Yes."

Herbert got up and went over to the window. He stood looking outside, not at the crowded streets, but at the sky — where, thanks to daylight-saving time, a faint sunset glow yet lingered.

"I wouldn't have known if I hadn't read the book," he said, turning around, the words coming out in a rush. "I'd just have known something big — big — was going to happen. But now I know. I read about it in my astronomy book.

"Look over here." He pointed to the west, where the sun had been. "Tomorrow it won't be like this."

"What do you mean?" Read cried, his voice sharp with anxiety. "What are you trying to say?"

"That . . . tomorrow the sun will be different. Maybe it's better this way. I wanted them to be happy. You mustn't hold it against me, Mr. Read, that I lied to them."

Read turned on him fiercely. "What is it? What's going to happen tomorrow? You've got to say!"

"Why, tomorrow the sun — I've forgotten the word. What is it they call it when a star flares up suddenly, when it becomes a billion times hotter than it was before?"

"A supernova?" Read cried.

"That's it. Tomorrow . . . the sun is going to explode."

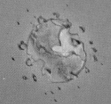

Diagrams Showing Parts and Whole

Look at Figure 1. From the caption, or title, you know that the diagram shows the parts of a bird. You might find this type of diagram in a science book or a birdwatcher's manual. The drawing includes the entire profile of a bird and a more detailed illustration of the underside of a bird's wing. Notice that lines are used to show the exact location of most labeled parts. As you study the labels, you can see that other names for some parts are given in parentheses. What is another term for the nape? What are the longest feathers at the fore edge of the wing called?

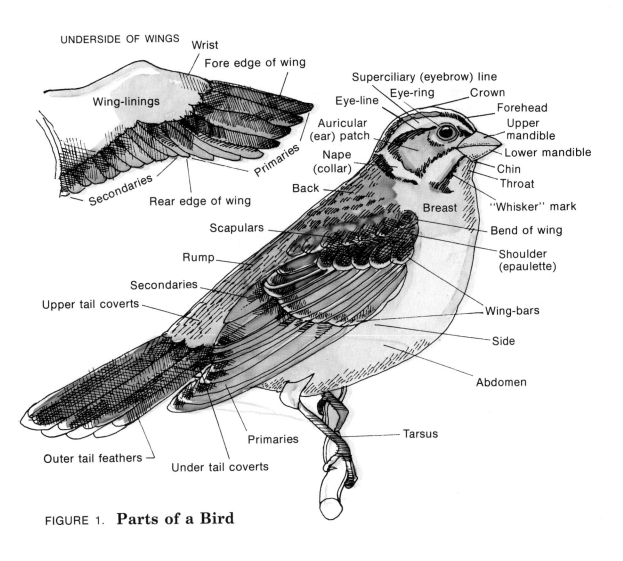

FIGURE 1. **Parts of a Bird**

Figures 2 and 3 also show part-whole relationships. Both diagrams illustrate teeth. Figure 2 shows the upper and lower teeth of an adult human with the various types of teeth labeled. Notice that lines and brackets are used to indicate how many teeth there are of each kind. What are the four front upper and lower teeth called? How many premolars does an adult have?

Figure 3 is a cross section of a human incisor. This is a detailed drawing that illustrates the inside of a tooth from the crown to the root and includes the surrounding membrane, bone, and gum. Lines and dots are used to show where the various parts are located. What is the outer layer of the crown of the tooth called? What is the part next to the pulp called?

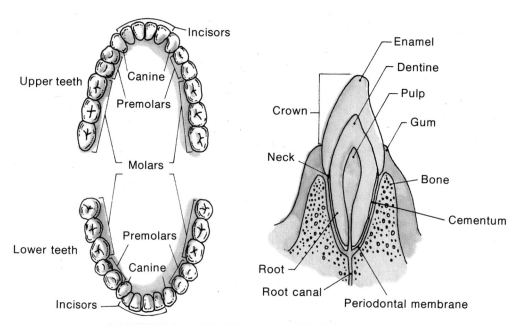

FIGURE 2. **Upper and Lower Teeth of an Adult**

FIGURE 3. **Cross Section of a Human Incisor**

Diagrams Showing How Something Works

The following paragraph and diagram describe how a hot-air balloon works. Without the diagram, it would be difficult to understand the placement and relationship of parts. As you read the text, refer to Figure 4 to picture how a balloon operates.

While the balloon is still on the ground, a large fan blows air into the mouth of the bag. When the bag is half-inflated, the pilot starts the burner to heat the air. As the air inside the bag becomes warmer and lighter than the air surrounding it, the balloon begins to rise. The pilot can burn more fuel to go higher and less fuel to lose altitude. For a rapid descent, the cooling vent may be used to release hot air. The balloon

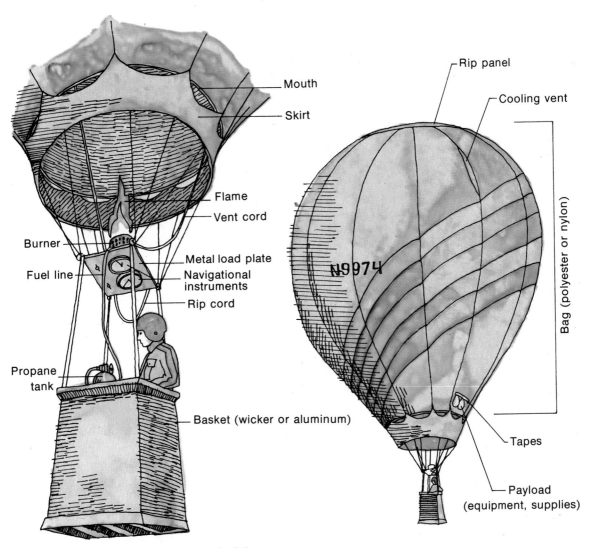

FIGURE 4.

Inflated Hot-Air Balloon

cannot be steered horizontally, but the vertical flight can be controlled. By varying altitude, the pilot can usually find wind blowing in the desired direction. Upon landing, the balloon is deflated by pulling the rip cord to open the rip panel.

Where is the burner of a hot-air balloon located? Where are the navigational instruments located?

Charts

In contrast to a diagram, which shows how something is put together or how something works, a chart is a drawing that shows organization or relationships through the use of words, pictures, or symbols, sometimes in combined form. A chart can demonstrate how the government of a country is organized, for example, or show the relationships among several generations of a royal family. You may find these kinds of charts in your social studies or history textbooks.

A chart can also show the steps involved in a particular process or procedure. From a chart of this kind, you could get information about the steps that are required to become a licensed balloon pilot or the steps to be followed in operating a fire extinguisher.

Charts Showing Sequence

Figure 5 is a chart that describes the steps involved in providing first aid for burns. If it appeared in a chapter or an article you were reading, you would want to note carefully the details in the accompanying text. From the chart alone, however, you can learn the steps that should be taken immediately to treat different kinds of burns.

Notice that burns are divided into three groups based on severity. Brief descriptions are given to help you identify each type of burn. Which type of burn is most serious?

It is important in reading a chart to understand how the information in it is organized. You can see that boxes have been used to organize the information in Figure 5 and that the boxes relating to the different types of burns are connected by lines. The information within the boxes describes the steps to be taken in treating each type of burn. The vertical lines indicate that the chart is to

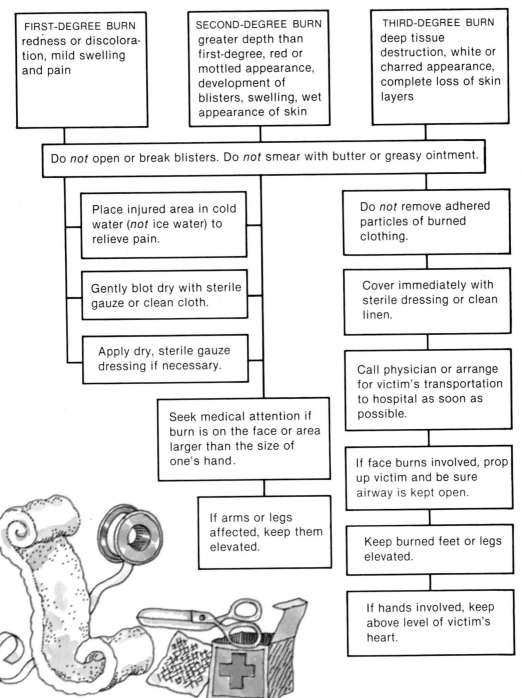

FIGURE 5. **Treatment of Burns**

FIRST-DEGREE BURN redness or discoloration, mild swelling and pain

SECOND-DEGREE BURN greater depth than first-degree, red or mottled appearance, development of blisters, swelling, wet appearance of skin

THIRD-DEGREE BURN deep tissue destruction, white or charred appearance, complete loss of skin layers

Do *not* open or break blisters. Do *not* smear with butter or greasy ointment.

Place injured area in cold water (*not* ice water) to relieve pain.

Gently blot dry with sterile gauze or clean cloth.

Apply dry, sterile gauze dressing if necessary.

Seek medical attention if burn is on the face or area larger than the size of one's hand.

If arms or legs affected, keep them elevated.

Do *not* remove adhered particles of burned clothing.

Cover immediately with sterile dressing or clean linen.

Call physician or arrange for victim's transportation to hospital as soon as possible.

If face burns involved, prop up victim and be sure airway is kept open.

Keep burned feet or legs elevated.

If hands involved, keep above level of victim's heart.

be read from top to bottom and the steps followed in the sequence given. The horizontal lines — or in one case a wide box — connecting more than one vertical line indicate which steps apply to more than one type of burn. What is the first step that applies only to the treatment of a third-degree burn? What is the last step that applies to the treatment of a first-degree burn?

Notice that some of the steps tell you what *not* to do. What two things should you *not* do in treating any burn?

Charts Showing Organization

Figure 6 is a chart that shows the organization of jobs within a newspaper company. Because the board of directors in this company has the most authority, it is listed at the top of the chart. You would read the chart from top to bottom if you wanted to determine for what other people a person or group is responsible. What people is the president of the company directly in charge of? For whom is the news editor directly responsible?

FIGURE 6. **Organization of the Prints Charming Newspaper Company**

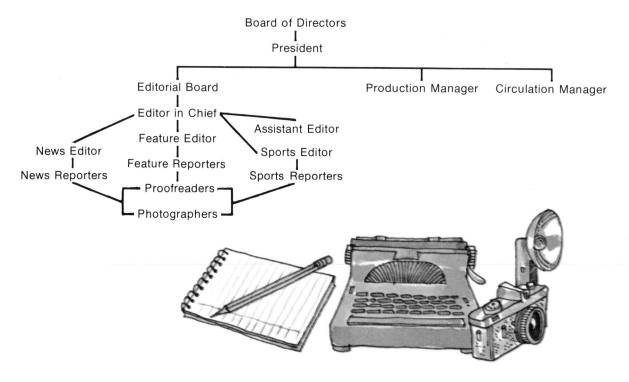

Except for the board of directors, each person or group in the company reports to one or more other individuals or groups with greater authority and responsibility. You would read the chart from bottom to top to determine to whom a person or group reports. To whom does the editor in chief report? To whom do proofreaders and photographers report?

READING DIAGRAMS AND CHARTS

1. According to Figure 1, what part of a bird is located directly below the nape?
2. What part forms a partial circle around the eye of a bird?
3. According to Figure 2, how many canine teeth does an adult have?
4. Which teeth are located beside the molars?
5. According to Figure 3, what word describes the part of the tooth between the root and the crown?
6. What material holds the tooth securely in place?
7. According to Figure 4, what part connects the propane tank and the burner?
8. Where is the rip panel located on the balloon bag?
9. According to Figure 5, what should be done first to help relieve the pain of a first- or second-degree burn?
10. What should be done if the victim's hands have received third-degree burns?
11. According to Figure 6, which members of the Prints Charming Newspaper Company report to the editor in chief?
12. For whom are the sports reporters responsible?

Susan Livingston

by MARGARET TRUMAN

My favorite woman of the American Revolution is someone many people have never heard of — Susan Livingston. Susan was pretty and fond of clothes, parties, and dancing. But when she found herself facing the most difficult crisis of her life, she proved she could also be daring and fearless.

I like Susan Livingston for several reasons. For one thing, she had a controversial politician for a father — William Livingston, the "rebel" Governor of New Jersey. For another, she lived in a big, comfortable house that she loved as much as I love my parents' old home in Independence, Missouri.

The Livingston homestead, Liberty Hall, still stands and continues to be owned by Livingston descendants. It is a rambling three-story structure tucked behind a stone wall on a busy highway just outside Elizabeth, New Jersey. When Susan Livingston lived there, the highway was no more than a dirt road, the house was surrounded by lush farmland, and Elizabeth was a small, sedate seaport known as Elizabethtown.

My father, I know, would have sympathized with William Livingston. Dad had only one child to cope with; Governor Livingston had three, all of them daughters.

Susan was the Governor's middle daughter. She was slightly less dignified than her two sisters and had a habit of frightening prospective suitors away with her sharp wit. In this and a number of other traits, Susan took after her father.

William Livingston loved an argument. He liked to think of himself as a man who had a love of freedom in his bones and was not afraid to risk everything for his beliefs. At the same time, he was an enormously affectionate man, a born father. He would leap up from a chair in his library, where he was often reading a book in Latin or French, and romp with his children like a five-year-old.

Susan's mother was an equally remarkable person. She was the calm, steadying influence in the family. She was also the money manager. In this department, the Governor was pretty close to inept. While he was busy fighting religious and political battles, Mrs. Livingston ran Liberty Hall and its 140-acre farm. She was more than able to hold her own as a separate and very independent personality, no small order for someone married to a man as unpredictable and dynamic as William Livingston. I suspect that this combination of a capable mother and a father who was a born fighter helped to make Susan Livingston the courageous woman she became.

No leader of the Revolution except George Washington had a more difficult task than the Governor of New Jersey. The state was split almost fifty-fifty between those who were loyal to the British (the Loyalists) and those who wanted independence. Morale was a constant problem. Thousands gave up the fight and signed secret agreements with the British to remain neutral in return for protection. Others took advantage of the chaos to loot and abuse their neighbors. Still others concentrated on getting rich. In the middle of the war, William Livingston wrote to George Washington, "I am so discouraged by our public mismanagement and the additional load of business thrown upon me by the villainy of those who pursue nothing but accumulating fortunes to the ruin of their country that I almost sink under it."

Nevertheless, Livingston had a strong spirit that could not be broken. "I have never desponded," he wrote another friend. "But I know at the same time that Providence will abandon us as a parcel of ingrates if we neglect to do for ourselves what we can do."

"To do for ourselves what we can do." That is a good definition of courage. Governor William Livingston lived it throughout the Revolution. So did his wife and daughters.

Liberty Hall was in disputed territory. The British and Loyalists held nearby New York, Long Island, and Staten Island, which was separated from Elizabethtown by a tiny strip of water known as the Sound. On almost any night they chose to do so, British raiders could cross the swift-running stream and roam through the town almost at will. Their goal, more often than not, was the capture of some well-known patriot, who was then dragged back to New York and thrown into a British army prison.

Number one on the royal kidnap list was Governor William Livingston. Knowing this, the Governor seldom spent a night at Liberty Hall. He switched his sleeping quarters from one friend's house to another's without advance notice, making it difficult for anyone to betray him. This left Susan, the other unmarried Livingston daughter, Kitty, Mrs. Livingston, and a handful of servants alone in the big mansion.

Governor Livingston worried about leaving his family unprotected and several times tried to persuade them to move to a safer location farther inland. All three women saw the anguish in his eyes when he made this proposal. Abandoned, Liberty Hall would almost certainly be looted and destroyed by the British or their Loyalist allies. No, they told him firmly, they would stay at Liberty Hall and take their chances. The Governor would ride off to Trenton to do battle with the legislature, worrying aloud but secretly relieved. He loved Liberty Hall, and it would have broken his heart to see it a charred ruin.

One evening in the spring of 1779, the British received word from one of their spies in New Jersey that Governor Livingston would be spending the night at Liberty Hall. The British commander on Staten Island, Brigadier Thomas Stirling, immediately decided to go after him.

At midnight the Livingston women were awakened by an angry pounding on their front door. Susan rushed to the window and stared out at an awesome sight. No fewer than a thousand British troops with fixed bayonets surrounded the house. Every few feet the ranks were illuminated by the glow of a torch held high to make sure that their quarry could not possibly escape.

Fortunately, the British had been given the wrong information. William Livingston was not at Liberty Hall. Susan elected herself to take charge in his absence. Turning to her mother and sister, she told them to remain upstairs. Then she put on a brightly flowered night-robe and calmly descended to admit the British officer and his staff.

"Miss," said Brigadier Stirling with a stiff bow, "your father, the Governor, is in the house. For his own safety we trust he will surrender to us without resistance."

With unconcealed triumph, Susan told the Brigadier he had been misinformed. "My father seldom spends the night here," she said. "I fear you have gone to a great deal of trouble for nothing."

"She's lying," snarled an officer on the Brigadier's staff.

Stirling nodded. "We will have to search the house," he snapped.

"Go right ahead," Susan replied coolly.

At this point, their conversation was interrupted by the distant boom of a cannon. The sound came from the west. In that same instant, a pillar of flame blazed on Hobart Mountain, the highest point in the Short Hills, some six miles inland. It was the alarm gun and signal tower calling the local militia out to attack the British invaders.

If the Brigadier recognized the sound, he gave no sign. He barked some orders to his aides, and several squads of redcoats were soon swarming through Liberty Hall. One group stomped down the cellar stairs to search the kitchen and the servants' dining room; another prowled through the upstairs bedrooms, terrifying Mrs. Livingston and Kitty.

Ten minutes of furious searching produced no Governor. At least one officer expressed his anger by hacking at the lovely mahogany banister with his sword.

The alarm gun on Hobart Mountain continued to boom. As the Brigadier well knew, this part of New Jersey could muster two or three thousand militia. At this very moment the men might be on the road to Elizabethtown. But Thomas Stirling was a stubborn man. He did not intend to lose a night's sleep and embarrass himself before his troops by returning empty-handed. "If we cannot bring back the Governor," he declared, "we must at least have the pleasure of examining his private papers."

"They aren't here," Susan solemnly assured him. "He carries most of them with him in a small trunk. The rest are in Trenton."

This was a bold-faced lie. The Governor's papers were only a few steps away in a locked desk. If the British found them, they would obtain priceless information about the state of the Revolution in New Jersey. They would be fascinated to learn, for instance, the detailed orders for mustering the militia and their places of rendez-vous. Even more interesting would be the lists of persons exempt from the strict prohibition against traveling to New York. These lists were in George Washington's handwriting. Those named were spies, and if the British should learn their identities, they would end up on the gallows.

The alarm gun still boomed, and from the distance came the faint sound of popping musketry. The militia were already fighting with the British pickets. Brigadier Stirling stormed out of the house to put his men in battle formation. His staff followed, leaving a major in charge of the search for Governor Livingston's papers.

The officer began methodically poking into every cabinet and chest in sight. Susan Livingston watched calmly until he reached her father's desk. Suddenly she stepped in front of the major and in a voice shaking with emotion begged him to leave the desk shut.

"In here," she said, placing her hand gently on the slanted top of the desk, "are letters that I have exchanged with a certain gentleman. If *you* are a gentleman, sir, you will not disturb them."

Like all British officers, the major prided himself on being a gentleman. He had no choice but to assure the charming young woman that he would not dream of touching her love letters. "But in exchange," he insisted, "you must show me where your father's papers are."

There were more popping sounds in the distance as the militia grew bolder. An officer rushed to the door to urge the major to hurry.

"Now, Miss Livingston, tell me where they are," the major commanded impatiently.

"All right," replied Susan with her sweetest smile, "I will. It's the least I can do for a *gentleman*."

She allowed the major to follow her back into the study, where she mounted the ladder to the upper shelves of the bookcases and began hauling down batches of papers. In a performance that would have done credit to an accomplished actress, Susan bitterly reproached herself for betraying her father's trust. The major tried to console her by pointing out that he probably would have found the papers anyway. Then he hastily handed them to his men, who stuffed the papers into their forage bags.

A brisk rattle of musketry shook the house. If they did not leave soon, the British would find themselves fighting a pitched battle with the gathering militia. Bowing his thanks to his seemingly guilt-stricken hostess, the major rushed out the door and joined Brigadier Stirling and the rest of the troops for the boat ride back to Staten Island.

Toward dawn, the major proudly opened the forage bags in the Brigadier's quarters. The entire staff was on hand to gloat over the biggest intelligence coup of the war. But instead of Governor Livingston's private papers, the redcoats found themselves staring at several dozen sheafs of old law briefs dating back to the 1750's, when William Livingston had been one of the busiest attorneys in New York.

DISCUSSION

1. Would you agree with the author that Susan Livingston's patriotic achievement during the American Revolution was worthy of recognition? Give reasons for your answer.
2. According to the author, what combination of qualities from her parents probably helped to make Susan the courageous person she became? Why did the author consider Mrs. Livingston to be as remarkable as her husband, the Governor?
3. Why was Governor William Livingston's task as a leader so difficult during the Revolution? What were some of the discouraging problems he faced?
4. What kept the Governor from sinking under the task of leadership? What do you think the author meant by saying that "to do for ourselves what we can do" is a good definition of courage?

5. Why were the Livingston family and their home in constant danger? What did the governor do to avoid being captured or betrayed?

6. Why did the Livingston women decide to stay at Liberty Hall instead of moving to a safer location while the Governor was away? What did their decision tell you about them?

7. What was Brigadier Thomas Stirling's purpose for conducting a midnight raid on Liberty Hall? Having failed to achieve his purpose, why did the Brigadier then order that a search be made for the Governor's private papers?

8. Why was a major left in charge of the search? What did Susan do to prevent him from removing her father's private papers from his desk?

9. Why, do you think, did the Governor leave his private papers at home instead of carrying them with him?

10. Why was the major convinced that Susan had given him the Governor's private papers? Do you think he used good judgment in hastily accepting the wrong papers without question? Give reasons to support your view.

11. Why was Susan's success in deceiving the major important to the cause of the American Revolution in New Jersey?

AUTHOR

Margaret Truman spent the first ten years of her life in Independence, Missouri. Her father's election to the United States Senate in 1934 necessitated a move to Washington, D.C. There she attended a private school and then George Washington University, where she earned a degree in history, an interest that was valuable to her during her father's presidency and one that has remained strong throughout her life. Following another of her interests, music, she decided on a vocal career. After intensive study, she made her debut as a soloist on national radio in 1947, and in the following years made many concert appearances across the country. In 1956 she married Clifton Daniel, a *New York Times* executive, and they subsequently had four sons. Her later activities have included summer theater performances and a nationally syndicated radio show. In addition, she fulfilled her father's prediction that she would one day turn to writing. Prior to the publication of her best-selling biography of her father, *Harry S. Truman,* she was the author of two successful books and a number of magazine articles. The selection "Susan Livingston" is from her book *Women of Courage.*

The Ballad of Mulan

by JO MANTON

In winter, when frost flowers cover the shuttered windows and the rower's oar breaks the ice with a tinkling sound, comes the time for telling stories. The parents drink fragrant tea, while the children sit together on top of the brick stove. Then the old ballad maker knocks at the gate, shambles across the snow-filled courtyard, and sitting down in the firelight, begins his story:

> Click, click, click-click-click,
> Quick and slow, slow and quick,
> Mulan sits at her parents' door
> Weaving her silk for evermore.

The old ballad maker curves his hand, as if around a weaver's shuttle, and throws it to and fro, so that the listening children, their father, their mother, and the servants who have gathered, gaping, seem to see the silk being woven by a young girl. Suddenly he crinkles his parchment face into a thousand sad lines as he asks:

> Why, what is this? The silk is lying
> Tangled and still. Mulan is crying.

And tears, actual tears, roll down the ballad maker's face as his voice changes to the faltering tones of a young girl:

> "Oh! How our land is ruined by war!
> Down from the north on China pour
> The Tartar riders, fierce, like a flood,
> A raging river, a river of blood,
> Drowning our peace. It tears down the peach,
> The willow, the silkworm mulberry. Each
> Home is a charcoal ruin, hut,
> Or hall, or carved pavilion. But
> The Emperor says this must not be.
> The Emperor sends a high decree
> To every town and village round
> The whole of China, at the sound
> Of which all run and listen. This
> Is what it says: 'Our Empire is
> In danger. Every man must go
> To fight the Tartars and to throw
> Them out of China. Young men and old,
> All, from all families, all are enrolled!'
> All men! Oh, then I knew that sorrow
> Would wake with me as I woke tomorrow.
> Last night I looked, I looked at the roll —
> My father's name stood black on the scroll!"
> Her father! That is who Mulan weeps for.
> These are the special tears she keeps for
> Him. Her father is sun and moon
> And stars to Mulan. Now, soon, soon,
> He will march off in soldier's dress,
> Never come back, unless, unless . . .

Now the ballad maker nods and shrugs mysteriously as he speaks in Mulan's voice again, but this time almost in a whisper:

"I must be able to do it, I must!
He who has given me love and trust,
Shall he die and his ashes blow over the plains,
Or drag out his weary life in chains,
A Tartar's prisoner? No, I must save
Him, now, in this hour, as a brave
Daughter should do. I must cloak my face
And ride with the soldiers to take his place!"

Lifting a corner of his ragged cloak sideways across his face, the ballad maker peeps in and out from behind it as he speaks first in his own voice and then in Mulan's:

Mulan goes to the Eastern Market!
There she buys a fiery horse.
"O my horse, my horse, carry me safely in the
    cruel war!"
Mulan goes to the Western Market!
There she buys a saddle and horsecloth.
"O saddle and cloth, sit well on my horse,
That he may carry me safely in the cruel war!"
Mulan goes to the Southern Market!
There she buys a bit and reins.
"O reins and fine silver bit, guide my horse
That he may carry me safely in the cruel war!"
Mulan goes to the Northern Market!
There she buys a tall whip.
"O riding whip, if need be, lick the sides
Of my fine horse that he may carry me safely,
Safely home again out of the cruel war!"

The ballad maker puts his finger to his lips and whispers as all lean forward, breathless, to hear what Mulan will do next:

Early next morning Mulan arose.
A gray mist like the river flows
Over the hemp fields, and the soft green
Of the mulberry leaves cannot be seen
For large gray drops. All is still.
No one chops wood upon the hill,
Or by the well no one draws water.

Mulan! Take your last look as a daughter
Over your father's home. The pigs
And sheep stir in their pen, the legs
Of the sleeping hens hang from their perch.
All quiet, but now is your time to march,
Mulan! Her flowing silken dress
She hangs on the wall. Instead, a coarse
Thick yellow tunic, leggings bound
With leather, and over all, sweeping the ground,
Her heavy soldier's cloak. Now she
Is like a warrior as can be.
Her face, so marred with weeping, looks
Like a man's too. Down she unhooks
Bridle, saddle, cloth, and whip;
Then, while the house is still asleep,
Goes to the wood where secretly
The horse is tethered, sets him free,
Then mounts, and rides him away, away,
Before the red sun lights the day
And she is missed. . . .

Where has she gone?
The army travels all day, on,
On, on, to the north. By nightfall
She camps, already a soldier, her rightful
Place taken — in her father's name —
And no one knows. The campfire's flame
Flickers by a great river. It is
The Yellow River. The boundaries
Of China used to end here; now
Tomorrow they must cross and go
On, to the war . . .
The next day, on
And on. Before the misty sun
Has risen, they cross the river. Floods
Sweep men in hundreds away. She goads
Her gallant horse with spur and whip.
He swims and struggles safely up
The farther bank, with her still on
His back. Others are wet to the bone;
But she is warm and dry. She shares
Her rations with her horse, the ears
Of barley given to horses and men,
Mulan the soldier! . . .
Now, can you count ten?

The ballad maker slowly stretches forward his bony knuckles
from his wide blue sleeves. One by one, as if they were mario-
nettes worked by wires, his ten fingers spring stiffly upright, each
one to represent the passing of a year in the story:

Ten years! It seems a whole life long —
Ten years of war. Only the strong
Are left to fight, those who have trod
Thousands of miles without a road,
Over mountain, torrent, desert, in ice
Freezing like armor, under skies
Now hot like a bronze gong, now cold
As echoing iron, young men grown old,
Fighting and wandering, men — and one
Besides — Mulan! Yes, though the sun

Has scorched her, the rain has beaten, the wind
Hardened her skin. You hardly find
A trace of her girl's face. She is
The captain of mighty victories,
A hundred attacks and battles done,
The leader of brave men.

Without warning, the ballad maker spins on his heel, snapping
his fingers for joy:

It is won,
The war! The war is over! The foe
Is fled at last, and all may go
Free to their homes!

Then the ballad maker leans forward once more and puckers his old face into a living question mark:

> Will Mulan remain
> A soldier ever, a leader of men?
> The Emperor offers riches galore
> To Captain Mulan, his warrior —
> Lands, wealth, power. Still with gruff voice
> Captain Mulan proclaims his choice:
> Nor riches, lands, nor wealth, nor power,
> But leave to return to her maiden's bower!
> Return — and be a girl once more!
> A girl once more at her parents' door!

The children clap their hands for glee to hear this, but the ballad maker has not quite finished. He smiles and asks:

> What did her mother and father say
> When they heard Mulan was coming? They
> Said nothing for tears of joy; they went
> To the gate of their house, old and bent,
> But in their best silk clothes, with joy.
> And here is her baby brother, a boy
> Now, a big boy. What does he do?
> He takes his knife with a "Hilloo!
> Hilloo!" startling the silly hens;
> He makes a dive for the fattening pens
> Where the pigs and sheep are kept — a feast,
> A gorgeous feast, is the very least
> That a boy who is too excited to speak
> Should expect for his long-lost sister's sake!

The children laugh as the ballad maker becomes the boy waving his imaginary knife. Then, like a magician, he changes his whole face and body again, to become Mulan once more, Mulan standing in front of her mirror in her own room:

> But can she forget the years that have passed?
> A girl again, a girl at last?
> By the window she binds her cloudy hair;
> Before the mirror, her gold combs there,
> She puts on again her silken dress,
> And her girl's face, smiling back from the glass,

Tells her, "You are yourself again.
This is your reward — to be Mulan!"

With light, fluttering fingers, the old ballad maker seems to dress himself in the girl's silken garment. With a girl's step, he solemnly breaks into a little dance of joy. Then he seats himself once more and curves his fingers around the invisible shuttle, tossing it to and fro in the firelight:

Click, click, click-click-click,
Quick and slow, slow and quick,
Mulan sits at her parents' door,
Weaving her silk for evermore.

It is the end of the story. The children clap their hands till they are red and stinging. The master of the house gives the ballad maker a string of cash,[1] and the mistress, throwing another log into the crackling flames, invites him to share their bowl of bean soup before he makes his way across the snow to tell the story of Mulan to another winterbound household.

---

[1]Traditionally Chinese coins are punctured and strung together to make up different amounts of cash.

DISCUSSION

1. What were some of the special talents the old ballad maker possessed as a storyteller? Do you think those talents made his storytelling more effective? Why do you think that?

2. Why, in your opinion, was winter "the time for telling stories"? Where do you think fine storytellers would be most likely to find employment today?

3. Read the first two lines of the ballad again. How did they help listeners to experience the sounds that Mulan made while weaving? How did the ballad maker's actions help his audience to "see" Mulan weaving the silk?

4. Why was Mulan crying at the beginning of the story?
5. What did Mulan decide she must do to save her father from going to the war? Why, do you think, did the ballad maker almost whisper while telling that part of the story?
6. Why was the choice of the right horse so important to Mulan? How do you know that she made the right choice?
7. When the war was over, what rewards did the Emperor offer to Mulan for her heroic leadership? Why do you think Mulan felt that her true reward was to be Mulan, herself, again?
8. In your opinion, is the view of war presented in this story romantic or is it realistic? Give reasons for your answer.
9. Under what circumstances might someone have to live in disguise for a long period of time? How would you feel about having to live that way?

AUTHOR

Jo Manton, author of several distinguished books for both adults and young people, was born in Hertfordshire, England, and educated at Cambridge University. For a time she worked for the British Broadcasting Company writing and producing history broadcasts to schools. She and her husband, Robert Gittings, a well-known poet and biographer, live in Sussex, England, where they often collaborate on books.

The story you have just read was selected from Jo Manton's book *The Flying Horses: Tales from China.* She worked on the book in the United States, in the Asian section of the Suzallo Library at the University of Washington, Seattle, while her husband was a visiting professor of literature at the university. She says of the book, "These stories have been written for all who feel themselves drawn to distant times and places, yet hope to find when they arrive there not fantasy but a real world, with real men, women, and children."

Billy Beans Lived Here

by JEAN McCORD

For the rest of her life, Ellie knew that every single solitary time she ever saw a white pigeon, she would think of her brother! She would be forced to think of her brother, sometimes thinking of him dead, which he was; most times remembering him alive and happy and working hard, and free.

FREE! The one in the family who had risen above their way of life. The one who shucked off bitterness and anger and would not allow a shred of meanness near him.

He had freed himself and was teaching Ellie to be free, when . . . but here, if Ellie's thoughts came wandering near the accident, little things in her head started dancing around . . . the way gnats do . . . of a summer evening. They hurt the backs of her eyes and made her clench her fists until the fingernails bit. And unless she quickly rushed around, did something to divert it, a gob of bitterness, the very thing that Billy had abhorred, rose up and choked within her throat.

But Time was slowly probing long

fingers of forgetfulness into her brain. Now the summer was almost over.

The family had moved away from that place, that hopeless farm they had been living on. The things that had filled her life were gone. The things that Billy had been and done were no more. Even her memories of him, she realized, were growing blurred, melting, running away. She could scarcely . . . straining her mind to remember what he looked like, she couldn't. She was scared; desperately she dug like a hunted gopher into her belongings for a couple of tattered old pictures.

She blew the dust away and peered closely, and yes, he was in there! He had really lived and walked on the earth and been laughing and smiling. And yes, she remembered now how his thick and shaggy hair had looked like straw piled on his head. And though he was sixteen, four years older, there had been only an inch difference in their heights.

She remembered clearly now. . . . They had just moved out onto the old Oliver place when he came home one day, swinging into the yard with his usual jaunty, fast-moving walk and carrying a small cardboard box under one arm.

"Look here," he said proudly, coming into the kitchen and setting the box carefully on the table. "I helped old Mr. Woody clean out his pigeon loft. He gave me these."

Lifting a top flap, he reached into the box and gently withdrew a small white bird. All the little kids in the family crowded round, pushing and jostling, each putting out a finger to touch or stroke the soft white feathers.

"Well, just what you aim to do with 'em, Billy?" his mother asked from the sink where she stood cleaning and cutting up carrots for their soup pot.

The three little boys and Ellie swung their eyes from the bird up to Billy's mouth for the reply.

"Thought I'd raise 'em up," he said slowly. "There's money in pigeons. You know, squabs. Raise 'em for restaurants, things like that. These here are homers, though. Let 'em grow, train 'em right, and they always come straight back to their loft." He smiled down at the little boys. "Can't ever get lost. How'd you like to be like that?"

"Well," his mother said. "Well, Billy . . ." And she waved her knife through the air in a futile gesture. It was plain she didn't think much of the idea.

"You wait, Ma," he promised. "They won't be no trouble to no one, and I'll feed them myself."

He picked up the box.

"Come along, Towhead." Hooking an elbow round Ellie's neck, almost choking her, he dragged her outside, but she liked it. She hung on to his arm and made him swing her off the ground. He was awfully strong for his age, Ellie thought.

She liked this one brother of hers better than anybody else in the world. There were other brothers in the family. Besides the three little boys there were Flinty and Brady and Pete. But the older brothers were different; they paid her no attention. They did things alone, and if they had money of their own, they spent it any way it pleased them. They took silly, lipsticked girls to the movies.

When Billy made a dollar or two, he gave half to his mother. With the rest he'd get things that were desperately needed then, maybe a part for the ancient, dying car they had traveled in all over the country. If there was any money left, he sometimes grabbed Ellie and they took in a movie too. They liked the same things, westerns and western music. At least Billy liked them, and whatever he liked was good enough for Ellie.

Right now, if he wanted to raise birds, she'd stand behind him. She'd even help him, if he wanted her to.

"Figured I'd put 'em up in the old barn," Billy was saying as he released her.

"Here." He handed her the box to carry. She felt proud and big inside that he trusted her so much.

They pushed open the sagging, warped doors and went inside the dark and musty barn.

It was a huge building, at least fifty years old. Once it had been sturdy and well built, but the weight of time was crushing it. Strong winds had tested themselves against it, and the west wind had won, forcing it to lean in and away.

At one end was a loft, built of big timbers, a ladder leading to it. It was filled with dust-layered junk — boxes of outmoded clothing, bits of harness, pieces of broken tools, the thousand and one things that accumulate around a farm, too broken to use, too good to throw away.

Within a week the two of them had thrown down the junk, only keeping emptied crates to make nesting boxes with, for they had big plans of things to come.

"With these two, Sis, we have all we need for a start," Billy stated, strong authority in his voice. "We'll get four, five hatchings from them in a year, and soon the little ones will be nesting and give us more. Before you know it, we'll have the best-sized pigeon loft in the state."

"And you said I get to name these," she reminded. "If I help."

"Sure. What'll it be?"

"Thought I'd call one Christy and one John. Which is which?"

He laughed. "I don't know. Never thought to ask old man Woody how to tell the ladies from the gentlemen. But whoever lays the eggs is Christy. Okay?"

They swept the loft over and over, always able to raise a cloud of dust that choked them and made them sneeze.

Finally Billy went out somewhere and brought home a load of straw in the old car. They spread it deep on the floor and put layers in all the nesting boxes. By now they had thirty-seven boxes lined up, sitting open and empty, waiting for Christy and John to get busy.

Their father looked on the venture with a jaundiced eye. "Foolishness, Bill. Git all tied up with stuff like that, won't have time for reg'lar things."

"Like what, Pop?"

"Takin' a little job here, a little work there. Make some money, not spend it on pidjuns!"

"Yeah. I know what you mean, Pop."

It was a joke in the family, among them all, that the old man spent more effort digging up little jobs for his kids to do for pennies than he ever would working any deal for himself. As for himself, he didn't believe in full-time jobs.

"Ties a man down too much. Can't make a million thetaway" was his ever-ready comment.

The older boys, and lately even Billy and Ellie, referred to him among themselves as "the Millionaire."

Billy was in high school, taking all the courses he could, but he still kept going at numerous small jobs. Every weekend found him laboring at some cleanup job or grocery delivery or helping out at a trucking place or organizing the junk that the small fry in the family collected. To sell or make something out of, Billy said. He was making avid collectors of them all, right down to the baby of the family, four-year-old Jim Dandy. Nothing was too small to escape Jim Dandy's notice, though sometimes he mistakenly contributed things like shiny stones or broken beetles to the common stockpile.

Since the old Oliver place sat outside the line of city limits, no restrictions gave the Beans family any law trouble. The older boys hauled home wrecked metal junk heaps, one after another, victims of the savage accidents that occurred up and down the fast-paced highway. They meant to salvage the still-usable parts to sell, or use, in case they ever had a use for them, but somehow other matters claimed their attention, so the wrecks lay scattered around the yard in rotting, rusting piles. Still, they made wonderful things for the little kids to play in.

Just before the end of school, Billy had said, "I've got a run this weekend, Sis, a long haul. The dispatcher at the truck company is letting me take out a big job alone." He carefully closed the cage door.

"Can I come this time, Billy?" Ellie asked softly.

He thought for a long moment before he answered, "I think ya better not. It's a long, tough haul. Besides, ya got school, and I won't be in till late Monday morning. Got to miss some school myself."

"Well," she sighed resignedly. "Well, it's finals week anyway."

"There ya are. Ya know ya can't when ya got exams comin' up."

They worked together, cleaning cages. Ellie fixed two crates to carry birds in. This would be a good training flight for them, over four hundred miles, and the birds could always use the practice. If one of their birds came in with a good time, Billy and Ellie decided they might even risk the entry fee and enter it in one of the local races.

Then it was suppertime, and they left the barn loft. Billy carried the two light wicker crates, holding fifteen racing birds.

"Where're ya goin', Bill?" asked the Millionaire.

"Over the mountains. Be back on Monday."

"Git good pay for it, will you?"

"Good enough." Billy glanced at the old man. What fancy money-making scheme was he going to propose now?

But the old man said only, "Well, do be careful 'bout thet downgrade. Shift yer gears low before you come over the top. It drops down in a hurry."

"Sure. Thanks, Pop." He shoved back from the table. Reaching out, he tweaked Ellie's nose. "Good luck in yer exam Monday."

Something fearful twisted down through Ellie's stomach, starting at the tip of her nose.

"Billy!" she cried, running out the back door after him. "Please! Let me come with you!"

He stooped for the bird crates. "Now, Sis. Exams. Remember?"

"But I can make them up," she pleaded desperately.

He patted her arm. "Next week. Then you'll be through school. Free all summer." Seeing the unreconciled look in her eye, he said persuasively, "They're goin' to let me take a Salt Lake run soon. You can come on that, and I'll even let ya drive across the desert."

And with that promise, she let him go, holding her right arm high in silent farewell.

All that night Ellie tossed fitfully on her cot, the bottom half of which she shared with Jim Dandy. Several times the little boy in his sleep protested at her movements, which twisted the blankets off him. Each time, Ellie woke up and, reaching down, gently covered him again.

In the gray, cold light before dawn, she finally arose and, tucking the little boy up firmly, dressed and went to the kitchen. Searching in the breadbox, she saw a new loaf of bread and the heel of an old loaf that was dried hard.

"Good for the teeth," she told herself, and took the hard crust.

She stood in the middle of the room a moment, listening to the sounds of the sleepers in their beds. Around her in the kitchen was a breath-holding silence, only her heartbeat sounding in it, and the dim, shadowy forms of tables and chairs, cupboards and stove, waiting for the life of the day.

She stepped quietly outside, and there on the northeastern edge of the world was the tip of a cold and pale sun. The weeds left cool, wet streaks on her legs when she tramped through them going to the barn. She climbed to the loft.

The birds huddled in near darkness, but her coming awoke them, and they stretched their wings and called softly to one another. Dangling her legs over the edge of the floor, she nibbled her bread, noticing for the first time that stale bread tasted sweeter than new bread if you chewed it long enough.

Ellie was only halfway through the bread when the birds began to arrive. The first one that came in startled her. She watched open-mouthed as it broke through the hanging wire trap and went into its own box. Then, while she was still puzzling over it, the others began to come home. Finally they came in a rush, too fast to count accurately, but she knew at least twelve birds had come in. Billy had taken out fifteen; he had told her that he would release them from their baskets at six o'clock sharp. The earliest she had expected any one of

them back was noontime. Yet she knew it wasn't even six yet. It was closer to five. AND THE BIRDS WERE COMING IN!

The pit of her stomach was sick and burning, and something seemed to be squeezing her throat where she had swallowed the bread. In that single moment she knew for sure what had happened.

Rushing down the ladder, she burst into the house and into her parents' bedroom.

"Ma!" she screamed. "Ma! Wake up, Ma!"

Her mother lifted her head, her gray hair straggling down around her temples and her eyes not yet focused.

"Ma!" Ellie threw herself down on her knees beside her. "Ma! Something's happened to Billy. The birds are in! It's only five o'clock!"

Mrs. Beans dropped her head back heavily onto her hard mattress. Then she waved her hand limply to drive her daughter away. "Stop . . . foolishness, now, Ellie. Just stop. . . . Something . . ." Almost immediately she was deeply asleep again, her mouth halfway open and her cheeks caved in.

Ellie's father rose on one elbow, his fingers digging into his eyes.

"Ellie," he said plaintively, "ifen you can't sleep, the rest of us would like to."

She rose slowly to her feet, staring down at them and bursting into a sobbing scream.

She ran away from them all then, up into the hills behind the house because she could not bear to be there, to hear the words confirming what she knew was true. Somewhere on the highway a fatal thing had happened! Ellie fought to keep away the swarm of sights that jostled for attention in her brain. Billy, tired and weary even before he had left, had drowsed a moment at the wheel . . . or a car . . . some other truck . . . had smashed head-on . . . or a tire blew, at high speed . . .

She knuckled her eyes until big red shapes flared and replaced the image of the truck crashing, the crates bouncing, bursting, the birds swifting out, the birds speeding home.

Later in the day, when the hills were hot and dry and a shimmering heat haze bent the house and the old outbuildings into crazy shapes, she slowly picked her way through the tall dead grasses. When Ellie reached their dusty yard, she could hear her mother's sobbing, muffled because her apron was thrown over her head. Ellie dragged her feet, trying to hold them back, but they took her through the door and into the kitchen.

Her father stood there, with both hands shoved in his pockets and his head hunched low. Jim Dandy was clutching his mother's skirts, howling lustily in fright.

Automatically Ellie bent down and picked him up, carrying him upstairs to the bedroom. When she had soothed him into sleep, she returned to the kitchen.

"He is dead, isn't he?" she demanded fiercely.

Her mother's louder outburst of sobbing and her father's shifting his weight from foot to foot answered her.

"The downgrade," her father said, his jaw working. "I warned the boy. I said, 'Go easy.' The Highway Patrol claims his brakes burned out." He hunched his shoulders. "Shouldn't ha' been usin' brakes nohow!"

"You shut up!" Ellie's mother screamed. "My good boy is gone! Don't you blame him now!"

By squeezing something in her head, Ellie closed her ears. She moved around the kitchen, fixing a bite to eat for them. And by another effort of will, she managed not to think about it. By dropping down the secret partition, the wall in her brain that separated the outside life from the things inside her head, she had just enough sense left to move herself around from one chore to another like a mechanical doll.

The birds came home, but Billy never did. The company he worked for gave him a funeral. Not a big funeral nor a grand one but satisfactory. And his fellow workers sent a big wreath of pretty pink roses in a horseshoe shape.

Ellie went with her folks and sat down in back.

"He's up there," she told herself, "in that gray box." But some great doubt, nesting inside her chest, refused to believe it. She knew she was expected to cry, as her folks were doing. Even big old lazy Brady was snuffling in a kerchief. But though she tried hard, squeezing her eyes painfully tight, no tears came. She tried pinching her leg, and it hurt bad. But no tears. And she couldn't even think of Billy. Instead, she kept seeing the birds coming in, wheeling gracefully round in big wagon-wheel circles.

The minister was talking, out where they went with Billy's gray box. She could see his mouth working, but all she heard in her ears was a soft, gentle cooing. And her eyes saw the place around her, a flat, treeless, barren section of graveyard, newly opened. Her mind saw nothing; at least not then. Later on, it grew and swelled to a rubbery, undulating picture in her brain.

When they went home, she climbed up to the loft, and the pigeons' cooing was soft and real in her ears. Somewhere, quite near, Billy slouched back on an upended crate, and he was very real and accepting and certainly not dead.

She found herself spending most of her time up there, doing nothing. Sitting on a sagging crate, listening to the birds cooing. She still took care of the birds daily; watering, feeding. There was a hundred-pound sack of mixed grains in one corner. She wondered vaguely what she would feed them when that ran out, but she didn't really give any worry-thought to it. Somehow it seemed too vague a trouble and too far away.

At dusk her mother called, piercing the silent gloom of evening.

"Ellie! You, Ellie!"

Her mother never spoke a thing in a normal voice. Every word she uttered came out a whining complaint, even if it was only a statement on the weather. And truly she had much to complain about. There had never been enough food to make the rounds of every plate. It was difficult to scrape things together. Every meal was a separate ordeal.

How many trips had Ellie made, trudging to the store, for a single loaf of bread or a few cents' worth of potatoes? She would never be able to count them! Yet, somehow, if their mother had been more cheerful, Ellie thought dully, the thing that had them in its tightening grip might have been forced to hold off just a little. There was still hope, perhaps seeded in the little boys. . . .

But their mother would not hope! Ellie thought about her older brothers. Brady, who tried working a few times, got into trouble, and quit for good. Now his time was spent hanging around the pool halls in town or slouching outside on the sidewalk.

Flinty and Pete both grew crankier every day. They snarled at the whole family; mostly they snarled at each other. And sometimes there were fierce flare-ups out behind the house when in seconds they would be at each other's throats; then gouging, kicking, kneeing fights down in the dust of the yard, till they both lay racked by exhaustion.

But Billy had been different. Billy had made her a promise. "Look, kid," he'd tried to tell her up in the barn, the soft pigeon sounds punctuating each of his words. "All life isn't like ours. What I mean is, well, we're poor and all that, but there are other things. I know there are, and I'm findin' out about 'em all the time. Life isn't all money, like the old Millionaire thinks it is, and it isn't just raisin' kids, tryin' to feed 'em more all the time, like Ma thinks it is. I can't tell ya what life really is, for you and me, 'cause I don't know yet. I can only tell ya what it ain't. It ain't what Brady and Flint and Pete think, chasin' girls all the time. And it ain't being unhappy all the time like Ma is, or walkin' around in a dream all the time like Pa.

"For you and me, anyway, it's somethin' all different, Ellie, maybe like books and pictures and music and a little more money, all rolled together. I kinda think it's goin' to be somethin' we can do and be proud in and that means somethin'. Anyway, when I find out more about it, I'll tell ya right away."

She had been squatting on her heels, the edge of her cotton dress dragging in the straw. She looked around at their tiers of boxes, filling up now with the new birds, and the old hens, sitting on more nests, hatching out more and more pigeons for them.

"Ain't our birds goin' to make us rich, Bill?" she had asked timidly. "I thought when we got to selling them, they'd bring in plenty."

"No!" He'd made a quick rasping sound that didn't quite sound like a laugh. "We ain't goin' to make no money off 'em. They eat up more than they can ever bring in."

"But you said, last summer . . ."

"I know! I know! But now we own ninety-two birds. And how many have we sold in a year? Just six!" Then he said softly, "And two of those I traded for corn."

"Well, why are we . . ." Her voice had trailed off in a plaintive sound.

"Why are we keepin' them?" He sighed. "Spendin' money on their feed and time on their care? I ain't sure, but I think it's 'cause they're Beauty. Can't you feel it, Sis, inside you, when we open the cote and let them all out? They swirl up in the sky like a . . . a scarf, a white scarf, or maybe a white flag; and then they sweep back and forth, wavin' through the air till we call them in."

Sometime near the end of August the whole Beans family moved away, off the decaying farm and clear across to the other side of town.

"Be better for us all," the old Mil-lionaire said. "We ain't gittin' ahead in the world, way we should." His wild dreams were growing, feeding on the fruit of their adversity, it seemed. His swollen schemes of millions, millions, leaped and twisted from the endless stream of his mouth.

"Makes no nevermind to me," Ellie muttered when her mother told her.

She had spent the whole summer huddled up in the loft, missing more than half her meals. Consequently, she was skinnier than the old blue scarecrow that flapped out in a barren field, guarding nothing.

Time didn't flow past and around her anymore. It stood suffocatingly still, wrapping her in a cloak of sodden grayness in which nothing happened, because anything that could happen, of importance, already had. The only thing she'd noticed in the last two months that puzzled her, and of course there was no one around to explain the Why of it, was that a certain stick of sunlight falling through a knothole in the barn had changed its angle.

They moved away then, no one caring much whether they did or not. They had to leave all the birds behind because, of course, there was no place to keep them in a house in town.

"There's no more feed anyway," Ellie said.

"Well, now," her father said, "those-there birds had it good long enough. They kin jus get out and rustle for themselfs."

"Sure," Ellie said, and firmly refused to think of cats and rats.

It didn't happen till after they had left the farm, abandoning the white birds and the sagging heaps of dead cars and the remaining small pile of salvage that Billy had not had time to turn in.

Then a new worry got inside of Ellie's head. It bored up from her mouth, tasting like that red ant she had once accidentally eaten, and though she swallowed and swallowed, she couldn't get rid of the fiery feeling. She walked long miles every day, turning her eyes this way and that on the new part of town. It walked right along, beside her, outside her, inside her. And the worry grew. It outwalked her, swelling, expanding, like the windy old Millionaire's dream of countless piles of money. Then the thought became a gray thing that, if she allowed it to, could double her over and twist her insides in cramps. There were tears, too, that had never been shed, and these would come surging into her head, making her whole face swell; but they would not come out, and she felt like a balloon, blown full up, ready to explode.

And the worst thought, the one that hurt as if a devil had thrust a hot fork into her heart and twisted it, was the absolute certain knowledge that if she had been along that night, just sitting there beside him in the truck, surely the accident would never have happened. Yes, surely this one thing was the worst. If only she'd been along . . . this thought said itself over and over in her head ten thousand times, till now it had grown into a sore spot like a canker, raw and painful, never getting any better. It wasn't exactly that she blamed herself for the accident — she was twelve years old and knew the difference between what one did and what one thought one did — but only that if she had really insisted that night, had maybe stowed away or something, her being there . . . her presence . . . might have *prevented* it!

Finally the day came when she absolutely knew she had to do something. She somehow had to change one fact. THERE WAS NO MEMORIAL! There was nothing around even to show he'd once been part of their family. No one mentioned his name anymore. The little boys had quit asking for him. Jim Dandy had put a puzzled frown on his pale face when she'd whispered in his ear, "Billy! Billy!" She shook him till he cried.

She formed her resolution lying stretched out flat in bed one night, staring at a jagged crack cavorting on the ceiling. Suddenly the whole thing came alive and leaped right out at her. She wondered in excitement why she hadn't thought of it before. It was the perfect, simple answer. It only needed a little money. "Two dollars would do it," she thought to herself.

At dawn, in the quiet strangeness of this new house, she rose and dressed carefully. She tiptoed into Pete and Brady's room and picked up the first pair of pants heaped on the floor. The pockets clinked softly, satisfactorily.

Very slowly, she walked downtown, touching each tree on the street as she passed. The morning breeze blew against her hot forehead and into her open mouth. She felt a little singing noise inside her head, and it was a good feeling. She waited outside the hardware store till it opened, patiently leaning against the wall, sliding one foot up and down on it.

Then, with her heavy burden and a coiled rope that she slung over one bony shoulder, she started walking out to the old farm. Most of the morning was gone when she got there. The sun was yellow-bright and hot overhead. But she had more time than she needed.

She didn't go near the empty house where both the front and back doors swung creakingly on broken hinges. Someone, boys most likely, had stoned out all the windows. Instead, she walked around it, keeping her eyes riveted on the side of the barn, the big, wind-tilted barn with boards that were plenty good yet.

Climbing once more up into the loft — and then never again, she knew — she pulled up her rope, which she had tied to a five-gallon bucket below. Her eyes looked quickly around the loft, though she didn't want them to and tried to prevent it. There were no birds.

She climbed out the small window of the pigeon trap and eased her way onto the roof, the rope tied to her wrist so it wouldn't drop.

Then, with a fierceness and determination born of a grinding desperation, she began her memorial. In big, black, dripping letters, six feet tall, she painted out his name. "BILLY BEANS," it said, bigger than life, clear across the shingled roof of the barn. She slid and jumped to the ground, half of her five gallons of black paint still left. Standing on an old pigeon crate, she wrote on the side of the barn fifty feet long, "LIVED HERE."

She threw her sticky paintbrush aside and jumped back to view her work. Too close. Running now, panting, fearful, as if she were leaving something horrible behind like a monster in a nightmare, her weak and rubbery legs bore her to a ditch beside the highway. At a safe distance she tumbled down into the weeds and lay there sobbing, dryly at first; and then like a spring that is released from pressure, the tears sprang up. They washed down her face, cleansing, purging, and they had been the sickness inside all the time.

Through the film over her eyes, two small watery windows, she saw her work standing out boldly, as it would

even from a distance. And everyone, no matter who, passing by, would see and wonder and remember! The stark black words would paint themselves upon each traveler's brain.

The wind might blow, and the barn might lean and someday fall, but as long as these marked and branded people lived, those four black words would live . . . within their brains.

DISCUSSION

1. Ellie thought of Billy as "free," and from him she was learning to be free. What did the word *free* mean to Ellie?
2. Of her four older brothers, why did Ellie like Billy best? What project did Billy and Ellie undertake together?
3. Why was life so difficult for Ellie's family? Why was her mother always complaining?
4. Long before the Highway Patrol notified her parents, how did Ellie know what had happened to Billy? After trying unsuccessfully to rouse her mother and father, why did she run off into the hills?
5. Why, do you think, did Ellie not cry at Billy's funeral? After the funeral, why, do you think, did Ellie spend most of the summer up in the barn loft?
6. What had Billy expected his future and Ellie's to be like? Do you think his dreams were in vain? Why do you think that?
7. Why did Billy keep the pigeons even after he found he was not going to make any money from them? How do you think Ellie felt about having to leave the pigeons behind when her family moved?
8. The thought that hurt Ellie most was that if she had gone on the trip with Billy, the accident would not have happened. Do you think that she could have prevented the accident if she had been with him? Why do you think that?

9. What kind of boy was Billy? In what ways was he quite different from his parents?

10. Why did it become so important to Ellie that there be a memorial to Billy? When she had written the memorial on the barn, why, do you think, was she finally able to cry?

11. If Ellie could have afforded a stone monument for Billy, would it have satisfied her more than the one she made? Why do you think as you do?

AUTHOR

Jean McCord's life has been one of changing scenes and varied occupations. She was born in Hayward, Wisconsin, but her family moved so frequently that she had attended sixteen different schools before completing high school at the age of fifteen. That she was successful in gaining an education in the face of great odds she credits to her love of books and her desire for knowledge. In 1946 Miss McCord graduated from the University of California, where she majored in biology. Her scientific training equipped her for positions she has held in hospital and research laboratories, but she estimates that over the years she has worked at more than forty other occupations.

Jean McCord's stories are based on incidents in her own adolescence or on experiences of young people she has known. She has been a contributor to magazines, textbooks, and anthologies, and she has had two collections of her short stories published.

Changing Times

Language, as you know, is alive. It grows, travels, adapts to new situations, discards what it no longer needs, and revitalizes old words by giving them new definitions. Many words in use today once had different and sometimes surprising meanings long ago. The word *explode* is one example. When you read in "The Boy Who Predicted Earthquakes" that the sun was going to explode, you knew it meant that the sun would burst apart in a sudden violent motion. It surely never occurred to you that *explode* meant what it did a few hundred years ago, "to drive an actor off the stage by clapping the hands."

When you think of the thunderous sound an audience produces by clapping, you can imagine how the new definition of *explode* developed from the old. In looking at other words whose definitions have altered, certain patterns of change appear.

Some words that once described a general class of things have narrowed their scope to specific items, sometimes within the same general class. For example, *cattle* once referred to any four-legged domestic animal, as *deer* did to any four-legged wild animal. *College* meant "a group of people" or "a crowd." *Corn* originally meant any kind of edible grain.

Other words traveled in the opposite direction, expanding their definitions from the specific to the general. *Lady* once meant "the wife of a lord"; it later referred to a woman who conducted herself like the wife of a lord, and it now includes all women under its definition. *Manuscript* has expanded its meaning to cover typed as well as hand-written material. You can probably also think of some brand names that have come into common use to describe particular types of products.

Some words have been promoted by a change in definition to a grander position in our language. *Queen* originally meant "woman"; *mansion* referred to any dwelling or abode; a *lord* was the head of a household; and *chiffon,* now the name for an elegant, silky fabric, once referred to an old rag.

As you might guess, while some words have been raised to loftier positions, others have been lowered in stature. *Silly* once meant "blessed"; a *villain* was once a farm laborer; to *persecute* meant "to follow something or someone to the end," but no evil purpose was implied; a *knave* was a male servant; and a *comedy* originally meant "a singer in the revels," and it later meant any play with a happy ending, even if it wasn't humorous.

Try to match the following words with their out-of-use definitions. Check your answers in a dictionary or with your teacher. Notice that dictionaries usually identify these out-of-use definitions as obsolete (*obs.*) or archaic (*arch.*).

1. That <u>brave</u> threatens the younger boys daily.
2. The <u>fond</u> youths believed the ridiculous rumor.
3. The village <u>snob</u> made boots for everyone in the area.
4. A <u>bachelor</u> on horseback emerged from the wood.
5. Feeling <u>clumsy</u>, he trudged on through the driving snow.

a shoemaker	numb from the cold	foolish
a young knight	a bully	

TOMB OF THE BOY-KING

by MILDRED MASTIN PACE

For years an English archeologist named Howard Carter had been excavating in a bleak and barren area of Egypt known as the Valley of the Kings. Sun-scorched by the unbearable heat in summer, hot and arid the year through, the valley is a desolate place of rocks and cliffs and mounds of sand. Cut into the faces of the rocks and cliffs are many openings. These are entrances leading to subterranean tombs built in the days of the ancient pharaohs (fay'rohs). The valley got its name from the fact that so many kings and their nobles were buried there.

Naturally the valley, honeycombed with royal tombs, attracted archeologists. But long before the archeologists, it had attracted tomb robbers. All the tombs had been plundered. Every mummy had been damaged.

Yet Carter believed that one small, unimportant king named Tutankhamen[1] had been buried somewhere in the valley and that his tomb had not been found. Other archeologists disagreed with Carter; they argued that the tomb and all its contents must have been plundered and destroyed long ago. Every inch of the valley had been dug out, they said. There was nothing more to find.

For five years Carter doggedly excavated, searching for the

---

[1] **Tutankhamen** (too'tahng-kah'muhn) was the pharaoh of Egypt during the late 14th century B.C.

tomb. He had no money of his own, but he had a wealthy English benefactor, Lord Carnarvon (kahr-nahr'vuhn), who was interested in Egyptian archeological finds. At long last Lord Carnarvon, too, decided there was nothing more to find in the valley. He asked Carter to visit him at his home in England, Highclere Castle, and there he reluctantly told Carter he was withdrawing his support.

One night, while still in England, Carter was poring over maps of the valley and pinpointed a small triangular space they had not explored. It was a barren area covered with loose rocks, sand, and rubble. Small, unpromising, and situated at the base of the great tomb of Rameses VI,[2] it was an unlikely spot for another pharaoh's tomb. Diggers, quite reasonably, had passed it by, but Carter pointed it out to Carnarvon and begged him to finance just one more season of digging. Carnarvon agreed.

Carter returned to Egypt, and on November 1, 1922, he and his crew began clearing the wedge of land. Three days later they discovered a step cut in the rock beneath an ancient hut they had uncovered. A little more clearing revealed this to be the first of sixteen steps leading down into more rock. At the foot of the

---

[2]**Rameses** (ram'uh-seez') **VI** was an Egyptian pharaoh who lived about two hundred years after Tutankhamen.

stairs there was a door, blocked with piles of stone. After workers removed the stones, Carter was excited to see impressions of seals pressed into the door, indicating a royal burial. He now knew, at long last, that he had found a royal tomb.

Carter later said, "I needed all my self-control to keep from breaking down the doorway . . . then and there." To open it at once, he felt, would not be fair to Lord Carnarvon, who was still in England. He went to the nearby city of Luxor (luhk'suhr) and cabled Carnarvon:

. . . MADE WONDERFUL DISCOVERY IN VALLEY.
A MAGNIFICENT TOMB WITH SEALS INTACT.
RE-COVERED SAME FOR YOUR ARRIVAL.
CONGRATULATIONS.

So the workers blocked the door once more and filled in the stairway with rubble. Carter placed guards on watch and, half mad with impatience, awaited Carnarvon's arrival.

Lord Carnarvon reached Luxor on November 23. By the following day the rubble and stones were again cleared, and the two men, accompanied by a few aides, went down to examine the door. To their bitter disappointment they saw now that Carter was mistaken. The seals had been broken and resealed. They removed the door and entered a narrow, empty corridor. At the end of the corridor was another door, the door to the tomb itself. To the men's despair, they saw that this door, too, had been forced open and resealed.

Grave robbers had been there before them! Would they find just another empty tomb?

With trembling hands, Carter made a small opening in the upper left-hand corner of the door. He held a lighted candle to the opening and peered in.

The candle sputtered. For a moment he saw nothing. Then, in Carter's own words:

As my eyes grew accustomed to the light, details of the room within emerged slowly from the mist, strange animals, statues, and gold — everywhere the glint of gold. For the moment — an eternity it must have seemed to the others standing by — I was struck dumb with amazement. And when Lord Carnarvon, unable to stand the suspense any longer, inquired anxiously, "Can you see anything?" it was all I could do to get out the words, "Yes. Wonderful things."

Carter handed Lord Carnarvon the candle.

When the door was removed, the men saw that all was in disorder. Thieves had been there — probably shortly after the young king's burial. Apparently they had been surprised and scared off by guards or priests before they did much harm. But they had left their greasy fingerprints where they had emptied valuable oils from alabaster vases. There was a footprint on the floor. In their haste to flee when discovered, they had left behind waterskins partly filled with oil. One thief had dropped a number of gold rings wrapped in a linen cloth. Two gold struts were broken from a golden chair. A small statue, probably of gold, was missing, ripped from its base.

But very little had been taken, very little damage done. Carter, Carnarvon, and their aides had entered a virtually intact tomb of a pharaoh — the only one that had ever been found.

This room, called the antechamber, and two smaller rooms they entered later were crammed with treasures. The wealth that had been buried with this boy-king for more than three thousand years dazzled the eyes and boggled the mind.

There was the young pharaoh's gold and silver throne, set with semiprecious stones. A whole fleet of model boats was ready to fill the pharaoh's every sailing wish. The ceremonial chariots the king had used on earth were there, dismantled because they were too large to be drawn through the narrow corridor into the small room. To serve him in his second life, there were more than a hundred statuettes of men and women servants. With them were almost two thousand tools and implements they would use in their king's service. In magnificently decorated chests were his royal robes, covered with gold sequins or decorated with gold rosettes, and his sandals worked with gold. Hundreds of other things were in the tomb, ready for his use in the next world.

Among the many objects of beauty, a few cast light on the shadowy figure of the young king, Tutankhamen. His marriage to a girl-queen is pictured as a happy one in many colorful scenes

from their daily life. The tomb tells us that the young king was a great hunter, he had a pet lion, he played a popular chesslike game, and he played the trumpet.

When Carter first entered the antechamber, his eyes were caught by two life-size statues of the king. Handsome in black and gold, holding scepters of gold, they stood at each side of a sealed door. Carter guessed at once that they guarded the royal sarcophagus. Behind that door he should find the mummy of the Pharaoh Tutankhamen.

If the sarcophagus had not been broken into, if the mummy remained intact, this would be the most important archeological find in all Egypt and one of the most important in all the world. This would be the first royal mummy ever found in its original coffins, its wrappings undisturbed.

As anxious as Carter and Lord Carnarvon were to see the sarcophagus, almost three months passed between the discovery of the tomb and the opening of the door to the burial chamber.

First they had to empty the antechamber. Every object in it was to be examined, cataloged, and photographed before it could be moved. Steps had to be taken, too, to preserve objects that might be harmed when exposed to outside air. For example, there were fragile objects that might disintegrate. Experts working with Carter hastened to preserve these in wax: the ostrich feathers of the king's fan, the wreaths of flowers standing against the walls.

Finally, only the two black and gold statues of the king were left in place, guarding the door.

By now the discovery of the tomb had attracted worldwide attention. When he was finally ready to open the burial chamber, Carter had an invited audience seated on folding chairs in the emptied whitewashed room. The antechamber was charged with excitement.

Carter made a small opening in the top of the sealed door. Using a flashlight, he peered in. There, within a yard of the doorway, he was astonished to see a solid wall of gold. It stretched as far as he could see and seemed to block the entrance to the chamber.

When the door was removed, Carter and Lord Carnarvon squeezed into the narrow passage between the "wall" of gold and the walls of the burial chamber. They found it was not a wall of gold. It was a large gilt shrine, apparently built around the sarcophagus for protection. It practically filled the burial chamber. Almost eleven feet wide, more than sixteen feet long, and nine feet high, it nearly touched the ceiling. The space between it and the four walls of the room was a little more than two feet. That left a very narrow space for the men to move around in.

There were two wide doors to the shrine, which Carter removed. Inside was another gold shrine. Now Carter's excitement was intense! The seals on the doors had never been tampered with. For the first time since the days of ancient Egypt, people would see the intact sepulcher of an Egyptian king, his mummy in its coffins just as it was on the day of his burial.

Removing the doors of the second shrine, Carter found a third one. And nested inside that, a fourth.

As the men carefully removed each shrine, they found rich and beautiful objects: elaborate lamps of milky alabaster, staffs of gold and silver, painted alabaster jars with lids of carved figures, small chests inlaid with gold. Over one shrine hung a sheer cloth canopy sprinkled with bright gilded daisies.

The fourth, and last, golden shrine contained the magnificent red quartzite sarcophagus. At each corner, in high relief, was the figure of a goddess, her winged arms spread out protectingly.

When the sarcophagus was opened, Carter found three coffins, each shaped like a mummy. They nestled tightly, one within another, so tightly that Carter could scarcely wedge his little finger between them. He and all who watched were astonished by the beauty of the coffins. Each was a figure of the young king wearing the false beard and headdress of the pharaohs. His hands, folded across his breast, held the crook and flail, symbols of Egyptian royalty.

The first and second coffins were of gilded wood, inlaid with gold and brilliant red and blue stones: carnelian and lapis lazuli.

The third coffin was of solid gold. Carter and those with him gazed in awe. The rich beauty of the golden figure of the young pharaoh was overwhelming. The coffin was massive. More than six feet long, it contained nearly twenty-five hundred pounds of twenty-two-carat gold. But there was a delicacy in its elegance, the flowing lines of the goddesses etched in gold, and the soft glow of stones set in graceful designs. Inside this coffin of gold was the mummy of the king.

Within the wrappings that enfolded him was found a whole treasury of ornaments: on his head the royal diadem of gold set with carnelian, lapis lazuli, and turquoise; collars and necklaces; golden girdles; amulets and pendants; pectorals — intricately wrought treasures of great beauty and exquisite detail. His slender hands were heavy with jewel-studded gold rings. Gold nail stalls were fitted on his fingers and toes.

Most wondrous of all was the portraitlike mask that had been placed on the bandaged face. Wrought of gold inlaid with gems, it covered the king's head and shoulders and extended down to the middle of his body. It was almost an exact likeness of the young king: the eyes wide open and luminous, the shining golden face noble and serene.

Tragically, Lord Carnarvon did not live to see the coffins opened and the young king's mummy revealed. Less than five months after the tomb was discovered, he was bitten by an insect in the Valley of the Kings. Blood poisoning set in, and he died in a hospital in Cairo (kie'roh).

Almost six years elapsed from the day the tomb was discovered by Carter until it was emptied and its treasures were moved to the museum in Cairo.

No, not emptied, for the mummy of the young king was left in its simple whitewashed tomb, lying in the second coffin, resting in the handsome quartzite sarcophagus where it had been placed more than three thousand years before.

DISCUSSION

1. Why, do you suppose, were treasures buried with the pharaohs? Judging by the objects found in the boy-king's tomb, what do you think the pharaohs expected life after death to be like?
2. What was Howard Carter's purpose for excavating in the area of Egypt known as the Valley of the Kings? Who provided the financial support for Carter's excavations?
3. In what year did Carter find a royal tomb? About how long had it taken him to discover it?
4. Why didn't Carter have the door to the tomb opened at once when he found it? What do you think was his reason for having the door of the tomb blocked again and its stairway filled in with rubble?
5. What details in the selection indicate that Howard Carter was a person of extraordinary determination and conviction?
6. How did Carter react when he looked into the small opening in the door to the tomb?
7. What evidence did Carter and Lord Carnarvon find indicating that thieves had been in the tomb? Why had the thieves done so little damage?

8. Judging from the objects buried with the boy-king, in what branches of knowledge do you think the ancient Egyptians were far advanced?
9. What did the discoveries in the tomb reveal about the personal life of young King Tutankhamen?
10. How old was the mummy of Tutankhamen? Why was its discovery one of the most important archeological finds ever to be made?
11. Do you think you would have enjoyed being one of the workers on Howard Carter's search for the tomb? Why or why not?
12. Which of the many interesting objects found in the boy-king's tomb would you most like to see? Why?

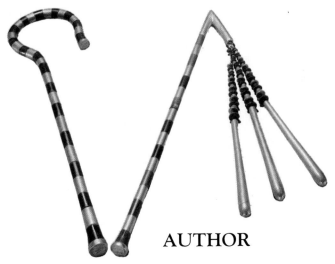

AUTHOR

Mildred Mastin Pace, a Cornell College graduate, has been a magazine writer in New York, a free-lance radio writer for the National Broadcasting Company, and a writer in the publicity department of a New York advertising agency. Since 1940 she has been writing books for young people. Her first, a biography of Clara Barton, won a prize in the *New York Herald Tribune* Spring Book Festival. A later book for young children was given the Dorothy Canfield Fisher Award. While researching material for radio shows between 1936 and 1940, Mrs. Pace developed skills that made possible her definitive book on the Egyptian mummy, *Wrapped for Eternity,* from which the excerpt you have just read was taken.

CRICKETS AND FROGS
GRILLOS Y RANAS

A Fable by GABRIELA MISTRAL

Translated and Adapted by DORIS DANA

In the beginning there was only one Old Cricket in the gully. He chirped.

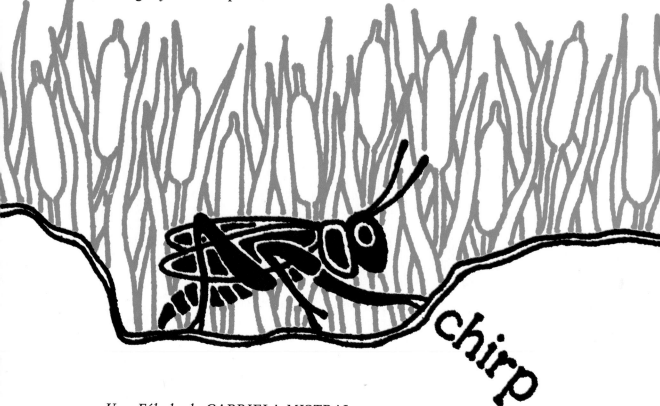

Una Fábula de GABRIELA MISTRAL

Traducción y Adaptación de DORIS DANA

En el principio había un solo Grillo Viejo en la quebrada. Cantó.

Suddenly from a little patch of grass nearby came another chirp. Then another one, and again another. Soon the whole gully was chirping and singing. The song spilled out over the entire field and spread over the land with a great sweetness.

De pronto, de una hierba punzada por sus notas, fueron saliendo otros y otros. Unas noches después, cantaba la quebrada entera; más tarde llegaron al llano donde el canto extendido fue cobrando una gran suavidad.

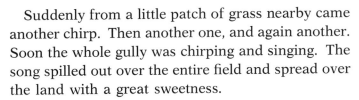

The Old Cricket became very worried. "Where am *I*?" he cried. "This cricket song is everywhere. Which song is *my* song? Which cricket am *I*?"

La desesperación del Grillo Viejo era ésta: ¿Dónde se encontraba él ahora, si cantaba en todas partes?

365

For a time everything grew very still and quiet in the Old Cricket's kingdom. There was a long silence that lasted many weeks.

Por un tiempo todo fue silencio y quietud en el dominio del Grillo Viejo. La calma duró varias semanas.

Then all at once a great croaking chorus of frogs shattered the stillness of night.

Pero de pronto un inmenso coro de ranas rompió la quietud de la noche.

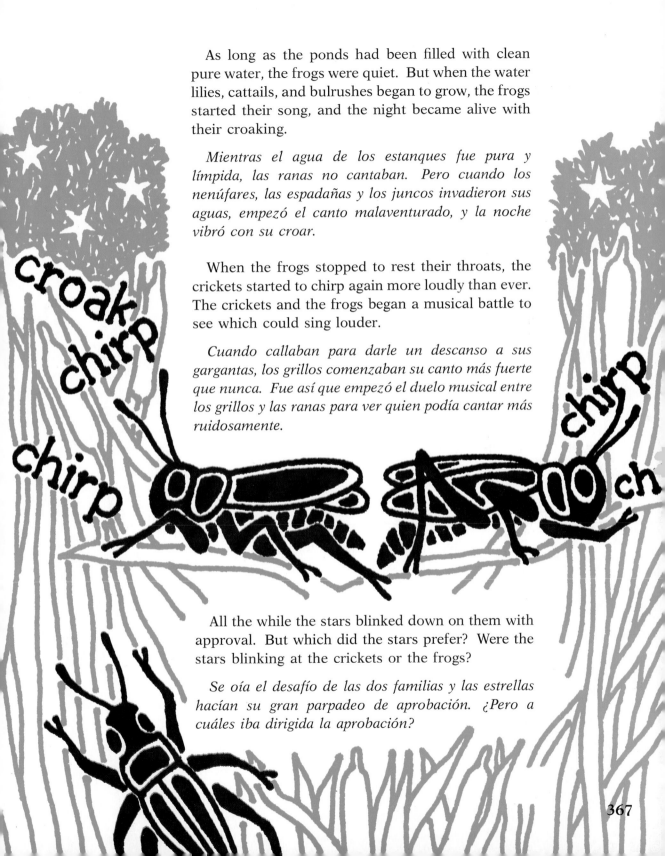

As long as the ponds had been filled with clean pure water, the frogs were quiet. But when the water lilies, cattails, and bulrushes began to grow, the frogs started their song, and the night became alive with their croaking.

Mientras el agua de los estanques fue pura y límpida, las ranas no cantaban. Pero cuando los nenúfares, las espadañas y los juncos invadieron sus aguas, empezó el canto malaventurado, y la noche vibró con su croar.

When the frogs stopped to rest their throats, the crickets started to chirp again more loudly than ever. The crickets and the frogs began a musical battle to see which could sing louder.

Cuando callaban para darle un descanso a sus gargantas, los grillos comenzaban su canto más fuerte que nunca. Fue así que empezó el duelo musical entre los grillos y las ranas para ver quien podía cantar más ruidosamente.

All the while the stars blinked down on them with approval. But which did the stars prefer? Were the stars blinking at the crickets or the frogs?

Se oía el desafío de las dos familias y las estrellas hacían su gran parpadeo de aprobación. ¿Pero a cuáles iba dirigida la aprobación?

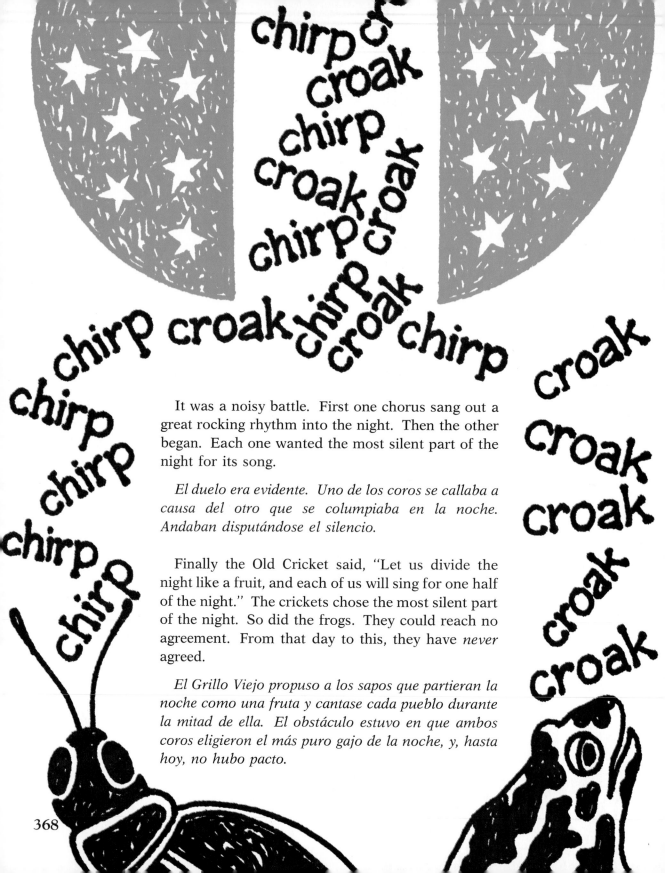

It was a noisy battle. First one chorus sang out a great rocking rhythm into the night. Then the other began. Each one wanted the most silent part of the night for its song.

El duelo era evidente. Uno de los coros se callaba a causa del otro que se columpiaba en la noche. Andaban disputándose el silencio.

Finally the Old Cricket said, "Let us divide the night like a fruit, and each of us will sing for one half of the night." The crickets chose the most silent part of the night. So did the frogs. They could reach no agreement. From that day to this, they have *never* agreed.

El Grillo Viejo propuso a los sapos que partieran la noche como una fruta y cantase cada pueblo durante la mitad de ella. El obstáculo estuvo en que ambos coros eligieron el más puro gajo de la noche, y, hasta hoy, no hubo pacto.

368

Which cricket am I?
Where am I?

And ever since, the Old Cricket keeps chirping, "Where am *I*? Which cricket am *I*?" And all the other crickets sing the same song: "Where am *I*? Which cricket am *I*?"

Desde entonces el Grillo Viejo sigue cantando: "¿Dónde estoy? ¿Cuál soy yo?" Y todos los grillos cantan el mismo canto: "¿Dónde estoy? ¿Cuál soy yo?"

From here to the starry sky you can hear the Old Cricket chirping everywhere. He will never again be *one* cricket — never again.

Y desde aquí hasta el cielo estrellado, se lo escucha por todas partes. No será uno nunca más, nunca más.

AUTHORS

Gabriela Mistral was a well-known poet and educator born in 1899 in a small town in the mountains of northern Chile. At fifteen she began her long teaching career in the rural schools of Chile. For a time, she was an advisor to the Mexican Ministry of Education and helped with the reorganization of rural schools in Mexico. In 1925 she was awarded the Chilean title "Teacher of the Nation." As a young teacher, she began to write poetry and gained recognition as a sensitive poet. In 1945 she became the first Latin American to receive the Nobel Prize for literature. She was a representative to the League of Nations and the United Nations before her death in 1957.

Doris Dana, the translator and adapter of "Crickets and Frogs," was a friend of Gabriela Mistral's and has translated many of her poems. A poet herself and a short-story writer, she has received Chile's Order of Merit for promoting cultural understanding between the Americas.

Kansas Boy

by RUTH LECHLITNER

This Kansas boy who never saw the sea
Walks through the young corn rippling at his knee
As sailors walk; and when the grain grows higher
Watches the dark waves leap with greener fire
Than ever oceans hold. He follows ships,
Tasting the bitter spray upon his lips,
For in his blood up-stirs the salty ghost
Of one who sailed a stormbound British coast.
Across wide fields he hears the sea winds crying,
Shouts at the crows — and dreams of white
   gulls flying.

The Trophy

by MARY ALEXANDER WALKER

Azure, a senior in high school, had been uprooted from her hometown in Breaux Bridge, Louisiana. At first Azure was sure she would hate living in California, but through a part-time job in the school cafeteria, which was run by her grandmother, a Paris-trained chef, Azure made new friends quickly. Azure's closest friend, Betsy, was more interested in art than her academic subjects. When Betsy had difficulty with an English assignment, Azure, an excellent student, was quick to offer an ingenious solution.

On Thursday when Betsy came by the cafeteria for me, she was all groans.

"Azure, you've got to come to the library and help me. I have to do this oral report on Ben Jonson for my English class. It's a matter of life or death."

"I can't go, Betsy, but how come Mr. Moray assigned you Ben Jonson again? You had an assignment on him last month," I said.

Betsy looked at me. "Uh . . . no . . . it's not exactly like that, Azure. It's the same one, and I haven't done it yet."

"Good grief, when is it due?"

"Monday," she said, making a horrible face.

"You mean you're starting on it *now*?" I couldn't believe it. I had to keep after that girl. I said, "You know that girl who makes all the *A*'s in your class? I'll bet she started on it last month."

"Sure. That's the reason she makes all *A*'s. I can't stand her, that Carry Win. What that girl needs is a personality transplant. But, you know, she made Mr. Moray smile once, and we all had to pay her a dime."

"What are you talking about? You never told me that," I said.

"Well, you know what a grouch Mr. Moray is. We have a deal in the class that if anybody makes Mr. Moray smile, we all pay that person a dime." She stopped and drew her face down. "Carry Win made him smile with her midterm paper. Then she stood outside the door with her hand out, and everybody who had a dime paid up. Ugh, *pain,* to give Carry Win a dime!"

I laughed. "Well, at least an oral report is easier than a written. You jus' have to have some notes and tell it."

"Easy? You're mad, Azure. Maybe you can do it, but I'm a disaster when I get in front of the class." Betsy looked woebegone. "I'm going to fail English, and Mr. Moray is going to send my parents a failing pink slip, and they'll ground me, and my whole life is going to be ruined forever and ever, all because of Ben Jonson. Who was he, anyway?"

Betsy was just too funny. It was so like her to blame the whole thing on Ben Jonson.

"Betsy, you sit you'self down in the library today and find out who Ben Jonson was, yes! Take some note cards, and every time you read something interestin', write it down, and then you memorize that. You'll be all done. Then we can go to Stinson Beach on Saturday, and you can paint some water colors."

"You know, Azure, you make it sound so simple."

I steered her to the door and shoved her out. "That's jus' how simple it is, Betsy, but you have to *do* it. Now, march straight to the library. Don't look to the right or the left, and don't stop at the art store."

Her feet were already dragging when I turned back to the kitchen.

Betsy must have come into the cafeteria very quietly the next morning. Gran and I were about to have our tea, and suddenly Betsy was standing there when I turned to pick up my teacup. She was not smiling.

"There *is* nothing interesting about Ben Jonson," she said flatly.

"Betsy! You didn't get anything for your report, no?"

"No, there just wasn't anything interesting to get." She reached into her jacket pocket, pulled out the blank note cards, and waved them in front of my face. I couldn't understand it, and I just stood there with my mouth open.

"I kept reading and waiting for something interesting, like you said, Azure." She nodded to me, then she started smiling slowly. Her smile had Gran and me smiling too, because it said, "Something's happened."

"There was this boy with red hair sitting at the next table, and he had freckles all across his face, and he had on an old blue denim shirt. Gee." Betsy rolled her eyes and we laughed. "He looked over at me — he had the bluest eyes — and I kind of got flustered and was turning pages, and I ended up at a chapter in the book that told about this fabulous guy named Inigo Jones. I probably never would have read it, but the boy left then, so there was nothing else to do. But Inigo Jones, now there's an interesting man."

"Oh, Betsy," I said, "spending your time reading about somebody besides Ben Jonson! No wonder Mr. Moray never smiles."

"But, Azure, listen. Inigo Jones designed sets for Ben Jonson's plays. He made the most fascinating sets way back there in the dark ages — I mean 1600 — or something. Look." She pulled the cards out of her pocket again and began to draw with a stubby pencil. With four lines she made a drawing that suggested the ocean.

"Now, he made this thing on wheels, with ropes like this, so that the whole thing could roll out onto the stage and move like the tides. Isn't that great?"

She was so excited that she didn't wait for an answer but whipped out another card and started to draw again.

"For another play, for King Somebody-or-other, he made a set like this."

I watched, somewhat stunned, as she sketched rapidly. I turned to Grandmother. "And she's doing all this without even any *notes*. She *knows* it."

Suddenly an idea hit me.

"Listen, Betsy, why don't you ask Mr. Moray if you can do your report on Ben Jonson's set designer, Inigo Jones? Go ask him," I coaxed, even though *I* wouldn't have wanted to ask him. "Jus' think! You might pass English."

"You think he might let me?" Betsy asked Gran.

"Betsy, I don't think you have a thing to lose," Gran said.

"I can't understand why he didn't tell me to do Inigo Jones in the first place. I mean, something that was worth doing!" Betsy said on the way to the door. "I'm going to go ask him right now." She had hardly gone before she was back, her face pleading.

"I can't face him by myself. Please come with me, Azure."

"Okay, okay," I said reluctantly, and followed her out the door. She ran so fast across the campus I could hardly keep up with her.

"Good grief, Betsy," I panted, "slow you'self down."

"I can't," she said. "I might turn back and run away." And she kept right on going until we reached the building where Mr. Moray teaches. She was rehearsing the conversation to herself as we went inside and walked down the long dark corridor. After being in the bright sun, I could barely see. I ran right smack-dab into somebody who loomed over me.

"What are you doing over here running people down in the hall?" he said.

It was my friend Ray John, and I could have hugged him; it was so good to hear his solid voice, with Betsy in a nervous fit. I grabbed his hand. "Come with us, Ray John. Betsy's goin' to take on Mr. Moray. I'm goin' to wait outside. *I* need moral support, yes."

He grinned and let me pull him along. We could see Mr. Moray's open door and the morning light pouring out through it into the dingy hall. Ray John tugged at my hand and motioned with his head toward Betsy. She was staring straight ahead and her lips were moving furiously. When we got to the door, she stopped dead.

"Go on, Betsy," I whispered. "We'll be right here." I cringed against the wall, pulling Ray John with me.

"It's okay, Betsy," said Ray John. "Mr. Moray has never eaten a student yet." With that, Betsy swallowed and sailed into the room. Ray John muttered to me, "Though he's sure chewed a lot of them up. . . ."

We turned at the sharp *tap, tap* of heels and saw Zack strutting toward us. I strained to hear what Mr. Moray was saying to Betsy above the sound of Zack's steps.

"*Sh-hh!*" I put my finger to my lips.

"What's happening?" Zack asked, ignoring Ray John.

"Betsy's in there with Mr. Moray," I whispered.

Zack laughed. "You cats scared of Little Daddy Moray? He thinks he is Big Daddy, but Zack the Man always calls him Little Daddy."

Ray John shifted slightly. Then he said quietly, "To his face?"

Zack's head jerked back.

"Sure, to his face."

Suddenly the little light in which we stood was blotted out as a huge figure appeared in the doorway.

"To what do I owe this unaccustomed popularity?" Mr. Moray boomed, a hollow echo bouncing back into the empty hall. "Did you want to see me, Zack?"

Zack was already taking a step away.

"No, sir, Mr. Moray. I was just on my way from a math conference, sir," and he fairly flew on down the hall. Mr. Moray looked after him and shook his head slowly.

"'To be a man, stand strong against time, and tide, and strong winds, and all other things.'" Mr. Moray looked at me. "Do you know who said that?"

"Shakespeare?" I quavered.

"No," he said, "my father. Now, what do you want?"

"We're just waiting for Betsy, Mr. Moray," said Ray John as I sank back against the wall.

Mr. Moray motioned us toward the room. "Well, if you're her friends, come in. Maybe without the commotion in the hall, Betsy can collect her thoughts and we can get on with it," Mr. Moray said. Betsy was standing in front of his desk, looking pale. When she saw me, she managed a wan smile.

Mr. Moray flopped into his chair, and Ray John and I sat at the first desks we came to.

"Well, Betsy, what is it now?" he asked.

"What I was trying to ask you, Mr. Moray, was can I make my oral report on Inigo Jones, Ben Jonson's set designer?"

Mr. Moray sighed, a deep rumble. He sat there for a few seconds without saying anything, looking rather dejected. Finally he asked, "Betsy, are you trying to tell me that you are just starting on this term project *now*?"

"Well, no, sir, not exactly. I have researched it — some. . . ." Betsy's color seemed to be returning to normal.

"Well, frankly, I can't see that you have anything to lose. You might as well do it on Inigo Jones."

"Thank you, Mr. Moray," and she started out of the room at almost the same clip she had come in but, this time, rosy and smiling.

Once we were out the door, I said, "Good. It's all set. Now we can picnic at Stinson."

"You two can talk about a picnic," Betsy said. "*I'm* going back to the library and get all those set designs and write down those dates and stuff. If I get up there in front of the class without something in my hands, I'll drop dead!"

I didn't dare mention the beach again, and Sunday night she called me. She was scared stiff but pleased with herself for making a series of pictures of the set designs in bright poster colors.

I didn't see her until Monday lunch. She was grinning from ear to ear when she opened her hand. It was full of dimes, a scrap of paper, and a dollar bill.

"Okay, congratulations," I said. "I know you made Mr. Moray smile. I know dimes when I see them, but what's with the dollar bill?"

"Azure, I got up there and went completely blank. Carry looked bored, on purpose, and when Jonathan Barlow made a face at me, I dropped the pictures. When I looked down and saw the one on the top, I was clued in. I picked them up and started talking and even got kind of comfortable. I looked around and nobody even looked sleepy, and Mr. Moray moved to the back so he could see the pictures too. And, Azure, when I finished, Jonathan Barlow started clapping, and they all applauded . . . *me!* Can you imagine? And Mr. Moray smiled."

"Oh, Betsy, that's wonderful," I said.

"Well, there was a little that was not wonderful. I started to leave, and Carry Win walked up to me and — right in front of Mr. Moray — handed me this I.O.U. When the kids saw her do that, they all filed by, dropping dimes in my hand. I could have killed them all."

"Oh, no, Betsy, what did Mr. Moray say?"

"Not a word, Azure. He just kept staring at me, even after they had gone, so I had to tell him about the deal."

"Oh, Betsy! What did he do then?" I asked, horrified.

"Azure, he laughed. He laughed and he laughed. Then he reached in his pocket and got this dollar bill, and he said, 'If a smile is worth a dime, a good laugh ought to rate a dollar.'"

I was too surprised to say a word.

"I'm not ever going to spend it, Azure. It's not just a dollar, you know. It's a trophy."

DISCUSSION

1. Judging by the story, do you think Azure and Betsy had a good friendship? Tell why you think as you do. What qualities do you think people need in order to become good friends? Why?

2. Why was Betsy worried about her assignment for English class? Do you agree that it is important to start an assignment as soon as possible instead of putting it off? Why do you think that?

3. What "deal" did Betsy's English class have regarding their teacher, Mr. Moray? How did Carry Win profit from the deal?

4. Why did Azure think that an oral report was easier to do than a written report? Do you agree with her? Why or why not?

5. What gave Azure the idea of having Betsy ask Mr. Moray if she could do her report on Inigo Jones instead of Ben Jonson? Why did she think that her idea might be helpful to Betsy?

6. Why was Betsy in such a hurry to reach Mr. Moray's room? How do you think she felt before entering the room? Why do you think that?

7. Why did Mr. Moray ask Azure and Ray John to come into his room instead of waiting outside for Betsy? Do you think having them there made it easier for Betsy to speak to him? Why or why not?

8. When Betsy first got up to give her report, she "went completely blank." How do you account for her ability to give an outstanding oral report after starting out so badly? Have you ever had a similar experience? If you wish to do so, tell about it.

9. How did Mr. Moray react when Betsy told him about the deal that the class had? What did his response tell you about him as a person?

10. What do you think Betsy meant when she said that the dollar was not just a dollar to be spent, but a trophy? Have you ever saved something as a personal symbol of victory? If you wish to, tell why you did so.

11. Do you think Mr. Moray had the qualities a fine teacher should have? Why do you think that?

AUTHOR

Mary Alexander Walker, author of short stories, novels, and plays, was born in Beaumont, Texas, and grew up in that state, attending Lamar College and Texas Women's University. Out of memories and feelings about her childhood came Mrs. Walker's book *Year of the Cafeteria,* a part of which you have just read. It was nominated for the Dorothy Canfield Fisher Award, and Mrs. Walker received a fellowship to the Breadloaf Writers' Conference as the author of a distinguished book for young people. Mary Alexander Walker lives and writes in Greenbrae, California, and teaches writing at Dominican College of San Rafael.

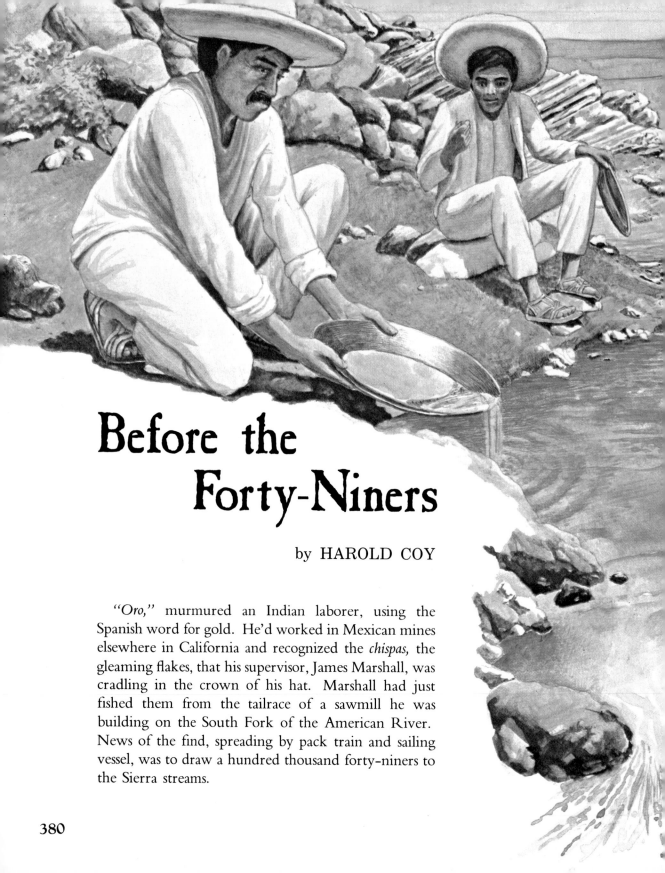

Before the Forty-Niners

by HAROLD COY

"*Oro,*" murmured an Indian laborer, using the Spanish word for gold. He'd worked in Mexican mines elsewhere in California and recognized the *chispas,* the gleaming flakes, that his supervisor, James Marshall, was cradling in the crown of his hat. Marshall had just fished them from the tailrace of a sawmill he was building on the South Fork of the American River. News of the find, spreading by pack train and sailing vessel, was to draw a hundred thousand forty-niners to the Sierra streams.

Before the forty-niners came the forty-eighters, mostly Spanish-speaking. The discovery took place on January 24, 1848, nine days before California passed from Mexico to the United States under the Guadalupe Hidalgo peace treaty. Gold mining had been going on along the California coast since 1842, when a Mexican ranch hand made a strike near Los Angeles. But the rich inland deposits along the mountain streams were then unknown except to Indians, who placed little value on the yellow pebbles. However, the native California Mexicans did prize them and were close by when the rush began. Nor were Mexicans from Sonora far behind. They came humbly attired in sandals and white cotton but wise in mining lore. They used the *batea,* a flat-bottomed wooden bowl, washing the pay dirt in it, then separating the lighter sand from the particles of gold. If water was lacking, as it often was in the dry diggings below Sacramento, they tossed the mixture into the air and relied on the wind or their own lungs to blow the sand away.

Upstream from the placer mines, where the gold was loose, were ridges where it came encased in quartz and could be freed only by milling. Under their broad-brimmed sombreros the Sonorans carried the know-how for making a simple mill called an *arrastre.* It consisted of a paved enclosure with an upright post to which a beam was attached. A mule, hitched to the beam, dragged a block of granite round and round over the quartz until it was pulverized. After that, the gold was extracted by treating it with quicksilver, which came from the great New Almaden mine near San Jose.

Though more Spanish-speaking gold seekers arrived from Chile and Peru in 1849, they were greatly outnumbered by the Anglo-Americans who crossed the plains or came by sea. Friction developed, and "foreigners," including native Californians, were forcibly expelled from many of the bonanzas, or rich strikes, they had taught others to exploit.

The gold rush drew Americans of every sort into sparsely settled backcountry. Yet the newly established camps were soon operating under miners' codes regulating the size of claims and the conditions under which they could be worked and retained. The forty-niners, having little mining background of their own, turned to laws and customs that had been tested by centuries of experience in Mexico and Spain. From California they were to carry throughout the West the Hispanic principle that ownership of mines depends on discovery and development. Mining law in the United States rose on these foundations.

Mexican labor was in heavy demand as mining became big business. Ore carriers climbed from pits with hide sacks containing two-hundred-pound loads suspended by straps from their foreheads. Mexican smelter operators were rated tops around the copper mines that, later on, were to supply an essential metal for electrification. Their skill went back to the Spanish-discovered Santa Rita mine in western New Mexico, where basic copper-mining techniques were evolved. It was a Mexican who first recognized that Nevada's Comstock Lode was fabulously rich in silver. He could have been from Sonora, where his people had been mining silver since 1763.

Mexico's silver far exceeded its gold and was in fact so abundant that for two centuries the Spanish dollar, or more correctly the Mexican peso, was a preferred currency in the Far East, the Caribbean, Africa, and much of Europe. It was legal tender in the early United States. When Paul Revere needed silver in his shop, he melted pesos.

In sixteenth-century Mexico, a forty-niner would have been one of the fortune seekers who in 1549 were rushing to Zacatecas, the site of a recent silver strike. Zacatecas became a roaring silver camp and the point of departure for places farther north. Within twenty years, the mining frontier moved into Durango, Coahuila, and Chihuahua. The recovery of silver was stepped up tremendously after a Pachuca miner had the inspired idea of treating the crushed ore with quicksilver. *Arrieros,* or mule drivers, moved freight over long stretches of lonely, arid country by pack train, an art that remained of utmost importance in Mexico and the Southwest until the railroad age. Stock ranches supplied the mines with work animals, food, and hides for cables and sacking. Lucky prospectors became *ricos mineros,* mining magnates, and *señores de ganados,* cattle lords. A few rose to be governors of provinces, and nearly all assumed the military title of *capitán.*

By the end of the eighteenth century, Mexico had three thousand silver mines and, among its scientific institutions, a School of Mines that was considered without equal on the new continent, not excluding the United States. All this was in the line of a Spanish mining tradition unbroken since ancient times when seagoing vessels carried Spanish tin to the Bronze Age civilizations of the Middle East. Mexico's miners and metallurgists carried this tradition into the Southwest, contributing their skills and the sweat of their backs to the growth of the United States.

DISCUSSION

1. The Mexicans made many contributions to the growth of mining and metallurgy. Which of their contributions do you consider most important? Why do you think that?
2. Since what year had gold mining been going on along the California coast? What incident in 1848 started the gold rush of 1849, when thousands of people came to the rich inland deposits along the mountain streams of California?
3. Who were the forty-eighters and what was the national origin of most of them? Why were they more informed about mining than the forty-niners?
4. How was gold separated from sand in streams? In dry diggings?
5. How was gold extracted when it was encased in quartz?
6. How was the word "foreigners" used to the disadvantage of the native California miners? Why do you think they were regarded as "foreigners" by the Anglo-American miners?
7. Why did the forty-niners adopt Mexican mining codes and customs?
8. Why was Mexican labor in heavy demand as mining became big business in New Mexico and Nevada?

AUTHOR

Harold Coy was born in La Habra, California, now a suburb of Los Angeles. He graduated from the University of Arizona, where he studied Spanish, and became a reporter of the St. Louis *Star* and later an assistant editor for the New York *Daily News*. He worked for many years in public relations until, in 1962, he and his wife moved to Mexico City.

For more than twenty-five years, Harold Coy has devoted his spare time to writing books for young people, an activity that he thoroughly enjoys. Two of his many books are *The Americans* and *The Mexicans*. "Before the Forty-Niners" is taken from his book *Chicano Roots Go Deep,* in which he deals with the histories of both the United States and Mexico in an attempt to explain how Mexican Americans became what they are today.

SKILL

Maps

Maps are drawings that show part or all of the earth's surface or objects beyond the earth, such as another planet. A variety of symbols and colors are used on maps to represent geographical features such as roads, mountains, bodies of water, and boundaries. Each feature is greatly reduced in size, of course, so that a large geographical area can be presented within a small space. To make the maps accurate, they are drawn to scale; that is, they are drawn in a way that shows the relationship between the actual size of an area and its size on the map. The scale used is usually indicated on the map and may represent distances in miles or kilometers or both. Most maps also include a drawing of a compass called a compass rose or an arrow indicating direction.

Maps are among the most helpful reference and study aids because they can be used for so many different purposes. You can use a map to plan a trip, compare sizes of areas, study weather patterns, or find mountain elevations.

First read the title of a map to make sure it will provide the information you need. Then study the key, or legend, to become familiar with symbols used on the map, read the distance scale, and note the compass rose or arrow that indicates north.

Latitude and Longitude

Some maps include a system of lines to help you locate the exact position of any place on the earth's surface. Grid lines that run east-west across the map are called parallels and are used to help you find the latitude, or distance in degrees north or south of the equator. Meridians are lines that run north-south and are used to find the longitude, or distance east or west of a specific line called the prime meridian.

Look at the two simple maps on the next page. Note that parallels are numbered from 0 degrees at the equator to 90 degrees north and south at the poles. Meridians range from 0 degrees to

LATITUDE

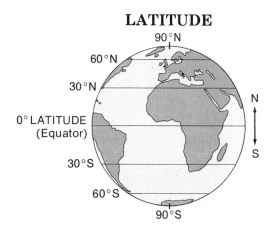

LONGITUDE

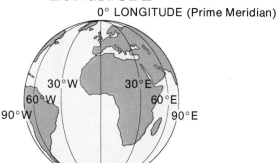

180 degrees east or west of the prime meridian, but not all these lines appear on the simple map shown.

Of course, most places that you look for on a map lie on points between numbered parallels and meridians and not directly on one of the lines. Therefore, you will discover that it is frequently necessary to estimate distances between lines. For example, look at the position of the city Veracruz, Mexico, on the following map.

You can see that Veracruz lies between the parallels labeled 15 degrees north and 20 degrees north, so you can estimate that the latitude is approximately 19 degrees north. To figure out the longitude, you should determine that the city lies between the meridians 95 degrees west and 100 degrees west, or about 96 degrees west. The approximate location of Veracruz may be written as 19° N, 96° W.

Political Maps

A political map shows land divisions of areas such as countries, states, provinces, and counties. Colors may be used to make political, or governmental, boundaries easier to see. Many political maps show major physical features, such as lakes, rivers, and mountains, as well as constructed features, such as cities, highways, and railroads.

The legend of a political map may contain a large variety of symbols, depending upon the number of features shown. Take a few minutes to read the political map of Mexico, and note the use of color to indicate land divisions and the symbols indicating features.

Look at the distance scale below the legend of the map. You can use such a scale and a piece of paper to help you figure out the distance between any two points on a map. To find out the

distance between Guadalajara (gwahd′l-uh-hahr′uh) and Mexico City, for instance, place the edge of a piece of paper along an imaginary line between the two dots that represent the cities. Make a mark on your paper opposite the center of each dot. Now place your paper directly below the scale, with the left mark lined up with the 0 on the kilometers line. Notice that the line on your paper is longer than the line of the scale, so make another mark on your paper to show the end of the kilometers line. Write 300 below the new mark, indicating the part of the distance already measured. Now move your paper to the left, lining up the mark labeled 300 with the 0 on the scale. The mark on your paper that is farthest to the right should be about three-quarters of the way between 100 and 200, or at a point that could be labeled 175 on the kilometers line. By adding 175 kilometers to the 300 kilometers already measured, you find that the distance from Guadalajara to Mexico City is about 475 kilometers.

Physical Maps

A physical map deals with landforms, such as hills, mountains, and plains, and often shows elevations, or heights of land. All elevations are measured in relation to sea level. Major rivers, lakes, deserts, and other geographical features are typically found on physical maps. On the physical map that appears on the next page, the boundaries of some of the political divisions are shown by red lines, but since the emphasis is on landforms rather than political geography, the countries are not labeled. The different colors on this map do not represent political land divisions as do the colors on a political map; color is used here to indicate elevations, as explained in the key. You can see, for example, that green represents elevations from sea level to 500 meters and dark brown stands for the highest elevations, ranging 4,000 meters and above. White and different shades of blue are used to show depths of water below sea level.

Shading may be used on a physical map to show land variations that exist within certain ranges of elevation. For example, look at the southern part of Africa and notice the large light brown area that represents an elevation of 1,000 to 2,000 meters. The shading within that area indicates that the land is uneven.

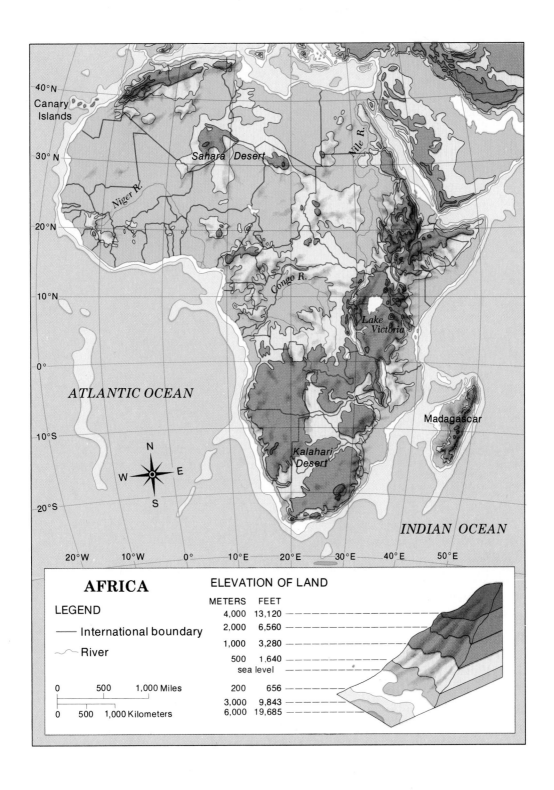

40°N

Canary
Islands

30°N

Sahara Desert

Niger R.

Nile R.

20°N

Congo R.

10°N

Lake Victoria

0°

ATLANTIC OCEAN

10°S

Kalahari Desert

Madagascar

20°S

INDIAN OCEAN

20°W   10°W   0°   10°E   20°E   30°E   40°E   50°E

AFRICA

LEGEND

—— International boundary

River

| 0 | 500 | 1,000 Miles |

| 0 | 500 | 1,000 Kilometers |

ELEVATION OF LAND

METERS	FEET
4,000	13,120
2,000	6,560
1,000	3,280
500	1,640
sea level	
200	656
3,000	9,843
6,000	19,685

389

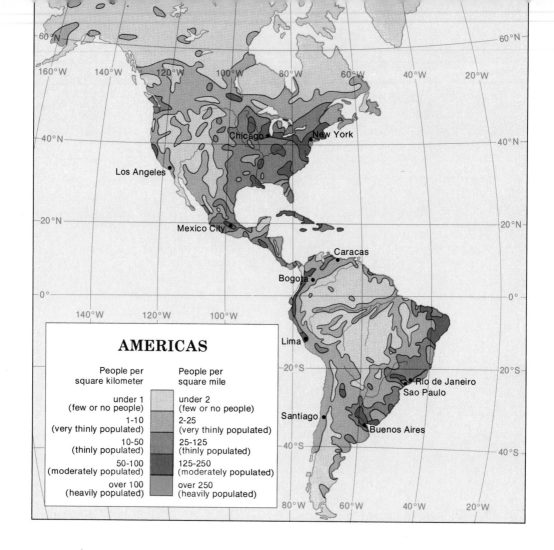

Population Density Maps

A population density map gives information about the number of people who live within an area. The legend of the following population map of North and South America explains how color is used on the map to represent numbers of people living in areas measured in square kilometers and square miles.

To get an understanding of population per square mile, imagine that the two continents shown are marked off into squares that are a mile on each side and that all the people living in a particular square are standing around to be counted. Picture crowded squares in which people would be standing very close together and also squares with so few people that they would be too far apart even to see one another. The key tells you that areas appearing in

390

beige on the map average fewer than two people per square mile. Because the southern tip of South America is shown in beige, you know that there are only one or two people per square mile living in that area. How many people per square mile live in the area surrounding Rio de Janeiro?

Road Maps

Perhaps the kind of map that is used most frequently is a road map. You can use a road map to find information about highways,

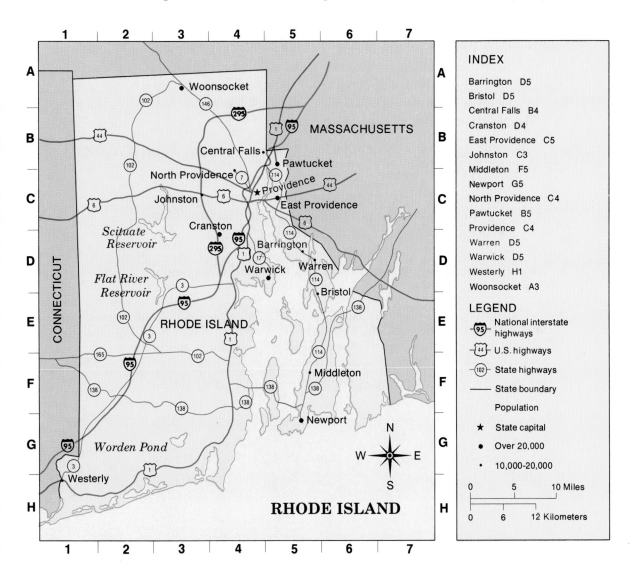

INDEX

LEGEND

National interstate highways
U.S. highways
State highways
State boundary

Population

★   State capital
●   Over 20,000
·   10,000–20,000

0   5   10 Miles

0   6   12 Kilometers

RHODE ISLAND

cities, recreational areas, and various points of interest. Road maps show locations of such places and provide information that is useful in making travel plans, such as choosing routes, measuring distances, and estimating time of travel.

Roads on a map are marked by numerals that appear in different shapes representing actual signs, called highway markers. Each shape represents a specific type of road. These and other symbols are explained in the legend. Look at the map of Rhode Island on page 391, and note the kinds of features it presents.

The small index on this map lists cities and towns. You can see that each name is followed by a letter and a numeral and that letters and numerals appear along the four sides of the map. Providence, for example, is followed by *C4* in the index. To locate it, find the *C* at the left of the map and then look to the right toward the other *C* until you reach the area below the numeral 4. Providence is located in that general area.

READING MAPS

Use the maps in this lesson to answer the following questions. On a sheet of paper, copy the number of each question and then write your answer.

1. What river forms part of the boundary between Mexico and the United States?
2. Of what state in Mexico is Hermosillo the capital?
3. What is the highest range of elevation in Africa?
4. What is the highest range of elevation shown on the island of Madagascar?
5. What is the population density of the area surrounding Santiago, Chile?
6. What population density per square mile is considered to be moderate?
7. What three U.S. highways go through Providence, Rhode Island?
8. In Rhode Island, what route would you travel to go from Barrington to Middleton?

ROBERTO CLEMENTE

by JERRY IZENBERG

I saw him play so often. I watched the grace of his movements and the artistry of his reflexes from who knows how many press boxes. None of us really appreciated how pure an athlete he was until he was gone. What follows is a personal retracing of the steps that took Roberto Clemente from the narrow, crowded streets of his native Carolina to the local ball parks in San Juan and on to the major leagues. But it is more. It is a remembrance formed as I stood at the water's edge in Puerto Rico and stared at daybreak into the waves that killed him. It is all the people I met in Puerto Rico who knew him and loved him. It is the way an entire island in the sun and a Pennsylvania city in the smog took his death.

393

The record book will tell you that Roberto Clemente collected 3,000 hits during his major-league career. It will say that he came to bat 9,454 times, that he drove in 1,305 runs, and played 2,433 games over an eighteen-year span.

But it won't tell you about Carolina, Puerto Rico, and the old square, and the narrow, twisting streets, and the roots that produced him. It won't tell you about the Julio Coronado School and a remarkable woman named María Isabella Casares, whom he called Teacher until the day he died and who helped to shape his life in times of despair and depression. It won't tell you about a man named Pedro Zarrilla, who found him on a country softball team and put him in the uniform of the Santurce club and who nursed him from a promising young amateur athlete to a major-league superstar.

And most of all, those cold numbers won't begin to delineate the man Roberto Clemente was. To even begin to understand what this magnificent athlete was all about, you have to work backward. The search begins at the site of its ending.

The car moves easily through the predawn streets of San Juan. It turns down a bumpy secondary road and moves past small shantytowns. Then there is another turn, onto hard-packed dirt and sand, and although the light has not yet quite begun to break, you can sense the nearness of the ocean. You can hear its waves, pounding harshly against the jagged rocks. You can smell its saltiness. The car noses to a stop, and the driver says, "From here you must walk." The place is called Punta Maldonado.

"This is the nearest place," the driver tells me. "This is where they came by the thousands on that New Year's Eve and New Year's Day. Out there," he says, gesturing with his right hand, "out there, perhaps a mile and a half from where we stand. That's where we think the plane went down."

The final hours of Roberto Clemente were like this. Just a month or so before, he had agreed to take a junior-league baseball team to Nicaragua and manage it in an all-star game in Managua. He had met people and made friends there. He was not a man who made friends casually. He had always said that the people you wanted to give your friendship to were the people to whom you had to be willing to give something — no matter what the price.

Just two weeks after he returned from that trip, Managua, Nicaragua, exploded into flames. The earth trembled, and people died. It was the worst earthquake anywhere in the hemisphere in a long time.

Back in Puerto Rico, a television

personality named Luis Vigereaux heard the news and was moved to try to help the victims. He needed someone to whom the people would listen, someone who could say what had to be said and get the work done that had to be done and help the people who had to be helped.

"I knew," Luis Vigereaux said, "that Roberto was such a person, perhaps the only such person who would be willing to help."

And so the mercy project, which would eventually claim Roberto's life, began. He appeared on television. But he needed a staging area. The city agreed to give him Sixto Escobar Stadium.

"Bring what you can," he told the people. "Bring medicine . . . bring clothes . . . bring food . . . bring shoes . . . bring yourself to help us load. We need so much. Whatever you bring, we will use."

And the people of San Juan came. They walked through the heat, and they drove old cars and battered little trucks, and the mound of supplies grew and grew. Within two days, the first mercy planes left for Nicaragua.

Meanwhile, a ship had been chartered and loaded. And as it prepared to steam away, unhappy stories began to drift back from Nicaragua. Not all the supplies that had been flown in, it was rumored, were getting through. Puerto Ricans who had flown the planes had no passports, and Nicaragua was in a state of panic.

"We have people there who must be protected. Black-market types must not be allowed to get their hands on these supplies," Clemente told Luis Vigereaux. "Someone must make sure — particularly before the ship gets there. I'm going on the next plane."

They had rented an old DC-7. It was scheduled to take off at 4 P.M. on December 31, 1972. Long before takeoff time, it was apparent that the plane needed more work. It had even taxied onto the runway and then turned back. The trouble, a mechanic who was at the airstrip that day conjectured, "had to do with both port engines. We worked on them most of the afternoon."

The departure time was delayed an hour, and then two, and then three. At 9 P.M., even as the first stirrings of the annual New Year's Eve celebration were beginning in downtown San Juan, the DC-7 taxied onto the runway, received clearance, rumbled down the narrow concrete strip, and pulled away from the earth. It headed out over the Atlantic and banked toward Nicaragua, and its tiny lights disappeared on the horizon.

Just ninety seconds later, the tower at San Juan International Airport received this message from the DC-7 pilot: "We are coming back around."

Just that.

Nothing more.

And then there was only a great silence.

"It was almost midnight," recalls Rudy Hernández, a former teammate of Roberto's. "We were having this party in my restaurant. Somebody turned on the radio, and the announcer was saying that Roberto's plane was feared missing. And then, because my place is on the beach, we saw these giant floodlights crisscrossing the waves, and we heard the sound of the helicopters and the little search planes."

Drawn by a common sadness, the people of San Juan began to make their way toward the beach, toward Punta Maldonado. A cold rain had begun to fall. It washed their faces and blended with the tears.

They came by the thousands, and they watched for three days. Towering waves boiled up and made the search virtually impossible. The U.S. Navy sent a team of expert divers into the area, but the battering of the waves defeated them too. Midway through the week, the pilot's body was found in the swift-moving currents to the north. On Saturday, bits of the cockpit were sighted.

And then — nothing else.

Rudy Hernández said, "I have never seen a time or a sadness like that. The streets were empty, the radios silent except for the constant bulletins about Roberto. Traffic? Forget it. All of us cried. All of us who knew him, and even those who didn't, wept that week. There will never be another like Roberto."

Who was he . . . I mean really?

He was born in Carolina, Puerto Rico. Today the town has about 125,000 people, but when Roberto was born there in 1934, it was roughly one-sixth its current size.

María Isabella Casares is a schoolteacher. She has taught the children of Carolina for thirty years. Most of her teaching has been done in tenth-grade history classes. Carolina is her home, and its children are her children. And among all of those whom she calls her own (who are all the children she taught), Roberto Clemente was something even more special to her.

"His father was an overseer on a sugar plantation. He did not make much money," she explained in an empty classroom at Julio Coronado School. "But then, there are no rich children here. There never have been. Roberto was typical of them. I had known him when he was a small boy because my father had run a grocery store in Carolina and Roberto's parents used to shop there."

There is this thing that you have to know about María Isabella Casares before we hear more from her. What you have to know is that she is the model of what a teacher should be. Between her and her students even now, as back when Roberto attended her school, there is this common bond of mutual respect. Earlier in the day, I had watched her teach a class in the history of the Abolition Movement in Puerto Rico. I don't speak much Spanish, but even to me it was clear that this is how a class should be, this is the kind of person who should teach, and these are the kinds of students such a teacher will produce.

With this as a background, what she has to say about Roberto Clemente carries much more impact.

"Each year," she said, "I let my students choose the seats they want to sit in. I remember the first time I saw Roberto. He was a very shy boy, and he went straight to the back of the room and chose the very last seat. Most of the time he would sit with his eyes down. He was an average student. But there was something very special about him. We would talk after class for hours. He wanted to be an engineer, you know, and perhaps he could have been. But then Roberto began to play softball, and one day he came to me and said, 'Teacher, I have a problem.'

"He told me that Pedro Zarrilla, who was one of our most prominent baseball people, had seen him play and that Pedro wanted him to sign a professional contract with the Santurce Crabbers. He asked me what he should do.

"I have thought about that conversation many times. I believe Roberto could have been almost anything, but God gave him a gift that few have, and he chose to use that gift. I remember that on that day I told him, 'This is your chance, Roberto. We are poor people in this town. This is your chance to do something. But if in your heart you prefer not to try, then, Roberto, that will be your problem — and your decision.'"

There was and there always remained a closeness between this boy-soon-to-be-a-man and his favorite teacher.

"Once, a few years ago, I was sick with a very bad back. Roberto, not knowing this, had driven over from Río Piedras, where his house was, to see me," Mrs. Casares recalled.

"Where is the teacher?" Roberto asked Mrs. Casares's stepdaughter that afternoon.

"Teacher is sick, Roberto. She is in bed."

"Teacher," Roberto said, pounding on the bedroom door, "get up and put on your clothes. We are going to the doctor whether you want to or not."

"I got dressed," Mrs. Casares told me, "and he picked me up like a baby and carried me in his arms to the car. He came every day for fifteen days, and most days he had to

carry me. But I went to the doctor, and he treated me. Afterward, I said to the doctor that I wanted to pay the bill.

"'Mrs. Casares,' he told me, 'please don't start with that Clemente or he will kill me. He has paid all your bills, and don't you dare tell him I have told you.'

"Well, Roberto was like that. We had been so close. You know, I think I was there the day he met Vera, the girl he later married. She was one of my students too. I was working part-time in the pharmacy, and he was already a baseball player by then, and one day Vera came into the store.

"'Teacher,' Roberto asked me, 'who is that girl?'

"'That's one of my students,' I told him. 'Now, don't you dare bother her. Go out and get someone to introduce you. Behave yourself.'

"He was so proper, you know. That's just what he did, and that's how he met her, and they were married here in Carolina in the big church on the square."

On the night Roberto Clemente's plane disappeared, Mrs. Casares was at home, and a delivery boy from the pharmacy stopped by and told her to turn on the radio and sit down. "I think something has happened to someone who is very close

to you, Teacher, and I want to be here in case you need help."

María Isabella Casares heard the news. She is a brave woman, and months later, standing in front of the empty crypt in the cemetery at Carolina where Roberto Clemente was to have been buried, she said, "He was like a son to me. This is why I want to tell you about him. This is why you must make people — particularly our people, our Puerto Rican children — understand what he was. He was like my son, and he is all our sons in a way. We must make sure that the children never forget how beautiful a man he was."

The next person to touch Roberto Clemente was Pedro Zarrilla, who owned the Santurce club. He discovered Clemente on the country softball team and signed him for a four-hundred-dollar bonus.

"He was a skinny kid," Pedro Zarrilla recalls, "but even then he had those large, powerful hands, which we all noticed right away. He joined us, and he was nervous. But I watched him, and I said to myself, 'This kid can throw, and this kid can run, and this kid can hit. We will be patient with him.' The season had been through several games before I finally sent him in to play."

Luis Olmo remembers that game. Luis Olmo had been a major-league outfielder with the Brooklyn Dodgers. He had been a splendid ballplayer. Today he is in the insurance business in San Juan. He sat in his office and recalled very well that first moment when Roberto Clemente stepped up to bat.

"I was managing the other team. They had a man on base, and this skinny kid comes out. Well, we had never seen him, so we didn't really know how to pitch to him. I decided to throw him a few bad balls and see if he'd bite.

"He hit the first pitch. It was an outside fast ball and he never should have been able to reach it, but he hit it down the line for a double. He was the best bad-ball hitter I have ever seen, and if you ask major-league pitchers who are pitching today, they will tell you the same thing. After a while, it got so that I just told my pitchers to throw the ball down the middle because he was going to hit it no matter where they put it, and at least if he decided not to swing, we'd have a strike on him.

"I played in the big leagues. I know what I am saying. He was the greatest we ever had . . . maybe one of the greatest anyone ever had. Why did he have to die?"

Once Pedro Zarrilla turned him loose, there was no stopping Roberto Clemente. As Clemente's confidence grew, he got better. He was the one the crowds came to see out at Sixto Escobar Stadium.

"You know, when Clemente was in the line-up," Pedro Zarrilla says, "there was always this undercurrent of excitement in the ball park. You knew that if he was coming to bat, he would do something spectacular. You knew that if he was on first base, he was going to try to get to second base. You knew that if he was playing right field and there was a man on third base, then that man on third base already knew what a lot of men on third base in the majors would find out — you don't try to get home against Roberto Clemente's arm."

Soon the major-league scouts began to make their moves, and in 1955 Roberto Clemente came to the Pittsburgh Pirates. He was the finest prospect the club had had in a long, long time. But the Pirates of those days were spectacular losers, and even Roberto Clemente couldn't turn them around overnight.

"I will never forget how fast he became a superstar in this town," says Bob Friend, who became a great Pirate pitcher. "Later he would have troubles because he was either hurt or thought he was hurt, and some people would say that he was loafing; but I know he gave it his best shot, and he helped make us winners."

The first winning year was 1960, when the Pirates won the pennant and went on to beat the Yankees in the seventh game of the World Series. Whitey Ford, who pitched against him twice in that Series, recalls that Roberto actually made himself look bad on an outside pitch to encourage Whitey to come back with it. "I did," Ford recalls, "and he unloaded. Another thing I . remember is the way he ran out a routine ground ball in the last game, and when we were a little slow covering, he beat it out. It was something most people forget, but it made the Pirates' victory possible."

The season was over. Roberto Clemente had hit safely in every World Series game, he had batted over .300, and he had been a superstar, but when they announced the Most Valuable Player Award voting, Roberto had finished a distant third.

"I really don't think he resented the fact that he didn't win it," Bob Friend says. "What hurt — and in this he was right — was how few votes he got. He felt that he simply wasn't being accepted. He brooded about that a lot. I think his attitude became one of 'well, I'm going to show them from now on so that they will never forget.'

"And you know, he sure did."

Roberto Clemente went home and married Vera. He felt less alone. Now he could go on and prove what it was he had to prove, and he was determined to prove it.

His moment finally came. It took eleven years for the Pirates to win a World Series berth again, and when they did in 1971, it was Roberto Clemente who led the way. I will never forget him as he was during that 1971 Series with the Orioles, a Series that the Pirates figured to lose and in which they, in fact, dropped the first two games down in Baltimore.

When they got back to Pittsburgh for the middle slice of the tournament, Roberto Clemente went to work and led his team. He was a superstar during the five games that followed. He was the big man in the Series. He was the MVP. He was everything he had ever dreamed of being on a ball field.

Most important of all, the entire country saw him do it on network television, and never again — even though nobody knew it would end so tragically soon — was anyone ever to doubt his ability.

The following year, Clemente ended the season by collecting his three thousandth hit. Only ten other men had ever done that in the entire history of baseball.

"When I think of Roberto now," says Willie Stargell, his closest friend on the Pirates, "I think of the kind of man he was. There was nothing phony about him. He had his own ideas about how life should

be lived, and if you didn't see it that way, then he let you know in so many ways, without words, that it was best you each go your separate ways.

"He was a man who chose his friends carefully. His was a friendship worth having. I don't think many people took the time and the trouble to try to understand him, and I'll admit it wasn't easy. But he was worth it.

"The way he died, you know, I mean on that plane carrying supplies to Nicaraguans who'd been dying in that earthquake, well, I wasn't surprised he'd go out and do something like that. I just never thought what happened could happen to him.

"But I know this. He lived a full life. And if he knew at that moment what the Lord had decided, well, I really believe he would have said, 'I'm ready.'"

He was thirty-eight years old when he died. He touched the hearts of Puerto Rico in a way that few people ever could. He touched a lot of other hearts too. He touched hearts that beat inside people of all colors of skin.

DISCUSSION

1. If Willie Stargell was correct in saying that Clemente was not easy to understand, how do you explain Clemente's great personal popularity?
2. What disaster led to Roberto Clemente's flight to Nicaragua on New Year's Eve in 1972? Why did Luis Vigereaux feel that Roberto Clemente was perhaps the only person who could help organize a relief program for the victims of the Nicaraguan earthquake?
3. How successful was Roberto Clemente in helping to organize the Nicaraguan relief program? Why did Clemente feel that he should personally fly to Nicaragua?
4. What happened to Clemente's plane and its occupants?
5. How did the people of Puerto Rico react to the news that Clemente's plane was believed missing?
6. Why did one team manager tell his pitchers to throw down the middle when they pitched to Clemente?
7. What really hurt Clemente about his failure to win the Most Valuable Player Award in 1960?
8. Why, do you think, did the author often use direct quotations in his memoir? Do you think that the use of direct quotations is an effective way of presenting a well-rounded picture of someone? Why do you think that?

AUTHOR

A graduate of Rutgers University, Jerry Izenberg has been the syndicated sports columnist for the *Newark Star Ledger* for many years. He has contributed to several leading magazines, including *Sport* and *Sports Illustrated*. He has had a weekly New York television sports program and has written, directed, and produced several TV sport documentaries, including "A Man Named Lombardi." The story that you have just read is from his book *Great Latin Sports Figures*.

Parting

by WANG WEI

I watch you travel slowly down the mountains
And then the sun is gone. I close my thatched door.
Grasses will grow green again next spring;
But you, beloved friend, will you return?

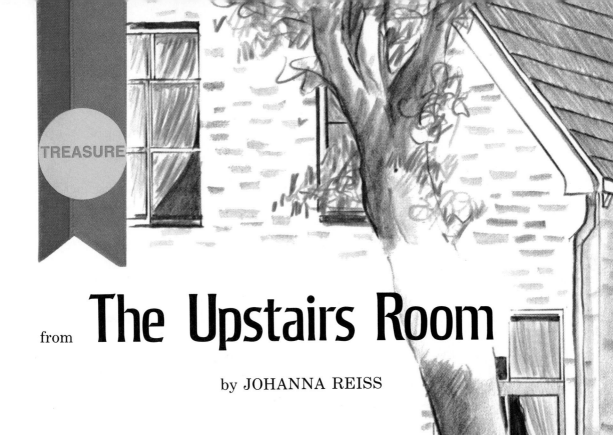

from **The Upstairs Room**

by JOHANNA REISS

One of the towns in Holland that was occupied by Nazi soldiers in World War II was Winterswijk (vin'ters-viek), where Annie de Leeuw (duh-layw') and her family lived. Because they were Jewish, the de Leeuws were forced to separate and go into hiding with different families so they wouldn't be killed.

Twelve-year-old Annie and her older sister Sini (see'nee) stayed with the Hannink (hah'nink) family in the village of Usselo (uhs'suh-lo) until it became unsafe. Then they moved to the remote farmhouse of Johan Oosterveld (yo'hahn ohs-tuhr-feld'), his wife, Dientje (deen'chuh), and Johan's mother, Opoe (oh'poo). To make a hiding place for the girls, Johan built a false wall in an upstairs closet. The girls were to crawl through a hole into the space behind the wall. Then one of the Oostervelds had to insert a piece of wood over the hole and lower a shelf in front of it.

Most people suffered some deprivation during the war. There was hunger. It was hard to buy clothes, hard to buy almost anything. Radios were forbidden so that the only news people received was propaganda provided by the Nazi government. For Annie de Leeuw, the greatest deprivation was being confined, day after day, to an upstairs room.

The Allies were running through Belgium. They would be in Holland next, the radio said. Every time I thought about it, I had to smile. If it was wonderful to be almost free, how wonderful it would be when the Allies really came. Wasn't Holland only a little bigger than Belgium? Say a few days' worth? Many people living in the south of Holland, near the Belgian border, could probably see the Allied soldiers already. They were lucky.

I turned to Opoe. "Will you come and see us when we're back in Winterswijk?" I asked her.

"Me?" She laughed. "No. I haven't been anyplace in twenty-one years. Winterswijk. What's next?"

"I'll come," Johan said, "and I won't be wearing these dumb overalls. I'll wear my suit."

"Johan, you're late for work again," Opoe said.

"Yes, Johan, hurry," Dientje urged.

He slammed the door when he left.

While Johan was on his way to work, Mr. Hannink came to see us. A truck was going from house to house, he said, checking.

"Checking what?" Dientje gasped, but Mr. Hannink had already gone.

Sini and I got into the hiding place as fast as we could.

"Dientje, don't close it yet," said Opoe.

"But they'll be here any minute. Mr. Hannink said so."

"You stay up here and sit in front of the window. When you see that truck, you close the opening to the hiding place."

"Where are *you* going?"

"To the kitchen, of course. Where else? Johan's coming home at twelve to eat."

Sini and I stood close together, listening, waiting for Dientje to come.

"Okay, okay." Dientje ran over to us. "They're here. They're here."

She closed up the hiding place with the piece of wood. We heard her lower the shelf and close the closet door. We heard her footsteps as she ran down the stairs. Then nothing.

Where were they? What took them so long? We could suffocate in here if they didn't come for a long time. I leaned up against Sini.

Footsteps. Loud ones. Boots. Coming up the stairs. Wooden shoes. Coming behind. Sini put her arms around me and pushed my head against her shoulder.

Loud voices. Ugly ones. Furniture being moved. And Opoe's protesting voice. The closet door was thrown open. Hands fumbled on the shelves. Sini was trembling. She tightened her arms around me. I no longer breathed through my nose. Breathing through my mouth made less noise.

A man was speaking German. Then another was saying, "We want to know where all those pieces of cloth came from."

"What's he doing? He can't just take all of that. It's mine," Opoe said. "Tell'm that."

A stick pounded once on the floor, and then again. The closet door was slammed. My heart was beating too loudly. What if they could hear us? Would they stick a bayonet through the closet wall? They could. All over the wall, to be sure to hit whoever was behind the wall.

My mouth was dry, yet I didn't dare breathe through my nose. They might still be there. But you clearly heard them storm down the stairs, didn't you? I know, but what if they had left a soldier behind? Sini must think so, too, or she wouldn't be holding me so tightly.

There were noises on the stairs again. They're coming back? No, only wooden shoes this time.

"They're gone, girls." Dientje removed the piece of wood. "We were lucky. One of 'em was standing right here. I was afraid he would hear you breathe."

We didn't move. Dientje bent in front of the hole. "They're gone."

"Girls, I brought you a drop of coffee," Opoe said. "You can come out now. They were nasty people. They took the pig we were going to kill and the cloth I've been saving for years."

Pig? Cloth? It could have been us.

"No, Opoe, we'll stay in here this morning. They might come back."

In the middle of September thousands of British parachutists were dropped at Arnhem (arn'em).

"You know, you can get from Arnhem to Usselo on the bike in one day?" Johan said. "Yep, if you have big legs like Dientje."

Sini laughed. While she was helping Johan with his English, I looked at her. Her face was flushed. I felt like crying. Remember how long they fought in Italy, Sini? Months. Why do you always forget these things? I know Arnhem is in Holland. Still . . . Tomorrow you may be miserable again.

In less than ten days it was all over. No, not the war, just the fighting. More German soldiers were in Arnhem than the Allies had thought, and the Allied soldiers that came up through the south of Holland to help the paratroopers had to go back. But not all the way back. Part of the south of Holland remained free, the part of Holland Usselo was not in. Today people in Eindhoven (ient'ho-vuhn) were probably singing and dancing and shouting.

And the rain continued, as if it were never going to stop. Leaves were fluttering around aimlessly and landing on the ground in soft, slippery piles. A few stuck against the window and stayed there, forming a pattern.

It was getting chilly, and there was no longer any coal. At night we went down to the kitchen to get warm. "Johan, are you sure nobody can see through the shades?" Dientje asked every time.

But who'd be there to look? Nobody was allowed out after dark anymore. "So, who'd come, eh?"

It was cozy in the kitchen. The oven door was open. Sini's and my feet were resting on it. Opoe got up and stuck her hand into the oven for a piece of dry wood. With a bent wire she tried to remove a disk from the top of the stove. "Fui-fui,[1] with just that oil lamp I can't really see what I'm doing. No electricity at night. What's next? Industry needs it. Pooh, industry. What's the matter with houses?"

"Ma, I remember what you used to say. 'Electricity, pooh. That's for young people. For the few years I'm going to be around, oil lamps suit me fine.' How many years ago did you say that?"

"Ja, ja.[2] I can't help it."

---

[1]**Fui-fui** (foo'ee-foo'ee), an expression similar to "My, my."
[2]**Ja, ja** (ya, ya): Yes, yes.

"Johan," Dientje said, "I don't know what to do with all those city people who come to the door for food. Six today. They said they were lucky they could still drag themselves around. People are lying in the streets, starved to death, they said."

"Johan, they're so thin." Opoe's voice trembled.

"What did you give them?"

"A couple of potatoes each," Dientje said. "You know they wanted to give me a lot of money for them?"

"Don't take it."

"I didn't."

"It's a disgrace. So many farmers charge all they can get away with. It's a scandal."

"Now's when you get to know people. And most of 'em are no good." Opoe shook her head.

"But I didn't, Johan," Dientje said.

"A scandal."

"A few came from that town where they were fighting, Johan. Arnhem. That whole town's a ruin, they said. People from there are just wandering around Holland. Fui-fui, and with winter coming."

Johan scratched his head. "We've got the girls, or I'd say let some of them sleep in the garage. But we can't have any strangers poking around."

Out in the street a car stopped suddenly. The gate opened, and loud footsteps sounded at the side of the house. Boots. Johan pushed us upstairs. "Into the hiding place, fast."

My goodness, what a long time. Weren't they coming? What was going on?

"Sini," I whispered.

"Hush."

Hush for what? I shifted my weight from one leg to the other. The closet was getting stuffy.

The Germans had not come back to search the house again, Johan told us after they had left. They had come to tell him that they needed part of the house for their headquarters. "'Look,' I said, 'you don't want to live here. We haven't got running water.' But it didn't matter. 'Well,' I said, 'upstairs is out; you wouldn't want to climb those steep stairs. The only thing that makes sense is to let you have the three rooms in the front of the house.' I showed them the rooms, and they said they were fine." Noisily Johan blew his nose. "And I bet they'll be here day and night."

My hands felt clammy. I stared at my feet. They were ugly, not the kind of feet I read about in books.

"Well," Sini said, "what now? Do you think Mr. Hannink can find us another place?"

"Eh? What d'you mean? You're going to stay here. What else? Right, Dientje?"

"You'll have to be very careful," Dientje said, "but we wouldn't send you away."

"I'll tell you something: you're going to be pretty safe here. As long as you don't make any noise. Because what fool would search our house for Jews? Eh? Nobody. Ha, ha, Germans and you in the same house! How's that for a dumb farmer?" Johan wiped the tears from his eyes.

"But, Johan," Dientje said, "what if they come up the stairs?"

"I thought of that. I'm closing those three rooms off from the rest of the house, so nobody can get through that way. The only other way they can get to the stairs is through the kitchen. Either you or Ma have got to be there all day."

"But what if they go up anyway?"

"Dientje," Opoe warned, "keep your wits together."

"How long are they going to be here?" Sini asked.

"How could I have asked them that? Till the end of the war, maybe."

That could be a long time. Nothing new was happening.

"You'll have to stay in the back room all day because the front room's right over their offices."

"But, Johan, the girls will freeze in there. That's the coldest room in the house."

"They'll have to stay in bed, then."

"The radio, Johan," Sini said.

"We can't hear the news anymore. I'll have to take the radio out of that place and put it somewhere else. Can't leave my radio in their office, can I?"

"Then how will we find out what's really going on, Johan?"

"Don't worry. I'll find out. What a thing to have — German headquarters. Ma, how's that for excitement?"

Opoe shook her head. "I don't like it. And then those telephones they'll put in. Telephones. What's next! Have you ever talked on one?" she asked Sini.

"Sure, Opoe."

"What's it like?"

"That's hard to explain."

"Ja, ja, I guess."

"Johan, he said they were going to use the garage. Now, what if the girls come too close to the window? Johan,

I want their hair dyed. That dark hair is no good."

"How are we going to do that?"

"Go to Mr. Hannink. Maybe he has some stuff for it."

He did. I hated myself with red hair. I was never going to go outside again. Not even when the war was over. Furiously I pushed my chair against the wall. I liked it here.

The next week the Germans moved in. At the same time Sini and I started to live in bed. October 17, 1944 — that's what the calendar said.

The days were long and silent. Evenings were just as long and silent. Sini hardly talked. Maybe she would if I made her mad enough, but how could we fight if we could only whisper?

Opoe brought our meals up in a towel. "In case I meet one of 'em. They keep coming in the kitchen. For coffee, all kinds of things. Oh, what's that noise?"

"That's the telephone."

"You can hear it all the way up here? That's scary stuff. I better go downstairs."

Where it was warm. To them. What kind of headquarters was this anyway? Where they went in and out of the kitchen all the time, day and night, drinking coffee. I stuffed my pillow in my mouth and bit it until I felt nauseated.

Would they never go away? Restlessly I rolled around the bed.

"Watch it, I have a needle in my hand."

Didn't Dientje have the time to mend socks? After all, she sat in that kitchen all day. "Sini, don't you think so too?"

"Yes," she said. "How dare they have fun with those soldiers. One of them even calls Opoe 'Opoe.' And Johan is boasting that he's learning so much German. I'm out of wool." Her voice had become more and more annoyed. "And I wanted to finish this sock. Now I'll have to wait till Dientje comes up here with more wool sometime today."

She threw the sock down. "We're always waiting for somebody." She sobbed in her pillow. "I can't stand it any longer, Annie."

Well, why should she? I sat up.

"Where are you going?"

"Downstairs to get some wool."

She grabbed my arm. "Let go, Sini." How was I going to do it? "Leave it to me," I said, imitating Johan. "Sure, I'll be careful. I'm not crazy."

Carefully I got out of bed and crawled to the door. With difficulty I stood up. I moved my legs up and down a little bit. They ached. Four weeks in bed was a long time.

"Did you change your mind?"

"No, I just have to wait a few minutes before I can walk."

"Come back to bed and forget it. I can wait."

"No, no, I'm fine."

There, I was through the door. It was chilly. I shivered in my pajamas. It would actually be nice to go back to bed. Later I would, after I got the yarn. I grabbed the railing. Hesitantly I lowered one foot, then the other one. I put my weight on them only when they were both together on the same step. Next. Very well. Halfway down. I stopped a minute. The only sound came from their typewriter. Good, they were in the front. Well, maybe I could go a little faster, then. My legs felt better too. Walking could only be good for me.

There. I was at the bottom of the stairs. I put my hand on the doorknob and looked through the glass part of the door. Was anybody on the other side of it? No, no one. I probably picked a very good time to do this job. As quickly as I could, I crossed the room. Well, that wasn't so bad, was it? I put my cheek against the kitchen door. Nobody seemed to be there.

Wait a minute. That was Johan's voice. "What d'you think, Ma, are we going to get snow today?"

"We could. My head hurts an awful lot."

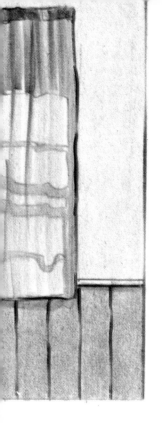

Then nothing. Dientje must not be in the kitchen. Maybe I should go back upstairs and try again later? No, Opoe probably knew where the wool was.

"We've got very little hay this winter. We're going to have a tough time."

"Ja, ja, I guess so."

Obviously there wasn't anybody in the kitchen but Opoe and Johan.

I touched the doorknob. I swallowed. Slowly I pushed the door open. And then faster. I stuck my head into the kitchen.

I saw only one face. It stuck out from a uniform. German.

I turned around, crossed the room, and went up the stairs.

"Didn't you get any yarn?" Sini asked. "Look at me. Something's wrong with you. What happened? Did you get to the kitchen?"

I stood by the door.

"Tell me what happened. Were they angry?"

I didn't move.

"Annie, what's going on? Come here." Sini was no longer whispering.

I couldn't move.

"Did you see Dientje?"

I shook my head. No.

"Who *did* you see. One of *them?*"

I nodded.

"Where."

"In the kitchen."

"But why did you go in there if they weren't by themselves?"

I licked my lips. "I thought they were."

Sini got out of bed. "Let's get dressed. Hurry up."

"Why are we getting dressed?"

"They'll be up here any minute to take us away."

With trembling hands, she opened the drawer and took out some clothes. Without looking at each other, we put them on.

We sat down on the bed in street clothes and waited. I was not even afraid. I felt nothing.

Was that them? No, Johan walked in. "You scared me, Annie. It was a good thing Dientje was in the stable. What came over you?"

I studied my nails. They needed cutting.

"Eh? Answer me."

"Johan, when are they coming?" Sini asked.

"Who?"

"The soldiers."

"They're not coming."

I looked up.

"For a minute I thought, 'What's going on?' I couldn't believe my eyes. There she was in her pajamas. 'Who's that little girl,' the German asked, 'and why is she so scared?' And then I came out with something pretty clever. I said, 'Oh, that's Rikie (ree'kee), Dientje's niece. She's been here for a day or two, and she's awfully shy. Maybe she'll come out later before she goes home.'

"So as soon as I could get away, I went to the stable to tell Dientje about it. 'Go to your sister and get the little girl. You can be back in a little over an hour.' 'But she's in school,' she said. 'So what?' I said to her. 'Go to the school and take her out.'

"'But my sister doesn't even know we've got Jews,' she said. 'Well,' I said, 'you've got to tell her.' 'But Rikie doesn't look like Annie,' Dientje said. She's right about that, but I figure the fellow didn't see you long enough to remember what you look like. What are you wearing those clothes for?"

"We thought they'd come upstairs and take us away."

"You didn't think I'd get you out of this mess? Eh? What's the matter with you?"

Funny to hear a girl's voice outside. What was her name again? Rikie? She should get together with the boy next door; then they could both laugh together.

I pulled my pajama sleeves down. Stupid kids. Bah. They don't know what is going on in the world. I'll bet they don't even know that Hitler is a maniac. I turned my back to the wall and stuck my fingers in my ears.

"I've got such a headache," Dientje said that night, "you can't imagine. What a day! And she didn't even know why she came with me."

"I had such a time keeping that little Rikie from going upstairs," Opoe said. "Fui-fui, she's a stubborn one. Nice enough, though. It wasn't smart what you did, Annie. He could've been nasty and followed you. And then what?"

And then what? Why were the Germans in the kitchen all the time? That's what I wanted to know. Maybe they even ate there, off plates. Unhappily I stared into the dark room. It wasn't right.

A week later we were startled by a lot of noise coming from the office, as if the furniture was being pushed around. We listened tensely. They were probably making room for more desks, Sini said. "They must have spread the word about what a wonderful house this is."

Yes, and what a warm kitchen.

But we were wrong.

"They packed up their stuff," Johan panted, "and they left, just like that. I'm glad. I was getting tired of having those fellows under foot all the time. Hey, Sini, I'm going to put the radio back in. Eh, for tonight?"

"Sure," she laughed. "Maybe the Allies are coming. Maybe that's why they left in such a hurry. I'll bet you that's what it is."

With wobbly steps I walked over to my window. It was covered with a layer of ice. I opened my mouth wide and breathed on it. Slowly the ice melted. I stopped when enough of the window was clear to let me see outside. Sky.

The Allies did not arrive in Usselo until the following spring. Then, at last, Annie and Sini were able to leave the upstairs room in which they had hidden for nearly three years and walk outside with the Oostervelds to celebrate the end of the German occupation.

DISCUSSION

1. From whose point of view was this story written? How do you know that? How would the story be different if it were told from Johan's point of view?

2. At the beginning of the story, what happened that forced Annie and Sini to go into the hiding place? Why was their experience in the hiding place so terrifying?

3. Why was Sini happy to hear that British parachutists had been dropped at Arnhem, Holland? What was Annie's reaction to the news? Why did she react in that way?

4. What did Johan's attitude toward farmers who took the city people's money for food tell you about him?

5. Why, do you think, were farm people like the Oostervelds able to survive better than most city people during the war?

6. Why, do you suppose, did Johan laugh heartily after describing himself as a "dumb farmer"?

7. Do you think the Oostervelds were sensible to act friendly with the German soldiers stationed in their home? Why or why not?

8. What were some of the things that made confinement to the upstairs room so hard for Annie and Sini to endure? If you had been in their situation, which one of those things do you think would have bothered you most? Why?

9. What made Annie finally decide to go downstairs? Why did Sini expect the Oostervelds to be angry at Annie for going there? What did they do instead to help insure the girls' safety?

10. At the end of the story, what do you think the sky outside might have represented to Annie? Why do you think that?

AUTHOR

Johanna de Leeuw Reiss, the Annie of the story you have just read, was born and brought up in Holland. There she and one of her sisters, in order to survive the Nazi holocaust during World War II, spent nearly three years hidden away in a tiny upstairs room. During that time she never went outside, and for several months she was not even allowed out of bed. She did not set out to write a book about her experiences; she simply wanted to record them for her own two daughters. "I didn't think it would take me more than a week," she says. "Not until I started to write did I find out how much I remembered, things I had never talked about with anyone because they were too painful." The resulting book, *The Upstairs Room,* received many awards and honors. It was selected as a Newbery Honor Book, an American Library Association Notable Children's Book, and a Jane Addams Peace Association Honor Book, and it won the Jewish Book Council Book Award and a prestigious German children's book award. It also appeared as a Dutch television special on Holland's Memorial Day.

After the war, Johanna de Leeuw graduated from high school and college in Holland and taught school there for several years before coming to the United States, where she married, raised two daughters, and worked as a consulting editor for a magazine. Every few years she returns to the Netherlands with her family to visit her sisters and to see the Oostervelds, the family who risked their lives to hide her.

Johanna Reiss tells more of her remarkable story in *The Journey Back,* a sequel to *The Upstairs Room.*

A Foot and a Half

Even as the boy-king of ancient Egypt, with all the wealth and power of that position, Tutankhamen was always subject to a higher power, as his name explains. When he came to power, the young boy's name was Tutankhaton, a combination of three pictorial symbols in Egyptian writing meaning *tut* ("pleasure") + *ankh* ("life") + *aton* ("the god Aton"). This translates to a meaning of "the life of Aton is pleasing." This name was given to the king to honor the god Aton, who was then the principal deity in Egypt. Somehow, with the passage of time, the god Aton lost favor and Amen took his place as the highest of the gods. This presented a problem for Tutankhaton, and he was forced to change his name to Tutankhamen. The substitution of *Amen* for *Aton* was a simple matter.

Like the name *Tutankhamen*, many other long and cumbersome words are understandable once they are divided into smaller parts. Some of them also tell stories. One of these is the name of such words, *sesquipedalian*. *Sesquipedalian* is itself a

417

sesquipedalian word, its parts *sesque-* ("one and a half") and *-ped-* ("foot") combining to mean "a foot and a half"; *-alian* is two suffixes that add the meaning "the means of." The word *sesquipedalian* means "having many syllables," "given to using long words," or "a long word." Someone concerned about even longer words coined the word *hippopotomonstrosesquipedalian* to describe them. You can see two parts of that word that suggest something huge: *hippopoto* and *monstro.*

Another such word is *antidisestablishmentarianism.* This seemingly endless word simply means a doctrine (*-ism*) based on the belief (*-arian*) that opposes (*anti-*) the idea of opposing (*dis-*) the state of being (*-ment*) of what is established (*establish*). This word does seem to twist and turn a bit more than necessary, but its length commands attention. Originally describing a doctrine held by a particular group of people in the 1800's, the word no longer has a use.

Fortunately, our language contains few such words. You can see that they have little practical value. Although *pneumonoultramicroscopicsilicovolcanokoniosis* is precisely the right term for a disease of the lungs that afflicts some miners, few people need to learn to pronounce or spell it! It would take most of a page to list the parts of that word and their meanings, but you would discover that they are not really so unfamiliar. A word with even less practical value is *supercalifragilisticexpialidocious,* an adjective meaning "atoning for extreme delicate beauty while highly educable." And what does that mean? It's pure nonsense!

You may be able to imagine only occasional use for such words as *floccinaucinihilipilification* ("the categorizing of something as worthless trivia"), *honorificabilitudinitatibus* ("with honorablenesses"), or *philisophicopsychological* ("both philosophical and psychological"). You can certainly see the usefulness of the Indian name for a Massachusetts lake, *Chargoggagoggmanchauggagoggchaubunagungamaugg,* which means "You fish on your side; I fish on my side; nobody fish in the middle."

If you looked in a dictionary for several sesquipedalian words, you might be surprised to find that some very long words are not so difficult to understand. Quite a few that have five or six syllables, such as *superintendent, unimaginable, supersaturated,* or *miniaturizing,* are words that you might even use.

Books to Enjoy

Escape to Freedom by Ossie Davis
In this play by a leading dramatist, the early years of Frederick Douglass, a major figure in American history, come alive.

Cromwell's Boy by Erik Christian Haugaard
A sequel to *A Messenger for Parliament* continues the adventures of the orphan Oliver, now a spy during the English Civil War.

Buffalo Woman by Dorothy M. Johnson
The engrossing story of Whirlwind, a courageous Sioux woman, spans the years 1820 to 1877 in the American West.

Mischling, Second Degree by Ilse Koehn
This is a vivid memoir of a young woman who grew up in Nazi Germany unaware that her paternal grandmother was Jewish.

Galloping Wind by Zoltan Malocsay
Set in the Rockies in 1896, this rousing wild horse story tells how the son of a mustanger tracks down the stallion the Cheval Indians call "The Wind That Gallops."

Behind the Sealed Door
by Irene and Laurence Swinburne
The discovery of the tomb and treasures of King Tutankhamen is presented in lustrous color photographs and brief text.

Awards

MAGAZINE FOUR

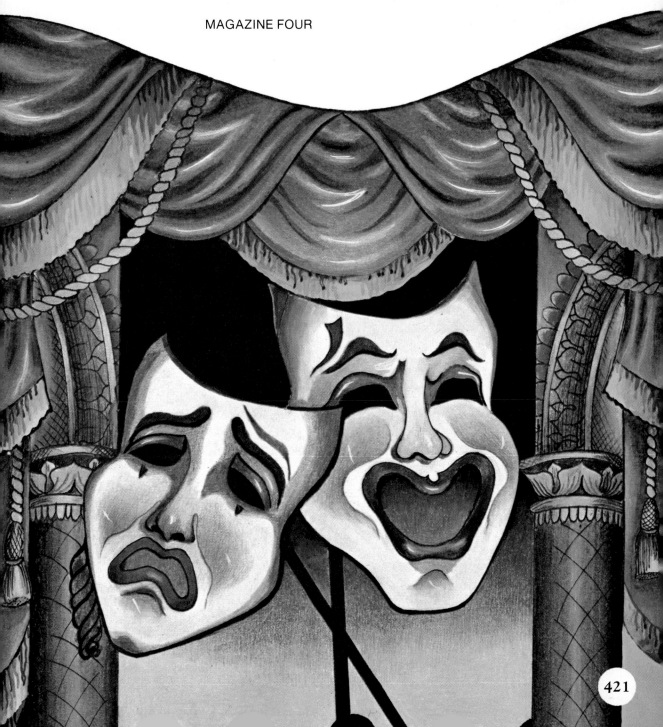

Contents

ROOTS

by ALEX HALEY

When I was a little boy of about five, I was living with my recently widowed Grandma Palmer in Henning, Tennessee. Each spring, to fill the void of Grandpa's absence, she used to invite various Murray family female relatives of hers to spend the summers with us. Averaging in her age range, the late forties and early fifties, they had names like Aunt Plus, Aunt Liz, Aunt Till, Aunt Viney, and Cousin Georgia.

When the supper dishes had been washed, they all would go out on the front porch and sit in cane-bottomed rocking chairs, and I would sort of scrunch myself down behind the white-painted rocker holding Grandma. Unless there was some local priority gossip, always they would talk about the same thing — snatches and patches of what later I'd learn was the long, cumulative family narrative that had been passed down across the generations.

The farthest-back person they ever talked about was a man they called "the African," who they always said had been brought to this country on a ship to some place that they pronounced "'Naplis." They said he was bought off this ship by a Massa John Waller, who had a plantation in a place called Spotsylvania County, Virginia. They would tell how the African kept trying to escape and how on the fourth effort he was captured by two white slave catchers, who apparently decided to make an example of him by cutting off one of his feet.

Massa John Waller's brother, a Dr. William Waller, was so mad about the maiming that he bought the African for his own plantation. Though now the African was crippled, he could do limited work in the vegetable garden.

Grandma and the others said that Africans fresh off slave ships were given some name by their massas. In this particular African's case, the name was Toby. But they said any time any of the other slaves called him that, he would strenuously rebuff them, declaring that his name was Kin-tay.

Toby — or Kin-tay — eventually became the mate of a woman slave, Bell, the big-house cook. They had a little girl who was given the name Kizzy. When she was about four to five years old, her African father began to lead her around, pointing out different things to her and repeating to her their names in his own native tongue. He would point at a guitar, for example, and say something that sounded like "ko." Or he would point at the river that ran near the plantation — actually the Mattaponi River — and say what sounded like "Kamby Bolongo." As Kizzy grew older and her African father learned English better, he began telling her stories about himself, his people, and his homeland — and how he was taken away from it. He said that he had been out in the forest not far from his village, chopping wood to make a drum, when he had been surprised by four men, overwhelmed, and kidnaped into slavery.

When Kizzy was sixteen years old, Grandma Palmer and the other Murray family ladies said, she was sold away to a new master named Tom Lea, who owned a small plantation in North Carolina. On this plantation Kizzy gave birth to a boy, who was given the name George.

When George got to be around four or five years old, his mother began to tell him her African father's sounds and stories until he came to know them well. George earned such a reputation as a game-cock trainer that he was given the nickname Chicken George.

Chicken George, when around eighteen, met a slave girl named Mathilda, who bore him eight children. With each new child's birth, Chicken George would gather his family within their slave cabin, telling them afresh about their African great-grandfather, Kin-tay.

The eight children grew up, took mates, and had their own children. The fourth son, Tom, was a blacksmith when he was sold along with the rest of his family to a Massa Murray, who owned a tobacco plantation in Alamance County, North Carolina. There Tom met a half-Indian slave girl named Irene, who eventually also bore eight children. With each new birth, Tom continued the tradition his father, Chicken George, had begun, telling his family about their African great-great-grandfather and about all those descending from him.

Of that second set of eight children, the youngest was a girl named Cynthia, who became my maternal Grandma. She was two years old when her father, Tom, and grandfather, Chicken George, led a wagon train of freed slaves westward to Henning, Tennessee, where Cynthia met and, at the age of twenty-two, married Will Palmer.

Invariably it would astonish me when the narrative finally got to Cynthia . . . and there I sat looking right at Grandma — as well as Aunt Viney, Aunt Matilda, and Aunt Liz (her older sisters), who had ridden right along with Grandma in the wagon train.

Almost three decades later, while working as a free-lance writer, I was sent to London on an assignment by a magazine. Poking about one day in the British Museum between appointments, I found myself looking at the Rosetta Stone.

Discovered in the Nile Delta, I learned, the stone's face had chiseled into it three separate texts: one in known Greek characters, the second in a then-unknown set of characters, the third in the ancient hieroglyphics, which it had been assumed no one ever would be able to translate. But a French scholar, Jean Champollion (zhahn shahn-po-lyohn′), matched, character for character, both the unknown text and the hieroglyphics with the known Greek text, and he offered a thesis that the texts read the same. Essentially, he had cracked the mystery of the previously undeciphered hieroglyphics in which much of humanity's earliest history was recorded.

The French scholar had deciphered an ancient unknown by matching it with something that *was* known. That presented me a rough analogy: In the oral history that Grandma, Aunt Liz, Aunt Plus, Cousin Georgia, and the others had always told, I had an unknown in those strange words or sounds passed on by the African. "What specific African tongue was it?" I wondered. "Is there any way in the world that maybe I can find out?"

Now, over thirty years later, the sole surviving one of the old ladies who had talked the family narrative on the Henning front porch was the youngest among them, Cousin Georgia Anderson. Grandma was gone, and all of the others too. In her eighties now, Cousin Georgia lived in Kansas City, Kansas. I flew to Kansas City to see Cousin Georgia.

I think that I will never quite get over her instant response when I raised the subject of the family story. Wrinkled and ailing, she bolted upright in her bed, her excitement like echoes of the front porch of my boyhood, exclaiming, "Yeah, boy, dat African say his name was Kin-tay! . . . He say de guitar a *ko,* de river Kamby Bolongo, an' he was choppin' wood to make hisself a drum when dey catched 'im!"

I explained to her that I wanted to try to see if there was any way that I could possibly find where our Kin-tay had come from . . . which could reveal *our* ancestral tribe.

"You go 'head boy!" exclaimed Cousin Georgia. "Your sweet grandma an' all of 'em — dey up dere *watchin'* you!"

Soon after, I went to the National Archives in Washington, D.C., and asked for the Alamance County, North Carolina, census records just after the Civil War. Tiring after studying several of the long microfilm rolls, I found myself looking down on: "Tom Murray, black, blacksmith," "Irene Murray, black, housewife." They were followed by the names of Grandma's older sisters. "Elizabeth, age 6" — nobody in the world but my great-aunt Liz! At the time of that census, Grandma wasn't even born yet!

Then living in New York, I returned to Washington as often as I could manage it — searching in the National Archives, in the Library of Congress, in the Daughters of the American Revolution Library. Wherever I was, whenever black library attendants perceived the nature of my search, documents I'd requested would reach me with a miraculous speed. From one or another source during 1966, I was able to document at least the highlights of the cherished family story.

Now the question was, where and how could I pursue those strange phonetic sounds that it was always said our African ancestor had spoken? There in New York City, I began arriving at the United Nations around quitting time. It wasn't hard to spot the Africans, and every one I was able to stop, I'd tell my sounds to. Each of them gave me a quick look, a quick listen, and then took off. I can't say I blame them — trying to communicate some African sounds in a Tennessee accent.

Increasingly frustrated, I had a long talk with a friend who told me about a renowned Belgian linguist, Dr. Jan Vansina, who had lived in several African villages and had written a book about oral history. I telephoned Dr. Vansina at the University of Wisconsin, where he now taught, and he invited me to see him. When I arrived in Madison, Wisconsin, I told him every syllable I could remember of the family narrative heard since little boyhood. Dr. Vansina said he felt certain that the sounds were from the Mandinka

tongue, the language spoken by the Mandingo people. The word *ko,* he said, could refer to the *kora,* one of the Mandingo people's oldest stringed instruments. Dr. Vansina said that without question *bolongo* meant, in the Mandinka tongue, a moving water, as a river; preceded by *Kamby,* it could indicate the Gambia River.

Speaking at a seminar held at Utica College, Utica, New York, I learned of a Gambian student at nearby Hamilton College, Ebou Manga. I found him in an agricultural economics class. Ebou tentatively confirmed my sounds. In his dormitory room, I told him about my quest. We left for The Gambia at the end of the following week.

Arriving in Dakar, Senegal, the next morning, we caught a light plane to small Yundum Airport in The Gambia. In a passenger van, we rode into the capital city of Banjul (then Bathurst). Ebou and his father assembled a group of men knowledgeable about their small country's history. I told these men the family narrative that had come down across the generations. When I had finished, they said, almost with wry amusement, "Well, of course Kamby Bolongo would mean the Gambia River; anyone would know that." They showed a much greater interest in the fact that my 1760's ancestor had insisted his name was Kin-tay. "Our country's oldest villages tend to be named for the families that settled those villages centuries ago," they said. Sending for a map, pointing, they said, "Look, here is the village of Kinte-Kundah. And not far from it, the village of Kinte-Kundah Janneh-Ya."

They told me of very old men called *griots* (grih'oz), still found in the older backcountry villages, men who were in effect living, walking archives of oral history. A senior *griot* would be a man usually in his late sixties or early seventies; below him would be progressively younger *griots* — and apprenticing boys. A boy would be exposed to those *griots'* particular line of narrative for forty or fifty years before he could qualify as a senior *griot*, who told on special occasions the centuries-old histories of villages, of clans, of families, of great heroes.

Since my forefather had said his name was Kin-tay — properly spelled *Kinte*, they said — and since the Kinte clan was old and well known in The Gambia, they promised to do what they could to find a *griot* who might be able to assist my search.

Back in the United States, I began devouring books on African history. It grew quickly into some kind of obsession to correct my ignorance concerning the earth's second-largest continent. It embarrasses me to this day that up to then my knowledge about Africa had been so limited.

After some weeks, a registered letter came from The Gambia; it suggested that, when possible, I should come back.

I again visited Cousin Georgia in Kansas City. Something had urged me to do so, and I found her quite ill. But she was thrilled to hear both what I had learned and what I hoped to learn. She wished me Godspeed, and I flew to Africa.

The same men with whom I had previously talked told me now that a *griot* very knowledgeable about the Kinte clan had indeed been found. His name, they said, was Kebba Kanji Fofana. To see this *griot*, I had to organize what seemed, at least to me then, a kind of minisafari. It took me three days of negotiating through unaccustomed, endless African palaver finally to hire a launch to get upriver; to rent a lorry and a four-wheel-drive vehicle to take supplies by a roundabout land route; to hire a total of fourteen people, including three interpreters and four musicians, since I had been told that the *griots* wouldn't talk without background music.

In the launch *Baddibu*, vibrating up the wide, swift "Kamby Bolongo," I felt queasily, uncomfortably alien. Did they all have me appraised as merely another pith helmet? Finally, ahead was James

430

Island, for two centuries the site of a fort over which England and France waged war back and forth for the ideal vantage point to trade in slaves. Asking if we might land there a while, I trudged amid the crumbling ruins yet guarded by ghostly cannon. Picturing in my mind the kinds of atrocities that would have happened there, I felt as if I would like to go flailing an ax back through that facet of black Africa's history. Then we went on, and upon arriving at a little village called Albreda, we put ashore. Our destination, now on foot, was the yet smaller village of Juffure.

There is an expression called "the peak experience" — an experience that nothing else in your life ever transcends emotionally. I've had mine, that first day in the backcountry of black West Africa.

When we got within sight of Juffure, the children who were playing outside gave the alert, and the people came flocking from their huts. It's a village of only about seventy people. Like most back-country villages, it was still very much as it had been two hundred years ago, with its circular mud houses and their conical thatched roofs. Among the people as they gathered was a small man wearing an off-white robe and a pillbox hat over an aquiline-featured black face, and about him there was such an aura of "somebodiness" that I knew he was the man we had come to see and hear.

As the three interpreters left our party to converge upon him, the seventy-odd other villagers gathered closely around me, in a kind of horseshoe pattern, three or four deep all around; had I stuck out my arms, my fingers would have touched the nearest ones on either side. They were all staring at me.

431

The eyes just raked me. Their foreheads were furrowed with their very intensity of staring. A kind of surging or a churning sensation started up deep inside me; bewildered, I was wondering what on earth was this . . . then in a little while it was rather as if some full-gale force of realization rolled in on me: Many times in my life I had been among crowds of people but never where *every one was jet black!* My glance fell upon my own hands' brown complexion, and another gale-force emotion hit me; I felt myself some variety of hybrid. I felt somehow impure among the pure; it was a terribly shaming feeling. About then, abruptly, the old man left the interpreters. The people immediately also left me now to go crowding about him.

One of my interpreters came up quickly and whispered in my ear, "They stare at you so much because they have never here seen a black American." When I grasped the significance, I believe that hit me harder than what had already happened. They hadn't been looking at me as an individual — I represented in their eyes a symbol of the twenty-five millions of us black people whom they had never seen, who lived beyond an ocean.

The people were clustered thickly about the old man, all of them intermittently flicking glances toward me as they talked animatedly in their Mandinka tongue. After a while, the old man turned, walked briskly through the people, past my three interpreters, and right up to me. His eyes piercing into mine, seeming to feel I should understand his Mandinka, he expressed what they had all decided they *felt* concerning those unseen millions of us who lived in those places that had been slave ships' destinations — and the translation came: "We have been told by the forebears that there are many of us from this place who are in exile in that place called America — and in other places."

The old man sat down, facing me, as the people hurriedly gathered behind him. Then he began to recite for me the ancestral history of the Kinte clan as it had been passed along orally down across centuries from the forebears' time. Spilling from the *griot's* head came an incredibly complex Kinte clan lineage that reached back across many generations: who married whom; who had what children; what children then married whom; then their offspring.

Simplified to its essence, this is the saga that the *griot* told me: The Kinte clan had begun in the country called Old Mali. Then the Kinte men traditionally were blacksmiths, those "who had conquered fire," and the women mostly were potters and weavers. In time, one branch of the clan moved into the country then called Mauretania; and it was from there that one son of this clan, Kairaba Kunta Kinte — a holy man of the Moslem faith — journeyed down into the country called The Gambia. He went first to a village called Pakali N'Ding, stayed there for a while, then went to a village called Jiffarong, and then to the village of Juffure.

In Juffure, Kairaba Kunta Kinte took his first wife, a Mandingo maiden whose name was Sireng. And by her he begot two sons, whose names were Janneh and Saloum. Then he took a second wife, Yaisa. And by Yaisa, he begot a son named Omoro.

Those three sons grew up in Juffure until they became of age. Then the elder two, Janneh and Saloum, went away and founded a new village called Kinte-Kundah Janneh-Ya. The youngest son, Omoro, stayed on in Juffure village until he was thirty rains — years — of age; then he took as his wife a Mandingo maiden named Binta Kebba. And by Binta Kebba, roughly between the years 1750 and 1760, Omoro Kinte begot four sons, whose names were, in the order of their birth, Kunta, Lamin, Suwadu, and Madi.

The old griot had talked for nearly two hours up to then, and perhaps fifty times the narrative had included some detail about someone whom he had named.

Now, after he had just named those four sons, again he appended a detail, and the interpreter translated: "About the time the King's soldiers came" — another of the griot's time-fixing references — "the eldest of these four sons, Kunta, went away from his village to chop wood . . . and he was never seen again. . . ." And the griot went on with his narrative.

I sat as if I were carved of stone!!! This man whose lifetime had been in this backcountry African village had no way in the world to know that he had just echoed what I had heard all through my boyhood on my Grandma's front porch in Henning, Tennessee . . . about an African who always had insisted that his name was Kin-tay; who had called a guitar a ko and a river, within the state of Virginia, Kamby Bolongo; and who had been kidnaped into slavery while not far from his village, chopping wood to make himself a drum.

I managed to fumble from my duffel bag my basic notebook, whose first pages containing Grandma's story I showed to an interpreter. After briefly reading, clearly astounded, he spoke rapidly while showing it to the old griot, who became agitated. He got up, exclaiming to the people, gesturing at my notebook in the interpreter's hands, and they all got agitated. They formed a wide human ring

around me, moving counterclockwise, chanting softly, loudly, softly; their bodies close together, they were lifting their knees high, stamping up reddish puffs of the dust. . . .

The woman who broke from the moving circle was one of about a dozen whose infant children were within cloth slings across their backs. Her jet-black face deeply contorting, the woman came charging toward me, her bare feet slapping the earth, and snatching her baby free, she thrust it at me almost roughly, the gesture saying "Take it!" . . . and I did, clasping the baby to me. Then she snatched away her

baby; and another woman was thrusting her baby, then another, and another . . . until I had embraced probably a dozen babies. I wouldn't learn until maybe a year later that I was participating in one of the oldest ceremonies of humankind, called "the laying on of hands"! In their way, they were telling me, "Through this flesh, which is us, we are you, and you are us!"

Later the men of Juffure took me into their mosque built of bamboo and thatch, and they prayed around me in Arabic. The crux of their prayer was translated for me in these words: "Praise be to Allah for one long lost from us whom Allah has returned."

Since we had come by the river, I wanted to return by land. As I sat beside the wiry young Mandingo driver who was leaving dust pluming behind us on the hot, rough, pitted, backcountry road toward Banjul, there came into my head a staggering awareness. I realized that *if* any black American could be as blessed as I had been in knowing a few ancestral clues — if he or she could know *who* was either the paternal or maternal African ancestor or ancestors, and about *where* that ancestor lived when taken, and finally about *when* the ancestor was taken — then only those few clues might well see that black American able to locate some wizened old black *griot* whose narrative could reveal the black American's ancestral clan.

In my mind's eye, rather as if it were mistily being projected on a screen, I began envisioning descriptions I had read of how, collectively, millions of our ancestors had been enslaved. Many thousands were individually kidnaped, as my own forebear Kunta had been, but millions had come awake screaming in the night, dashing out into the bedlam of raided villages, which were often in flames. The captured able survivors were linked neck-by-neck with thongs into processions called coffles, which were sometimes as much as a mile in length. I envisioned the many dying or left to die when they were too weak to continue the torturous march toward the coast, and those who made it to the beach being greased, shaved, probed, often branded with sizzling irons. I envisioned them being lashed and dragged toward the longboats; I saw their spasms of screaming and clawing with their hands into the beach, biting up great choking mouthfuls of the sand in their desperate efforts for one last hold on the Africa that had been their home. I envisioned them shoved, beaten, jerked down into slave ships' stinking holds, and chained onto shelves, often packed so tightly that they had to lie on their sides like spoons in a drawer. . . .

My mind reeled with it all as we approached another, much larger village. Staring ahead, I realized that word of what had happened in Juffure must have left there well before I did. The driver slowed down, and I could see this village's people thronging the road ahead when it suddenly registered in my brain what they were all crying out. They were all crying out together, *"Meester Kinte! Meester Kinte!!!!"*

Let me tell you something: I am a human being. A sob hit me somewhere around my ankles; it came surging upward, and flinging my hands over my face, I was just bawling as I hadn't since I was a baby. *"Meester Kinte!"* I just felt as though I was weeping for all of history's incredible atrocities against fellow human beings.

Flying homeward from Dakar, I decided to write a book. My own ancestors would automatically also be a symbolic saga of all African-descent people — who are without exception the seeds of someone like Kunta who grew up in some African village, someone who was captured and chained down in one of those slave ships that sailed him or her across the same ocean, into some succession of plantations and, since then, into a struggle for freedom.

In New York, my waiting telephone messages included one saying that in a Kansas City hospital, Cousin Georgia had died. Later I discovered that she had passed away within the very hour that I had walked into Juffure. I think that as the last of the old ladies who talked the story on Grandma's porch, she had had the job of getting me to Africa before she joined the others up there watchin'.

Always, Grandma and the other old ladies had said that a ship brought the African to "somewhere called 'Naplis." I knew they had to have been referring to Annapolis, Maryland. So I felt now that I had to try to see if I could find *what* ship had sailed to Annapolis from the Gambia River with its human cargo, including "the African."

I needed to determine a time around which to focus search for this ship. In the village of Juffure, the *griot* had timed Kunta's capture with "about the time the King's soldiers came."

Returning to London, midway during a second week of searching in records of movement assignments from British military units during the 1760's, I finally found that "King's soldiers" *had* to refer to a unit called "Colonel O'Hare's forces." The unit was sent from London in 1767 to guard the then British-operated Fort James, a slave fort on the Gambia River.

I went to Lloyd's[1] of London. In the office of an executive, what I was trying to do just poured out of me. He promised to help as much as he could. It was a blessing, for through Lloyd's, doors began to open for me to search among myriad old English maritime records.

I can't remember any more exhausting experience than my first six weeks of seemingly endless, futile, day-after-day searching in an effort to isolate and then pin down a specific slave ship on a specific voyage from within cartons upon cartons, files upon files, of records

---

[1] **Lloyd's,** a corporation founded in 1688 that originally specialized in marine insurance and shipping data. Today it is noted for the variety of insurance written.

of thousands of triangular-trade slave-ship voyages made between England, Africa, and America. Along with my frustration, the more a rage grew within me, the more I perceived to what degree the slave trade, in its time, was regarded by most of its participants simply as another major industry.

I hadn't found a single ship bound from The Gambia to Annapolis when in the seventh week, one afternoon about two-thirty, I was studying the 1,023rd sheet of slave-ship records. A wide rectangular sheet, it recorded the Gambia River entrances and exits of some thirty ships during the years 1766 and 1767. Moving down the list, my eyes reached ship No. 18 and automatically scanned across its various data entries.

On July 5, 1767 — the year "the King's soldiers came" — a ship named *Lord Ligonier,* her captain a Thomas E. Davies, had sailed from the Gambia River, her destination Annapolis. . . .

The airline confirmed the last seat available that day to New York. There simply wasn't time to go by the hotel where I was staying; I told a taxi driver, "Heathrow Airport!" Sleepless through that night's crossing of the Atlantic, I was seeing in my mind's eye the book in the Library of Congress, Washington, D.C., that I had to get my hands on again — a book called *Shipping in the Port of Annapolis* by Vaughan W. Brown.

From New York, the air shuttle took me to Washington; I taxied to the Library of Congress, ordered the book, almost yanked it from the young man who brought it, and went riffling through it . . . and there it was, confirmation! The *Lord Ligonier* had cleared customs at Annapolis on September 29, 1767.

Renting a car, speeding to Annapolis, I went to the Maryland Hall of Records and asked the archivist for copies of any local newspaper published around the first week of October, 1767. She soon produced a microfilm roll of the Maryland *Gazette.* At the projection machine, I was halfway through the October 1 issue when I saw the advertisement in the antique typeface: "JUST IMPORTED, In the ship *Lord Ligonier,* Capt. Davies, from the River Gambia, in Africa, and to be sold by the subscribers, in Annapolis, for cash, or good bills of exchange on Wednesday the 7th of October next, A Cargo of CHOICE HEALTHY SLAVES. The said ship will take tobacco to London on liberty at 6s. Sterling per ton." The advertisement was signed by John Ridout and Daniel of St. Thos. Jenifer.

On September 29, 1967, I felt I should be nowhere else in the world except standing on a pier at Annapolis — and I was; it was two hundred years to the day after the *Lord Ligonier* had landed. Staring across those waters over which my great-great-great-great-grandfather had been brought, again I found myself weeping.

The 1766–1767 document compiled at James Fort in the Gambia River had included that the *Lord Ligonier* had sailed with 140 slaves in the hold. How many of them had lived through the voyage? Now, on a second mission in the Maryland Hall of Records, I searched to find a record of the ship's cargo listed on arrival — and found it, the following inventory, written in old-fashioned script: 3,265 "elephants' teeth," as ivory tusks were called; 3,700 pounds of beeswax; 800 pounds of raw cotton; 32 ounces of Gambian gold; and 98 "Negroes." Its loss of 42 Africans en route, or around one third, was average for slaving voyages.

I realized by this time that Grandma, Aunt Liz, Aunt Plus, and Cousin Georgia also had been *griots* in their own way. My notebooks contained their centuries-old story that our African had been sold to Massa John Waller, who had given him the name Toby. During his fourth escape effort, when cornered, he had wounded with a rock one of the pair of professional slave catchers who caught him, and they had cut his foot off. Massa John's brother, Dr. William Waller, had saved the slave's life; then, indignant at the maiming, he had bought him from his brother. I dared to hope that some record might exist.

I went to Richmond, Virginia. I pored through microfilmed legal deeds filed within Spotsylvania County, Virginia, after September, 1767, when the *Lord Ligonier* had landed. In time, I found a lengthy deed dated September 5, 1768, in which John Waller and his wife, Ann, transferred to William Waller land and goods, including 240 acres of farmland . . . and then, on the second page, "and also one Negro slave named Toby."

DISCUSSION

1. Do you think it is valuable for people to know about their roots? Why or why not?

2. How had the stories Alex Haley heard as a child been passed down through several generations? Why did he remember them so well?

3. What African words did Alex Haley's first American ancestor use to name himself, a guitar, and a nearby river? How were

these African words useful in Alex Haley's research? How did he find out that his ancestor had been speaking the Mandinka language and had probably lived near the Gambia River?

4. How did Ebou Manga's father and his friends confirm Alex Haley's being on the right track? Why were they particularly interested in the name that Mr. Haley's ancestor had insisted was his name?

5. What did the men Alex Haley met in the Gambia do to help him find out more about the Kinte clan?

6. In your opinion, what made Mr. Haley call his first day in the African backcountry "the peak experience" of his life?

7. What one thing did Mr. Haley remember that later helped prove that he had found the African village from which his ancestor had come? Why did the *griot* and the villagers become so excited when they heard about the story Mr. Haley had learned from his grandmother?

8. Do you think the work of the *griots* is important? Why do you think as you do? Why did Alex Haley feel that his grandmother and other relatives "had been *griots* in their own way"?

9. In what ways is Alex Haley's story like a detective story?

AUTHOR

Alex Haley is a self-taught writer who developed his talent during a twenty-year career in the United States Coast Guard. When he retired, he embarked on a new career as a professional writer. Since then he has written magazine articles, screenplays, and books, including an adult best-selling biography of Malcolm X. In 1976, after twelve years of genealogical detective work, he completed his book *Roots,* from which this selection was taken. In recognition of this outstanding work, he was awarded a special Pulitzer prize, and the United States Senate honored him by passing a resolution of tribute.

Alex Haley has established the Alex Haley Roots Foundation to provide scholarships for post-graduate study in black history and to help build bridges between Africans and Americans.

African Proverbs

by KOFI ASARE OPOKU

African proverbs express the wisdom of the African people and are a key to the understanding of African ways of life in the past and in the present.

All people are believed to possess wisdom, and the Akan (ah-kahn) people of Ghana (gah'nuh) tell an interesting story of how it spread to all parts of the world:

Long, long ago there lived a man called Kwaku Ananse (kwah'koo ah-nahn'sih). Ananse possessed all the wisdom in the world, but so selfish was he that he did not want to share it with anybody. He decided to collect it in a big pot and hide it at the top of a big, tall tree in the forest. Ananse's wife got him the largest pot she could find, and Ananse began to fill it with wisdom. He told no one what he was doing.

When he had finished, he fastened a rope around the pot, tied the rest of it around his neck, and sneaked out of the house in the dead of night, the pot hanging on his belly. Ananse walked clumsily into the thickest part of the forest until he came to the tree that he thought would serve his purpose and stopped.

Ananse did not think that any of the members of his house had seen him, but he was mistaken. His son, Ntikuma (ntee-koo'mah), had been awakened by the noise his father made and had followed Ananse, curious to see just what Ananse was going to do. Ntikuma hid himself behind a tree a good distance away and gazed intently at his father.

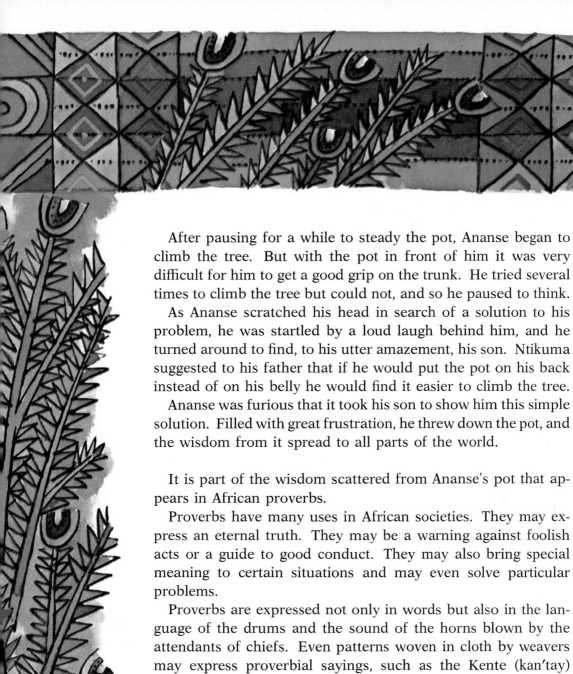

After pausing for a while to steady the pot, Ananse began to climb the tree. But with the pot in front of him it was very difficult for him to get a good grip on the trunk. He tried several times to climb the tree but could not, and so he paused to think.

As Ananse scratched his head in search of a solution to his problem, he was startled by a loud laugh behind him, and he turned around to find, to his utter amazement, his son. Ntikuma suggested to his father that if he would put the pot on his back instead of on his belly he would find it easier to climb the tree.

Ananse was furious that it took his son to show him this simple solution. Filled with great frustration, he threw down the pot, and the wisdom from it spread to all parts of the world.

It is part of the wisdom scattered from Ananse's pot that appears in African proverbs.

Proverbs have many uses in African societies. They may express an eternal truth. They may be a warning against foolish acts or a guide to good conduct. They may also bring special meaning to certain situations and may even solve particular problems.

Proverbs are expressed not only in words but also in the language of the drums and the sound of the horns blown by the attendants of chiefs. Even patterns woven in cloth by weavers may express proverbial sayings, such as the Kente (kan'tay) pattern *Ti koro nko agyina* (tih ko-ro nko ahg'yee'nah) — "One head does not go into council (It is better if two heads make a decision)" — which the Republic of Ghana presented to the United Nations. It may be seen hanging on one of the walls in the delegates' lounge in the United Nations Building in New York City.

The Yoruba (yo'roo-bah') of Nigeria (nie-jeer'ee-uh) emphasize the value of proverbs by saying "A proverb is the horse that can carry one swiftly to the discovery of ideas." The following proverbs will give some insight into an important aspect of African culture and help to increase human understanding.

If you are greedy in conversation, you lose the wisdom of your friend.

The hand of the child cannot reach the shelf, nor can the hand of the adult get through the neck of a gourd.

To forget is the same as to throw away.

To own only a few things is better than to be a thief.

People are the home.

When a fowl is eating your neighbor's corn, drive it away, or someday it will eat yours.

Even the greatest bird must come down from the sky to find a tree to roost upon.

When the right hand washes the left and the left hand washes the right, then both hands will be clean.

The wise person who does not learn ceases to be wise.

If you see wrongdoing or evil and say nothing against it, you become its victim.

When two antelopes are fighting and a lion approaches, the antelopes run off together (forgetting their quarrel).

The one who asks the way does not get lost.

DISCUSSION

1. What uses do proverbs have in African societies? Do you think proverbs may have some of the same uses in your own society? Tell why you think as you do.
2. What do you think the Yoruba of Nigeria meant by saying, "A proverb is the horse that can carry one swiftly to the discovery of ideas"?
3. In what other ways besides words are African proverbs expressed? Do you think the proverbial saying that was presented to the United Nations by the Republic of Ghana was appropriate? Why do you think that?
4. Why, do you think, did the author include the African story about how Kwaku Ananse spread wisdom to all parts of the world in this selection?
5. Using your own words, explain the meaning of a proverb that you feel gives good advice. Can you think of a situation in which to apply that advice? If so, describe that situation.
6. According to the author, African proverbs are a key to the understanding of African ways of life. How do you think understanding the proverbs of different peoples might help to increase international understanding among peoples?

AUTHOR

Kofi Asare Opoku is a Ghanaian whose primary work has been researching African culture, religion, and oral literature. A graduate of the University of Ghana, Mr. Opoku spent six and a half years in the United States, where he studied at Yale University Divinity School, as well as a year in West Germany at the University of Bonn. He has traveled extensively in the United States, Canada, Europe, and Africa.

Mr. Opoku's hobbies are photography, traveling, and collecting African stories and proverbs. He says that his book *Speak to the Winds: Proverbs from Africa* is an attempt to introduce young people to the traditional wisdom and values of Africa.

Klondike Kate

by LYNN HALL

Some dogs live out their lives without ever seeing their owners. They are born, raised, exhibited, retired, and buried at the kennel of a professional handler or trainer. Often the owners are wealthy people whose life-styles are incompatible with dog ownership but who have a genuine love for either fine dogs or, perhaps, well-filled trophy cases.

Klondike Kate was one such dog. Her legal owner was a Philadelphia industrialist, but she had no knowledge of his existence. Her entire three years had been spent in the fourth run on the right in the kennel of Arthur West, professional handler of show dogs, sporting breeds a specialty.

For a golden retriever, Kate was small — at least she gave the appearance of being small, partly because she spent every waking moment in a frightened crouch. When the door from her pen to her run was opened, she bolted in or out, in terror of being touched. If a person stood above her and looked directly down into her

eyes, the tension was enough to send her spinning in a frenzy at our feet.

To my almost certain knowledge, Kate had never in her life been mistreated or spoken to in a harsh tone. The only humans she had any contact with at all were Mr. or Mrs. West or myself, and all three of us were dog lovers of the highest order. Kate's was a classic case of kennel shyness. It happens sometimes to a dog who has inherited a tendency toward neurotic behavior and who, in those crucial first weeks of life, does not receive a great deal of human socializing.

I was working that spring for Arthur West, helping with the kennel work and, on weekends, assisting him on the dog-show circuits, so for those months most of Kate's care fell to me. With twenty setters, pointers, and retrievers to take care of, I had little time to spend with Kate, but because I was too young to have learned my limitations and because I had romantic notions of the power of love, I did try to break down Kate's fear.

After the other dogs were fed, brushed, and turned out by pairs into the orchard for their exercise, and after all the runs had been cleaned, hosed, and disinfected, and after Arthur had given me my daily lesson in such arts as how to pose a thin-fronted dog to hide the fault or to razor-trim an Irish setter's throat so that it didn't look trimmed, I worked with Kate.

I crawled into her pen and sat on the wooden bed-platform while she cowered in the far corner. I sang "K-K-K-Katy" in what I hoped was a low, reassuring voice and let my hand touch her paw or her tail tip. No response. I tried staying in her pen when I brought her pan of food, but she refused to eat in my terrifying presence.

When my period of employment was over and it was time to leave, Kate and I were not one fraction closer than we had been on the day I arrived.

On a golden morning in early June, I began packing my old sedan for the trip toward a destination as yet undecided. I hoped to find another job with a professional handler because I wanted to learn the business, but as yet I had had no firm job offers.

From house to car I went, back and forth, jamming the trunk with boxes and bags of personal belongings. I was in a low mood. This had been a pleasant job, often grindingly hard but filled with dogs, dog lore, and learning. I'd have been sorry to leave even if I had known where I was going.

Just as I finished stuffing the car trunk, Arthur came up the drive from the mailbox. He was walking slowly, reading a letter as he came.

On the third attempt I was able to slam the trunk lid hard enough for the latch to catch and hold. I turned and waited for Arthur to come and tell me good-by, wish me luck, say I'd done a good job — something to encourage me.

What he said was, "Got a letter from Kate's owner." He waved the sheet thoughtfully. "He says I should go ahead and have her put to sleep. Kind of hate to . . ."

"Why does he want to do that?" I demanded, knowing the answer.

"Why, she's not ever going to be any good for showing, as shy as she is. I can see his point. He's put out a lot of money for her board all these years. Listen, why don't *you* take her? See if you can do anything with her. Sometimes dogs like that will come out of it if you make house pets out of them."

I hesitated. I had very little money and no job in the offing, and if I was lucky enough to find work in another kennel, there would almost certainly be a ban against my keeping a dog of my own. As far as I could see, Kate was hopeless anyhow. I just couldn't imagine any amount of socializing curing her at this advanced stage of her neurotic development.

But on the other hand, if it meant saving her life . . . Besides, it would be nice to have a companion as I set out to seek my fortune, even a companion like Kate.

"Sure, I'd be glad to take her."

Ten minutes later we were on our way, Kate and I. Arthur had given me Kate's pedigree, which was almost solid bench and field champions, and had even donated an old nylon show lead and a paper sack of dog meal.

Kate was not much company. All morning she remained pressed against the back floor between my typewriter and a carton of old dog magazines Arthur had discarded. We were traveling south through Wisconsin on little-traveled blacktop highways that wandered among deep-green pine and birch forests.

The destination for tonight was a town in northern Illinois where tomorrow there was to be an informal dog show primarily for the benefit of pups and inexperienced exhibitors, a sort of dry run for regular dog-show competition. I had promised to come to the match to help a friend who had five corgis to show and too few relatives to handle all of them.

Kate and I stopped for lunch at a drive-in stand so that I wouldn't have to leave her alone in the car. After much coaxing, I was able to get her out and walk her in a grassy area.

By midafternoon the car was uncomfortably warm. I opened the windows on the far side a couple of inches and rolled mine all the way down. I was stiff from sitting, and it felt good to be able to rest my arm on the opened window and shift my weight a little.

Suddenly something struck the back of my head, knocking it against the steering wheel. The car was going at highway speed and very nearly careened into the ditch before I was able to get hold of it again. I pulled off the road and turned around just in time to see Kate streaking across an open field, her lead lashing the air behind her.

I fumed. "If that's the way you want it, you just go ahead and run away. Who wanted you in the first place? I've got to get to Rockford by tonight. I can't spend all afternoon chasing you."

I locked the car and, of course, spent all afternoon chasing her.

She was out of sight by the time I had wriggled through the barbed-wire fence. It was a pasture, a very large pasture from the looks of it. I plodded straight ahead through the hummocks of long grass, keeping one eye out for a flash of gold, the other for cattle.

About the time I was seriously considering leaving the dog to her chosen destiny, I came to the bank of a stream. There, about five feet out and belly-deep in muddy water, stood Kate. Her expression was foolish, pitiful, and thoroughly hangdog.

"Okay, girl, come on out of the water," I coaxed. Her head drooped lower.

"Oh, honestly." I kicked off my tennis shoes, rolled up my pant legs as far as they would go, which wasn't very far, and waded in. As my feet sank into the muddy bank, I thought about water snakes, crawdads, and all the stinging, biting, and pinching things that might be living in the ooze. I expected Kate to retreat from my grasp, but when I caught the trailing lead and said, gently but firmly I hoped, "All right, come on out now," she came.

She stood patiently and without spinning while I tried to wipe the worst of the mud from both of us with a handful of grass, and she followed meekly all the way back to the car.

It was a turning point, of sorts, in our relationship. We were not yet friends, but it seemed that she had concluded that I was perhaps the least of the evils that surrounded her at the time.

At the match the next day, Kate stayed in the car, occasionally daring to raise her head high enough to peer out the windows. The match was held in a well-shaded park, and there was not much of a crowd, so I didn't worry about leaving her in the car.

When the corgis had been shown, I told my friend about Kate. "Why don't you show her just for the fun of it, as long as she's here?" my friend said. "They're doing sporting breeds in about an hour. We'd have time to get her brushed up."

At first I declined, but finally curiosity overcame caution and I went to the card table where entries were being taken. I had Kate's pedigree with me, so there was no problem about getting her entered.

We took Kate from the car and set her up on my friend's grooming stand. Kate was somewhat accustomed to this from the routine at Arthur's kennel, and she seemed less frightened by the surroundings than I had anticipated.

Most of yesterday's mud had dried and fallen off by now, and we brushed out the rest of it. Then I went to work, cautiously, trimming around the pads of her feet and rounding off her tail tip. Bushy hunks of pale yellow fur stood up in front of her ears, making the ears look unattractively high; but when I tried to trim them, she began cringing and shaking, so I decided not to press my luck.

"Who's judging retrievers?" I asked as I brushed.

"Glen Aberfeldy. He should be good," said my friend from the other side of Kate. "He's applied for a license to judge sporting breeds. Going to give up handling and become a full-time judge just as soon as his license is approved."

I was beginning to dread going into the ring with Kate. She'd be too frightened to gait properly, if I could get her around the ring at all, and she almost certainly wouldn't stand calmly for the judge's examination.

I was right. She balked all the way around the ring, pressing herself against my legs in a pitiful attempt to disappear. Mr. Aberfeldy took one look at her and said loudly, "That dog has no business in a show ring." He gave the first- and second-place ribbons to the only other dogs in the ring but declined to award Kate third place in a class of three. This was the ultimate insult a judge could give.

Kate and I left the ring and the match and the town, united suddenly in an us-against-them fury. At least that was my mood. Although I had been more than half convinced, myself, of Kate's shortcomings before the match, I certainly wasn't going to let any non-judge insult us that way. After all, Kate wasn't *that* bad.

The money ran out, jobs eluded me, and eventually Kate and I went to my parents' home in Iowa. I took a job writing radio commercials for a small local station, and in my spare time I continued to work with Kate.

By now she accepted me but was still terrified of other people, loud noises, strange places, and sudden movements. Gradually the weeks passed, and Kate relaxed just the slightest bit. She gained weight. With daily brushing and treats of bacon fat, her golden coat began to gleam. I was allowed certain liberties now, so I removed the ear tufts and trimmed her toenails. She seemed taller because she no longer crouched.

Part of the rehabilitation program was to take her, each evening after work, to the town square and make her sit quietly beside me while the traffic swished by and strangers passed. At first she spent the entire time cringing against my knees, but after several weeks she began to relax. She still hated it but not quite so much.

In August, Doc Petry called from his home near Chicago. Doc was not a doctor at all; he was a dog handler I had gotten to know while traveling the circuits with Arthur West. He was planning to make the Kentucky circuit, he said, and his crate handler had just quit, leaving him without help. Would I be interested in working those shows for him? I'd get regulation pay and room for one more dog on the load, if I had one I wanted to bring.

"I sure would be interested, and yes, I do have a dog I'd like to show, a golden retriever."

We agreed on the details, and I hung up, elated at the chance to get back into the fray and to see what Kate would do now.

"Are you ready to give it another try?" I asked her as I made out her entry blank. She thumped the floor with her tail and pressed close to my legs.

"Well," I said with a sigh, "I guess you're as ready as you'll ever be."

It was a three-show circuit over the Labor Day weekend, beginning at

Lexington, Kentucky, and ending at Louisville. The Lexington show was held on the grounds of the beautiful Keeneland Racetrack.

Like most of the other exhibitors, Doc and I set up shop in the broad alleyway of the most storybooklike stable I'd ever seen. It was built of dark weathered brick and oak beams, and it smelled of clean straw and neat's-foot oil. Unfortunately there were no horses in residence that day.

Most of Doc's dogs were shown in the morning, so I had the afternoon free to put finishing touches on Kate. She was taking the whole thing with relative aplomb, only trembling and salivating a little inside the dark and roomy crate Doc had provided.

An hour before her class was called, I realized that I hadn't even checked to see who was judging goldens. Some professional I was. After all, knowing the preferences of the various judges was one of the most important tools in a professional handler's bag of tricks. I didn't yet know much about any of the judges, but I went through the motions anyway and looked up the golden retriever judge in my show catalog.

"Golden retrievers, four o'clock, ring one, Glen Aberfeldy, judge," I read to myself.

"Oh, dear!"

"What's the matter?" Doc said as he approached with two paper cups of iced tea.

"Thanks. I need that." I took one cup and drank. "I just found out the judge who's doing goldens is the same guy who, just last June, told me Kate had no business in a show ring. She was third in a class of three, and he withheld the ribbon."

Doc was thoughtful for a moment. "Does he know you?" he asked finally.

"No. Saw him just that one time, and I don't think he paid much attention to me. Why?"

Doc was looking at my shoulder-length hair. "How would you like a haircut?"

For an instant I was confused, but then I understood what he was thinking. If Mr. Aberfeldy recognized me, he was bound to remember Kate and his first impression of her. She wouldn't have a chance at an impartial opinion today.

In a few minutes, I was perched on Doc's grooming crate, with a dog towel around my shoulders, while he went at my hair with his dog shears. He did a surprisingly good job, probably from all his practice with poodles. Twenty minutes later my hair was reduced to a length of about two inches all over. Doc even wet the comb in a drinking fountain and shaped my hair into a more or less fashionable style. The change in my appearance was rather exciting and was surely enough to fog any memory Mr. Aberfeldy might have had of a long-haired girl and a cringing retriever seen briefly three months ago.

450

When our class was called, Kate followed me to ringside with only a suggestion of hesitancy in her gait. I dared to hope.

It was a large class of golden retrievers, at least for this part of the country — five in addition to Kate. I glanced at the others briefly. A strong class. A couple of nothings, but the others would definitely provide serious competition.

Kate and I led into the ring on the theory that the first dog might have a very slight advantage. Kate gaited well, and when the time came to line up for examination, she held her pose like a statue. But I could feel, through the lead, that she was trembling.

Mr. Aberfeldy began his examination at the far end of the line. Kate's trembling grew more and more pronounced as the seconds passed. I kept up a steady murmur of encouragement. She watched me from the corner of her eye. When neither Kate nor I could have borne the tension another moment, Mr. Aberfeldy came to judge Kate.

He reached slowly for her head. Every muscle in Kate's body turned to iron. The judge's deft fingers separated her lips just long enough to ascertain that her teeth were in proper alignment. Then the hands passed over her neck and shoulders, down her rib cage, and then over her hips and hindquarters.

As Mr. Aberfeldy examined Kate, I carefully kept my head low and my face averted.

With a swift, practiced motion he reached beneath her tail, lifted her hindquarters a few inches off the ground, and dropped them. Kate's legs remained rigid; her feet landed not one millimeter from where they had been.

Mr. Aberfeldy gave Kate's rump a quick pat and said, "Well trained."

He moved toward the table that held his judging book and the rows of ribbons. He marked the book. I was sweating from every pore.

Mr. Aberfeldy approached finally, paused dramatically, then handed me the blue ribbon.

"Dandy little golden," he murmured appreciatively.

DISCUSSION

1. From reading the story, does it seem likely that Kate's trainer will become a fine professional handler of show dogs? Give reasons for your answer.
2. What had kept Kate from becoming a show dog earlier? What causes this problem in some dogs?
3. Why did Arthur West offer to give Kate to the young trainer? What made the trainer accept his offer?
4. On the trip to Rockford, Kate jumped out the car window and tried to run away. How did that incident mark a turning point in the relationship between Kate and her new owner?
5. When she entered the show at Rockford, what did Kate do to make the judge say, "That dog has no business in a show ring"? How did Kate's owner react to the "ultimate insult" the judge gave Kate?

6. Have you ever played a game or entered a contest that caused you to become fearful and tense? If so, how did you deal with your fear? What are some of the ways in which fear can affect someone's ability to perform?

7. Later, at her parents' home, the young trainer continued working with Kate. What were some of the things she did there that helped turn Kate into a show dog?

8. Do you think that Arthur West showed good judgment as a dog handler? Why do you think as you do?

9. At the beginning of the story, Kate's young trainer said that she had "romantic notions of the power of love." What do you think she meant? Judging from the outcome of the story, would you say that she was right about the power of love? Give reasons for your answer.

AUTHOR

Lynn Hall knows a great deal about animals, especially dogs, because of her experience as a veterinarian's assistant, then as a handler on the dog show circuit, and now as a breeder of her own show dogs. It was after she started working as a copy writer in an advertising agency that she realized she wanted to write books, and since 1968 she has had over two dozen books published. "Klondike Kate" was taken from a collection of her short stories, *Lynn Hall's Dog Stories*.

Ms. Hall lives in northeastern Iowa in a stone cottage named Touchwood that she designed and helped to build. When she is not writing books for young people or working with the dogs, she keeps herself busy with building and landscaping projects, a large garden, and twenty-five acres of woods that supply fuel for her house and endless hours of enjoyment for her and her dogs.

Poem

by WILLIAM CARLOS WILLIAMS

As the cat
climbed over
the top of

the jamcloset
first the right
forefoot

carefully
then the hind
stepped down

into the pit of
the empty
flowerpot.

Duke Kahanamoku (kah-hah-nah-moh'koo) was a famous Hawaiian surfer and an Olympic swimming champion. Here he describes an unforgettable surfing experience off Waikiki Beach, Honolulu.

That Legendary Ride

by DUKE KAHANAMOKU

Much seems to have been made of that once-in-a-lifetime ride of mine from the outer steamer lane off Waikiki, and now is as good a time as any to put the record straight. The incident has been written up before but might bear repeating. I can remember the details as though it all happened yesterday, for, in retrospect, I have relived the ride many a time. I think my memory plays me no tricks on this one.

Pride was in it with me in those days, and I was still striving to build bigger and better boards, ride taller and faster waves, and develop more dexterity from day to day. Also, vanity probably had much to do with my trying to delight the crowds at Waikiki with spectacular rides on the long, glassy, sloping waves.

But the day I caught the Big One was a day when I was not thinking in terms of awing any tourists or *kamaainas*[1] on Waikiki Beach. It was simply an early morning when mammoth ground swells were rolling in sporadically from the horizon, and I saw that no one was paddling out to try them. Frankly, they were the largest I'd ever seen. The yell of "The surf is up!" was the understatement of the century.

In fact, it was that rare morning when the word was out that the big "bluebirds" were rolling in; this is the name for gigantic waves that

---

[1] **kamaainas** (kah'mah-eye'nahs), old-timers.

sweep in from the horizon on extraordinary occasions. Sometimes years elapse with no evidence of them. They are spawned far out at sea and are the result of certain cataclysms of nature — either great atmospheric disturbances or subterranean agitation like underwater earthquakes and volcanic eruptions.

True, as waves go, the experts will agree that bigness alone is not what supplies outstandingly good surfing. Sometimes giant waves make for bad surfing in spite of their size, and the reason often is that there is an onshore wind that pushes the top of the waves down and makes them break too fast with lots of white water. It takes an offshore wind to make the waves stand up to their full height. This day we had stiff trade winds blowing from the high Koolau (koh'oh-lah'oo) Range, and they were making those bluebirds tower up like the Himalayas. I was pulling my breath from way down at sight of them.

It put me in mind of the winter storm waves that roar in at Kaena (kah-ay'nah) Point on the North Shore. Big-wave surfers, even then, were doing much speculating on whether those Kaena waves could be ridden with any degree of safety. The bluebirds facing me were easily thirty-plus waves, and they looked as though, with the right equipment — plus a lot of luck — they just might be makable.

The danger lay in the prone-out or wipe-out. Studying the waves made me wonder if any person's body could withstand the unbelievable force of a thirty- to fifty-foot wall of water when it crashes. And, too, could even a top swimmer like myself manage to battle the currents and explosive water that would necessarily accompany the aftermath of such a wave?

Well, the answer seemed to be simply — *don't get wiped out!*

From the shore you could see those high glassy ridges building up in the outer Diamond Head region. The bluebirds were swarming across the bay in a solid line as far northwest as Honolulu Harbor. They were tall, steep, and fast. The closer-in ones crumbled and showed their teeth with a fury that I had never seen before. I wondered if I could even push through the acres of white water to get to the outer area where the build-ups were taking place.

But, like the mountain climbers with Mount Everest, you try it "just because it's there." Some days you do not take time to analyze what motivates you. All I knew was that I was suddenly trying to shove through that incoming sea — and having the fight of my life. I was using my *Papa-nui* (pah'pah-noo'ee), the sixteen-foot, 114-pound semihollow board, and it was like trying to jam a log through the flood of a dam break.

Again and again it was necessary to turn turtle with the big board and hang on tightly underneath — arms and legs wrapped around a thing that bucked like a bronco gone berserk. The shoreward-bound torrents of water ground overhead, making all the racket of a string of freight cars roaring over a trestle. The prone paddling between combers was a demanding thing because the water was wild. It was a case of wrestling the board through block-busting breakers, and it was a miracle that I ever gained the outlying waters.

Bushed from the long fight to get seaward, I sat my board and watched the long humps of water peaking into ridges that marched like animated foothills. I let a slew of them lift and drop me with their silent, threatening glide. I could hardly believe that such perpendicular walls of water could be built up like that. The troughs between the swells had the depth of elevator shafts, and I wondered again what it would be like to be buried under tons of water when it curled and detonated. There was something eerie about watching the shimmering backs of the ridges as they passed me and rolled on toward Waikiki.

I let a lot of them career by, wondering in my own heart whether I was passing them up because of their unholy height or whether I was really waiting for the big right one. One begins to doubt oneself at a time like that. Then I was suddenly wheeling and turning to catch the towering blue ridge bearing toward me. I was prone and stroking hard at the water with my hands.

Strangely, it was more as though the wave had selected me, rather than I had chosen it. It seemed like a very personal and special wave — the kind I had seen in my mind's eye during a night of tangled dreaming. There was no backing out on this one; the two of us had something to settle between us. The rioting breakers between me and shore no longer bugged me. There was just this one ridge and myself — no more. Could I master it? I doubted it, but I was willing to die in the attempt to harness it.

Instinctively I got to my feet when the pitch, slant, and speed seemed right. Left foot forward, knees slightly bent, I rode the board down that precipitous slope like a person tobogganing down a glacier. Sliding left along the watery monster's face, I didn't know I was at the beginning of a ride that would become a celebrated and memoried thing. All I knew was that I had come to grips with the tallest, bulkiest, fastest wave I had ever seen. I realized, too, more than ever, that to be trapped under its curling bulk would be the same as letting a factory cave in upon you.

This lethal avalanche of water swept shoreward swiftly and spookily. The board began hissing from the traction as the wave leaned forward with greater and more incredible speed and power. I shifted my weight, cut left at more of an angle, and shot into the big Castle surf which was building and adding to the wave I was on. Spray was spuming up wildly from my rails, and I had never before seen it spout up like that. I rode it for city-long blocks, the wind almost sucking the breath out of me. Diamond Head itself seemed to have come alive and was leaping in at me from the right.

Then I was slamming into Elk's Club surf, still sliding left and still fighting for balance, for position, for everything and anything that would keep me upright. The drumming of the water under the board had become a mad tattoo. Elk's surf rioted me along, high and steep, until I skidded and slanted through into Public Baths surf. By then it amounted to three surfs combined into one; big, rumbling, and exploding. I was not sure I could make it on this ever-steepening

ridge. A curl broke to my right and almost engulfed me, so I swung even farther left, shuffling back a little on the board to keep from purling.

Left it was; left and more left, with the board veeing a jet of water on both sides and making a snarl that told of speed and stress and thrust. The wind was tugging my hair with frantic hands. Then suddenly it looked as if I might, with more luck, make it into the back of Queen's surf! The build-up had developed into something approximating what I had heard of tidal waves, and I wondered if it would ever flatten out at all. White water was pounding to my right, so I angled farther from it to avoid its wiping me out and burying me in the sudsy depths.

Borrowing on the Cunha surf for all it was worth — and it was worth several hundred yards — I managed to manipulate the board into the now towering Queen's surf. One mistake — just one small one — could well spill me into the maelstrom to my right. I teetered for some panic-ridden seconds, caught control again, and made it down on that last forward rush, sliding and bouncing through lunatic water. The breaker gave me all the tossing of a bucking bronco. Still luckily erect, I could see the people standing there on the beach, their hands shading their eyes against the sun, and watching me complete this crazy, unbelievable one-and-three-quarter-mile ride.

I made it into the shallows in one last surging flood. A little dazedly I wound up in hip-deep water, where I stepped off and pushed my board shoreward through the bubbly surf. That improbable ride gave me the sense of being an unlickable guy for the moment. I heisted my board to my hip, locked both arms around it, and lugged it up the beach.

Without looking at the people clustered around, I walked on, hearing them murmur fine, exciting things that I wanted to remember in days to come. I told myself this was the ride to end all rides. I grinned my thanks to those who stepped close and slapped me on the shoulders, and I smiled to those who told me this was the greatest. I trudged on and on, knowing this would be a shining memory for me that I could take out in years to come and relive in all its full glory. This had been *it*.

I never caught another wave anything like that one. And now with the birthdays piled up on my back, I know I never shall. But they cannot take that memory away from me. It is a golden one that I treasure, and I'm grateful that God gave it to me.

DISCUSSION

1. In your opinion, was Duke's achievement worth the risk he took? What makes you think that?
2. What were the "bluebirds" referred to by Duke? How often do they occur?
3. What causes the bluebirds to roll in? Why does an offshore wind make for the best surfing?
4. In what ways would Duke's life have been endangered by the water if he had not succeeded in riding the wave all the way in?
5. About how large and heavy was Duke's surfboard? What was the first challenge Duke faced before he could attempt to ride a bluebird?

6. What two things did Duke have to do over and over again in alternation to get his surfboard out beyond the breakers? What did he then have to do to start riding the wave he chose?

7. Have you ever tried, like Duke, to do something dangerous just to prove to yourself that you could? What was it? Did you have enough knowledge and skill to give you a good chance of success? If you wish to do so, tell about your experience.

8. What were some of the different emotions that Duke probably felt as he rode toward the shore?

9. Do you think the people watching Duke knew much about surfing? What makes you think that? Do you think that Duke's warm reaction to their praise showed that he was conceited? Tell why you think as you do.

10. Suppose no one had been watching. Do you think Duke would have treasured the memory of his feat as much as he did? Why do you think as you do?

AUTHOR

Duke Paoa Kahanamoku was born in Honolulu, Hawaii, in 1890. Duke was his given name, not a title or nickname. His medal-winning swimming performance at the Stockholm Olympics in 1912 brought him his first acclaim and focused the attention of the aquatic world on his Hawaiian homeland. He was a member of three later United States Olympic swimming teams. At one time or another he held almost every swimming record there is. But surfing was his real love, and many experts consider "the Duke" the master surfer, the greatest of all time. The ancient Polynesian sport of surfing had fallen into decline by the turn of the century, and Duke Kahanamoku was the person primarily responsible for reviving it and bringing it to its present popularity.

In spite of his fame, Duke Kahanamoku remained a modest and friendly man. He served thirteen terms as Sheriff of Honolulu, and he was ambassador-at-large for the state of Hawaii until his death in 1968.

"That Legendary Ride" is an excerpt from the book *Duke Kahanamoku's World of Surfing*, written in collaboration with sports writer Joe Brennan.

SKILL

Doing Well on Tests

> Mark was beginning to panic. He couldn't concentrate. Seeing the people around him hard at work made him still more nervous. His palms grew moist and his mouth got dry.

Did you guess that Mark was taking a test? Have you ever had a similar reaction to a test? You know that as long as you are a student, you will have to take tests in school. However, you will also be faced with tests throughout your life. In the next few years you may have to take tests in order to qualify for a driver's license, to be admitted to a college, or to determine your job aptitude. Other tests you may have to take include civil service examinations or tests that qualify you to sell real estate or practice law.

There is no formula that will guarantee you success on a test, but there are some techniques you can learn that will help you to prepare for tests and others that will help you do well on them. Although the techniques in this lesson refer directly to tests in school, most of them also apply to the kinds of tests you may have to take as an adult.

Preparing for a Test

The preparation for a test should actually begin on the first day of class and continue until the course ends. Regular studying and organized reviewing are important parts of preparing to take a test; they give you self-confidence and help you avoid feeling panicky. If you have listened carefully to the teacher, completed and reviewed assignments, and used SQRRR or another study method throughout the course, your preparation just before a test will be much easier.

During a course you should think not only about the content but about the way the teacher approaches it. Does the teacher stress main ideas and relationships? Does the teacher consider details important? Does the teacher keep returning to a particular topic? Thinking about the things the teacher emphasizes may give you a good idea of what to review and study for the test.

You should also be sure you understand the vocabulary the teacher uses. Try to ask any questions you have about terms, ideas, or skills well before the time comes for a test.

When you learn that you are going to have a test, give yourself plenty of time to review for it. Sometimes a teacher will tell you what to study and what kind of test it will be. Be sure to listen carefully and jot down what the teacher says. That will help you know what to concentrate on when studying for the test.

Go over any notes you have taken during the course, whether they are from information discussed in class, from the textbook, or from other sources you have read. You and other students may wish to share your notes in order to fill in any gaps. As you review your notes, you may find it helpful to underline key words and phrases. Try to identify the main ideas stressed in the course and be aware of supporting details and correct vocabulary.

These steps should be helpful as you prepare for a test:

- Form questions that you think may be included.
- Answer any questions at the ends of chapters in your text.
- Write summaries or make outlines of what you have learned.
- Reread your notes, summaries, and outlines.
- Recite facts, names, dates, and vocabulary words to yourself.
- Practice math problems or formulas.
- Look over assignments you have completed.
- Review what the textbook and the teacher emphasized.

Whichever ways you choose to prepare for a test, allow yourself plenty of time; otherwise you will wind up tired and tense.

Just before test time arrives, organize whatever you will need. Depending on the type of test, you may need pencils or pens, eraser, paper, dictionary, slide rule, calculator, ruler, and textbook. Have with you anything the teacher has mentioned.

Take the time to use effective study and review techniques and gather the items you need beforehand. Then you can be well prepared and self-confident, ready to do your best.

Essay Tests

One of the most common types of tests given in schools is the essay test. An essay test usually focuses on important topics and main ideas and requires you to write out your answers. A short-answer item on an essay test may be answered in a single well-written sentence. However, some items may require several sentences or paragraphs as an answer.

At the beginning of an essay test, first read the directions carefully and then read through all the items before you start to answer any of them. Look for such key words as *contrast, compare, describe, explain, discuss, list,* and so on. These words will help you plan how to present your answer. During the first reading, jot down on an extra sheet of paper, so that you won't forget them, any facts, dates, ideas, and definitions that you know you will need to include. Finally, figure out about how much time to spend on each item. If the number of points given to each item is indicated, you might allot extra time to items that are worth the most points. Once you start, concentrate on one item at a time, but allow time to write something for each item.

Begin by working on the items you think are the easiest for you. Plan your answer before you start writing so that your response will be well-organized and clear. You may find it helpful to make a quick outline.

In a paragraph-length essay, you might begin with a sentence that gives the main idea. Often this can be done by restating the item as part of your first sentence. For instance, suppose one item was *Describe the migration of the humpback whale.* Your first sentence might begin, "The migration of the humpback whale follows a yearly pattern. . . ." After you state the main idea, you should include facts and ideas to support it. You may wish to illustrate a point with a specific example. When appropriate, include special terms or vocabulary. Try to complete each answer with a summary statement. Write neatly and read over your answer to check sentence structure, spelling, punctuation, and content.

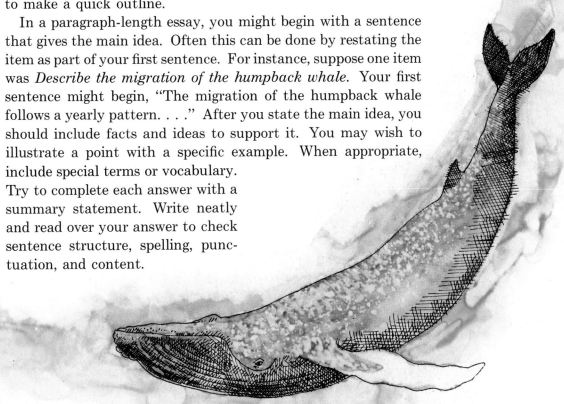

Study the following examples of items that might be included on an essay test, noticing in particular the key words that tell what to do for each item:

1. Explain why Europeans came to the New World in the 1600's.
2. Describe the Panama Canal and explain its importance.
3. Explain how a pinhole camera forms an image.
4. What is a short circuit? Draw a circuit that has a "short."
5. What is moonstone?

Did you find the key words? The answers to those items could vary in length from a single sentence for item 5 to several paragraphs for item 2. Notice also that a diagram is required in the answer to item 4 but that item 3, which could be answered with a diagram, requires a written response.

Objective Tests

On an essay test you are required to discuss important ideas and to write out your answers in full sentences and paragraphs. In contrast, on an objective test you must recall and identify specific facts and details and your answers must be brief. On some objective tests you must be able to choose correct answers from among incorrect answers.

Since an objective test may include different types of items, you should first look over an entire objective test to see what kinds of items are included. Estimate the amount of time you can spend on each section of the test. Then read the first set of directions carefully and note how to record your answers. Answer the items you are sure of first. If you are unsure of an answer, place a small mark by the item so you can come back to it. Avoid wasting time on an item if you don't know the answer. However, unless you will be marked down for guessing, answer every item.

Types of Objective-Test Items

There are several types of objective-test items. Knowing about different types should help you make fewer mistakes.

One common type of item on objective tests is sentence completion. A sentence-completion item is a statement that contains one or more blank spaces in which to write one or more words, symbols, or numerals. You must think of an answer that will complete the statement logically, using the context that is provided. Ask yourself, "Is a synonym required? Is the missing word defined or described? Is a date or number needed?" The pattern of blanks may give you a clue to the number of words needed. The following are examples of sentence-completion items:

1. *Tom Sawyer* was written by _____ _____.
2. _____, or soybean curd, is a valuable source of protein.
3. A marathon is a cross-country footrace of _____ miles and _____ yards.
4. Cactuses can survive long periods without rain because
   _____.

A multiple-choice item presents a stem — a question, a statement, or an incomplete statement — followed by three to five answers. You must evaluate the answers and choose the correct one. Sometimes the directions ask you to choose the best answer, which implies that more than one answer could be correct. Some items include as responses *all of these* or *none of these*. Others may require you to choose two or three answers; on these a choice may read *a and b* or *a, b, and c.*

You can see that each multiple-choice item must be read carefully. First read the stem; then read all the answers. Remember that if the directions ask you to choose the best answer, you may have to choose between two that are very close. If the answers include a choice reading *a and b,* read the other answers very carefully; do not choose that answer unless you know that both *a* and *b* are correct. There are several ways of recording answers on a multiple-choice test. Be sure to follow the directions given.

Careful reading and thinking are required on multiple-choice tests. Study the following examples of multiple-choice items to notice the variations:

1. The card catalog in a library contains
   a. author cards
   b. subject cards
   c. title cards
   d. all of these

2. Who was Grandma Moses?
   a. a movie star of the 1930's
   b. Hank Aaron's grandmother
   c. a character in the novel *Little Women*
   d. none of these

3. The highest mountain in the world is
   a. Mount McKinley
   b. Mount Everest
   c. Mount Fuji
   d. none of these

4. Which of the following countries have red, white, and blue flags?
   a. Mexico
   b. France
   c. United States
   d. b and c

Objective tests often contain sections that require you to identify one item and match it with a related item. Usually there are two columns of items to be matched. You are to record letters or numerals from items in one column next to the related items in the other column. Read the directions carefully to find out how many times each item can be used. Where one column has more items than the other, usually not all the items are used.

It is usually helpful to make a mark by an item as you use it so that you don't use it more times than you are supposed to. First match the items you are sure of; that reduces the number of choices for the more difficult ones.

The following example shows a typical matching section:

Match each word with its definition by writing the letter of the definition in the blank before the word.

1. _____ isthmus
2. _____ peninsula
3. _____ island
4. _____ continent

a. a small land mass completely surrounded by water
b. a narrow strip of land connecting two large masses of land
c. a long projection of land into water
d. a principal land mass on the earth
e. a cliff at the edge of the sea

A variation on matching requires you to mark a letter before each item. The directions explain what the letter stands for, as in the example that follows:

Identify each of the following people as real or fictional by writing the letter *R* for *real* or *F* for *fictional* in the blank before the name:

1. _____ Jesse James
2. _____ Cinderella
3. _____ Mohandas Gandhi
4. _____ Ty Cobb
5. _____ Brenda Starr
6. _____ Harriet Tubman

Many objective tests include a section in which you are asked to decide whether a given statement is true or false. Usually you must indicate your answer by writing the word *True* or *False* or by writing only the initial letter *T* or *F.* You must read each statement very carefully. Be especially careful when you see the word *not,* since it completely changes an idea or concept.

The following are examples of true or false items:

Write *True* or *False* in the blank before the statement.
1. _____ All snakes are poisonous.
2. _____ The ostrich is the biggest living bird.
3. _____ The largest mammal is the elephant.
4. _____ A whale is not a mammal.

Reasons for Testing

Teachers do not give tests in order to make you nervous and anxious. They usually give tests to determine the progress of the class and of individuals and to get information on which to base grades. You can make a test useful for yourself, too. Knowing that you must take one may motivate you to study and review regularly. You can use a test to demonstrate what you have learned and to evaluate your own efforts. By identifying your strengths and weaknesses as you work on a test, you can decide if you need to change the way you study.

You yourself determine how well you will do on tests. Success depends on your efforts to master the skills and content of the course you are taking. Consistent study at regular intervals should help you do well on tests, since knowing the material is the most important requirement for success. But it also helps to be test-wise, to know how to take tests. If you remember and apply the techniques of test-taking discussed in this lesson, you will find that you, too, are test-wise.

Now, relax, and good luck!

TAKING A TEST

Practice responding to the various types of test items by answering those on page 470. Copy the numerals on a sheet of paper and then write the answers.

Completion:

1. The two main kinds of tests discussed in this lesson are
_____ and _____.

2. Some of the special terms that might be found in questions requiring essay answers are _____, _____, _____, and _____.

Multiple-choice:

Write the letter of the group of words that best completes the statement.

3. When preparing for a test, you should think of:
   a. assignments you have completed
   b. what the textbook stressed
   c. what the teacher emphasized
   d. all of the above
   e. none of the above

Matching:

4. ____ 1) Sentence completion

    ____ 2) Multiple choice

    ____ 3) Matching

    a. Choose the best answer from those given.
    b. Add one or more words, symbols, or numerals to blank spaces.
    c. Pair related items.
    d. Write answers in sentences or paragraphs.

True-false:

_____ 5. Test preparation should take place continuously throughout the duration of the course.

_____ 6. Objective tests are always easier than essay tests.

Short-answer essay:

7. What is an essay test?

Essay:

8. Explain how to prepare for a test.

Billie Jean King

by FRANCENE SABIN

On September 20, 1973, more than thirty thousand people came to the Houston Astrodome to watch twenty-nine-year-old Billie Jean King, the world's top-ranked woman tennis player, take on fifty-five-year-old Bobby Riggs, a man who had been a national champion years before Billie Jean was born. The crowd was perhaps the largest live tennis audience ever, and millions of other fans in thirty-seven countries would see the game on television. Billed as the Battle of the Sexes, it was the most talked-about match in tennis history.

Billie Jean had already proved that she was the greatest female champion in a generation. She had won the annual singles championship at Wimbledon, England, six times, and in 1971 she had become the first woman athlete in any sport to win $100,000 in prize money in a single year.

On and off the tennis court, Billie Jean had fought for women's rights to equal opportunity in sports. As one of the first women tennis players to turn professional — not as a teacher but as a competitor — she had helped establish the first independent women's tennis tour. For years she had carried on an outspoken battle to increase the prize money available to women.

Billie Jean's crusade had won little support from the men who ran international tennis. But her most vocal detractor was Bobby Riggs, former tennis pro, self-proclaimed "male chauvinist pig," and well-known tennis hustler.

Early in 1973, Bobby proclaimed that women tennis players didn't deserve to win as much money as the men because they didn't play as well. He insisted that women's tennis was a farce and that even he could beat the best female tennis player alive. Then he dared the leading women to play him for five thousand dollars. Billie Jean turned him down, but another champion, Margaret Smith Court of Australia, accepted the challenge.

On Mother's Day, 1973, Riggs and Court met for a nationally televised best-of-three-sets match. Court, who had expected to play tough tennis, was totally unprepared for the series of "junk" shots (high-looping lobs and drop shots) Riggs threw at her. More important, the great publicity build-up for the game — and Riggs's expert needling — had put Court so on edge that she fell apart, losing 6–1, 6–2 in less than an hour.

Then the hoopla began. Bobby Riggs next proclaimed himself the women's tennis champion and repeated his challenge to Billie Jean, boasting that he could smash her as easily as he had Margaret Court. Billie Jean smiled and waited, certain that the publicity was the best thing that could happen to her and to women's tennis. Then she agreed to play Riggs.

Various commercial tie-ins and side bets raised the winner's estimated profit to about $200,000, but there was much more than money at stake. It was beginning to seem as if the whole future of women's tennis was on the line. If the best woman player of the day couldn't beat a man almost twice her age, how could women hope to be considered equal on the court? The pressure on Billie Jean was almost unbearable.

Finally the contest took place. The match was played by men's rules, the winner having to take three sets out of five. Using her strong, twisting serve, her phenomenal speed, and her blazing backhand drives, Billie Jean ran Bobby Riggs into the ground. She was fast, she was sure, and she was the winner in straight sets (6–4, 6–3, 6–3).

After the match was over, Billie Jean flung her racket in the air, wiped away her tears of joy, and said, "I feel this is the culmination of nineteen years of tennis for me."

In a way, Billie Jean Moffitt King had spent most of her life preparing for that victory. Born in Long Beach, California, on November 22, 1943, she had been a chubby, active little girl. Her father considered sports an important part of every child's life and encouraged Billie Jean and her younger brother, Randy, to be physically active. Every day after school, the two young Moffitts would head for the Houghton Park playground or a nearby beach.

At the age of ten, Billie Jean, whose family nickname was B.J., was the youngest member of the Houghton Park girls' baseball team. A fast runner and an accurate ball handler, she was shortstop and leadoff batter. Her fielding and timely hitting helped Houghton Park win the Long Beach Recreation Park Championship — her first sports triumph. Although the Moffitts were proud of their daughter's athletic ability, they didn't see much of a future for her in baseball. One morning, her father suggested that Billie Jean might be better off trying golf, swimming, or tennis. "I didn't swim well," Billie Jean recalled, "and I considered golf an old man's game. But I always liked to run a lot, so I chose tennis."

At that time, about the only thing eleven-year-old Billie Jean knew about tennis was that it involved running. She actually didn't know what a tennis racket was. And she certainly didn't know the rules of the game. In fact, B.J. had never even seen anybody play tennis. Still, she was willing to give it a try.

To earn money to buy her own racket, Billie Jean did odd jobs around her neighborhood. When she had eight dollars stashed in a glass jar in a kitchen cupboard, she went out to buy her first tennis racket. "It was maroon and had a velvet grip," she remembered. "It had real thick nylon and was loosely strung, factory style. But I was in seventh heaven."

Racket in hand, she went to Houghton Park, where free group tennis lessons were given to neighborhood kids every Tuesday afternoon. It was there, on a cement court, that Billie Jean Moffitt took her first lesson from instructor Clyde Walker.

That day's lesson didn't cover much more than the proper racket grip, but B.J. happily stayed on the court for four hours. When her mother came to pick her up, Billie Jean announced, "Mother, this is what I want for my life. I want to be the best tennis player in the world."

From that day on, tennis became the focus of her life. Clyde Walker coached youngsters at a different Long Beach park every day, and B.J. followed him around as if he were the Pied Piper. She would show up at every session, at every park, ready to learn more. Not surprisingly, Walker noticed her determination and began giving her special attention.

Billie Jean played a strong game right from the beginning. She was fast on her feet and, thanks to her shortstop experience, could start and stop, wheel, turn, and cover the court with unusual ease. She played an aggressive game, rushing the net, never letting up for a moment, showing the same drive and desire that would later make her a great champion. The talent was there, the determination was there, and Clyde Walker was there to provide instruction in the fine points of the game.

When she was eleven and a half, B.J. played her first real tennis match against a sixteen-year-old named Marilyn Hester. B.J. won the first set 6–3 and was ready to leave the court when she was told that the match wasn't over yet. So she kept playing and won the second set 6–4 to wrap it up. "I didn't know you had to play two sets," she explained later. Everyone had assumed she knew that in women's tennis a player must take two sets out of three to win the match in regular competition.

B.J. continued to work with Clyde Walker, practiced eight hours every day there was no school, and strove to acquire the skills she needed to be a topnotch player. She won her first tournament — the Long Beach Recreation Class D, women's division — when she was thirteen. The six-inch trophy she received for that victory was the first real sign that her dreams might come true. It still sits in a place of honor today, in the midst of the more impressive international awards Billie Jean later collected.

Billie Jean's toughest problems as a teen-ager were her tendency to gain weight in the off-seasons and, even more serious, her extreme nearsightedness. At the age of thirteen, she began to wear glasses on and off the court. Her eyesight was so poor that many experts considered it a miracle that she played tennis at all and a double miracle that she played so well. Even with the glasses, Billie Jean had trouble seeing. The frames blocked certain areas from vision, creating blind spots on both sides. To make things worse, sweat tended to run down the lenses during a game, and heat caused them to fog over. To combat the fogging of her lenses, Billie Jean learned to rub a smear of soap over each lens just before a match. As she grew accustomed to wearing eyeglasses and solved the problems they caused, her tennis got even better.

When she was fifteen, B.J. was introduced to America's tennis immortal, Alice Marble, an international star in the late 1930's. She watched B.J. in action, recognized the potential in the hard-hitting teen-ager, and offered to coach her. "I could have fallen over backward — and probably did," said Billie Jean as she remembered that moment.

Alice Marble knew that Billie Jean's strength was her aggressive attack at the net and that this phase of her game didn't need very much work. Alice helped B.J. to strengthen her forehand and develop her backcourt ground strokes. "I think she helped me mentally as much as anything else," Billie Jean later said. "More than anything, I think she gave me confidence. She showed me that the more you know about the game, the more confidence you have."

The coaching paid off handsomely. Billie Jean's ranking in U.S. amateur tennis went to nineteenth in 1960. By 1961, the year she graduated from high school, Billie Jean was ranked fourth. Her plans for the future were divided — to be a tennis star and to do well in college. She enrolled at Los Angeles State College, intending to get a degree in social studies and then teach at the

junior-high or high-school level. "I feel I don't want to go on playing a long time," Billie Jean said then. "There's more to life than just tennis." But that was before she realized just how much the game would change her life.

In 1961, Billie Jean competed in her first Wimbledon tournament. Although she was already well known to American tennis fans, she was a complete unknown on the international scene. When they first saw the five-foot-six, somewhat plump Californian, the British spectators were less than impressed. B.J.'s behavior on the court — talking to herself, making faces, looking up in mock despair, sighing, grinning, and frowning — shocked audiences accustomed to the deadpan manner of most tennis players. So it was a surprise when seventeen-year-old Billie Jean Moffitt and eighteen-year-old Karen Hantze Susman won the doubles championship, the youngest team in Wimbledon history to do so.

B.J. lost her first match in singles play, but her appetite for the championship was whetted. When asked if she was disappointed by the loss, she answered, "That's all right. I'll come back here and win this little old tournament."

After Wimbledon, everything began to click for Billie Jean. She took the Pennsylvania State Championship, the Philadelphia District Championship, and was named to the U.S. Wightman Cup team. The Cup is awarded annually to the nation that wins that year's U.S.–Great Britain women's competition. The 1961 team was described as the youngest and weakest ever — until B.J. won the singles and doubles matches. The U.S. squad went on to take the Wightman Cup against tremendous odds, recapturing the coveted trophy from the British women, who had held it for three years.

Billie Jean returned to Wimbledon in 1962, ranked fourth among American women. This high status, however, meant little to Wimbledon officials. To them, the fact that she had never won a major singles tournament was far more significant, and they didn't rank her at all. In the opening round of play in the women's singles, Billie Jean was scheduled to face Margaret Smith of Australia, the number one player in the world. It seemed like a sure win for the tall, strong Australian, who was accustomed to winning in top international tournaments.

But B.J. wasn't troubled by the reputation of her opponent. She practiced for the match with a close friend, Carole Caldwell. Carole kept reminding Billie Jean that she had to concentrate on playing to Smith's forehand. In fact, entire practice sessions were devoted to that strategy. As Billie Jean recalled later,

"Everybody said, 'You can do it — just play her forehand.' But Carole's saying it, and repeating it, instilled it in my mind."

On nights before a crucial match, Billie Jean usually had trouble falling asleep, but she slept soundly before this one. And she stepped onto the court with confidence. The first set, which the Australian won 6–1 in only eighteen minutes, might have crushed a player with less self-assurance. But Billie Jean wasn't shaken a bit. In the second set, an aggressive B.J. bounced back to win the first five games. One more game would give her the set and send the match into the third and final set. But then, as Billie Jean recalled, "Margaret started catching up, and I started getting nervous. She started putting in some good shots, and I started missing easy ones. It went to 5–3, and then I got over it."

With B.J. ahead 5–3, and needing only one more point to win the second set, it was Margaret Smith's turn to be nervous. She hit into the net, and Billie Jean tied the match at one set apiece.

In the final set, Margaret took a commanding 4–1 lead. Things looked bad for the young American. Using her powerful running backhand, Billie Jean began fighting to catch up. She broke Margaret's service, won her own, and began to unnerve the Australian champ.

477

Ripping a steady stream of shots to Margaret's forehand, B.J. successfully worked on her rival's weak spot. When Billie Jean went ahead 6–5, the capacity crowd in the stadium again fell silent. An upset was in the making. But B.J. double faulted as she tried to drive her serves past her opponent, and the tension increased. Then, with a backhand volley to Margaret Smith's forehand, Billie Jean won the set — and the match. With a whoop of absolute joy, she threw her racket in the air and bounded to the net to shake the hand of her defeated opponent.

In the quarterfinals, B.J. was eliminated by Ann Haydon of Great Britain. Yet even though she hadn't achieved her goal of winning "this little old tournament," Billie Jean's performance left no doubt that she was on her way to tennis stardom.

Now nothing but winning the most important tournaments would satisfy Billie Jean, and she couldn't seem to do that. She felt torn between school and tennis, convinced that it was impossible to do well in both at the same time. Early in 1965, with less than a year left until graduation, B.J. decided it was now or never in her tennis career. So, with the encouragement of her parents and her fiancé, Larry King, Billie Jean dropped out of college.

"My heart was really in tennis," she said. "I decided to go to Australia for three months and change my game. I had a very weak forehand, and I didn't think my serve was powerful enough. A lot of your power is in just playing — playing all the time. It's timing and rhythm.

"In Australia, the great coach Merv Rose helped me. He changed my forehand and my serve. He taught me all about the game as far as percentage tennis is concerned. That is what the pros use. You have certain patterns. There are certain points that you go for at a given time. Anyway, it was the decision to put my whole life into the sport that took me from number four to number one."

Billie Jean came home from Australia to play in the tournaments on the summer circuit. She reached the finals of the U.S. Nationals, only to lose to Margaret Smith. Still, she finished the season as the second-ranked female player in the United States.

In 1966, Billie Jean won every tournament on the winter circuit, including the U.S. hard court and the U.S. indoor singles titles. But those were only preparation for the real thing — Wimbledon.

It was a new Billie Jean who took the court at Wimbledon Stadium in 1966. This time, there was quiet on her side of the net. She wasn't going to break her concentration with the chatter that had marked her earlier matches. This time,

Billie Jean was playing percentage tennis, using strategy and a game plan against each opponent. This time, Billie Jean was not going to be stopped in the finals. With her overpowering serve, her speed in sprinting to the net, and her new stronger strokes, she defeated Maria Bueno of Brazil for the 1966 women's crown at Wimbledon.

In 1967, she won every championship in sight: the U.S. indoor, the Eastern grass court, the U.S. Nationals, and Wimbledon. Naturally, she was awarded the rank of number one woman tennis player in the world.

Her childhood fantasies had come true, but B.J. felt there was still more to do. First, she wanted to make life a little easier for her husband, Larry, whom she had married in the fall of 1965. Billie Jean was still an amateur, and although her expense money helped the couple's strained budget, Larry was working forty hours a week to help make ends meet while taking a full load at law school. B.J. believed that now it was her turn to earn their keep so that Larry could give up his job. Besides, Billie Jean had a new goal now. "This is a pro-oriented country," she said. "You can't be the best here unless you're a pro."

In the spring of 1968, B.J. signed a pro contract and set to work. Winning Wimbledon for the third straight year, she took her place alongside former tennis greats Maureen Connolly Brinker, Louise Brough, Fred Perry, Helen Wills Moody, and Suzanne Lenglen, the only others to accomplish that feat.

With Larry as her business agent, B.J. set out on the professional tour. But she quickly discovered that being a female tennis pro, even a superb one, didn't bring in very much money. A man who won a tournament might earn ten thousand dollars, but a woman was supposed to be satisfied with two thousand dollars. The women, led by Billie Jean, boycotted the official U.S. Lawn Tennis Association tournaments, publicized the inequities in prize money, and began to organize their own tour. "As the women's player representative," Billie Jean said, "I will attempt to represent the women's position along with what I view to be the best interests of the sport."

Her arguments were forceful and articulate, but victory didn't come easily. The late 1960's and early 1970's were years of turmoil for women, particularly for Billie Jean King. Winning tennis matches and drawing crowds were no longer enough for her; now only total acceptance as a pro and equal prize money would do.

In 1971, B.J. won $117,000, followed by $119,000 in 1972. She repeated her Wimbledon victory in 1972, 1973, and 1975; was U.S.

champion in 1971, 1972, and 1974; and became the best-known female athlete in history. Still, she had one more dream: to make tennis a popular spectator sport.

Billie Jean's success in promoting the joys of tennis could hardly be doubted. In the year after her smashing victory over Bobby Riggs, she became the player-coach of the Philadelphia Freedoms, the most successful team in the new World Team Tennis league. She helped start a tour for women pros that reached new heights of popularity, and she established a new magazine about women's sports to convey the idea that sports are for both sexes.

She was so busy that it seemed only a matter of time before the game itself would take a back seat to her related interests. But by then, of course, Billie Jean King had already made her point in competitive tennis. She had set the standard against which other women tennis players would measure themselves for years to come.

DISCUSSION

1. Both on and off the tennis court, how has Billie Jean King fought for women's rights to equal opportunity in sports?

2. Under what circumstances did Billie Jean take up tennis? Why did Clyde Walker notice her in his classes?

3. What natural abilities did Billie Jean possess that helped to make her a champion? What abilities did she develop with help from others? Which abilities do you think were more important? Why do you think that?

4. Why did Bobby Riggs challenge women tennis players to a match? What do you think Billie Jean's reason might have been for refusing Riggs's challenge the first time?

5. What do you think made Billie Jean decide to play Riggs after he had defeated Margaret Smith Court?

6. Why, do you think, was Billie Jean certain that the publicity about the proposed match between her and Riggs was "the best thing that could happen to her and to women's tennis"?

7. When she was a teen-ager, in what ways was Billie Jean physically handicapped as a tennis player?

8. Why does the trophy Billie Jean won at age thirteen occupy a place of honor among all her more impressive ones?

9. The article mentions two people, besides her first instructor, who coached Billie Jean. What special help did each provide?

10. Why, do you think, could Billie Jean be satisfied with nothing less than "total acceptance as a pro and equal prize money"?

11. Do you think that Billie Jean will be remembered longer for her victory over Riggs or for her victories at Wimbledon? Which do you consider to be more important? Why do you think that?

AUTHOR

Francene Sabin is a prolific author who has written articles and stories for magazines as well as several books. Her combined interests in sports and women's rights made it natural for her to write a book about women successful in the sports world. The book is *Women Who Win,* in which "Billie Jean King" appears.

Mrs. Sabin is married to a writer, Louis Sabin, with whom she sometimes collaborates. They and their son make their home in Milltown, New Jersey.

The Case of the Punjabi Ruby

by FRANK WILLMENT

Characters

Madame Martine, *owner of a jewelry shop*
Mona La Marr, *movie actress*
Silas Small, *financier*
Sardu Singh, *representative of a rajah*
Bradford Cabot, *museum curator*
Sergeant O'Shea *of the police*
Officer Akimoto *of the police*
Inspector Conlon *of the police*
Agatha Pritchett, *retired schoolteacher*

Time: *Late afternoon.*

Setting: *A small room in the rear of **Madame Martine's** jewelry shop. There is a table with five chairs around it at center. There are a few other chairs, an end table, etc., around room. There is a telephone on a table upstage. Doors are at right and at left.*

At rise: ***Sergeant O'Shea** stands at center in front of table talking to **Mona La Marr,** who is seated at one end of table. **Bradford Cabot** stands behind her, listening. **Madame Martine** is seated at opposite end of table, examining contents of her pocketbook. **Sardu Singh** is pacing back and forth at rear of room. **Silas Small** sits at left, lost in thought, and **Officer Akimoto** is guarding door at right.*

Mona La Marr (*Angrily; excited*): Why are you keeping us here, Sergeant? We've all been thoroughly searched by you or the policewoman. (*She waves hand in direction of Akimoto.*) None of us has the missing ruby! I have an important film premiere tonight, and I simply must get back to my hotel to get ready.

O'Shea: A few minutes more, Miss La Marr. I know you Hollywood stars have busy schedules, but Inspector Conlon should be here any second. I called him at home as soon as the robbery was reported. It isn't every day we have a half-million-dollar jewel theft in this precinct.

Singh (*Angrily*): It was more than just a jewel. It was the Punjabi[1] Ruby, a national treasure of my country, taken from us years ago.

Small (*Rising and crossing to center*): *You* say it was the Punjabi Ruby, Singh. All we know is that we were looking at an extremely valuable stone. The lights went out and it was gone. (*To O'Shea*) What can the inspector do, Sergeant, that you and the policewoman haven't already done? You've searched us; you've searched the room. The gem isn't here. Why not let us go home while you continue your investigation?

O'Shea: My orders are not to let anyone leave, Mr. Small.

Small: What rubbish! I'm a busy man. (*He returns to seat.*)

---

[1] **Punjabi** (puhn-jah′bee), of the Punjab, a region and former province of northwest India.

483

Singh (*Confronting O'Shea*): And I am the representative of one of the wealthiest and most powerful men in India. If the rajah knew you were keeping me prisoner here . . .

O'Shea: You're not a prisoner, Mr. Singh. You'll be free to go shortly, I'm sure. (*Knock on door is heard.*) That must be the inspector now. Let him in, Officer Akimoto.

Akimoto: Right, Sergeant. (*She opens door right, and **Inspector Conlon** and **Agatha Pritchett** enter.*)

Conlon: Hello, Akimoto. Hello, O'Shea. Everybody still here?

O'Shea: They're all here, Inspector. They've been squawking, but we didn't let them go.

Conlon (*Sitting on edge of table as others gather around him*): Sorry to inconvenience you folks, but we'll have a better chance of solving this case if we keep you all together. (*Indicating **Agatha**, who nods and smiles*) This is Miss Agatha Pritchett, who taught me a few things years ago when she was my eighth-grade teacher. She happened to be paying me a visit when the sergeant's telephone call came, and she asked to tag along to see a police investigation firsthand.

O'Shea: You picked a good one, Miss Pritchett. This case is a real humdinger.

Agatha: Please call me Miss Agatha. Everyone does. Now, all of you pretend I'm not here. I'll just sort of fade into the draperies, and you won't even know I'm around.

Conlon: I'm sure nobody minds, Miss Agatha. Now, then, let's get down to work. Will you fill us in on the facts, O'Shea?

O'Shea: Sure, Inspector. (*Indicating **Martine***) This is Madame Martine, the owner of this shop, Martine's Jewels. (***Conlon** nods.*) You passed through the main shop to get to this room. This is where she conducts private auctions of rare jewels.

Conlon: And I gather that an auction was going on here this afternoon.

Martine: Yes, we were holding a discreet auction of a valuable ruby. I had invited four clients who had expressed an interest in purchasing the gem.

Conlon: Are all four of the clients present?

Martine: Yes, Inspector. This is Mona La Marr, the actress. (*She indicates **La Marr**.*)

La Marr: I realize that you have your job to do, Inspector, but if you could be brief ——

Conlon: I'll do my best.

Martine: This gentleman is Sardu Singh. (*She indicates **Singh**.*) The rajah he represents is an old client of mine.

Singh: I am his *official* representative. I do not believe the rajah will be kindly disposed toward the police when he hears that I have been held like a common criminal.

Cabot: The ruby was worth half a million dollars! I'd say whoever stole it was an *uncommon* criminal, Singh.

Conlon (*To Cabot*): And who are you, sir?

Cabot: I'm Bradford Cabot, the curator of the City Museum. I attended the auction to see if I could secure the ruby for our collection.

Agatha: Pardon me for interrupting. Mr. Cabot, most curators have a specialty. Do you, sir?

Cabot: Yes, madam. I am in charge of our collection of minerals, metals, fossils, and gems.

Martine: There is one more client you have not met, Inspector. This is Silas Small, a prominent financier. (*She indicates **Small**.*)

Small: I trust this won't take too long, Inspector. I'd like to get back to the stock exchange before closing time.

Conlon: I understand. Tell me, Mr. Small, were you representing some business organization at the auction this afternoon?

Small: No, I'm strictly a private collector. As a matter of fact, I would appreciate as little publicity as possible. The fewer people who know I collect rare gems, the less chance I have of being robbed.

Agatha: I take it that you don't display or exhibit your collection, Mr. Small.

Small: Never! I enjoy my jewels for their own sake. I share that pleasure with no one.

Conlon: Now, let's see if I have the facts straight. Madame Martine was conducting a private auction in this room this afternoon, with four clients bidding on a valuable ruby.

Martine: We were sitting around this table, with the ruby on a black cloth in the center.

Conlon: You, Madame Martine, were sitting at the head, I suppose?

Martine: Yes. Miss La Marr and Mr. Small were on my right, and Mr. Cabot was on my left.

Conlon: Then, at the far end of the table was Mr. Singh, the representative of the rajah. Now, Madame Martine, tell us about your ruby.

Martine: It wasn't mine, Inspector. I merely had it on consignment for another client. I was working on a commission basis.

Conlon: How much of a commission would you have received?

Martine: Twenty per cent of the price the ruby brought. That's the standard fee in jewel auctions.

Agatha: Then if the gem had been auctioned for half a million dollars, your commission would have been $100,000.

Martine: Quite true. However, with the ruby gone, I receive nothing. You can see why I am anxious for its return.

Conlon: Who is the owner of the ruby, Madame Martine?

Martine: A wealthy European who wishes to remain anonymous.

Conlon: There's no doubt that the ruby was genuine, I take it.

Cabot: No doubt at all. I inspected it carefully, using a jeweler's loupe. In all modesty, I must say that I am an expert with jewels.

Small: Naturally I consider myself something of an expert also. I examined the gem, and I can say with certainty that it was genuine.

Singh: I may not be an expert, but I would know the Punjabi Ruby anywhere. The gem on the table an hour ago *was* the Punjabi Ruby!

Conlon: I'll accept the fact that it was genuine. Now, what actually happened at the auction?

Martine: We met here at one P.M., examined the ruby, placed it in the center of the table, and began the bidding.

La Marr: We hadn't been bidding too long before there was a power failure. The lights went out, and since there are no windows in the room, it was completely dark.

Conlon: Sergeant O'Shea told me about the power failure when we spoke on the phone. How long were the lights out?

La Marr: Perhaps ten or fifteen seconds, Inspector Conlon. Not very long.

Singh: But quite long enough! When the lights went on again, the Punjabi Ruby was missing! What will I tell the rajah?

Small (*Heatedly*): Tell him what you did with it! You took it, didn't you? You came here to get the gem by hook or by crook!

Singh: How dare you make such an accusation! The rajah does not need to steal. He is one of the world's wealthiest people. I came prepared to outbid all of you. Had it not disappeared, the gem would be mine at this moment!

Conlon: Mr. Small, let's not make unfounded charges. Now, could anyone have entered the room while the lights were out?

Martine: Impossible. There are two doors, and both were securely locked. And, of course, the room has no windows.

Conlon: Could anyone have hidden in the room before the auction began?

O'Shea: That's impossible, Inspector. There's no place to hide. There isn't even a closet in the room.

Conlon: Then that brings us back to the five people at the table when the lights went out. Now, what happened when the lights went on?

Small: We discovered immediately that the ruby was missing.

Cabot: I insisted that the police be called at once and that no one leave the room.

Agatha: There is a telephone in the room, I presume?

Martine: Yes, over on the corner table. I did not leave the room to make a phone call, if that is what you're suggesting, Miss Aggie.

Conlon: How long did it take Sergeant O'Shea and Officer Akimoto to arrive?

La Marr: Less than five minutes, I would say.

Akimoto: That's about right, Inspector. The station house is only two blocks away. We left as soon as we got the message.

Conlon: What did you do when you arrived here, Sergeant O'Shea?

O'Shea: Akimoto and I searched the premises thoroughly after we questioned the witnesses.

Singh: Witnesses? The lights were out. We witnessed nothing.

Small: What you mean to say is that we couldn't see you grab the ruby.

Singh: Another insult!

Conlon: As I told you two before, stop the bickering. Did you turn up anything in your search, O'Shea?

O'Shea: Not a single clue. And, of course, no sign of the ruby.

Akimoto: After that, we decided to search the people who were present when the robbery took place.

O'Shea: Akimoto searched the two women; I searched the three men.

Cabot (*Earnestly*): We insisted on a thorough search.

La Marr: It was obvious that the ruby must still be in the room, so each of us insisted on clearing himself or herself.

Conlon: I gather the personal search also proved fruitless.

O'Shea: That's right. None of them had the ruby.

Conlon: Did anyone leave the room — even for a moment, perhaps?

La Marr: No one left the room at any time. We were watching one another like hawks!

Conlon: It looks as if we have the elements of a first-rate mystery on our hands, doesn't it?

O'Shea: I'll say! We made a complete list of everything found on the suspects during the search.

La Marr: Suspects! I've never been so insulted in my life.

Agatha (*Gently*): But, one of you has to be guilty, Miss La Marr. So, naturally, all of you are suspects.

La Marr: You're right, I suppose. It just doesn't sound very nice.

Conlon: Do you have the lists of the suspects' possessions, Sergeant?

O'Shea (*Taking notebook from pocket and giving it to* **Conlon**): Here they are, Inspector. Nothing of any importance in them.

Conlon (*Glancing at lists*): So I see. Combs, keys, handkerchiefs — but nothing out of the ordinary.

Agatha (*Timidly, to* **Conlon**): May I see the lists, Bill?

Conlon: Well, I don't know. You're not on the force, Miss Agatha.

Small: Why do you want to poke your nose into our affairs?

Agatha: You seem to have reached a dead end, and I thought that something on the lists might be helpful — give the inspector a lead, you know.

La Marr: I have nothing to hide.

Cabot: Read them aloud. Somebody may get an idea. I'm sure we all want to find the ruby and get home.

Conlon: No objections? (*He looks around group.*) All right, read the lists out loud, Miss Agatha. (*He gives her the lists.*)

Agatha: Let's see. The first list is Mr. Small's. (*Reading*) "Handkerchief, aspirin, jeweler's loupe, checkbook, wallet, change."

Cabot: Nothing incriminating there.

Small (*Dryly*): Thanks for the vote of confidence.

Agatha: Mona La Marr: (*Reading*) "Compact, lipstick, doctor's prescription, credit cards, money clip, address book, sunglasses, keys, change purse, tissues."

La Marr (*Bored*): Makes me sound like a member of Murder Incorporated, doesn't it?

Conlon: I'll admit it sounds pretty harmless. Carry on, Miss Agatha.

Agatha: This is Mr. Singh's list. (*Reading*) "Passport, letter of introduction, traveler's checks, wallet, eyedrops, vitamin pills, cold tablets."

O'Shea: I thought the eyedrops were a little odd.

Singh: Not at all! This climate bothers my eyes and sinuses. In my country, we don't have industrial smog!

Agatha: Madame Martine's list. (*Reading*) "Perfume, compact, lipstick, chewing gum, appointment book, tissues, keys, pocket calculator, brush, and comb."

Singh: The pocket calculator was to figure her twenty per cent commission on the Punjabi Ruby, no doubt!

Martine: That is a normal, legal commission!

Agatha: Here's the last list — Mr. Cabot's. (*Reading*) "Pipe, tobacco, handkerchief, wallet, credit cards, nail file, parking ticket, comb, keys, jeweler's loupe."

Small: Parking ticket, eh?

Cabot: I put it in my pocket to pay later today. That hardly makes me a criminal.

Martine: Are we quite finished with all this nonsense?

Agatha: I've read all the lists, if that's what you mean.

La Marr: And they weren't much help, were they?

Agatha: Oh, I wouldn't say that. I found them to be most interesting.

Conlon: If you saw something we didn't see, tell us, Miss Agatha. You know, in school we always said that you had eyes in the back of your head. We couldn't put anything over on you, as I remember.

Agatha (*Smiling modestly*): Frankly, I did notice one or two things, but they're probably not important.

Akimoto: Then, where do we go from here, Inspector?

Conlon: Let's review the facts. Fact one: The ruby must still be in this room. Fact two: It hasn't been found in the room or on anyone who was in the room when it disappeared. An interesting case!

Small (*Impatiently*): Interesting to you, maybe, but it's wasting my valuable time.

Agatha: When I was a girl, we used to say there's more than one way to skin a cat.

La Marr: What do you mean by that?

Agatha: It means that there are many ways of looking at a problem. When you reach a dead end, try another angle.

Singh: What angle do you suggest?

Agatha: Let's see what the ruby's loss would mean to everyone. Perhaps this will show us who had a motive for the theft.

Small: We all had a motive. We wanted a half-million-dollar gem!

Agatha: But that jewel might have been more important to one person than to another. Now, Madame Martine, if the gem had been sold for $500,000, your commission would have been $100,000. Is that correct?

Martine: Yes, the theft cost me $100,000. How can that possibly give me a motive?

Agatha: Wasn't the ruby insured?

Martine: Of course, for its full value by the owner in Europe. He will collect the insurance.

Agatha: I see. The owner loses nothing. You lose your commission.

Martine: That is correct.

Agatha: Actually, the others have lost nothing except the chance to bid on the gem. Perhaps it would be enlightening to see what each person at the auction intended to do with the ruby and how much each was prepared to pay.

Conlon: That's a good angle to pursue, Miss Agatha.

Agatha: Let's start with you, Miss La Marr. Why did you want the stone?

La Marr: Frankly, wearing fabulous jewels is part of my image. They write it up constantly in the gossip columns. The ruby would be worth tons of publicity to me. It would have given my career an enormous boost.

Agatha: I quite understand. And how much were you willing to pay?

La Marr: Unfortunately, this auction caught me at a bad time. I could only raise $275,000.

Agatha: I see. And how high had the bidding gone when the lights went out?

Martine: The bidding was at $130,000. And the auction was far from over.

Agatha: Mr. Cabot, you said you wanted to purchase the ruby for your museum. How high were you authorized to go, may I ask?

Cabot: I suppose there's no harm in telling you now. My top figure was to be $350,000. But I hoped to get it for less.

Agatha: If you had been the successful bidder, the gem would have been put on display at the museum?

Cabot: Correct.

Agatha: Mr. Small, if you, however, had bought the ruby, it would have been hidden from the world.

Small: That's not a crime! As a private collector, I have no wish to share my treasures with the common herd of humanity. I have no philanthropic inclinations. Gems are my hobby.

Agatha: I see. And how much were you prepared to spend on your hobby?

Small: The auction was called at an inauspicious moment, to tell you the truth. Ordinarily, I would not have permitted anyone to outbid me, but I had to use most of my liquid assets to cover a margin call on the stock market last week. A bid of $225,000 would have been my top offer for the ruby today.

Agatha: Then you, like Miss La Marr, would have lost to Mr. Cabot and the City Museum.

Small: It would seem so.

Singh: Not quite! You seem to have forgotten that I was also bidding on the stone!

Agatha: I was coming to you, Mr. Singh. What did you intend to do with the ruby?

Singh: It was the Punjabi Ruby! I was to return it to my homeland and to the rajah, the rightful owners! Eighteen years ago it was stolen from the Shrine of Jind.

Agatha: Then it would have been displayed in the shrine?

Singh: Yes, along with the other sacred relics. But this time it would be placed under constant armed guard.

Small: There's your man, Inspector. A fanatic who wanted the ruby any way he could get it!

Singh: Yes, I wanted the ruby desperately, but there was no reason to

491

steal it. My instructions were to out-bid you all, and the rajah is wealthy enough to do just that!

Agatha: According to the others, the top bid would have been Mr. Cabot's $350,000.

Singh: Then I would have secured the ruby for $360,000.

Agatha: I see. I thank all of you for your frank answers, but I haven't been too much help so far, I'm afraid.

Conlon: Oh, one can't have too much information in a case like this. One slip of the tongue could provide the key to the mystery. (*All talk informally with one another as* **Agatha** *leads* **Conlon** *to one side.*)

Agatha (*To* **Conlon**, *conspiratorially*): My thoughts exactly, Bill. One slip of the tongue.

Conlon: Then we must watch for it.

Agatha: Oh, it's already happened.

Conlon: It has? Do you know where the ruby is and who stole it?

Agatha: I think so, but I'm not certain of my facts yet. May I make one more suggestion?

Conlon: Of course. You seem to have missed your vocation, Miss Agatha. You would have made quite a detective. What do you suggest?

Agatha (*Turning to others; brightly*): I think we should re-enact the crime.

Singh: Re-enact the crime? What an idiotic idea!

Agatha: Everybody could sit around the table. We could go through the bidding, turn out the lights at the proper moment, turn them on after ten seconds or so, and see if we learn anything.

Cabot: It sounds silly. What could we possibly learn?

Agatha: Perhaps where the jewel is and who took it.

Conlon: What can we lose? The ruby is already gone. Let's try it. Take the places you had at the time of the auction. (*They take seats around table, with* **Martine** *at head,* **Singh** *at opposite end,* **La Marr** *and* **Small** *to right of* **Martine**, **Cabot** *to her left.*) Now, let's put the black cloth in the center — without the Punjabi Ruby, of course. (**Martine** *unfolds cloth on display stand on table.*)

La Marr (*Snippily*): This is a waste of time, Inspector!

Conlon: Perhaps not, Miss La Marr. Please conduct the auction, Madame Martine. Sergeant O'Shea, go over by the light switch. (*Motions left*) When the bids reach $130,000, as they did earlier today, turn off the lights for ten seconds, and then switch them back on again.

O'Shea (*Going left to light switch*): Will do, Inspector.

Conlon: Go ahead, Madame Martine. (**Conlon** *stations himself behind table;* **Miss Agatha** *stands at head of table behind* **Martine**; **Akimoto** *is at the other end of table behind* **Sardu Singh**.)

Martine: Very well. You have all examined the ruby. May we begin the bidding?

Small: I bid $50,000.

La Marr: Make that $60,000.

Cabot: I say $70,000.

Singh: Let's stop these trifling bids. I'll bid $100,000.

Small: Make it $110,000.

La Marr: $120,000.

Cabot: It's $130,000 here. (**O'Shea** *flips light switch, and there is a blackout for ten seconds. Lights come up again. Large ruby is in center of table on black cloth.*)

493

Singh (*Incredulous*): Look! The ruby is back in place! Praise be!

Conlon: Jumping catfish! It is back!

Akimoto: Is it the real Punjabi Ruby?

Cabot (*Taking out jeweler's loupe and examining gem*): It's the real thing, all right.

Small: Let me see it! (*He takes ruby from* **Cabot**, *takes out his loupe, and examines it.*) He's right! It is the Punjabi Ruby!

Martine: It has been found! Wonderful! We can continue the auction.

Singh: No auction is necessary. That Miss Agatha woman had us reveal our top bids. I am obviously the high bidder at $360,000. Can anyone here top it?

Conlon: You can't bid on stolen merchandise, Mr. Singh. A crime is involved.

Martine: But the ruby is back, even if we don't know who returned it!

Agatha: I know who returned it.

La Marr: You do?

Agatha: Yes. I returned it.

Cabot: You? But you couldn't have. You weren't even here when the gem was stolen!

Agatha: Oh, I didn't steal the ruby. I simply discovered who did, guessed where it was hidden, and returned it to the table while the lights were out. That's why I wanted a re-enactment of the crime. I thought it would be more dramatic that way.

O'Shea: Well, don't keep us in suspense! Who did it?

Agatha: Let me first explain how I came to my conclusions. Miss La Marr wouldn't steal the ruby. She wanted publicity, and she couldn't wear a stolen jewel in public.

Conlon: And Mr. Cabot couldn't have displayed a stolen gem in his museum.

Agatha: Precisely. Mr. Singh wanted to return the ruby to his native land. Since he claims it was originally stolen from a temple, he might have been willing to steal it back.

Small: So it was Singh all the time! I knew it!

Singh: Don't be ridiculous! Why should I steal a gem I was about to buy?

Agatha: That's true. Also, if Mr. Singh had stolen the gem, how would he have gotten it out of the country? Both the police and the customs officials would have been watching him closely.

La Marr: Then it must have been Silas Small! I should have known. I never did like that shifty look of his!

Small: Be careful what you say, Miss La Marr! A suit for slander isn't exactly the kind of publicity you want.

Agatha: Mr. Small seemed an obvious suspect in the beginning. Once the ruby was in his private collection, no one would know he possessed it. On the other hand, any one of you might have stolen it, hoping to sell it later to some other private collector who wouldn't question where it came from.

Akimoto: Then we're right back where we were, Miss Agatha.

Agatha: Not quite. While anyone might have had a motive for stealing the ruby, everyone except the thief lacked one important thing.

Akimoto (*Fascinated*): What was it they lacked?

Agatha: Opportunity!

O'Shea: But everyone at the table had the same opportunity. They were all there when the lights went out.

Agatha: But only one person *knew* that the lights would go out and *when* they would go out.

Akimoto: Who did?

Agatha: The thief. (*To Conlon*) Do you remember, Bill, that I stopped to chat with the attendant at the door when we entered the building?

Conlon: Oh, yes. What did you say?

Agatha: Sergeant O'Shea had mentioned the power failure when he talked to you on the telephone. I asked the attendant about it.

Conlon: And what did he say?

Agatha: He wasn't aware of a power failure.

Martine: It lasted only ten seconds. He might not have noticed it.

Agatha: I thought that too. So as we walked through the lobby, I spoke to a woman who was leaving the building. I asked her if the blackout had inconvenienced her. She wasn't aware that there had been a power failure either.

Akimoto: Then what caused the lights to go out during the auction?

Agatha: I wondered about that too. I looked around rather carefully when I first arrived. You have rather elaborate lighting, don't you, Madame Martine?

Martine: Yes, to show off jewels to their advantage. It's one of the tricks of the trade.

Agatha: At home I have a timing device attached to my radio. It allows me to go to sleep to the sound of music and to awaken to it. It turns off my radio at night and turns it back on in the morning.

Martine: So you like music. So what?

Conlon: Do you mean that by using a timing device, the thief could know exactly when the lights would go off and come on?

Agatha: It occurred to me that it could explain why the lights went out in this room and nowhere else.

Conlon: Madame Martine, do you own such timing devices?

Martine (*Indignantly*): What if I do? If that's what caused the lights to go out, any one of us could have set the timer!

Agatha: I suppose that's true, but first let me explain how I found the ruby.

Akimoto: Please do. I can't wait!

Agatha: It all started when Madame Martine called me Miss Aggie.

Martine: I did?

Agatha: Yes. It was then that I suspected you must have been a former student of mine.

Martine: But the inspector — you said that he was a former student of yours — and he's been calling you Miss Aggie.

Agatha: No, he's been calling me Miss Agatha. As a matter of fact, I asked everyone to call me Miss Agatha.

Martine: So what?

Agatha: In class, students always called me Miss Agatha. Behind my back some students called me Miss Aggie, and you were one of them, Molly.

Martine: Molly! Why did you call me that? What are you talking about?

Agatha: When you said "Miss Aggie," it started to come back. *Martine*, I said, *Martine*. Take off the *e* and you have *Martin*. Molly Martin, a freckle-faced, gum-chewing eighth grader!

Martine: I don't know what you're talking about.

Agatha (*Ignoring her*): That's what I was looking for when I went over the lists. If you were Molly Martin, you'd still chew gum, I was certain. Sure enough, chewing gum was one of the things on your list.

Martine: All right, I used to be in your class, and I still chew gum. How does that add up to a jewel theft?

Agatha (*To Conlon*): Bill, did you chew gum in school?

Conlon (*Trying to remember*): Yes, I guess I did.

Agatha: Did you chew it in my class, Bill?

Conlon: In your class? Of course not! You had no mercy for gum chewers.

Agatha: Then what did you do with your gum when you came to my class?

Conlon (*Thinking a moment*): Why, we parked it under our chairs.

Agatha: I thought you would remember that. And I thought that Molly Martin would too! When the sergeant turned off the lights, I reached under her chair and found what I expected to find — a wad of chewing gum.

Conlon: With the Punjabi Ruby in the middle!

Agatha: Correct! I pulled the ruby out of the gum and put it back on the table before the lights came on again!

Conlon: The ruby was under Madame Martine's chair! She was the only one who could really have arranged for the lights to go out. She must have been the one who planned the whole thing!

Martine: You're crazy! Why would I steal the gem? I would lose a huge commission.

Agatha: Yes, you'd lose the commission, but you would have the ruby. At another time, when the stock market was better, Mr. Small would have paid you the gem's full worth — $500,000.

Small: I would have, and Madame Martine, or whatever her name is, knows it.

497

Martine: All right, so I hid the ruby under the chair. What's the charge?

Conlon: It seems to me that you were trying to steal the ruby from its present owner. We'll hold you for questioning and get in touch with the owner to see if he wishes to press charges. In any case, I'm pretty sure he won't want you to handle any more auctions for him. (***Akimoto and O'Shea*** *escort* ***Martine*** *out.*)

Agatha (*Shaking her head*): Molly Martin was never able to get away with anything, not even back in eighth grade.

Conlon: Miss Agatha, you should have been a detective.

Agatha: No, Bill, I'll let you be the detective. I'm just a retired school-teacher. You know, all I really did was use one of the tricks of my trade. (*Quick curtain*)

DISCUSSION

1. Do you think Madame Martine would have succeeded in stealing the ruby if Miss Agatha had not helped the police? Why do you think as you do?
2. Who owned the ruby Madame Martine was selling? Why did it seem unlikely at first that Madame Martine had stolen the ruby?
3. Why was it certain that the ruby was still somewhere in the room?
4. When Inspector Conlon asked Miss Agatha if she had discovered something in the lists of suspects' possessions, why did she say, "I did notice one or two little things, but they're probably not important"?
5. Why was Sardu Singh so eager to have the ruby?
6. Judging by their behavior during the investigation, which one of the suspects do you think acted most guilty? Why do you think that?
7. Miss Agatha said she suggested re-enacting the crime because that would be dramatic. What other reason did she probably have for suggesting the re-enactment?

8. As a result of Miss Agatha's questioning, why did it seem unlikely that the actress, the museum curator, or the rajah's representative had stolen the jewel?

9. How did Miss Agatha know that the lights had gone out only in the room where the auction was being held?

10. What did Madame Martine say that gave Miss Agatha a clue to her real identity?

11. What did Miss Agatha see in the lists of items found on the suspects that confirmed her suspicion of who Madame Martine was? Why was that item also an important clue to the location of the ruby?

12. Do you think Madame Martine had devised a clever scheme for robbery? Why or why not?

AUTHOR

Frank Willment taught English and drama at the junior- and senior-high-school levels in Georgetown, Delaware, and Ridgewood, New Jersey, for many years before concentrating on educational writing. He is currently public information officer for the Ridgewood Public Schools. Most of his plays were written for production in his own drama classes when he was teaching. Now he writes for young people as a change of pace after working on articles explaining school budgets and math curriculums.

Roots from Roots

In Alex Haley's "Roots," one man tackled a mystery of life that interests us all. To fully understand who we are, we must look back to where we came from. Alex Haley's roots extended to a small village in The Gambia, and further back to a country called Old Mali. For each of us the search would take its own course: perhaps also to Africa, or to Asia, to South America, to Europe, or to America before Columbus came. We each carry clues to the past: our names, physical characteristics, and family customs. These are clues to the mystery of each person's past, if we use them. So it is with language.

Anyone who reads a great deal often comes across unfamiliar words. The English language has approximately half a million words. The language is so complex that even a lexicographer cannot know the meanings of all its words. But we do have familiar clues to the mysteries of unfamiliar words. Roots, prefixes, suffixes, and sentence context are all helpful if you know how to use them.

If, for instance, you did not know the meaning of the word *lexicographer*, you could figure it out if you knew that it is made up of the following smaller parts: the Greek word *lexicon*, meaning "a book pertaining to words," from the Greek word *lexis*, meaning "speech, word, phrase"; the root *-graph-*, meaning "write"; and the suffix *-er*, meaning "a person or thing that." Thus, a lexicographer is a person who writes books describing words, or a writer or compiler of a dictionary. An unfamiliar puzzle, the word *lexicographer,* has been added to your stockpile of familiar words. Now you understand why a lexicographer would know more words than almost anyone else.

In the article "Roots," you read a number of words that are each built around a single root from ancient Latin or Greek. Some of these words are *envisioning, circular, surviving, imported,* and *phonetic.* The word *envisioning* appeared in the sentence, "In my mind's eye, rather as if it were mistily being projected on a screen, I began envisioning descriptions I had read of how, collectively, millions of our ancestors had been enslaved." If you did not know the exact meaning of *envisioning* when you read it, the sentence context probably helped you. The word *envision* itself gives you clues to its meaning. The root of *envision, -vis-,* means "to see." This root is common to a number of words that have something to do with seeing: *vision, visible, invisible,* and *visual.* If you also know the meanings of the prefix *en-,* meaning "in," and the suffix *-ion,* meaning "the act of," you might come up with the rough definition "the act of seeing in (the mind)," or "to picture in the mind," or "to imagine."

Here are the roots of the other words listed above. Try to match each root with its correct definition from the bottom of the page. Each root is listed with two sentences containing words in which it appears.

1. *-Circ-* is a root meaning _____. The <u>circulation</u> is the path of blood through the body and back to the heart. Some day you may wish to <u>circumnavigate</u> the earth.
2. *-Viv-* is a root meaning _____. Some of the <u>vivid</u> colors used by contemporary painters were not discovered until this century. You might know someone with a <u>vivacious</u> personality.
3. *-Port-* is a root meaning _____. A <u>portable</u> appliance can be moved from place to place. Have you ever <u>portaged</u> on a canoe, kayak, or rafting trip?
4. *-Phon-* is a root meaning _____. A <u>phonetic</u> spelling shows how to pronounce a word correctly. What do a <u>xylophone</u>, a <u>saxophone</u>, and a <u>sousaphone</u> have in common?

life   carry   ring   sound

Settlers in Space

by GERARD K. O'NEILL

"Jan. 15, 1996: Jennie and I have been in Transfer Station One, in low orbit around the earth, for 24 hours. We have decided to start this journal while our thoughts are still fresh.

"There were 150 of us on the shuttle from Earth to the transfer station. The video panels gave us a good view of our liftoff, but it was quite different from watching a rocket lift off on a television show. This time, we knew we were on top of all those fireworks. Lying in narrow bunks, however, we weren't bothered much by the acceleration, and after 10 minutes, the engines shut down. A few more minutes of coasting in zero gravity, and we docked onto Station One. As we walked down a ramp leading to the outer rim of the rotating station, gravity built up to normal.

"They have a nice mobile hanging from the ceiling of the Orbiter Hotel lobby. The earth and moon are two points of an equal-sided triangle, and a small green light at the third point marks L5, where we are headed. Dots of white light that move around the green point in a big kidney-shaped orbit are all the colonies, including Colony Two, our final destination.

"Every six hours another shuttle arrives. The hotel is about two-thirds full now, and there's quite an international mix among the new colonists. Jennie and I are starting to try our Russian and Japanese, even though we are pretty shy about it still.

"Jan. 17, 1996: Yesterday we boarded the *Konstantin E. Tsiolkovsky* (tsee-ohl-kahv′skih), named after the Russian space pioneer, for the eight-day trip to L5. It's a huge ship, holding about 2,000 passengers. It runs on three separate schedules, eight hours apart, that match the Moscow, Cape Canaveral, and Western Pacific time zones on Earth. One nice custom they have is seating us by place cards at breakfast with a couple from another time zone having dinner. The Japanese couple we met this morning are in power-plant construction, too, so we talked shop for a while.

"Jan. 20, 1996: Everyone was excited today when we passed the *Tsiolkovsky's* twin, the *Robert H. Goddard*,[1] on its way back to Station One. The *Goddard* was in view for more than an hour, and our crew gave us some nice telescope views on the video screens. It was beautiful.

"Jan. 24, 1996: We docked at Colony Two this morning and got a good view of it on the video screen in our room as we came in.

---

[1] **Robert H. Goddard,** an American physicist who pioneered in the study of rockets.

It's quite a sight. Two parallel cylinders rotate slowly in space, about 10 kilometers [6 miles] apart. Each one is about 700 meters [0.4 mile] in diameter and 3,400 meters [2.1 miles] long. Three big mirrors rotate with each cylinder, sweeping over a wide area as they gather solar energy. As we docked, we passed between the colony and the sun for a few minutes, and we could look right into the mirrors and see the reflected valley areas inside, green with crops.

"The colonists live in terraced apartments in the end caps of the cylinders. Jennie and I have one of the smaller apartments, but it still has two large rooms, plus kitchen and bath, and a nice garden. The climate, controlled by opening and closing mirrors, is like springtime in Hawaii, so there are masses of flowers and fruit in the garden.

"Jan. 25, 1996: Edward has gone off to the power-plant construction factory, so I'll take over the writing for a while.

"Sunning ourselves in the garden yesterday, we could look up and see the gardens of the apartments on the other side of the cylinder. For some reason, it doesn't seem as strange to have trees growing straight down as it does to have them coming out sideways, as they do from the gardens a quarter circle away. Everyone spends a fair amount of time outside.

"Looking out and across, we can see the big disk that seals us off from the main part of the cylinder, where the crops are grown. It is about 50 centimeters [20 inches] thick, to block the cosmic rays. The disk is gently curved like a dish. On our side it is steeply terraced and planted with tropical flowers, a mass of green and bright colors. Early each morning there is a rain shower, so everything is fresh when we wake up, and the air has a nice, clean smell of rain and flowers. Our colony is not quite big enough to have weather of its own, though, so the 'rain' comes from spray pipes that are just a bit too high and too thin to be seen.

"After Edward gets home, we are going down to the little beach for a swim. Maybe tomorrow we'll walk up the garden paths, past the shops and restaurants, and into the park. They have zero-gravity clubrooms there where we can try flying under pedal-power and slow-motion diving in low gravity — that pool must be fun."

Those journal entries may sound like science fiction about life hundreds of years from now, but every detail described is practical in terms of today's technology. We need no new breakthroughs, no super-strength materials, not even any new inventions to carry through a giant space-colonization program. As many as one million people could be living and working in space by the year 2000.

The idea of such a program grew out of an informal seminar that I held in 1969 for a few of my first-year physics students at Princeton University in New Jersey. When we studied whether a planetary surface was really the best place for a growing industrial civilization, we found some surprising answers. For one thing, enclosing atmospheres in cylinders was more than a billion times more efficient than trying to hold an atmosphere by gravity, as a planet does.

The seminar lasted only a few weeks, but I continued to work in my spare time on the concept of a space community. By 1972, I was lecturing about space colonies at other universities. In 1974, the first small, informal conference on the subject was held at Princeton. Suddenly, the idea became front-page news, and hundreds of letters began to pour in from interested and enthusiastic people who wanted to help make the idea a reality. Magazine and newspaper articles appeared in many other countries, conferences were held, and the National Aeronautics and Space Administration awarded a grant to finance further study at Princeton.

Resourceful Use of Space

Although the idea of space colonization can be traced back more than eighty years, a serious plan, based on available technology, could never have been formed before the Apollo astronauts landed on the moon. Within just a few years, the Apollo program greatly advanced rocket technology. More, it proved that people could live far from the surface of our planet. Above all, it gave us samples of the lunar surface to study. We know that the lunar surface is a rich mine of aluminum, iron, silicon, oxygen, titanium, calcium, and other useful elements. And we know that Earth plants can grow in lunar soil if they are given water and fertilizer.

Space has an abundance of the two key requirements for continuing industrial progress — energy and materials. A colony in space could have a clean, unlimited, absolutely reliable energy source — the sun. Even today's solar technology would be effective and economical in the space environment. In space, the sun shines twenty-four hours a day, even in the middle of winter, and it is never hidden by clouds or rain. With no atmosphere to penetrate, the intensity is about 50 per cent higher than it is on Earth when the sun is directly overhead.

Abundant materials for industry can be taken from the moon and, later, from the asteroids, those chunks of rock that orbit the sun between Mars and Jupiter. The asteroids and the moon share one great asset — no one owns them, and there are no living creatures on them whose needs and wishes must be weighed against exploitation.

The first colony will probably be built about 386,000 kilometers (240,000 miles) from the earth in orbit around a point in space known as L5, the third point of an equilateral triangle formed with the earth and moon. At L5, the gravities and centrifugal forces of the earth and moon cancel each other out. This means that any object placed nearby would orbit the point forever without drifting away. The stable orbit would be kidney-shaped, because of the influence of the sun, and it would be large enough to hold several thousand colonies.

Before we can build the first colony, we will need careful studies on such subjects as architecture for space, growing crops in constant bright sunshine and in an oxygen-rich, low-pressure atmosphere, and adapting chemical and industrial processes to make full use of low-cost energy and zero gravity. In a few years, we may begin building pilot plants, special-purpose machines, and prototypes of two essential devices. One is a crewless freight rocket that can carry tens of tons of material. The other is a Transport Linear Accelerator, or mass driver, that can catapult raw materials mined from the surface of the moon to the L5 region where the colonies will be built.

The first space station built at L5 will contain living quarters, greenhouse areas, and a large spherical working area where the first colony will be assembled. A processing plant will turn lunar ores into aluminum for the colony structure, glass for its windows, oxygen for its atmosphere, and industrial slag to be crushed into sand and soil.

Slowly, the pieces of the colony structure will begin to take shape.

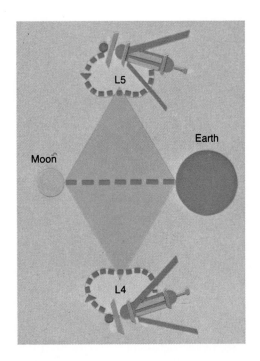

Each time one of the large curved sections is finished, the working area will be temporarily depressurized and opened. The new section will be floated out and welded to the growing shell by remotely directed machines using solar heat.

Design of Colony One

The first colony may take the form of two parallel cylinders, each 1,000 meters (1,100 yards) long and 200 meters (220 yards) in diameter, with round caps at the ends. Each cylinder will have three land areas running lengthwise on its inner surface, alternating with window areas of the same width. Aluminum cables that are rather like bridge cables will run lengthwise along each

507

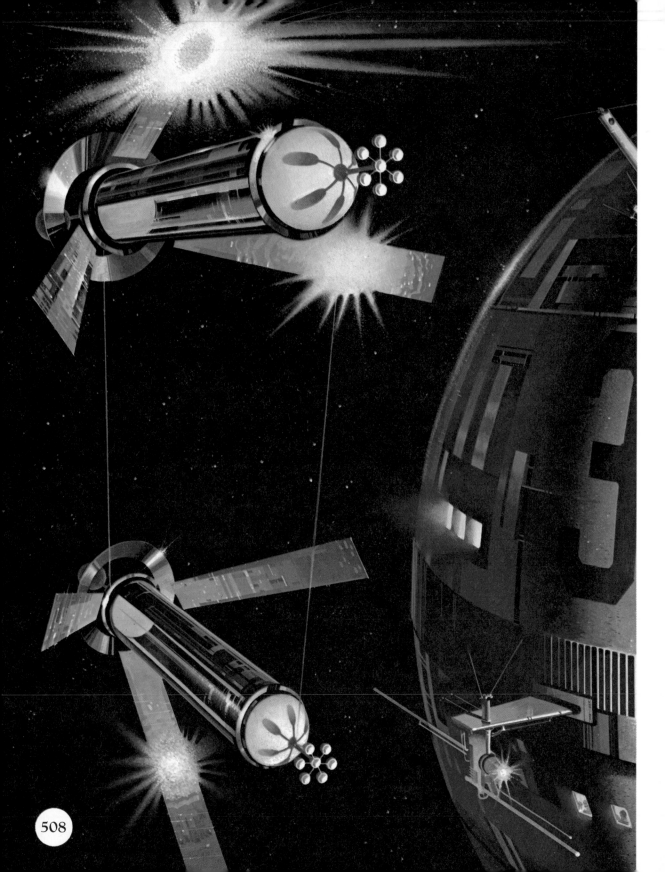

cylinder and will also circle it every few meters or yards to give it strength. An aluminum frame will strengthen the window areas, dividing the glass into small panels. Large, flat mirrors, fixed to each cylinder by cables, will rotate with the cylinder, reflecting the sun's rays into the land areas. At one end of each cylinder, a round aluminum mirror will concentrate the sun's rays for the colony's power station. A network of lightweight beams will keep the cylinders parallel and pointing toward the sun.

It will take several years to finish the cylinders and make them airtight. The store of liquid oxygen accumulated during the industrial processing of oxide ores can then be warmed by solar heat, releasing gaseous oxygen that will slowly build up inside each cylinder. Motors will begin to turn the cylinders in opposite directions until they are finally rotating three times per minute, providing normal Earth gravity for people standing on the land areas inside. This machine-made gravity will slowly decline as one moves toward the axis, reaching the weightlessness of zero gravity at the center.

Once the colony is finished, colonists like Edward and Jennie can begin traveling to their new homes. A fleet of shuttle vehicles, each carrying from 50 to 150 passengers, will begin taking them from Earth to an orbit about 160 kilometers (100 miles) from the earth where they will meet the space liner that will carry them to L5. The huge, spherical space liner will be as different from the shuttle as a steamship is from a city bus. It may carry up to 6,000 passengers.

Colony One will hold about 10,000 persons. I hope that the early residents will include a wide spectrum of settlers from all countries — not only men and women in their working years but also children and older persons. Perhaps they will already have worked and studied together during a preparation program on Earth so that they will have built up friendships, confidence in each other, and trust. These settlers will find difficult conditions, but not nearly so hard as those faced by early colonists of the New World.

Agriculture, in the main land areas of the cylinders, will be intensive and highly mechanized. By controlling the solar mirrors, there can be long summer days all year, with never a cloud or storm. Temperatures can stay always near 35°C (95°F) so that corn, sweet potatoes, sorghum, and other fast-growing crops can be harvested four times a year. Chickens, turkeys, and pigs, raised on cuttings and grains, will round out the colonists' nutritious diet. Even though beef cattle may be too inefficient in converting grain

509

to meat to earn space in this first colony, there may be a small stock of dairy cows — children will still need their milk. There could be insects for the birds to eat, but perhaps we can do without mosquitoes and cockroaches. We can also do without other pests such as mice and rats.

The living areas of Colony One will be in the end caps of the cylinders, set off from the hot, humid agricultural areas. Homes may be terraced apartments, each with its own garden. Space clothes may be quite light, because the environment can be pleasant at all times.

Benefits and Hazards

Because all manufacturing dealing with large objects can be done most easily in zero gravity, almost all large-scale industry will be placed outside the spinning cylinders. One such industrial capsule may hold Colony One's electric power station. The early stages of ore processing, requiring the crushing of rock into powder, can also be done in space, where no noise can cross the vacuum to the colony.

A small part of Colony One's work force may engage in scientific work. They could build large optical telescopes, free from atmospheric interference and able to pick out planets around the nearest stars. Or they might assemble the delicate webs of huge radio tele-

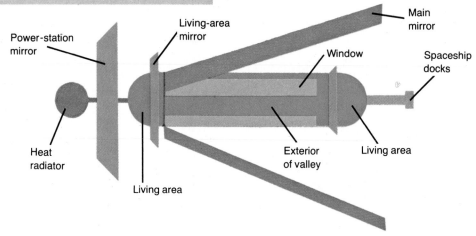

scopes that could stretch across vast areas of space, free from the restrictions of gravity. Large exploration ships built at the colony could visit the asteroids and outer planets of the solar system. A larger group of technicians, working to meet Earth's important need for energy, might build large solar power stations that could beam microwave energy down to Earth.

One of the diversions of space-colony planning is imagining the new choices that the colonists will have. The first is one that I call seasonal counterpoint. The two cylinders that form one colony will each be entirely independent in its day-night cycle, climate, and seasonal phase. One cylinder could have a New England climate, with brisk winters and crisp autumns, to turn leaves to rainbow colors. Its twin might have the year-round springtime of Hawaii, with moist air, palm trees, and beaches for warm, lazy swimming.

Many of the recreations will be those of a small, wealthy resort community on Earth — good restaurants, movie theaters, libraries, and perhaps small discotheques. Yet some things will be very different. There will be no cars and no smog; colonists will travel on foot or on bicycles in Colony One and perhaps use electric runabouts in the larger colonies. Some favorite colony sports would be impossible on Earth. There would be low-gravity swimming and diving, and surfing on waves that break as slowly as in a dream; human-powered flight near the cylinder axes, where gravity will approach zero; or mountain climbing at the end caps, where the gravity will become weaker as climbers mount higher, until at the top they will weigh nothing at all.

But along with the conveniences and pleasures, the colonies will also have their dangers. With no atmosphere outside to protect them, the window areas of Colony One will be exposed to a constant rain of meteoroids. Nearly all of these will be far tinier than a grain of sand. But occasionally a larger one will break a window panel. When this happens, there need be no panic, because it would take several days for Colony One to lose all its atmosphere. Within minutes of a break, workers can patch the hole, and a full repair can be made at leisure. Even if it takes an hour to patch the hole, the inside pressure will drop only as much as it does on Earth when we climb a small hill — not even enough to affect our eardrums. Oxygen losses can be made up from the oxygen released during industrial processing. Losses in water vapor will be more costly to replace because additional hydrogen must be brought from Earth. Still, an occasional small loss will not be hard to make up.

Pioneers in Space

As time goes on, larger colonies will almost certainly be built. However, people may prefer to live in smaller colonies where government, transportation, and life-styles might be simpler.

Quite early in colonial history, some families may choose to cut loose from the colonies and homestead the asteroid belt on their own. A colonist living at L5 could, with little trouble and at small cost, assemble a suitable spacecraft. The same spirit that fired the pioneers who settled the American West may drive people of great energy and skill to build their own worlds some day in the future.

At some point, it will become commonplace to build new colonies near asteroids. The ten largest asteroids would provide enough material to continue building new colonies for more than 2,000 years. Colonies farther from the sun than the earth could easily set up concentrating mirrors to obtain the same intensity of sunshine that exists near Earth.

The possible long-term effects of space colonization on the earth and on the human race raise many questions. Would it be possible that provision of low-cost energy for the earth, perhaps the earliest task of the colonies, could save millions of human lives by speeding up the spread of high-yield agriculture?

What would be the effect of the great diversity of social systems, governments, and life-styles likely to develop in the colonies? Psychological and sociological results are hard to predict, but the effect on the colonists might be a healthy one. Could the opening of a doorway into another set of worlds bring hope to many people trapped in a world growing ever more crowded and lacking in resources?

For the earth itself, space colonization may offer the chance to return to a natural environment that will be greener, less crowded, and less burdened with industry. Earth's remaining inhabitants may enjoy remolding it into the open, pastoral state that existed before the industrial age. It may finally become a sort of worldwide park, which the space colonists may visit as tourists. To them, life on a planet may seem as strange as life in space will at first seem to us.

Eventually, many millions of colonists may be scattered over the solar system, and at least a few explorers may begin to venture out to our nearest neighbor stars. After 1,000 years of living in space, our descendants may find those unimaginable voyages as natural as we find journeys to other countries. How lucky we are to be the generation that has the power to take the first giant step by which humankind will climb to the stars!

DISCUSSION

1. If you had a choice, would you prefer to live in a space colony or on Earth? Why?
2. Why, do you think, did the author start this article with an imaginary diary?
3. Why, do you think, did Dr. O'Neill's idea of space colonies become front-page news soon after he began to develop it?
4. About how long before this article was written did people first conceive the idea of space colonies? What three contributions to planning for such colonies did the Apollo moon landings make?
5. The author states that there would be abundant energy and materials in space for industrial development. Where would the energy and materials come from?
6. Why would living areas in space colonies provide more desirable living conditions than many areas on Earth?
7. What advantages would the space colony described by Dr. O'Neill have in agricultural production?
8. If you were to go to the first space colony as a pioneer settler, what would you probably do for amusement? What special forms of recreation would be available that are impossible on Earth? What forms of recreation that are common on Earth would probably be impossible or forbidden in such a colony?
9. What are some possible dangers in the space colony described? Why does the author say that they would not be catastrophic? What other possible dangers can you think of?
10. What effect does Dr. O'Neill think space colonization would eventually have on the earth itself?

AUTHOR

Gerard K. O'Neill is a distinguished scientist whose main area of research has been high-energy-particle physics. A graduate of Swarthmore College with high honors in his field, he received his Ph.D. from Cornell University and then went to Princeton University as a professor of physics. Since 1969 Dr. O'Neill has been developing the space-colony concept. In his spare time he is a pilot and holds an International Diamond Badge in soaring.

the
Round table
mystery

by MAXEY BROOKE

It came to pass in those days that a great calm descended on Merry England. For five years and more the Danes had not disturbed the north. Nowhere was there oppression or injustice or hunger or want, and the knights of the Round Table lolled around the court and waxed fat.

A few very young knights fared forth to seek adventure and found none. Indeed, it seemed that the day of great deeds was past, and the winning of golden spurs was only a dream.

The knights gathered at the Round Table night after night for feasting and telling of tales. The Great Hall rang with the song of a wandering minstrel, or the rafters echoed with hearty laughter at the antics of a buffoon. Other times they would stare open-mouthed at the feats of my master, Merlin. For the most part, my master performed what he called small tricks, whose lore he had entrusted to me. Already I knew the secret of coating one's mouth with storax and secreting therein a small ball of wool soaked in the spirit called *al-kohl.* When this was done, one had but to blow one's breath on a lighted taper and a great rush of flame would issue from one's mouth. Already I had done this in the stables, and such was the fear of the stable hands that even now they turned pale at my approach. But when my master heard of this, he punished me and threatened to teach me no more of his art.

"For a magician must never perform cheaply," he had said, "and the awe of stable hands is not worth the risk of exposing one's secrets." I recognized words of wisdom and promised never to perform again until he pronounced me ready.

Now, in my seventeenth year, I was allowed to participate in some of the small tricks. Once King Arthur himself commended me on my bravery in entering a large basket and allowing my master to pierce it with many swords and pikes. I thanked him gravely, although I knew that at no time had I been in danger. It was after that that Merlin decided my apprenticeship was over and that I should be initiated into the deeper mysteries of sorcery.

No one was more surprised than I to find that sorcery was performed without the aid of spirits and followed the laws of nature.

"We magicians mask these things with incantations and rituals," explained Merlin, "not to protect ourselves but to prevent the knowledge from falling into evil hands. For if everyone were a magician, no one's life would be safe. Knowledge begets knowledge, and each new knowledge is dangerous."

"And our king," I asked, "does he know this?"

"He is well aware of it. And so long as we use this knowledge to amuse and to further good works, he suffers us to continue our deceptions."

And so by day we studied the writings of the ancients and experimented with our vials and powders, hoping to add a grain to the sands of knowledge. By night we performed our small tricks for the knights of the Round Table assembled, to amuse them and to help hold them together against the time of England's need.

But these were brawny men and full-blooded, given much to boasting and jokes. They were also men of honor, high of temper, and quick to take offense. And in these easy times of inaction, many were the quarrels that flared up and that were deemed settled only in combat.

Time and again our good king forestalled bloodshed with wise decisions. When words would not suffice, he allowed the knights to settle their quarrel on the jousting field, but only with blunted lances. Yet all could feel the tension growing and growing. All knew that soon even the king's wisdom would not maintain the uneasy peace.

"Were I but king," I once said to my master, "I would disband the court and do away with these quarrels once and for all."

"Aye," answered Merlin quietly, "and when the knights returned to their holdings, there would be half a hundred trouble spots instead of one."

'Twas then I recognized that much of the king's wisdom was in reality my master's. And 'twas then I knew why our king closeted himself with my master before and after each gathering of the Round Table.

But strong men's anger must burst when kept pent up overlong. And so it was that one evening, in a small room adjoining the Great Hall, a servant found the body of Sir Alain sprawled face down in a pool of blood.

Now, let it be said that the servant did not lose his wits and spread abroad a hue and cry. Rather, as though he were answering a summons, he entered my master's apartment and announced his discovery.

Merlin, albeit annoyed at having his studies interrupted, said to me, "Go, my son, and stand guard over the body. Let none enter the room until I arrive with the king."

I hurried posthaste to the small room. There, even as the servant had said, lay Sir Alain's body. And one could easily see that his death had come of no misadventure, nor was it the result of a fair fight. He had been struck down from behind, murdered most foully. The wound between his shoulder blades was from the blow of a wide Danish dagger, such as many of the knights of the Round Table affected. A brutal crime and a callous one, as could be seen by the black footprint on Sir Alain's white tabard where the murderer had placed one foot in order to withdraw the dagger.

I arrived none too soon. Scarce had I time to note the condition of the corpse when a servant entered the room on some mission. On seeing the blood, the lad drew up and stood, mouth agape, for the space of six heartbeats. He turned and ran from the room, screaming at the top of his voice, "'Tis blood, 'tis blood, 'tis blood!"

Hard on his outcry came the knights, the squires, the servants, the court rabble. They stopped at my raised hand, and all but the knights disbanded at my word, for my fame as a sorcerer was waxing. The knights continued to press around the door, held back only by fear of the magic five-pointed star I was tracing in the air with my finger.

Their anger was exceeded only by their disbelief that such a deed could have been done. To them it was readily evident that this was murder. And to them it was equally evident that one of their own company was the murderer, none but a knight who had warred with the Danes and had won in fair combat such a weapon as had struck down fair Sir Alain.

As the first shock wore off, I could see the knights drawing back and eyeing one another with distrust and suspicion. 'Twas an ugly thing to see — the breakdown of the bond amongst them. Full glad was I at the appearance of the king, followed closely by my master.

The king's face was white behind his huge red beard, and his brows were drawn together in anger. And only I knew the effort of my master in keeping his face calm and reposed. The king turned to the knights assembled, and well did they draw back at his anger, though they were strong men and brave.

I expected a great roar, for the king had a full voice; but the king spoke softly, which was all the more frightening because of the softness.

"Let him that did this step forth."

There was no movement.

"Let him that did this step forth, and I will slay him honorably with my own hands."

There was no movement.

And the king's voice then arose to a roar that could be heard to the utmost parts of the castle. "Then I will seek you out, strip you of your knighthood, and see you hanged from the highest battlements." Even Sir Lancelot could not conceal a quaking at the king's intensity.

The king turned to my master. "What will you need to reveal this foul knave who calls himself a knight?"

My master stood a full minute, his head bent in contemplation.

"His blood will tell. I will need Sir Alain's blood-soaked tabard and the bloodstained stones whereon he lies. At moonrise let the knights be assembled in the Great Hall — barefoot, to prove their humbleness, and clad only in singlets. Let each man be seated at his appointed place at the Round Table. Let no squires nor servants be present, for there is to be revealed a great mystery. And let none touch aught that he sees on the Round Table."

Without hesitation, although these were strange requests, the king said quietly, "So be it."

He turned on his heel and marched away toward the chapel. One by one the knights followed to offer up prayers for Sir Alain's soul. My master looked me full in the eyes; then he, too, departed, leaving me strangely aware of what I was to do.

Not for long was I alone with the corpse. Soon came two black-robed friars. They removed Sir Alain's befouled tabard and handed it to me. They then bore Sir Alain away to prepare him for burial.

Hard on the friars came workers with bars and mauls to remove the bloody stones. Only my presence and the fear of some meaningless but strange passes I made with my hand overcame their fear of the death chamber.

The stones I had carried to the Great Hall. Then, closing the door, I chalked a few Arabic symbols thereon, knowing full well that none but my master would enter.

Thereupon I retired to our chambers, where Merlin awaited me. Wordlessly he held out his hand for the tabard and, having spread it on a table, studied it full long. Though I wished mightily to talk of the day's happenings, I knew to hold my peace until my master finished his meditations. I pretended to study an ancient scroll. At last my master looked up from the table.

"My son, an hour before moonrise, take yonder small chest to the Great Hall. Then station yourself at the door to see that all the knights are garbed as I directed. When the knights are assembled, enter with them and await my coming." He took the scroll from my hand, glanced at it, and smiled, "When you read Hebrew, hold the scroll thus." He reversed the scroll and returned it to me.

I spent the remainder of the day studying the mysteries of Pythagoras to atone for the error in the manner of my reading of the Hebrew scroll. When at last the glass showed it to be an hour till moonrise, I put aside the mysteries without being much wiser. The chest my master had indicated I now took to the Great Hall and set therein. I removed the signs from the door and awaited the knights.

One by one they came, each looking darkly at the others. Each paused beneath where his shield was hung, removed his outer garments and shoes, and entered the Great Hall. Not a word was said.

On the dais, where the king was accustomed to sit, lay the bier of Sir Alain, lit at head and toe with tall tapers. In the dim light sat the knights, even the king, shorn of their trappings, each in his place at the Round Table.

All eyes turned ever and anon to the eastern casement. As the silver edge of the moon appeared over the horizon, all turned toward the door. There in a great rush of flame and smoke appeared my master, clad in his magician's robes and wearing a great coned cap.

He advanced to the foot of the Round Table, eyed each knight in turn, and intoned solemnly, "Does the murderer wish to confess now, or shall I call upon the powers of darkness to seek him out?" There was a stir around the table as each knight shuddered, but none spoke. "Then so be it." He nodded to me.

I lifted the basket of stones torn from the floor of the murder room and stained with the blood of the dead man. I carried them around the table, and my master placed one stone in front of each knight.

"The blood of the stones seeks the blood on the murderer's hands!"

Each knight sat far back in his chair, eyes fixed on the stone in front of him. Fear was on every face.

Next I brought forward the chest. From it my master removed a device most cunningly contrived: an arrow with an iron head mounted on a pivot, so that it could swing freely. This he set in the middle of the Round Table.

"Now I call on the greatest forces known: blood and iron! The blood of the murdered man cries for vengeance. The iron is thirsty for that blood. I shall swing the arrow around, and it shall come to rest pointing to that bloody stone before the murderer."

He gave the arrow a twirl. Around and around it went, slower and slower. And at last it came to a stop, pointing to the stone before Sir Warfield.

Sir Warfield's face was white behind his black beard. He cried in a mighty voice, "'Tis chance! 'Tis but chance!"

"Nay, 'tis not chance," said Merlin quietly. "'Tis the power of darkness. 'Tis the attraction of a murdered man's blood for iron."

He gave the arrow another twirl. Again it made its ever-slowing rounds, and again it stopped, and again it pointed to the stone before Sir Warfield.

Sir Warfield stood up, his mouth working for a moment; then once more he cried out, "'Tis trickery! Yon Merlin spun the arrow in such a manner as to make it stop here!"

With those words he gave the arrow a mighty buffet. And for the third time it stopped directly before him.

Sir Warfield stood looking at the arrow for a time one could count to ten slowly. Then he collapsed into his chair.

"'Tis sorcery," he gasped in a strangled voice. "'Tis sorcery. Aye, I killed him. I did him in even as that hateful arrow says. I killed him."

There was a silence in the Great Hall — a silence in part of relief and in part of revulsion. And King Arthur said slowly, "Take him away."

521

He was taken away and given over to the executioner. Even as the king had ordered, he was hanged from the highest battlements at dawn.

Back in our chambers I awaited my master's pleasure, but when he saw fit to say nothing, I asked, "Sir, riddle for me this mystery. Did you truly call on the powers of darkness?"

"Nay, my son. There are no powers of darkness save in the mind."

He reached into a leather case. "Do you recognize this stone?"

"'Tis one of the cobbles from the floor whereon Sir Alain died."

"Nay. 'Tis a stone from the shores of a far land, and it is ofttimes called a lodestone. It has the strange power of attracting iron unto itself. I simply put it before Sir Warfield, knowing full well that the arrow, with its iron head, would always stop turning when it pointed toward the stone."

I tried to resume my studies, but another thought occurred.

"How did you know to put the stone before Sir Warfield, sir?"

"I had the knights remove their shoes — not to humble themselves, as I said, but rather to enable me to examine each shoe. The stitching on the sole of Sir Warfield's right shoe matched the print on Sir Alain's tabard. Remember, no cobbler, however clever, can ever sew two shoes so that the stitching on them is exactly the same."

DISCUSSION

1. Do you think "The Round Table Mystery" is a good mystery story? Tell why or why not.
2. From whose point of view is the story being told? How would the story have been different if it had been told from Merlin's point of view?
3. What surprising discovery did Merlin's young apprentice make when he was first initiated into the mysteries of sorcery? Why did Merlin say that magicians masked their tricks and knowledge with incantations and rituals?

4. What was King Arthur's attitude toward the magicians' deceptive use of incantations and rituals? What details in the story indicate that his attitude was a wise one?

5. Why were King Arthur's knights unusually quarrelsome during easy times of inaction? What happened to confirm the king's fear that their quarrels might eventually result in bloodshed?

6. When the body of Sir Alain was found, what evidence was there to show that he had been "murdered most foully"? What clues were there to the murderer's identity?

7. How did the knights react to the crime? Do you think they were more horrified by the murder itself or by the dishonor it had cast upon them as a group? Why do you think that?

8. What things did Merlin say he would need to discover who murdered Sir Alain? Do you think Merlin had planned his strategy for solving the crime already? Why do you think that?

9. According to the story, Merlin served the king as a trusted adviser as well as a magician. Do you think he was more important to the king as an adviser or as a magician? Tell why you think as you do.

10. Why do you think many people enjoy watching magicians perform even though they know that there is a natural explanation for their "magic" tricks?

AUTHOR

Maxey Brooke, born in Oklahoma and a graduate of the University of Oklahoma, has had a long career as a chemist for petroleum companies in Texas, and he is the holder of sixteen patents. He is also a versatile writer. He has had many technical articles and occasional short stories published in periodicals. As a result of his special interest in the theory of numbers, he has written several books of number puzzles, tricks, and games.

Mr. Brooke is a resident of Sweeny, Texas.

SKILL

Effective Use of Language

Did you ever find yourself thinking about a story long after you had read it? You may have imagined yourself in a story character's place or vividly pictured the setting. A story that you remember is usually one that was especially well written. The author used language so effectively that the setting, characters, and situation became real to you.

Colorful Words and Jargon

Perhaps you have found yourself thinking about Sancho, "one of the walking Texas longhorns." J. Frank Dobie, the author of "Sancho," made the story memorable partly by his use of colorful language. The story is set in Texas, and Dobie used words that gave it a southwestern flavor. For example, the English of the Southwest is peppered with Spanish words and words of Spanish origin; Dobie included several such words: *mesquite, frijoles, coyotes, tamale, chiltipiquín, remuda, chili, vaqueros.* He also used some of the jargon, or specialized language, of the old West of cattle drives and cowhands: *dogie, brand* (and examples of brands, **7Z** and **CR**), *range, paint steer, drag drivers, pitched a loop, chuck wagon.* By using colorful words and jargon typical of the Southwest and the old West, J. Frank Dobie made his story of a remarkable steer seem real and vivid, a story that stays in the mind.

Repetition

Another technique that the author of "Sancho" used effectively is repetition. In describing the long journey from Texas to Wyoming, he used forms of the verb *trail* several times: "Meantime the cattle were trailing, trailing. . . . On into Kansas they trailed. . . . For two thousand miles . . . they trailed." The repetition emphasized the distance and the slow pace of the cattle drive. A colorful rhyming word introduced a variation and also stressed the pace: ". . . they *snailed* on across the Wichita. . . ."

In "A Distant Eye," Mavis Thorpe Clark also used repetition for emphasis. If you remember sharing the characters' feelings of fear at being trapped in a cave, it may be partly because of the repetition of the word *dark* and variations of it, such as *darkness, thick dark,* and *heavy darkness.* The repetition of those words and of some contrasting words continually reminded the reader of how dark and frightening the tunnel was. For example, when Louise imagined that the entrance to the tunnel was just ahead, the author repeated the word *light* twice and also used the word *sunlight.* Louise's despair when the light didn't appear was understandable because the earlier repetition of *dark* had helped the reader feel the character's longing for light.

Sensory Words

Mavis Thorpe Clark also used sensory words — words that appeal to one or more of the five senses — to increase the reader's feeling for the plight of the story characters. In most writing, sight is probably the sense most often appealed to. The words relating to darkness are the most important words used to appeal to the sense of sight in "A Distant Eye." But Clark also emphasized the characters' inability to see by using words that appeal to the senses of hearing and touch. For example, she often used words telling how the characters sounded when they spoke: *whispered, quietly, lazy, ordered, calm, tired, cried out, screamed, shouted.* Those words reminded the reader that the characters' main contact with one another was through their voices and that they were very much aware of the feelings the others' voices expressed.

In the excerpts that follow, the author's use of words that appeal to the sense of touch gives a vivid impression of the characters' steadily increasing feelings of being trapped:

> There was only . . . a darkness that grew narrower and narrower — she could feel it pushing on her shoulders, . . . her jeans kept catching on sharp edges. . . . She felt the walls moving in, beginning to clasp her. . . . The rocks were wrapping around her. . . . The weight of the earth must be resting on [the boys]. . . . She wormed through damp and cold. . . . The earth and rock pressed down closer.

As you can see, Mavis Thorpe Clark used language very effectively in "A Distant Eye." No wonder readers find themselves remembering the story characters and their situation.

Characters' Ways of Speaking

Sometimes stories are memorable not so much for the setting or the situation as for the characters themselves. You know that authors tell you about characters in a variety of ways: through descriptions of a character's thoughts, feelings, and actions and through the thoughts, feelings, and actions of other characters. If you find yourself thinking about a particular story character, wondering how he or she might react in another situation, wishing you could know the character, chances are that the author has used language effectively to give that character a distinctive "voice."

You may have noticed that people you know have different ways of speaking. Some of them may speak quickly, others more slowly; some may use rather formal language, others a lot of slang. Authors take advantage of the different ways people speak to create story characters who seem real, who have their own ways of speaking.

Both "Blue Beach" and "Raymond's Run" are told by a first-person narrator. Carlota and Squeaky were both active, athletic girls but their personalities were completely different. Scott O'Dell, the author of "Blue Beach," made Carlota seem stern and calm. Her sentences were usually fairly short and were clear and precise: "There were four horses saddled. . . . We chose the north bank . . . we had ridden for two hours." Carlota seemed to express little or no emotion; even when she was caught by the burro clam, she said nothing of being afraid of drowning. Only at the end of the story did she say that she wanted to tell her father that she had been scared and still was. And it was only then that she admitted feeling angry at her father, apparently for expecting her to take her dead brother's place.

Carlota's life was hard. Scott O'Dell made us see how she reacted to it by attempting to please her father yet holding back and hiding all her feelings, both of pleasure and of unhappiness. The author tried to make her real by using what he imagined would be her own words, and he succeeded.

Squeaky in "Raymond's Run" seemed equally real, but her own words, as imagined by Toni Cade Bambara, showed her to be a very different sort of person from Carlota. Squeaky sometimes used very short sentences, but at times she expressed her strong feelings in sentences that went on and on. She did not hide her feelings, was very honest with other people, and disliked people who were not equally honest. She did not hesitate to express dislike or anger or her opinions about people and activities.

Unlike Carlota, who used plain and precise language to describe things, Squeaky was more likely to exaggerate or to use figurative language, such as similes and metaphors. You probably remember that similes and metaphors are comparisons of things that are basically quite different but are alike in one way. A simile uses the words *like* or *as* to express the comparison; a metaphor does not.

Imagine Carlota describing a tall man. She might have said, "He was six feet four inches tall." Squeaky used first a metaphor and then a simile to describe Mr. Pearson's height: "He sticks out in a crowd 'cause he's on stilts. . . . He looks around for Gretchen like a periscope in a submarine movie."

Carlota and Squeaky seem about as different in personality as two girls can be. Yet, each girl is believable; that is true because the language given to each as a first-person narrator by her author is distinctive and consistent. Both girls seem real, and so the reader remembers them.

In stories written in the third-person, authors also consider what their story characters should sound like and often try to give each one a distinct voice. "The Boy Who Predicted Earthquakes" shows how effectively an author, in this case Margaret St. Clair, can do this.

Wellman, the producer of Herbert's show, was nervous and excitable. He talked a great deal and was given to repeating himself for emphasis: "I don't blame you, wouldn't dream of blaming you. . . . Herbert is very simple, very quiet, very, very sincere. . . . I'm sincere about this, Read, terrifically sincere."

Read, the scientist who intended to investigate Herbert, always spoke briefly and asked a question nearly every time he spoke. Only at the end of the story, when he began to realize what was going to happen, did he lose his control.

Herbie, the boy who made the predictions, spoke on television and to Read very plainly and politely. He used simple, everyday language. Even his predictions were made calmly and undramatically. Only on his last television broadcast did he use colorful words and figurative language: "We've seen the wealth of the world wasted shamelessly, the rivers running black with washed-off soil. . . . From pole to pole the world will be one great garden, full of richness and fruit. . . . We're going to be wiser and happier and richer than any people have ever been." The contrast between the language he used in the earlier program and the language he used on the last one is quite sharp; if you read the story carefully, you may have noticed the difference and wondered about it — exactly as the author meant you to do.

The three characters in "The Boy Who Predicted Earthquakes" may not seem as real as Carlota and Squeaky do because they were not first-person narrators and did not say as much. But each of them was clearly different from the others: Weller, the excitable man from the high-pressure world of television; Read, the calm, questioning scientist; Herbie, the quiet boy with the amazing talent. Margaret St. Clair created their different personalities through her effective use of language, giving each one a different way of speaking.

Effective Writing

You can see that authors use language in many ways and to create many different effects. They may use colorful words and jargon to help you visualize a particular setting. They may use sensory words and repetition to help you share the experiences of the story characters. They may use language in different ways even within a single story in order to make story characters different from one another and to give each one a distinct voice.

Authors do not all use language in the same way even for the same purpose. But if you find yourself remembering a setting, a character, or a situation long after you read a story, you can be sure the author used language effectively. Effective writing is memorable.

Recognizing Effective Use of Language

Read these examples of effective use of language, taken from selections you have read. Write the numeral of each example on a sheet of paper and then write whether it contains jargon, repetition, sensory words, or figurative language.

1. Then a skeleton came out from among the trees. It was the skeleton of a Union soldier. . . . [The hair] fell over the skeleton's forehead and down into its eyes.
2. Twisted hard, [the hay] burned with a brief, hot flame. [Caroline's] palms were soon raw and bleeding from handling the sharp, harsh stuff, but she kept on twisting it.
3. The horses suddenly swept together like dark leaves in a gust of wind.
4. He hit the first pitch. It was an outside fast ball and he never should have been able to reach it, but he hit it down the line for a double.
5. They made very little sound; the wheels hardly whispered. . . . It came as a shock when the thump of Drew's hoofs and the grating of the wheels . . . echoed suddenly from planking overhead.
6. His feet [were] swollen and as awkward as stumps of wood.

Characters in several of the selections you have read faced frightening situations. The examples below give the words spoken or thought by three characters during or after such a situation. Write the numeral of each example on your paper. Then think about each character's words and decide which of the characters listed following the examples spoke or thought those words. Write the letter of the correct answer after the numeral. Note that there is one extra name.

7. What took them so long? . . . Footsteps. Loud ones. Boots. Coming up the stairs. . . . My heart was beating too loudly.
8. How do I know what *I'd* be like if I was sick and scared and hopeless; how does *anyone* know that ain't been there?
9. What is the matter with you? Brace up and show a little decent spunk! It's only a storm.

    a. Anna Solden, a Canadian girl of 1939 who must help her brother overcome his blindness
    b. Caroline, a pioneer girl who must survive a prairie winter alone with her baby
    c. Annie de Leeuw, a Jewish girl of the 1940's who is hiding from Nazi soldiers
    d. Jethro Creighton, a boy of Civil War days who must decide how to help a deserter

The
Sacred Drum
of
Tepozteco

by M. A. JAGENDORF and R. S. BOGGS

Long ago, in the valley of Tepoztlan (tah-pohsh'tlahn), a valley in Mexico where there is much copper, Tepozteco (tah-pohsh'tah-ko) was born. He was born to be different from other children, for he was destined to be a god.

In a short time he was a fully grown man, rich in wisdom and great in strength and speed. He could hunt better than others, and he gave counsel that brought success; so the people made him king. And as he grew in wisdom and understanding and strength, they worshiped him and made him a god.

He was known for his virtues even to the farthest corners of his kingdom, and he was loved and respected by all. The other kings feared him, although they never dared to say so.

One day the king of Ilayacapan (ih-lah′yah-kah-pahn) asked Tepozteco to come to a great feast to be given in Tepozteco's honor. Other kings and nobles and men of strength were also invited.

The king told his cooks to prepare food such as had never been eaten before. He had new dishes painted in bright colors, and he ordered new mats of lovely designs.

And the most beautiful mat of all was to be for Tepozteco to sit upon. This was to be a feast of feasts.

On the appointed day, the kings and nobles arrived, wearing their richest robes and jewels of jade and gold. It was a wonderful sight to see the great company seated on the many-colored mats, with the richly painted dishes before them. All around were handsome servants ready to bring the fine food.

They sat and they sat. They were waiting for the great guest, Tepozteco.

They waited and they waited. After a long time they heard the *teponaztli* (tah-poh′nahs-tlee), the drum that always announced the coming of Tepozteco.

Soon he was seen, approaching with his followers. But he was not dressed for the feast. He was dressed in hunting clothes, with an ocelot skin thrown over his shoulders and weapons in his hands. His followers also were dressed in hunting clothes.

The king and his guests looked at them in silent surprise. Then the king spoke.

"Noble Tepozteco," he said, "you have put shame on me and my land and my guests. This feast was in your honor, and we came properly dressed to honor you, but you have come in your hunting clothes and not in your royal garments."

Tepozteco looked at the king and his company and did not say a word. For a long time he was silent. Then he spoke.

"Wait for me. I shall soon return in my royal clothes."

Then he and his followers vanished into the air like a cloud.

Again the company waited a long time, and finally the drum of Tepozteco was heard once more. Suddenly the whole company saw him.

He was alone, dressed more beautifully than anyone there. He was all covered with gold. From his shoulders hung a mantle in colors that gleamed more richly than birds in the sunlight. His headdress was of the most brilliant quetzal feathers ever seen. Gold bands bound his arms, and jade beads encircled his neck. In his hand he held a shield studded with jewels and richly colored stones.

The king and his company were greatly pleased at the sight.

"Now you are dressed in a manner befitting this noble gathering in your honor. Let the food be served."

Tepozteco did not answer. He seated himself on a mat, and the food was served. Everyone ate except Tepozteco, who took the dishes and poured his food on his mantle.

Everyone stopped eating and looked at the guest of honor in surprise.

"Why do you do this?" asked the king.

"I am giving the food to my clothes, because it was they, not I, that you wanted at your feast. I was not welcome here in whatever clothes I chose to wear. Only when I came in these, my feast-day clothes, were you pleased; therefore this feast is for them, not for me."

"Leave my palace," said the king sharply.

Tepozteco stood and left.

When he had gone, a great cry of anger rose from all the guests.

"He is not fit to live among us," they cried. "We must destroy him!"

Everyone agreed to this, and the kings and nobles gathered a great army of warriors and marched on Tepoztlan.

Tepozteco knew he could not do battle against this great army, for his soldiers were too few. So he went up on the Montaña del Aire (mahn-tah'nyah del ie'reh) — the Mountain in the Air — where a vast temple had been built for him by his people.

There he stood, drawn up to his full height, almost reaching the sky. He raised his hands and waved them in all directions. The earth quaked and trembled and roared. Trees fell and rocks flew. Masses of earth rose into the air. Everything fell on the army that had come to destroy Tepozteco and his people, and the enemy was wiped out.

The temple of Tepozteco still stands on that mountain, and at night, when the wind screams through the canyons that the earthquake created along the Montaña del Aire, one can hear the sacred drum of Tepozteco, telling his people that he is still there to guard and protect his city.

DISCUSSION

1. What natural phenomenon is explained by this story?
2. What virtues did Tepozteco possess that made him so admired and respected?
3. What special preparations did the king of Ilayacapan make for the feast in honor of Tepozteco?
4. How did Tepozteco appear when he first arrived at the feast? What had he been doing just before he arrived there?
5. How did the king react to Tepozteco's appearance? Do you think the king was right in feeling insulted that Tepozteco had come to the feast in his hunting clothes? Why do you think as you do?
6. How was Tepozteco's appearance changed when he later returned to the feast?
7. What did Tepozteco do that angered the king and the other guests after he returned to the feast? How did they respond to his action?
8. Why did Tepozteco pour his food on his mantle? Do you think his action brought the result he expected?
9. How did the king and the nobles feel that honor and respect should be shown? How did Tepozteco's view differ from theirs?
10. How did Tepozteco take revenge on the king and nobles?

AUTHORS

M(oritz) A(dolph) Jagendorf was born in Austria in 1888. At thirteen he came to the United States with his family and later attended Columbia University. There he took an active part in dramatics, beginning a theatrical career that included translating, producing, and directing. Meanwhile, a long-standing interest in folklore led him into the work for which he is best known, collecting and rewriting folktales from Europe and different regions of the Americas. "The Sacred Drum of Tepozteco" is from *The King of the Mountains: A Treasury of Latin American Folk Stories,* which Mr. Jagendorf collected with R. S. Boggs.

R(alph) S(teele) Boggs was born in Indiana in 1901 and graduated from the University of Chicago. He taught English at the University of Puerto Rico before teaching Spanish and folklore at the University of North Carolina and later at the University of Miami. Professor Boggs compiled many collections of Spanish folktales and legends and contributed over a hundred articles to folklore and literary magazines in the Americas.

Canada  Geese

by JACK DENTON SCOTT

In the dark of a late October moon, in the far north of Canada, geese begin to wing across the cold face of the sky. Beneath them, the grass in the vast marshlands stands stiff. The tundra is slicked with the soft silver sheen of frost, and the waters of James Bay and Hudson Bay, capped with waves stirred up by winds of coming winter, gleam in the moonglow.

The mighty migrations of Canada geese, some three million strong, have begun. They are leaving their breeding grounds in this northernmost land, uninhabited by people, to fly south to warmer temperatures.

The birds burst from the marshes singly and in groups, the flights at the beginning seemingly without pattern. But as they gain altitude, the straggling lines of geese begin to straighten. At first, it looks like a single line of birds, with one flying faster, becoming the leader. But that follow-the-leader group slowly shapes into a loose V outline, with the birds churning closer together, as if obeying commands from a flight leader.

High now (probably about one thousand meters, but sometimes as high as three thousand meters), dark shapes moving away from the moon, the flight of geese looks like a squadron of aircraft flying in tight formation. The V is precise; the point is one bird — the leader; the others are spaced evenly behind. It is as perfectly formed as the head of an arrow.

Many of us have watched and listened to migrating geese in the sky. As they speed south, we know that winter is on its way.

We have wondered why the flocks fly in that tight V formation. And is the leader always a wise old bird that knows the way south? Science does not have all the answers, but it does have some.

It is believed that the lead bird, the one at the extreme point of the V, breaks up the air directly ahead, creating updrafts with the tips of its wings. Each bird following takes advantage of these updrafts by flying slightly to the outside of the bird immediately in front of it. In this way the flock can increase its flight range by seventy per cent. The air to the side of a flying bird is less turbulent than the air behind it. One bird flying directly behind another would be similar to someone trying to swim behind a motorboat. The alignment, or V formation, of the birds also permits each bird to see ahead and avoid hazards. Thus the whole flock is not entirely dependent on the leader.

The lead bird is not necessarily a wise old gander that knows the route south. And it does not make the entire flight as the leader. The leader is changed often and may be a female goose or a gander. Positions are switched because the lead bird breaking the air waves tires more quickly than those following. The V, however, remains as perfect as the birds can make it. In their fixed flight positions, there is no misalignment on the updrafts and flying is easier.

The sounds of migrating Canada geese are as stirring as the sight of them. Each of us has our own reactions, referring to the sounds as honking, calling, or crying. They have been described in various ways: a cry of wildness; an exultant scream of freedom; one of the last pure wild sounds left in a world overwhelmed by civilization. There is nostalgia in it. And poetry. The Cree Indians of the Hudson Bay region call these Canada geese, barking across the sky, the hounds of heaven.

Color and Light

by CHARLOTTE WILLARD

Color is the essence of painting and its chief delight. Painting is for those who are willing to plunge into a sea of color, the mysterious, exhilarating child of light. Light is a force of nature that you cannot touch, smell, feel, or taste. In nature, light makes color, and in art, color makes light. Adventurers in color leave the traditions of art behind and depend on their intuition and personal observations.

Color itself has no form. The artist who uses color to convey feelings and thoughts must create a world in which color is free — free to become space, to create depth, to suggest weight, to acquire shapes, and to convey the whole range of emotions. In the instinctive language that everyone seems to understand, red, the color of blood, is the color of life, of joy, and of danger; white is the color of purity; blue, of the heavenly or divine. These are the most obvious aspects of the color alphabet that artists use and that are universally recognized and enjoyed.

Henri Matisse (ahn-ree' mah-tees') was born in the north of France in 1869. His father, a wealthy merchant, hoped that his son would study law, and young Henri entered the University of Paris. But after copying a picture when he was about twenty, Matisse knew that painting was the only career for him. He said, "I felt transported into a paradise in which I was gloriously free."

His father finally allowed him to study painting with Bouguereau (boo-groh'), then the most successful painter in Paris. When Matisse saw the photographic quality of that painter's work, he despaired of

540

Henri Matisse. SELF-PORTRAIT AS AN ETCHER. (c. 1903).
Collection, The Museum of Modern Art, New York. Gift of Mrs. Bertram Smith.

becoming an artist, and his teacher discouraged him, saying, "You'll never learn to draw." He was about to give up art when he came upon the last, loosely painted work of the great Spanish painter, Goya (go'yah). "I can paint like that," he said, and went back to his studies. Later, rejecting Bouguereau's standards, Matisse said, "Exactitude is not truth."

In the late nineteenth century an artist was regarded as an outcast who broke all rules of behavior. Matisse, however, promised his father he would be a conventional, well-behaved family man. He was, all his life — except in his art.

In 1905, Matisse became the leader of a group of artists who wanted to break the back of classic art. They maintained that faces could be green or violet, that water could be red, that perspective was old-fashioned and classic art finished. They were attacked by the critics and called the Fauves (fohvz), that is, Wild Beasts.

At the famous Armory Show in New York in 1913, the first major exhibition of modern European painting in the United States, Matisse's work was again attacked. It was not until 1927, when he won first prize at an international exhibition in Pittsburgh, that he was recognized as one of the great masters of painting.

Henri Matisse. VIEW OF COLLIOURE AND THE SEA. 1911. Collection, The Museum of Modern Art, New York. Bequest of Nelson A. Rockefeller.

Henri Matisse. HORSE, RIDER AND CLOWN, Plate 5 from JAZZ. 1947. Collection, The Museum of Modern Art, New York. Gift of the artist.

Almost from the start, Matisse was fascinated by color. Although his first paintings were in the somber browns and grays popular in the 1890's, he soon began to use bright colors. In 1898, he painted a human figure, not in flesh tones, but entirely in blue, breaking all the traditions of art.

He noticed as he worked how much light seemed to come from the contrasts of pure, bright colors. He observed that other contemporary artists were able to suggest the near and far by colors alone or to express emotions through violently contrasting hues. A magician of color, he created harmonies and contrasts that few earlier painters had dared to use.

Matisse favored light, transparent color effects. Working with a brush and a rag full of turpentine, which thins out color, he would fill in with the brush and rub out with the rag. He kept working until he got the exact form and color he wanted, directly, without painting one layer of color over another. The most difficult task was getting the wild color and spontaneous forms he was after. He said, "Order above all in color. Put three or four touches of color that you have understood upon the canvas; add another if you can. If you cannot, set this canvas aside and begin again."

Toward the end of his life, Matisse said, "What I dream of is an art of balance, of purity, of serenity, devoid of all depressive subject matter, an art that is an appeasing influence, like a good armchair in which to rest." Matisse's paintings, full of light and joy, great outbursts of color, are witnesses to his success.

DISCUSSION

1. What experience made Henri Matisse decide to become a painter?
2. Why did Matisse almost give up art while studying with Bouguereau? What made him change his mind?
3. In rejecting Bouguereau's standards, what do you think Matisse meant when he said, "Exactitude is not truth"?
4. How did the group of artists called the Fauves want to change traditional art? Why, do you think, were the ideas of the Fauves attacked by the art critics at the time?
5. Why did the author refer to Matisse as "a magician of color"?
6. Why did Matisse feel that art should be "devoid of all depressive subject matter"? Do you agree with that view? Why or why not?
7. Which one of the works by Matisse shown in this article do you like best? Why?

AUTHOR

Charlotte Willard, a graduate of New York University, was the author of several books on modern art. She was art critic for the New York *Post,* contributing editor for *Art in America* magazine, and art consultant for *Look* magazine. Her articles appeared regularly in several other magazines until her death in 1977.

Dragonwings

by LAURENCE YEP

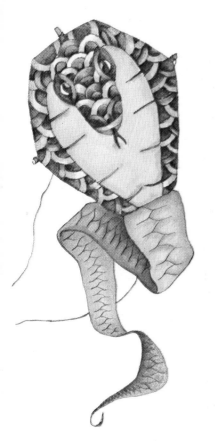

In the early 1900's, young Moon Shadow left China to join his father, Windrider, in San Francisco's Chinese community. Together they lived and worked, along with Lefty and several other Chinese, in the building that housed the laundry company founded by old Uncle, an earlier immigrant and now a patriarch of the community. Despite the harsh realities of the hostile new land, Uncle tried to guide his people with precepts about the kind of behavior that distinguished a "superior" person.

The talented Windrider's interests lay not in the laundry company, however, but in mechanical devices, and his dream was to build a flying machine. Uncle was hurt and angry when Windrider, to further this dream, left the Chinese part of the city to become a free-lance mechanic.

Windrider rented space for Moon Shadow and himself in the stable behind the Polk Street home of tiny, silver-haired Miss Whitlaw and her orphaned niece, Robin. Miss Whitlaw had once been a wealthy woman, and the unusual octagonal house she had inherited contained an imported treasure, a stained-glass window. Soon Windrider and his son became friends with their landlady and her niece. In the following excerpt from Laurence Yep's book *Dragonwings,* named for the flying machine that Windrider finally built, young Moon Shadow tells how the four friends were drawn even closer together during the great San Francisco earthquake of 1906.

It was thirteen days after the Feast of Pure Brightness[1] that the earthquake hit. Just a little after five A.M. I had gotten dressed and gone out to the pump to get some water. The morning was filled with that soft, gentle

[1] **Feast of Pure Brightness,** a traditional Chinese springtime festival.

twilight of spring, when everything is filled with soft, dreamy colors and shapes; so when the earthquake hit, I did not believe it at first. It seemed like a nightmare where everything you take to be the rock-hard, solid basis for reality becomes unreal.

Wood and stone and brick and the

very earth became fluidlike. The pail beneath the pump jumped and rattled like a spider dancing on a hot stove. The ground deliberately seemed to slide right out from under me. I landed on my back hard enough to drive the wind from my lungs. The whole world had become unglued. Our stable and Miss Whitlaw's house and the tenements to either side heaved and bobbed up and down, riding the ground like ships on a heavy sea. Down the alley mouth, I could see the cobblestone street undulate and twist like a red-backed snake.

From inside our stable, I could hear the cups and plates begin to rattle on their shelves, and the equipment on Father's work table clattered and rumbled ominously.

Suddenly the door banged open, and Father stumbled out with his clothes all in a bundle. "It's an earthquake, I think," he shouted. He had washed his hair the night before and had not had time to twist it into a queue, so it hung down his back long and black.

He looked around in the back yard. It was such a wide, open space that we were fairly safe there. Certainly more safe than in the frame doorway of our stable. He got into his pants and shirt and then his socks and boots.

"Do you think one of the mean dragons is doing all this?" I asked him.

"Maybe. Maybe not." Father had sat down to stuff his feet into his boots. "Time to wonder about that later. Now you wait here."

He started to get to his feet when the second tremor shook, and he fell forward flat on his face. I heard the city bells ringing. They were rung by

no human hand — the earthquake had just shaken them in their steeples. The second tremor was worse than the first. From all over came an immense wall of noise: of metal tearing, of bricks crashing, of wood breaking free from wood nails, and all. Everywhere, what people had built came undone. I was looking at a tenement house to our right, and it just seemed to shudder and then collapse. One moment there were solid wooden walls and the next moment it had fallen with the cracking of wood and the tinkling of glass and the screams of people inside.

Mercifully, for a moment, it was lost to view in the cloud of dust that rose up. The debris surged against Miss Whitlaw's fence and toppled it over with a creak and a groan and a crash. I saw an arm sticking up from the mound of rubble, and the hand was twisted at an impossible angle from the wrist. Father pulled at my arm. "Stay here now," he ordered and started for Miss Whitlaw's.

I turned. Her house was still standing, but the tenement house to the left had partially collapsed; the wall on our side and part of the front and back had just fallen down, revealing the apartments within: the laundry hanging from lines, the old brass beds, and a few lucky if astonished people just looking out dazedly on what had once been walls. I could see Jack sitting up in bed with his two brothers. His mother and father were standing by the bed holding on to Maisie, their whole family crowded into a tiny two-room apartment. Then they were gone, disappearing in a cloud of dust and debris as the walls and floor collapsed. Father held me as I cried.

Miss Whitlaw came out onto her porch in her nightdress and a shawl. She pulled the shawl tighter about her shoulders. *"Are you all right?"*

"Yes," Father said, patting me on the back. "Aren't we, Moon Shadow?"

"Yes." I wiped my eyes on my sleeves.

"Is everything okay inside?" Father asked Miss Whitlaw.

She nodded. We joined her on the porch and walked with her into her house. Robin was sitting on the stairs that led up to the second floor. She huddled up, looking no longer like the noisy, boisterous girl I knew. The front door was open before her. She must have gone outside to look. *"Just about the whole street's gone."*

Miss Whitlaw looked up the stairs. *"Everything's all right here."*

"Are you sure?" Father asked her quietly.

Miss Whitlaw laughed. *"From top to bottom. Papa always built well. He said he wanted a house that could hold a herd of thundering elephants — that was what he always called Mama's folks. He never liked them much."*

"It's gone," Robin repeated. *"Just about the whole street's gone."*

"Oh, really now." Miss Whitlaw walked past Robin. We followed her out the front door to the front porch. Robin was right. No one had constructed the houses along the street as well as Miss Whitlaw's father had built his.

A strange, eerie silence hung over the city. The bells had stilled in their steeples, and houses had stopped collapsing momentarily. It was as if the city itself were holding its breath. Then we could hear the hissing of gas from the broken pipes, like dozens of angry snakes, and people, trapped inside the mounds, began calling. Their voices sounded faint and ghostly, as if dozens of ghosts floated over the rubble, crying in little, distant voices for help. Robin and I pressed close to one another for comfort. It was Miss Whitlaw who saved us. It was she who gave us something important to do and brought us out of shock.

She pressed her lips together for a moment, as if she were deciding something. *"We must get those people out."*

"It would take four of us weeks to clear tunnels for them," Father said.

"We'll draft help. After all, we were put on this earth to help one another," Miss Whitlaw said.

Father suppressed a grin. *"I see what can do. But better put on clothes."*

"What? Oh, my." Miss Whitlaw was suddenly horrified to be found in her nightgown in public. *"Come, Robin."* She took her by the hand and practically pulled her up the steps.

Father shook his head affectionately. He sat down on a chest in the hall and he and I began braiding up his queue. On his advice, we both pinned our queues into tight buns at the back of our heads. When we got outside the house, though, Father stopped. "I've put my boots on the wrong feet." Sure enough, he had his left boot on his right foot and vice versa. We both laughed a little louder than the joke actually deserved, but we were just so relieved that we were still alive after the disaster. Father sat down on the sidewalk and got his boots on right. He stood up, stamping his feet back into his boots. Then we looked around.

We had gone to sleep on a street crowded with buildings, some three or four stories high and crowded with people; and now many of the houses were gone, and the ones that remained were dangerously close to falling too. There was a hole in the cobblestone street about a yard wide and twenty feet long. As we watched, a cobblestone fell over the edge, clattering ten feet to the bottom.

I heard one person compare it to being on the moon. It was that kind of desolate feeling — just looking at huge hills of rubble: of brick and broken wooden slats that had once been houses. On top of the piles we would see the random collection of things that had survived the quake: somebody's rag doll, an old bottle, a fiddle, the back of an upholstered chair . . . and a woman's slender wrist, sticking out of the rubble as if calling for help.

And then the survivors started to emerge, and I saw that there were as many hurt in mind as in body. Some people wandered out of the buildings almost naked, others still in their nightclothes. I saw one man with the lather on one side of his face, the other side already clean-shaven. In his hand was a lather-covered razor. One woman in a nightgown walked by, carrying her crying baby by its legs as if it were a dead chicken. Father caught her by the shoulder and gently took the baby from her.

"Fix her arms," Father told me. I set her arms so she could cradle the baby — as if the mother were a doll. Then Father put the baby back into her arms. She dumbly nodded her thanks and wandered on.

Other people who had taken the time to dress had dressed in the oddest things, choosing things they wanted to save rather than what would be appropriate for a disaster. I saw one girl go by in a ball gown with the ruffles sounding crisp in the morning air. Perhaps she had saved for a year to buy it. I don't know. But I saw another man in formal tails go by. His wife carried the baby while he pushed a baby carriage filled with jewelry, a frying pan, and a candelabrum.

Then along came a big healthy man with ginger whiskers. He had slipped his trousers on over his red *long johns.* In his arms he had a chest.

Father tried to stop the man. *"Please — need help."* Father pointed to the mound behind us, from which the ghostly voices were calling.

"Be off with you," said the man.

Father tried grabbing him by his

blue suspenders, but the man dodged away and started running. We tried to get other survivors to help. One or two came out of their daze and started to work on the mound, clearing rocks and broken boards again, but most of them ignored Father and went on their way as if they were made of stone. Some even cursed him.

Then Miss Whitlaw and Robin joined us. Both of them were in clean dresses, with their hair braided and coiled around their ears. You would have thought they were going to church. *"Please help us save the others,"* Miss Whitlaw said to two sturdy young men, but they were in a hurry pushing their wheelbarrow.

"Out of the way, you old bat."

"Well," sniffed Miss Whitlaw as they trundled past. *"You . . . you selfish fools,"* she called after them, as if it were the worst thing she could think of. She stood for a moment in the street, fingering the ends of her shawl. Then she turned around with a determined set to her jaw. *"Mr. Lee, I think we are going to have to use a more forceful argument than moral persuasion."* With that, she marched back into her house.

Father scratched his head. *"What kind that?"* he asked Robin.

She shrugged. *"Maybe we'll pay them."*

Miss Whitlaw came out with one of her heavy wooden kitchen chairs. She set it down in front of Father. *"Please break this, Mr. Lee."*

Father shrugged and grasped the chair. He lifted it up high over his head and brought it down with a loud, splintering crash. Miss Whitlaw sifted through the broken wood. She handed one chair leg to Robin, one to me, and one to Father. She waved her own chair leg like a club. *"There never was anything like a swat across the fundament to wake up a sluggish conscience."* She pointed her club across the street. *"You take that side, Mr. Lee. I'll take this. Don't let anyone through."*

It was a wonder to watch Miss Whitlaw sail up the block and gather people behind her like a hen collecting her chicks. In her gentlest but firmest way, she gathered up the survivors and set them in work crews to clearing the mounds from which people were calling.

Watching her with open admiration, Father shook his head. "Now just look at her." For myself, I could not help thinking that she had missed her vocation as a shanghaier.

The next moment I learned why we had clubs. A man came toward us in a suit and balancing three hats on his head; two were derbies and the last was a top hat. In either hand he had a suitcase. His eyes glanced up continually toward his hats.

"Please help," Father asked him.

"Go on with you," the man said, and tried to push past.

Father shoved the end of his club into the man's chest. *"You help."*

The man dropped his suitcases and swung at Father, but Father ducked easily. He clubbed the man lightly on the back of his head. The man grunted and fell to his knees. Father raised his club menacingly.

The man held up his hand. *"All right. All right. Just don't hurt the hats. Watch where you're stepping."*

"You go over there." Father pointed to where Miss Whitlaw stood supervising one reluctant work crew. The man picked up his suitcases while Father picked up his hats, dusted them off, and set them on his head one by one.

I don't think the people were necessarily bad for not wanting to help others. They might have been scared, or so shocked they could not really know how selfish they were being. Now that there were other people actually helping to save those who were trapped, we did not seem to have as much trouble as before. Some people were glad to pitch in, though we still had to use the clubs on some others. When we had work crews at every mound from which there was a voice — about fifty people in all — we tucked our clubs into our belts and joined them. Miss Whitlaw had managed to salvage shovels, pickaxes, and crowbars from the various places for at least a dozen workers. The rest of us used our hands or the ends of boards.

Father deliberately chose to work on one mound that stood under a wooden wall. It was the last wall of the tenement — one of the buildings he had worked in — and at any moment the wall threatened to collapse. When I climbed up the hill of rubble to stand beside him, he turned to me. "You work somewhere else," he told me.

But I figured I had as much right to make a fool of myself as he did. I picked up a rock and sent it clattering down the slope of the hill-like mound.

Father tapped me on the shoulder. "Did you hear me, boy? You go someplace else."

"The faster we can clear this stuff away, the sooner we can leave this mound. Maybe we can even get away before the wall collapses."

Father grinned suddenly. "You're getting as unruly as a demon." He slapped me on the back, and together we went back to work.

It was a little bit like playing *jackstraws,* where you toss all the straws down in a pile and then try to take one away without disturbing the others. There was a kind of science to freeing the people from the mound. A building does not collapse completely. There are little pockets inside the mound where the people are trapped. The trick is to not dig away the whole mound, but to work tunnels to those pockets. But you have to be careful not to make the mound collapse on that pocket or on you. We picked up bricks, the rocklike broken bits of concrete blocks, the wooden boards.

And Miss Whitlaw was everywhere, encouraging here, helping there. I wondered again at the strength within her slender body.

About an hour after we started, Miss Whitlaw came over with Robin in tow. All our sweating faces were covered with a fine film of dust. We all looked like the mountain trolls who live deep, deep within the earth. "Moon Shadow, *you and Robin make some sandwiches and hot tea. We'll all be needing a break.*"

I glanced up at the tottering wall. "It's all right," Father told me. "We're almost finished here." We had already pulled four people from the mound. Only one of them had any injury, and that was a broken leg.

Robin and I went around to the back. We were going to try to wash our hands and faces at the outdoor pump, but no matter how much we primed the handle no water would come out, so we decided to use the one in Robin's kitchen. But the indoor pump was dry too. There was only the steady crea-creak-creak as we took turns working the handle.

"That's funny," she said. *"It's never been this slow before."*

"What do we use for water?"

"Get the water from the pitchers in the rooms," Robin said. There was a pitcher of water and a washbasin in each bedroom for washing up. She wagged a finger at me. *"And don't let me catch you wasting any of it by washing your face."*

"I wouldn't think of it," I said, though I really had been.

It was a good thing that Miss Whitlaw had just baked the other day, so there was plenty of white, fresh, sweet-tasting bread. For filler we had ham and some of that fermented cow's milk called *cheese*. There were also a lot of jellied preserves. Robin carried the sandwiches out on trays. I lugged the pail of water with the pitcher.

As the people quit working to gather round, Robin warned them that it was all the water we had until the pump started working, so they were to go easy.

Father paused, his sandwich in his hand.

"What's the matter?" I asked him. He seemed troubled.

"Nothing," he said and went back to eating.

After breakfast, we went back to work. By that time, we had saved about twenty people. Poor Maisie and Jack had not been among them. Their bodies were still somewhere in the ruins of their tenement. We had put the three injured on makeshift stretchers, made out of blankets and long boards we salvaged from the ruins, and taken them into Miss Whitlaw's house, which was the only one standing intact on the block. Then she had sent one of the neighborhood boys — one of my former tormentors — after a doctor.

We had not been at work again for more than a half hour when we heard

an indignant yell that carried along the street. It was Robin. *"Hey, you, drop that."* Father and I turned to see a man standing on the porch of Miss Whitlaw's house. He cradled a small metal chest in his arms. Father and I were working on a mound next to the house. Father jumped over Miss Whitlaw's fence. I was still climbing over it as Father ran across the garden to the bottom step. The thief stared at Father for a moment.

Then the thief tried to kick Father, but Father caught his leg and gave it a vicious twist. The thief had to turn around or lose his leg. Father shoved and the thief went face down on the porch. He rolled over, his hands reaching for his belt, but Father already had one knee on his throat. The thief lay still. Father slipped the knife out of his belt and threw it into the doorway. He handed the chest of money back to Miss Whitlaw.

She took it with a nod of thanks. *"Let him go now, Mr. Lee."*

"But —"

"This earthquake'll bring out the best and worst in folk." Miss Whitlaw waved her hand as if the thief were some stray dog. *"Go on."*

The thief got up, not quite believing that he was free. Rubbing his throat, he limped down the steps and down the street with everyone staring.

"Better take inside and hide," Father said. Miss Whitlaw nodded and left. We heard her quick, light steps on the stairs. We both watched the thief slip around the corner, out of sight. "People," Father said with a shake of his head. "And this is probably only the start."

"Father?"

"There's a whole city in ruins, and more of his kind willing to take advantage of others' misery," he explained. He touched the club in his belt. "But there's no helping other people's souls. We can only try to help the people trapped inside the rubble."

About an hour later, we stopped. My throat was dry from the dust and dirt. I went to the outdoor pump and worked at it hard for about five minutes but still no water. And then, turning, I saw an ominous sight. There were three tall columns of black smoke rising from the south. They were apart from one another, but as I watched two more sprang up. I went quietly to Father and pulled at his sleeve. He turned, heaved a stone down. He looked in the direction I pointed. "Yes," he grunted. "I no-

ticed them. There's not enough pressure in the pipes for the water to come out of the fire hoses."

"They'll fix them soon."

"Not soon enough if there's fires. There won't be any water for the fire fighters to use." He put his hand on my shoulder. "But don't you tell anyone. No sense causing a panic. They might get the pipes fixed before there's a serious fire."

And he went back to work.

But it was not more than five minutes later that a buggy dashed by. There were a man and a woman and two frightened children clinging to it. To the top of the buggy were lashed a mattress, a nightstand, and other items. Pots and pans had been tied to the sides, and they clanked and rang as the man drove.

He had to stop when he came to the hole in the street. His horse was covered with sweat, as if the man had driven it too hard. The woman took the reins while he got down and threw his coat over the horse's eyes. He was wearing a bright pink nightshirt underneath. He guided the horse around the hole. Father went down to him then. *"What hurry?"* he asked.

"There's a fire south of Market," the man said. *Market Street* was the main street of the city and ran diagonally across it, dividing the city in half. *"There's no water for the hoses. They're still going to try to make a stand on Market, but I don't see what they can do. The fire'll just spread and spread."*

Others had stopped work to look at the man. They began to throw down their tools and leave the rubble mounds. Miss Whitlaw stepped to the center of the street and held out her arms. *"We still have time,"* she pleaded. *"Please help."*

But they all ignored her. The man got back into his buggy and slapped the horse's rump with the reins. The buggy clattered on over the cobblestones. When I looked back, the entire street was abandoned, except for a few people trying to save something from the ruins of their homes. The others had gone to their own places to rescue what they could.

Father went over to Miss Whitlaw. *"You did your best,"* he said.

"But the people."

"I no hear calling in last hour. No one alive left there," Father said.

"Yes," Miss Whitlaw said. *"I guess you're right. I hope you're right."*

The boy Miss Whitlaw had sent out came back without a doctor. *"They've declared martial law all over the city,"* he said, wide-eyed with fear. *"And there's a fire to the southeast, a big one, already across Market."* And then he left hurriedly to join his family across the street, salvaging what they could before they fled for safety — though where they were going to go to escape the fire, no one knew as yet.

It was not until months later that we learned how it started. The white people would call it the Ham and Eggs fire: A woman whose house had survived the quake began to make a breakfast of ham and eggs, but the earthquake must have damaged the flue of her chimney, for sparks from the fire caught on the walls, and the whole quarter of wooden houses had gone up in flames. Because the fire companies were off to *Market Street,* there was no real effort to stop it. It was just spreading.

The army came marching in about four hours after the earthquake. The soldiers had on broadbrim hats with the crown of the hat shaped into a cone. Over their shoulders they wore blanket rolls, in which they had rolled up their belongings so that they looked like they were wearing doughnuts. On their rifles were bayonets. They were headed by an old man with V stripes on his sleeves that Father said were *sergeant* stripes. *"You'll have to get out of here, ma'am,"* the sergeant said. *"There's a fire coming."*

"How much time do we have?"

"Mebbe six to ten hours."

"We have injured here."

"Take them to Golden Gate Park. They'll be safe there. The fire'll be going more north than west."

"I don't see how we're going to get there, sergeant."

He seemed to have sized up Miss Whitlaw and liked what he had seen. *"Now, I'm supposed to keep a lookout for looters and the like, but if I was someone who needed a horse underneath me, I'd try on Van Ness, where I just saw a horse tied to a wagon."*

"But surely there's an owner."

"Yessum. He must have gone back into his house for one too many things, 'cuz the house fell on top of him while he was getting it."

"Thank you, sergeant," Miss Whitlaw said.

"My pleasure, ma'am." He touched the brim of his hat in a kind of a salute. *"Just step lively before the next patrol comes through."*

The Whitlaws and I spent an anxious ten minutes while Father went to get the wagon. We sat down by the front door, clubs in hands, watching for looters. We saw two sleazy individuals, but they took one look at us and slunk on, picking at the rubble as they tried to find something worthwhile to take.

It was a relief to hear the rumble of a wagon and the clatter of hoofs and see Father perched on top of the wagon. We loaded the sick onto the wagon, along with some bedding, some clothes, a frying pan or two, and other things. That plus Miss Whitlaw's bags and our own boxes of possessions took up the wagon. The whole southward side of the city was covered with black smoke now. I could not see the sun, even.

As she climbed onto the wagon, Miss Whitlaw asked Father, *"Don't you want to throw away your club?"*

"Not yet." Father looked grim. *"I no like what I see, come back here."* He did not elaborate, and we did not ask for details.

The streets were strangely empty now. The houses that were standing were tilted every which way. Rubble covered the streets. We saw dead horses everywhere, and now and then heard rifle shots. I asked Father what they were, and he replied grimly, *"Soldiers shoot looters."*

Well, we got everyone to *Golden Gate Park,* where there were thousands of others. Healthy as well as injured, all had taken refuge there. We got our patients to the doctors and found a site for a camp, and the people right next to the site agreed to watch our things.

Then we headed back to Miss Whitlaw's house. On her lap Miss Whitlaw now had an antique pistol which had once belonged to her father. She had taken it along in one of her bags as a souvenir but had gotten it out — just in case we met more than Father's club could handle.

Our friend Lefty was waiting for us on the stoop, munching on a chicken drumstick. Father laughed with relief and jumped off the wagon. "Well, you did all right for yourself."

"I might say the same." Lefty looked up at me. "You're both rather filthy, but otherwise intact."

"How about the others?"

"Equally as filthy and equally as intact. Uncle sent me to check on you."

"You can see we'll be all right."

"I also came to get your help,"

557

Lefty added. "Uncle won't leave the building."

"The old fool," Father muttered.

"Will you come?" Lefty asked.

"Of course, but let us help our friend first."

Lefty got up then. He had been sitting on a silk napkin that must have belonged to one of his customers. He fastidiously wiped his fingers on the napkin and laid it on his right arm, folding it neatly with his left. Then he slipped it into his pants pocket. "Are you hungry?"

"Can't you hear the rumbling in our stomachs?"

"I thought it was another tremor in the earth."

He produced a big basket of chicken, enough to feed a dozen people. I suddenly realized how hungry we were. Father beckoned to the Whitlaws. *"Come on,"* he said. *"It for all."*

Father helped Miss Whitlaw down, while Robin just jumped. They stood shyly around the basket on their front porch. *"This is Lefty,"* Father said.

"How do you do?" Miss Whitlaw held out her hand. Lefty took it.

After we finished the meal, we put the rest of Miss Whitlaw's valuables into the wagon. There were her *stereopticon*, her *slides*, her world globe — almost all the essentials of life, Miss Whitlaw said, disregarding food, clothes, and bedding. It was Robin who got out the clothes they would need, and blankets, mattresses, and other things. The wagon was quite full when we finished. Miss Whitlaw arranged a kind of soft nest in the middle of the wagonload. *"And now the stained-glass window,"* she said.

Father helped her ease it out of the window frame. Lefty let out a low whistle when he saw the window. "Surely it is the very jewel of heaven," he said. We did not need to translate that. Miss Whitlaw beamed. We wrapped it carefully in newspaper and then in a second layer of blankets before we put it in the wagon in the little nest. Miss Whitlaw turned then and took the door key out of her purse. *"Oh, dear, I feel so silly."*

"Go on, Auntie," Robin said.

"Who know, maybe they will stop fire," Father said, even though he knew they would not. But Miss Whitlaw had been born and raised in that house.

"Well, when you put it that way," Miss Whitlaw said. She walked quickly back up the path to her door and locked it. Then she put the key back into her purse. It was the last time she would be able to do that. Her home would be burned down that night. We started to get onto the wagon with her, but Miss Whitlaw told us to get down. *"Your kinfolk may need help."*

"You need help yourself unloading all this and this," Father said.

"I'm sure I'll find some people there to help."

"You sure?" Father asked.

"Yes, I'm quite sure."

"You not know how handle horse."

"Who do you think Papa took camping with him?" Miss Whitlaw took up the reins. *"Don't you worry about us, now."*

"You sure you be all right?"

"We'll meet in the park," Miss Whitlaw said firmly.

"See you there," Father said. We watched until we were sure she could control the horse. The route to the park was clear of holes and rubble in the actual street, so it would not be that much of a problem. Robin now had the antique pistol and looked so eager to use it that I was sure she would discourage any would-be thief.

We waited until they were out of sight, and then Lefty turned to us. "She seems nice."

"She is a superior woman," Father said.

DISCUSSION

1. Why did Mr. Lee go to Miss Whitlaw's house shortly after the earthquake? When she came out of the house, why did Miss Whitlaw ask, *"Are you all right?"*

2. What did Miss Whitlaw do that brought Moon Shadow and Robin out of shock?

3. How did Miss Whitlaw plan to save the people who were trapped under the rubble?

4. Why was it difficult at first to get any survivors of the earthquake to work in rescue crews? Later, what "forceful argument" did Miss Whitlaw think of for getting survivors to help? Was it a good idea? Why do you think that?

5. What did Moon Shadow mean by saying that rescuing people from the mounds of rubble was "a little like playing jackstraws"? How do you know that the work was dangerous?

6. What happened to make Miss Whitlaw say, "This earthquake'll bring out the best and the worst in folk"? Would you agree with the view that disasters usually have that effect on people?

7. How did Mr. Lee react when he saw his friend Lefty sitting on Miss Whitlaw's front stoop? Judging from details in the story, what would you say Lefty was like as a person?

8. Which one of the valuables that Miss Whitlaw collected from her home do you think she treasured most? Why?

9. Why did Miss Whitlaw think it was silly to lock her door before leaving? How do you think she really felt when she finally returned to lock it?

10. At the end of the story, why did Miss Whitlaw refuse to let Mr. Lee and Moon Shadow return with her and Robin? What characteristics did she have that caused Mr. Lee to describe her as "a superior woman"?

AUTHOR

Laurence Yep was born in San Francisco of Chinese-American parents. "I was raised in a black neighborhood," he says, "but commuted to a grammar school in Chinatown so that I did not really meet white culture until I went to high school. In a sense, I have no one culture to call my own, since I exist peripherally in several. However, in my writing I can create my own." Later, he attended Marquette University, was graduated from the University of California at Santa Cruz, and received his Ph.D. from the State University of New York at Buffalo.

Laurence Yep's first story reflected his early interest in science fiction. It was published in the science fiction magazine *The Worlds of If* and then reprinted in a book entitled *World's Best Science Fiction.* Soon his stories were being widely anthologized in adult science-fiction collections. His first book for young people, *Sweetwater,* was a blend of fantasy and science fiction in which people from Earth strive to perpetuate their way of life on another planet. Dr. Yep feels that his frequent use of themes that deal with strange, unknown lands expresses his first reactions to white culture.

In *Dragonwings,* a part of which you have just read, Dr. Yep conveys those reactions as well as the Chinese American's cultural heritage. "I finally confronted my own Chinese-American identity," he says. "I tried to understand the background that shaped me. It took some six years of research in the libraries of different cities to find the bits and pieces that could be fitted into Chinese-American history."

Dragonwings was given the International Reading Association Children's Book Award and the Carter G. Woodson Book Award, and it was named a *Boston Globe-Horn Book* Award Honor Book, a Jane Addams Children's Book Award Honor Book, a Newbery Award Honor Book, a Notable Children's Book in the Field of Social Studies, and an American Library Association Notable Children's Book.

Laurence Yep lives and writes in California. Another of his award-winning books for young people is *Child of the Owl.*

The Old Walking Song

by J. R. R. TOLKIEN

The Road goes ever on and on
Down from the door where it began.
Now far ahead the Road has gone,
And I must follow, if I can,
Pursuing it with eager feet,
Until it joins some larger way
Where many paths and errands meet.
And whither then? I cannot say.

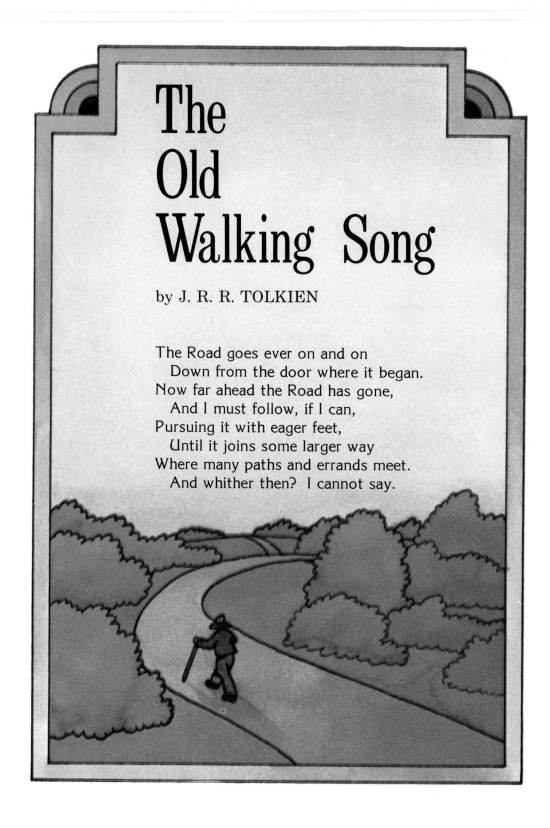

Earth to Spaceship

Thirty years ago the idea of space travel was pure fantasy.

"Spaceship to Earth. Spaceship to Earth. Come in please."

"Earth to Spaceship. Go ahead. Over."

"Spaceship to Earth. We have adjusted our movable wings. We are opening the parachute. We are falling to the moon's surface."

This sort of dialogue was typical of science fiction movies about space flight thirty years ago. But today space flight is a reality, and space terminology has become more sophisticated. You would scarcely have any difficulty understanding a similar conversation in its present form:

Eagle: Contact light! O.K., engine stop. Descent command override off. Houston, Tranquility Base here. The *Eagle* has landed!

Houston: Roger, Tranquility. We copy you on the ground.

Eagle: The auto targeting was taking us into a crater. That final phase required flying manually to find a good landing area. Over.

Houston: Roger, we copy. It was beautiful from here, Tranquility.

Perhaps not all of these terms are familiar, but this is the sort of dialogue used to describe the first moon landing in 1969.

"Settlers in Space" included a fictional journal about travel and everyday life in space. Few existing space terms were actually used, yet the journal had a convincing quality. As a scientist interested in space settlement, the author used a number of terms that are likely to become part of our vocabulary as we adapt to life in space. Examples are *transfer stations, rotating stations, power-plant construction factories,* and *video screens,* all terms that we might well use in the future. Among some scientists these terms are already in common use.

The following is a description of a moon landing. Find as many examples of space terminology as you can in this description, and look up any you don't know in a dictionary or a book about space exploration.

Because the moon is a moving target, a spacecraft must be aimed at a point far ahead of the moon's position in its orbit so that both the moon and the spacecraft reach that point at the same time. After extensive preparation, a date is set for the launch.

Following liftoff, two successive stages of the spacecraft ignite to propel it away from the earth and are then jettisoned. A third stage ignites to send the spacecraft into a parking orbit around the earth. The third stage then re-ignites to send the spacecraft to the moon. Later in the journey the third stage is jettisoned, and the spacecraft, now composed of a command module, a service module, and a lunar module, enters a parking orbit around the moon. Two astronauts transfer to the lunar module and, as the spacecraft remains in orbit, the lunar module descends and lands on the moon.

After the astronauts' mission is completed, the lunar module lifts off from the moon and ascends to the parking orbit, where it docks with the spacecraft. The astronauts then return to the command module, and the lunar module is jettisoned. The service module ignites to send the spacecraft back to the earth. Eventually the service module is also jettisoned, and the command module re-enters the earth's atmosphere. Parachutes are released to prepare for splashdown.

Books to Enjoy

The Life of the Harp Seal by Fred Bruemmer
The noted Canadian photographer's splendid pictures of the harp seal make this book memorable.

I Greet the Dawn: Poems by Paul Laurence Dunbar
selected by Ashley Bryan
This collection of the lyric poems of the noted turn-of-the-century black poet contains an introductory biography.

Run to Starlight: Sports Through Science Fiction
edited by Martin H. Greenberg and others
Twelve stories give a futuristic look at eight different sports.

Belonging by Deborah Kent
Wanting to be an ordinary teen-ager rather than a person set apart, Meg was determined to go to Ridge View High School instead of the school her parents wanted her to attend, the Institute for the Blind.

The Visitors by John Rowe Townsend
In this fantasy, the lives of a young man and his family become enmeshed with those of three people who have time-traveled from the year 2149 to present-day England.

Child of the Owl by Laurence Yep
A motherless girl goes to live with her wise grandmother in San Francisco's Chinese community and learns to appreciate her Chinese heritage.

Glossary

Glossary

Some of the words in this book may have pronunciations or meanings you do not know. This glossary can help you by telling you how to pronounce those words and by telling you the meanings with which those words are used in this book.

You can find out the correct pronunciation of any glossary word by using the special spelling after the word and the pronunciation key at the bottom of each left-hand page.

The full pronunciation key below shows how to pronounce each consonant and vowel in a special spelling. The pronunciation key at the bottom of each left-hand page is a shortened form of the full key.

FULL PRONUNCIATION KEY

Consonant Sounds

b	bib	k	cat, kick, pique	t	tight
ch	church	l	lid, needle	th	path, thin
d	deed	m	am, man, mum	*th*	bathe, this
f	fast, fife, off,	n	no, sudden	v	cave, valve, vine
	phase, rough	ng	thing	w	with
g	gag	p	pop	y	yes
h	hat	r	roar	z	rose, size,
hw	which	s	miss, sauce, see		xylophone, zebra
j	judge	sh	dish, ship	zh	garage, pleasure, vision

Vowel Sounds

ă	pat	ī	by, guy, pie	o͞o	boot, fruit
ā	aid, they, pay	î	dear, deer,	ou	cow, out
â	air, care, wear		fierce, mere	ŭ	cut, rough
ä	father	ŏ	pot, horrible	û	firm, heard, term,
ĕ	pet, pleasure	ō	go, row, toe		turn, word
ē	be, bee, easy,	ô	alter, caught,	yo͞o	abuse, use
	leisure		for, paw	ə	about, silent, pencil,
ĭ	pit	oi	boy, noise, oil		lemon, circus
		o͝o	book	ər	butter

Stress Marks

Primary Stress '	*Secondary Stress* '
bi·ol'o·gy (bī ŏl'ə jē)	**bi'o·log'i·cal** (bī'ə lŏj'ĭ kəl)

Pronunciation key and word meanings adapted from *The American Heritage School Dictionary*, © 1972, 1977, by Houghton Mifflin Company.

a·ban·don (ə băn′dən) *v.* **1.** To leave and stop looking after (someone); desert: *abandon one's family.* **2.** To give up completely: *abandon all hope.* —**a·ban′don·ment** *n.*

ab·do·men (ăb′də mən) *or* (ăb dō′-) *n.* **1.** In human beings and other mammals, the front part of the body from below the chest to about where the legs join, containing the stomach, intestines, and other organs of digestion. **2.** The hindmost division of the body of an insect.

ab·hor (ăb hôr′) *v.* **ab·horred, ab·hor·ring.** To regard with horror or loathing: *abhor violence in all forms.*

ab·o·li·tion·ist (ăb′ə lĭsh′ə nĭst) *n.* A person who favored the prohibition of slavery in the United States.

a·broad (ə brôd′) *adv. & adj.* **1.** In or to foreign places: *going abroad.* **2.** Broadly or widely: *scattering seeds abroad.* **3.** Outdoors and about: *There were people abroad in spite of the downpour.* **4.** In circulation: *There's a nasty rumor abroad.*

a·brupt (ə brŭpt′) *adj.* **1.** Unexpected; sudden: *an abrupt change.* **2.** Very steep: *an abrupt cliff.* **3.** Short and brief so as to suggest rudeness, displeasure, etc.; brusque: *an abrupt answer.* —**a·brupt′ly** *adv.* —**a·brupt′ness** *n.*

a·bun·dance (ə bŭn′dəns) *n.* A great amount or quantity; a plentiful supply: *an abundance of natural resources.*

a·bun·dant (ə bŭn′dənt) *adj.* **1.** Existing in great supply; very plentiful: *abundant rainfall.* **2.** Rich; abounding: *a forest abundant in trees.* —**a·bun′dant·ly** *adv.*

ac·cel·er·a·tion (ăk sĕl′ə rā′shən) *n.* The act or process of increasing in speed.

ac·ces·si·ble (ăk sĕs′ə bəl) *adj.* Easy to reach, approach, or obtain: *The lake is accessible from the highway.* —**ac·ces′si·bil′i·ty** *n.* —**ac·ces′si·bly** *adv.*

ac·cou·ter·ments (ə kōō′tər mənts) *pl. n.* **1.** Articles of clothing or equipment; trappings. **2.** A soldier's equipment other than clothing and weapons.

ac·cu·mu·late (ə kyōō′myə lāt′) *v.* **ac·cu·mu·lat·ed, ac·cu·mu·lat·ing.** To gather together; pile up; collect: *Snow has begun to accumulate on the sidewalk.*

ad·join (ə join′) *v.* **1.** To be next to or share a boundary with: *The bath adjoins the bedroom.* **2.** To lie side by side: *The rooms adjoin.*

ad·o·les·cent (ăd′l ĕs′ənt) *n.* A boy or girl, especially a teen-ager, in the stage of development between childhood and adulthood. —*adj.* Of or going through adolescence: *an adolescent youngster.*

ad·ver·si·ty (ăd vûr′sĭ tē) *n., pl.* **ad·ver·si·ties.** Great misfortune; hardship: *time of adversity.*

af·fect[1] (ə fĕkt′) *v.* **1.** To have an influence on; bring about a change in: *Geography affects people's ways of living.* **2.** To touch or move the emotions of: *How does rudeness affect you?* **3.** To attack or infect: *Anthrax affects cattle and sheep.* —**af·fect′ing** *adj.: an affecting tale of woe.*

af·fect[2] (ə fĕkt′) *v.* **1.** To imitate in order to make a desired impression; pretend to have; assume: *He affected an English accent because he thought it sounded better.* **2.** To like; prefer: *He affects striped shirts.* —**af·fect′ed** *adj.: an affected voice.*

a·gape (ə gāp′, ə găp′) *adv.* Wide open (of the mouth) in a state of wonder or amazement: *With mouths agape they stared at the great magician.*

ag·gres·sion (ə grĕsh′ən) *n.* **1.** The action of a country in launching an unprovoked attack on another country. **2.** The habit or practice of launching attacks. **3.** Hostile action or behavior.

ag·gres·sive (ə grĕs′ĭv) *adj.* **1.** Quick to attack or start a fight: *an aggressive youngster.* **2.** Vigorous; energetic: *an aggressive salesperson.* —**ag·gres′sive·ly** *adv.* —**ag·gres′sive·ness** *n.*

ag·i·tat·ed (ăj′ĭ tāt′ĕd) *adj.* **1.** Violently shaken or stirred up. **2.** Disturbed; upset.

aide (ād) *n.* An assistant or helper: *a Presidential aide.*

ă pat / ā pay / â care / ä father / ĕ pet / ē be / ĭ pit / ī pie / î fierce / ŏ pot / ō go / ô paw, for / oi oil / ŏŏ book / ōō boot / ou out / ŭ cut / û fur / th the / th thin / hw which / zh vision / ə ago, item, pencil, atom, circus

al·a·bas·ter (ăl′ə băs′tər) *or* (-bä′stər) *n.*
Any of various hard, translucent, often
tinted or banded minerals that consist
mainly of salts of calcium.

al·be·it (ôl bē′ĭt) *conj.* Even though; although: *an imaginative, albeit somewhat
impractical, idea.*

al·cove (ăl′kōv′) *n.* A small room opening
on a larger one without being separated
from it by a wall.

a·li·en (ā′lē ən) *or* (āl′yən) *adj.* **1.** Of or
coming from another country; foreign.
2. Not of one's own society; unfamiliar;
strange. —*n.* **1.** A person living in one
country though a citizen of another; a
foreigner. **2.** In science fiction, an intelligent being from anywhere other than
earth.

a·light (ə līt′) *v.* **a·light·ed** *or* **a·lit** (ə lĭt′),
a·light·ing. **1.** To come down and settle
gently: *A bird alighted on the windowsill.*
2. To get off: *alight from a train.*

al·lied (ə līd′) *or* (ăl′īd′) *adj.* **1.** Joined
together in an agreement. **2.** Similar; related: *Biochemistry and biophysics are
allied sciences.* **3. Allied.** Of allied countries, especially the countries that fought
against Germany and its allies in World
Wars I and II.

al·ly (ə lī′) *v.* **al·lied, al·ly·ing, al·lies.** To
join or unite for a specific purpose: *The
United States allied itself with Russia during World War II.* —*n.* (ăl′ī′) *or* (ə lī′),
pl. **al·lies. 1.** A person or country that is
allied to another. **2. Al·lies.** A group of
allied countries, especially the United
States, Great Britain, France, Russia, and
other countries that fought together in
World Wars I and II.

al·tim·e·ter (ăl tĭm′ĭ tər) *n.* An instrument that measures and indicates the
height at which an object, such as an
aircraft, is located.

am·u·let (ăm′yə lĭt) *n.* A charm worn to
ward off evil or injury, especially one
worn around the neck.

a·nal·o·gy (ə năl′ə jē) *n., pl.* **a·nal·
o·gies. 1.** A reasoning that if two unre-
lated things are alike in some ways, they
are probably alike in others. **2.** A parallel:
*The beehive finds its human analogy in the
city.*

a·nat·o·my (ə năt′ə mē) *n., pl.* **a·nat·
o·mies. 1.** The structure of a plant or an
animal or of any of its parts. **2.** The scientific study of the shape and structure of
living things. **3.** The dissection or cutting
apart of a plant or animal in order to
study its structure.

an·ces·tral (ăn sĕs′trəl) *adj.* **1.** Of ancestors, or persons from whom one is descended: *ancestral spirits.* **2.** Coming
from ancestors: *ancestral wealth.* **3.** Being
an ancestor: *the ancestral Indo-European
language, from which English and Greek
are descended.* —**an·ces′tral·ly** *adv.*

an·es·thet·ic (ăn′ĭs thĕt′ĭk) *adj.* Insensi-
tive; without sensation or feeling. —*n.*
Any drug or agent that causes a condition
in which some or all of the senses, especially the sense of touch, stop operating,
either completely or in part.

an·guish (ăng′gwĭsh) *n.* A pain of the body
or mind that causes one agony; torment;
torture.

an·i·mos·i·ty (ăn′ə mŏs′ĭ tē) *n., pl.*
an·i·mos·i·ties. Hatred, enmity, or hos-
tility that is shown openly.

a·non (ə nŏn′) *adv.* **1.** Again; then. Used
chiefly in the phrases *ever and anon* and
now and anon. **2.** *Archaic.* Soon; presently: *"Of this discourse we more will hear
anon."* (Shakespeare).

an·tag·o·nist (ăn tăg′ə nĭst) *n.* A person
who opposes and actively competes with
another; an adversary; opponent.

an·tag·o·nize (ăn tăg′ə nīz′) *v.* **an·tag·
o·nized, an·tag·o·niz·ing.** To earn the
dislike of: *He antagonized his father
by acting bored.*

an·te·cham·ber (ăn′tē chām′bər) *n.* A
smaller room at the entrance to a larger
and more important room.

an·thro·pol·o·gist (ăn′thrə pŏl′ə jĭst) *n.*
A scientist who specializes in the scientific study of the origins and physical,
social, and cultural development and behavior of human beings.

an·ti·bi·ot·ic (ăn′tē bī ŏt′ĭk) *n.* Any of a
group of substances such as penicillin
and streptomycin that are widely used in
the treatment and prevention of diseases.
—*adj.* Of, using, or acting as an antibiotic
or antibiotics.

an·tic (ăn′tĭk) *adj.* Odd; ludicrous. —*n.* Often **antics.** An odd or extravagant act or gesture; a caper; prank.

an·ti·freeze (ăn′tĭ frēz′) *n.* A liquid added to another liquid, such as water, to lower its freezing point so that the other liquid will not freeze.

anx·i·e·ty (ăng zī′ĭ tē) *n., pl.* **anx·i·e·ties.** **1.** A feeling of uneasiness and distress about something in the future; worry: *He was filled with anxiety about his mother's return.* **2.** Eagerness or earnestness, often marked by uneasiness: *anxiety to do well.*

ap·er·ture (ăp′ər chər) *n.* A hole or opening: *an aperture in the wall.*

a·plomb (ə plŏm′) *or* (ə plŭm′) *n.* Self-confidence; poise; assurance: *She handles difficult situations with aplomb.*

ap·pease (ə pēz′) *v.* **ap·peased, ap·peas·ing.** **1.** To calm or pacify, especially by giving what is demanded: *He appeased the child with an ice-cream cone.* **2.** To satisfy; relieve: *A glass of water appeased his thirst.*

ap·pend·age (ə pĕn′dĭj) *n.* **1.** Something added or attached. **2.** Any part or organ of the body that hangs or projects from another part: *A finger is an appendage of the hand.*

ap·pre·hen·sive (ăp′rĭ hĕn′sĭv) *adj.* Anxious or fearful; uneasy: *an apprehensive glance; apprehensive about the future.* —**ap′pre·hen′sive·ly** *adv.*

ap·pren·tice (ə prĕn′tĭs) *n.* **1.** A person who works for another without pay in return for instruction in a craft or trade. **2.** One, usually a member of a labor union, who is learning a trade. **3.** Any beginner. —*modifier: an apprentice carpenter.* —*v.* **ap·pren·ticed, ap·pren·tic·ing.** To place as an apprentice: *His father apprenticed him to a silversmith.*

ap·pren·tice·ship (ə prĕn′tĭs shĭp′) *n.* **1.** The condition of being an apprentice: *His apprenticeship prevented him from marrying.* **2.** The period during which one is an apprentice.

ap·pro·pri·a·tion (ə prō′prē ā′shən) *n.* **1.** The act of setting something aside for oneself or for a specific use. **2.** Public funds set aside for a specific purpose.

aq·ui·line (ăk′wə līn′) *or* (-lĭn′) *adj.* Curved or hooked like an eagle's beak: *an aquiline nose.*

Ar·a·bic (ăr′ə bĭk) *n.* The Semitic language of the Arabs. —*adj.* **1.** Of the Arabs or their language. **2.** Of the script used in writing Arabic, Persian, and some other languages.

ar·che·ol·o·gist *or* **ar·chae·ol·o·gist** (är′kē ŏl′ə jĭst) *n.* A person who scientifically studies the remains of past human activities, such as burials, buildings, tools, and pottery.

ar·chives (är′kīvz′) *pl. n.* **1.** The records or documents of an organization, institution, or nation. **2.** The place where such records are kept.

ar·chi·vist (är′kə vĭst) *or* (är′kī-) *n.* One who is in charge of archives.

ar·du·ous (är′jōō əs) *adj.* Demanding great effort; difficult: *arduous training; an arduous undertaking.* —**ar′du·ous·ly** *adv.* —**ar′du·ous·ness** *n.*

ar·id (ăr′ĭd) *adj.* **1.** Having little or no rainfall; dry; parched: *an arid desert; an arid wasteland.* **2.** Lifeless; dull: *a long, arid book.* —**a·rid′i·ty** (ə rĭd′ĭ tē) *n.*

ar·mor·y (är′mə rē) *n., pl.* **ar·mor·ies.** **1.** A storehouse for military weapons; an arsenal. **2.** The headquarters of a military reserve force. **3.** A weapons factory.

ar·tic·u·late (är tĭk′yə lĭt) *adj.* **1.** Spoken clearly and distinctly: *articulate speech.* **2.** Capable of speaking clearly and expressively: *articulate people.* —*v.* (är tĭk′yə lāt′) **ar·tic·u·lat·ed, ar·tic·u·lat·ing.** **1.** To utter (a speech sound or sounds) distinctly; enunciate: *Articulate the following words. He articulates well.* **2.** To express verbally: *She articulated the sentiments of the group in a lengthy report to the commission.* —**ar·tic′u·late·ly** *adv.* —**ar·tic′u·late·ness** *n.*

ă pat / ā pay / â care / ä father / ĕ pet / ē be / ĭ pit / ī pie / î fierce / ŏ pot / ō go / ô paw, for / oi oil / ŏŏ book / ōō boot / ou out / ŭ cut / û fur / th the / th thin / hw which / zh vision / ə ago, item, pencil, atom, circus

as·cer·tain (ăs′ər tān′) *v.* To find out: *ascertain the truth.* **—as′cer·tain′a·ble** *adj.*

as·set (ăs′ĕt′) *n.* **1.** A valuable quality or possession: *Her smile is a real asset. The water birds are the island's most spectacular asset.*

as·so·ci·ate (ə sō′shē ĭt) *or* (-āt′) *or* (-sē-) *n.* **1.** A partner; colleague: *my business associate.* **2.** A member without full status: *an associate of the museum society.*

a·stride (ə strīd′) *prep.* **1.** With a leg on each side of; bestriding: *He jumped astride the bronco's back.* Also used adverbially: *riding astride.* **2.** On both sides of or spanning: *a safe position astride the bridge.*

a·tone (ə tōn′) *v.* **a·toned, a·ton·ing.** To make amends for a sin, fault, etc.: *atone for tardiness by doing extra work.*

a·tro·cious (ə trō′shəs) *adj.* **1.** Extremely evil or cruel; wicked: *an atrocious crime.* **2.** Very bad; abominable: *atrocious weather conditions.* **—a·tro′cious·ly** *adv.* **—a·tro′cious·ness** *n.*

a·troc·i·ty (ə trŏs′ĭ tē) *n., pl.* **a·troc·i·ties.** Something atrocious, especially an extremely evil or cruel act: *victims of wartime atrocities.*

aught (ôt) *pron. Archaic.* Anything at all. Used especially in phrases like *for aught I care* ("for all I care"), *for aught I know* ("for all I know"), etc. *—adv.* At all.

au·ra (ôr′ə) *n.* A distinctive air or quality that characterizes a person or thing: *an aura of mystery about him.*

aus·tere (ô stîr′) *adj.* **1.** Having a stern personality or appearance; somber. **2.** Severely simple, as in living habits. **3.** Harsh or barren: *They found it an austere land in which to live.* **—aus·tere′ly** *adv.*

av·a·lanche (ăv′ə lănch′) *or* (-länch′) *n.* A large mass of material such as snow, ice, or earth that falls or slides down the side of a mountain.

a·vert (ə vûrt′) *v.* **1.** To turn away or aside: *avert one's eyes.* **2.** To keep from happening; prevent: *The successful handling of the problem could help us to avert other accidents.*

a·void (ə void′) *v.* **1.** To keep away from; stay clear of; shun: *avoid crowds.* **2.** To evade; dodge: *quick enough to avoid the blow.* **3.** To prevent; keep from happening: *a clumsy attempt to avoid getting wet.* **4.** To refrain from: *avoid taking sides in a personal argument.* **—a·void′a·ble** *adj.* **—a·void′ance** *n.*

awe (ô) *n.* A feeling of wonder, fear, and respect inspired by something mighty or majestic: *gazing in awe at the mountains.*

ax·is (ăk′sĭs) *n., pl.* **ax·es** (ăk′sēz′). **1.** A straight line around which an object or geometric figure rotates or can be imagined to rotate: *The axis of the earth passes through both of its poles.* **2.** A line, ray, or line segment with respect to which a figure or object is symmetrical. **3.** A reference line from which or along which distances or angles are measured in a system of coordinates: *the x-axis.* **4. the Axis.** The alliance of Germany, Italy, Japan, and other nations that opposed the Allies in World War II.

ax·le (ăk′səl) *n.* A supporting shaft or spindle on which one or more wheels revolve.

bac·te·ri·ol·o·gy (băk tîr′ē ŏl′ə jē) *n.* The scientific study of bacteria.

balk (bôk) *v.* **1.** To stop short and refuse to go on: *Her horse balked at the first jump.* **2.** To refuse; recoil; shrink: *They balked at the terms of the settlement.* **3.** To check or thwart: *The police balked the robbers' escape plans.*

bal·lad (băl′əd) *n.* **1.** A poem, often intended to be sung, that tells a story in a simple manner. **2.** Music to which a ballad could be sung. **3.** A popular love song.

ban·is·ter (băn′ĭ stər) *n.* The handrail supported by posts along a staircase.

barn·storm (bärn′stôrm′) *v.* **-stormed, -storming, -storms. 1.** To travel about the countryside presenting plays, lecturing, or making political speeches. **2.** To appear at county fairs and carnivals in exhibitions of stunt flying and parachute jumping. **—barn′storm′er** *n.*

barred owl. A large American owl with bars of dark brown on the breast.

bar·ren (băr′ən) *adj.* **1.** Lacking or unable to produce growing plants or crops: *a barren desert.* **—bar′ren·ness** *n.*

basque (băsk) *n.* A girl's or woman's close-fitting bodice.

bat·tle·ment (băt′l mənt) *n.* Often **battlements.** A wall with indented openings, built along the top edge of a tower, castle, fort, etc., and formerly used as protection and concealment for soldiers in warfare.

bay·o·net (bā′ə nĭt) *or* (-nĕt′) *or* (bā′ə-nĕt′) *n.* A knife attached to the muzzle end of a rifle for use in close combat.

bed·lam (bĕd′ləm) *n.* **1.** A place or situation of confusion, disorder, or noisy uproar: *After breakfast the happy bedlam of unwrapping presents began.* **2.** *Archaic.* An insane asylum.

be·drag·gled (bĭ drăg′əld) *adj.* Wet, drenched, messy, etc.: *bedraggled clothes.*

be·foul (bĭ foul′) *v.* To make dirty; soil: *smokestacks befouling the air.*

be·get (bĭ gĕt′) *v.* **be·got** (bĭ gŏt′), **be·got·ten** (bĭ gŏt′n) *or* **be·got, be·get·ting.** **1.** To father; sire. **2.** To cause to exist; produce: *Knowledge begets knowledge.* —**be·get′ter** *n.*

ben·e·fac·tor (bĕn′ə făk′tər) *n.* A person who gives financial or other aid to another person.

ber·serk (bər sûrk′) *or* (-zûrk′) *adj.* In or into a crazed or violent frenzy: *He went berserk and started screaming political slogans at everyone.*

be·sieged (bĭ sējd′) *adj.* **1.** Surrounded and blockaded: *Everyone in the besieged city suffered from hunger.* **2.** Hemmed in.

bier (bîr) *n.* A stand on which a dead person or a coffin is placed while lying in state or when being carried to the grave: *Thousands of mourners filed by the bier, paying their last respects to the great leader.*

bil·liard (bĭl′yərd) *adj.* Of the game of billiards: *a billiard table.*

bil·liards (bĭl′yərdz) *n.* (*used with a singular verb*). A game, played on a cloth-covered table with raised, cushioned edges, in which a cue is used to hit three balls against one another or the side cushions of the table.

bi·zarre (bĭ zär′) *adj.* Very strange or odd: *a bizarre hat; a bizarre idea.*

bleak (blēk) *adj.* **bleak·er, bleak·est.** **1.** Exposed to the winds; barren and windswept: *bleak moors.* **2.** Cold and harsh: *a damp, bleak wind.* **3.** Gloomy; somber; dreary: *bleak thoughts.* —**bleak′ly** *adv.* —**bleak′ness** *n.*

blind (blīnd) *n.* A shelter for concealing humans from wildlife.

blunt (blŭnt) *adj.* **blunt·er, blunt·est.** **1.** Having a thick, dull edge or end; not pointed. **2.** Abrupt and frank in manner. —*v.* **1.** To dull the edge of. **2.** To make less effective; weaken; deaden: *The army blunted the enemy onslaught.* —**blunt′ly** *adv.* —**blunt′ness** *n.*

bog (bôg) *or* (bŏg) *n.* Soft, water-soaked ground; a marsh; swamp.

bog·gle (bŏg′əl) *v.* **bog·gled, bog·gling.** To hesitate or evade, as if in fear or doubt: *He boggled at the thought of opening someone else's letter.*

bois·ter·ous (boi′stər əs) *or* (-strəs) *adj.* **1.** Rough and stormy; violent: *boisterous winds.* **2.** Noisy and lacking restraint or discipline: *boisterous cheers.* —**bois′ter·ous·ly** *adv.* —**bois′ter·ous·ness** *n.*

bow·er (bou′ər) *n.* A private room.

brace (brās) *n.* **1.** A device that holds two or more parts together or in place. **2.** A support, as a beam in a building. —*v.* **braced, brac·ing.** **1.** To support; strengthen. **2.** To prepare for a blow, shock, struggle, etc. **3.** To prop or hold firmly in place: *She braced her feet against the floorboard.* —**brace up.** To summon up lost courage or strength: *Brace up and do what has to be done in this difficult time.*

brawn·y (brô′nē) *adj.* **brawn·i·er, brawn·i·est.** Strong and muscular: *Six brawny figures appeared in the body-building competition.*

bra·zen·ly (brā′zən lē) *adv.* In a manner that is rudely bold: *He brazenly defied the rules.* —**bra′zen** *adj.* —**bra′zen·ness** *n.*

ă pat / ā pay / â care / ä father / ĕ pet / ē be / ĭ pit / ī pie / î fierce / ŏ pot / ō go / ô paw, for / oi oil / ŏŏ book / ōō boot / ou out / ŭ cut / û fur / *th* the / th thin / hw which / zh vision / ə ago, item, pencil, atom, circus

break·through (brāk'thrōō') *n.* A major achievement or success that permits further progress, as in technology.

breech·clout (brēch'klout') *n.* A cloth worn to cover the loins.

brig·a·dier (brĭg'ə dîr') *n.* Also **brigadier general.** A general of the lowest rank.

brood (brōōd) *n.* A group, as of young birds, hatched from eggs laid at the same time by the same mother. —*v.* **1.** To sit on and hatch (eggs). **2.** To think at length and unhappily; worry anxiously.

brusque (brŭsk) *adj.* Rudely abrupt in manner or speech; curt; blunt. —**brusque'ly** *adv.* —**brusque'ness** *n.*

buck·le (bŭk'əl) *n.* A bend, bulge, warp, or other distortion. —*v.* **buck·led, buck·ling.** To bend, warp, or crumple under pressure or heat: *the ever-changing crust of the earth buckling in some places, rising in others, and sinking in still others. Changing stresses buckled great rock masses along a fault.*

buff[1] (bŭf) *n.* **1.** A soft, thick, yellowish leather made from the skins of buffalo, elk, or oxen. **2.** The color of this leather; a yellowish tan. **3.** An implement covered with soft material and used for polishing. —*modifier: a buff jerkin.* —*adj.* Yellowish tan. —*v.* To polish or shine with a buff.

buff[2] (bŭf) *n. Informal.* A person who has great interest in, and some knowledge of, a subject: *an opera buff.*

buf·fet (bŭf'ĭt) *n.* A blow or cuff made with or as if with the hand.

buf·foon (bə fōōn') *n.* A clown or jester.

bump·er (bŭm'pər) *adj.* Abundant: *a bumper crop.*

buoy (bōō'ē) *or* (boi) *n.* A float used as a channel or anchorage marker. —*v.* **1.** To keep afloat. **2.** To cheer; hearten: *The news buoyed her spirits.*

ca·lam·i·ty (kə lăm'ĭ tē) *n., pl.* **ca·lam·i·ties.** Something that causes great distress and suffering; a disaster.

cal·ci·um (kăl'sē əm) *n.* Symbol **Ca** One of the elements, a silvery, moderately hard metal.

cal·i·co (kăl'ĭ kō) *n., pl.* **cal·i·coes** or **cal·i·cos.** A cotton cloth with a figured pattern printed on it in color: *Dozens of calicoes were used in the quilt.*

cal·lous (kăl'əs) *adj.* Unfeeling; unsympathetic. —**cal'lous·ly** *adv.* —**cal'lous·ness** *n.*

cam·ou·flage (kăm'ə fläzh') *v.* To conceal or disguise people, animals, or things through the use of colors or patterns that make them appear to be part of the natural surroundings. **cam·ou·flaged, cam·ou·flag·ing.**

can·de·la·brum (kăn'dl ä'brəm) *or* (-ăb'rəm) *or* (-ä'brəm) *n., pl.* **can·de·la·bra** (kăn'dl ä'brə) *or* (-ăb'rə) *or* (-ä'brə) *or* **can·de·la·brums.** A large decorative candlestick that has several arms or branches for holding candles.

can·ker (kăng'kər) *n.* An open sore on the lips or in the mouth.

can·o·py (kăn'ə pē) *n., pl.* **can·o·pies.** **1.** A kind of tentlike roof, usually held up on posts or poles, covering a bed, entrance, sacred object, or important person. **2.** Any similar covering: *a canopy of leafy branches.*

can·teen (kăn tēn') *n.* A container for carrying drinking water.

ca·pa·ble (kā'pə bəl) *adj.* Able; skilled; competent: *a capable teacher.* —**capable of. a.** Having the ability or capacity for: *a person capable of being a great athlete.* **b.** Open to; subject to: *a statement capable of several interpretations.* —**ca'pa·bly** *adv.*

ca·pac·i·ty (kə păs'ĭ tē) *n., pl.* **ca·pac·i·ties.** **1.** The ability to hold, receive, or contain: *a can with a capacity of three quarts; a theater with a small seating capacity.* **2.** Ability; capability: *a person's capacity for learning.* **3.** The maximum amount that can be contained. —*modifier:* Maximum; as large or numerous as possible in a given setting.

ca·pit·u·late (kə pĭch'ə lāt') *v.* **ca·pit·u·lat·ed, ca·pit·u·lat·ing.** To surrender under stated conditions; give in; yield.

ca·rafe (kə răf') *or* (-räf') *n.* A glass bottle for serving water or wine at the table.

car·bon di·ox·ide (kär'bən dī ŏk'sīd') *n.* A colorless, odorless gas that does not burn. It is composed of carbon and oxygen and is produced in any process, such as breathing, combustion, or the breaking down of organic matter, in which carbon combines with oxygen.

car·bu·re·tor (kär′bə rā′tər) *or* (-byə-) *n.* A part of a gasoline engine that vaporizes or atomizes the gasoline and mixes it with air in such a way that the gasoline will burn properly.

car·cass (kär′kəs) *n.* **1.** The dead body of an animal. **2.** Anything likened to a carcass: *the carcasses of old cars dumped in a junkyard.*

ca·reen (kə rēn′) *v.* **1.** To tilt (a ship) onto its side, on the shore, in order to clean or repair its bottom. **2.** To lurch or swerve while in motion: *The car careened on the icy road.*

car·i·ca·ture (kăr′ĭ kə chŏŏr′) *or* (-chər) *n.* A picture or description of a person or thing in which certain distinctive features are greatly exaggerated or distorted to produce a comic effect. —*v.* **car·i·ca·tured, car·i·ca·tur·ing.** To represent in caricature. —**car′i·ca·tur′ist** *n.*

car·nel·ian (kär nēl′yən) *n.* A pale to deep red type of clear quartz used as a gem.

case·ment (kās′mənt) *n.* **1.** A window sash that opens outward on hinges. **2.** A window fitted with such sashes.

cat·a·clysm (kăt′ə klĭz′əm) *n.* **1.** A sudden and violent change in the earth's crust. **2.** A great upheaval or disaster, such as a flood, earthquake, revolution, or war. —**cat′a·clys′mic** (kăt′ə klĭz′mĭk) *adj.*

cat·a·pult (kăt′ə pŭlt′) *or* (-pŏŏlt′) *n.* **1.** An ancient military device for hurling stones, spears, arrows, or other missiles. **2.** A mechanism for launching aircraft from the deck of a ship. —*v.* **1.** To hurl or launch from or as if from a catapult: *The volcano catapults boulders the size of small houses.* **2.** To move suddenly as if propelled from a catapult.

ca·vort (kə vôrt′) *v.* To leap about playfully; romp; frolic: *ponies cavorting about an open field.*

cen·sus (sĕn′səs) *n., pl.* **cen·sus·es.** An official count of population, often including statistics on age, sex, etc., and other factual information about people.

cen·trif·u·gal (sĕn trĭf′yə gəl) *or* (-trĭf′ə-gəl) *adj.* Moving or directed away from a center or axis.

chaff (chăf) *n.* **1.** Grain husks that have been separated from the seeds by threshing. **2.** Trivial or worthless matter.

cha·os (kā′ŏs′) *n.* Great disorder or confusion: *The flood left chaos behind it.*

chap·ar·ral (shăp′ə răl′) *or* (chăp′-) *n.* A dense growth of tangled, often thorny shrubs, especially in the southwestern United States and Mexico.

chau·vin·ism (shō′və nĭz′əm) *n.* **1.** Unthinking and boastful devotion to one's country or a cause; fanatical patriotism. **2.** Prejudiced belief in the superiority of one's own group: *male chauvinism.* —**chau′vin·ist** *n.*

Cho·pin (shō′păn′), **Frédéric.** 1810–1849. Polish composer and pianist.

chor·tle (chôr′tl) *v.* **chor·tled, chor·tling.** To chuckle throatily. —*n.* A snorting chuckle.

cir·cuit (sûr′kĭt) *n.* **1. a.** A closed curve, such as a circle. **b.** Any path that forms such a curve. **2.** A closed path through which an electric current flows or may flow. **3.** An association of theaters in which plays, acts, or films move from theater to theater for presentation. **4.** An association of teams, clubs, or arenas of competition: *the tennis circuit.*

claim (klām) *v.* **1.** To demand or ask for (something) as one's own or one's due. **2.** To declare to be true; assert. —*n.* **1.** A demand or request for something as one's rightful due. **2.** A right to ask for. **3.** A statement of something as fact. **4.** Something claimed, especially a tract of land claimed by a miner or homesteader.

claim jumper. Someone who takes land or rights from another by violence or fraud.

ă pat / ā pay / â care / ä father / ĕ pet / ē be / ĭ pit / ī pie / î fierce / ŏ pot / ō go / ô paw, for / oi oil / ŏŏ book / ōō boot / ou out / ŭ cut / û fur / *th* the / th thin / hw which / zh vision / ə ago, item, pencil, atom, circus

clam·or (klăm′ər) *n.* **1.** A loud, continuous, and usually confused noise: *the clamor of a crowd.* **2.** A strong or loud demand: *a clamor for less pollution.* —*v.* To make a clamor.

clas·sic (klăs′ĭk) *adj.* **1. a.** Long regarded as or serving as an outstanding example of its kind; model: *a classic case of neglect. The Derby is a classic horse race.* **b.** Well-known and typical: *the classic situation of boy meets girl.* **2.** Of ancient Greece and Rome or their literature or art: *classic times; classic styles of architecture; classic drama.*

cob·ble (kŏb′əl) *n.* A cobblestone. —*v.* **cob·bled, cob·bling.** To pave with cobblestones. —**cob′bled** *adj.: narrow cobbled streets.*

col·league (kŏl′ēg′) *n.* A co-member of a profession or organization; an associate.

col·lec·tive·ly (kə lĕk′tĭv lē) *adv.* In a group collected or assembled into a whole or considered as a whole.

comb·er (kō′mər) *n.* **1.** A person or instrument that combs. **2.** A long wave of the sea that has reached its peak or broken into foam.

com·mend (kə mĕnd′) *v.* **1.** To speak highly of; praise: *The mayor commended the commission for its painstaking report.* **2.** To recommend: *commend someone for employment.* **3.** To put in the care of someone: *commend him to his mother's care.*

com·mo·tion (kə mō′shən) *n.* Violent motion; agitation; tumult.

com·pe·tent (kŏm′pĭ tnt) *adj.* **1.** Able to do what is required; capable: *a competent worker.* **2.** Satisfactory; adequate: *a competent job.* —**com′pe·tent·ly** *adv.*

con·ceal (kən sēl′) *v.* To keep from being seen, noticed, or known; hide: *A bank of clouds concealed the setting sun.*

con·cept (kŏn′sĕpt′) *n.* A general idea or understanding, especially one based on known facts or observation: *the concept that all matter is made up of elements.*

con·cert·ed (kən sûr′tĭd) *adj.* Planned or accomplished together with others; combined: *a concerted fund-raising drive.*

con·duct (kən dŭkt′) *v.* To lead; guide: *conduct a tour.* —*n.* (kŏn′dŭkt). The way a person acts; behavior: *disorderly conduct; good conduct.*

con·firm (kən fûrm′) *v.* To support or establish the truth or reality of: *The news confirmed the rumors.*

con·front (kən frŭnt′) *v.* **1.** To come face to face with; stand before: *Allow the defendants to confront their accuser. The problems that confront us seem overwhelming.* **2.** To meet or face boldly or defiantly: *A couple of hoodlums confronted us on the street.* **3.** To bring face to face; challenge to accept or deny: *When confronted with all the evidence, the suspect confessed.*

con·jec·ture (kən jĕk′chər) *v.* **1.** To form an opinion or conclusion from incomplete or insufficient evidence; guess. **2.** To make a statement based on guesswork.

con·serve (kən sûrv′) *v.* **con·served, con·serv·ing.** To use (a supply) carefully, without waste: *conserve one's energy; conserve groceries.*

con·sign·ment (kən sīn′mənt) *n.* The delivery of something for sale. —**on consignment.** Sent to a retailer who is expected to pay after selling.

con·sole (kən sōl′) *v.* **con·soled, con·sol·ing.** To comfort in time of disappointment or sorrow.

con·spir·a·to·ri·al·ly (kən spîr′ə tôr′ē əl lē) *or* (-tōr′-) *adv.* In the manner of planning together secretly: *The prankster whispered conspiratorially to his friend.*

con·sump·tion (kən sŭmp′shən) *n.* **1.** The act of using up. **2.** A quantity used up. **3.** A wasting away of body tissues. **4.** *Archaic.* Tuberculosis of the lungs: *wasted by consumption.*

con·tem·pla·tion (kŏn′təm plā′shən) *n.* The act of thoughtful watching or thinking: *lost in contemplation.*

con·tem·po·rar·y (kən tĕm′pə rĕr′ē) *adj.* **1.** Living or occurring during the same period of time. **2.** Current; modern: *contemporary history.* —*n.,* pl. **con·tem·po·rar·ies.** **1.** A person of the same age as another: *John and I are contemporaries.* **2.** A person living at the same time as another: *a composer much admired by her contemporaries.* **3.** A person of the present age.

con•tend (kən tĕnd′) v. To compete, as in a race: *I could not contend with him in speed.* —**con•tend′er** n.

con•tort (kən tôrt′) v. To twist or become twisted severely out of shape.

con•tour (kŏn′tŏor′) n. The outline of a figure, body, or mass: *the contour of the American coast.*

con•trite (kən trīt′) or (kŏn′trīt′) adj. Feeling or caused by guilt: *a contrite sinner; contrite tears.* —**con•trite′ly** adv. —**con•trite′ness** n.

con•tro•ver•sial (kŏn′trə vûr′shəl) adj. Tending to cause argument or debate: *a controversial issue.* —**con′tro•ver′sial•ly** adv.

con•ven•tion•al (kən vĕn′shə nəl) adj. Following accepted practice, customs, or taste: *a conventional greeting; a conventional plan for a house.* —**con•ven′tion•al•ly** adv. —**con•ven′tion•al′i•ty** n.

con•verge (kən vûrj′) v. **con•verged, con•verg•ing.** To come together in one place: *The three roads converged in a lush green meadow.*

con•vert (kən vûrt′) v. To change into another form, substance, or condition: *convert carbon dioxide into sugar.*

con•vey (kən vā′) v. To make known; communicate: *Words convey meaning.*

con•voy (kŏn′voi′) n. A group of ships or vehicles acting as an escort.

con•vul•sive (kən vŭl′sĭv) adj. **1.** Having or causing violent involuntary muscular contractions. **2.** Of or like a fit or seizure.

cor•gi (kôr′gē) n. A dog of a breed having a long body, short legs, and a foxlike head; a Welsh corgi.

cosmic ray. A stream of radiation, consisting of high-energy atomic nuclei, fragments, and particles and some electromagnetic waves, that enters the atmosphere from outer space.

cos•mos (kŏz′məs) n. **1.** The universe regarded as an orderly, harmonious whole. **2.** Any system regarded as orderly, harmonious, and whole.

Cos•sack (kŏs′ăk′) n. A member of a people of southern Russia, noted as riders of horses: *The band of Cossacks burst into song.* —**Cos′sack′** adj.

cote (kōt) n. A shed or coop for small animals or birds.

coun•ter•point (koun′tər point′) n. **1.** A musical technique in which two or more distinct melodies are combined so that they can be performed at the same time as a single whole. **2.** A secondary melody designed to go along with a principal melody. **3.** A contrasting but parallel element, item, or theme.

coup (kōo) n., pl. **coups** (kōoz). A brilliantly executed move or action that obtains the desired results: *The ambassador pulled off quite a coup with the signing of the new agreement.*

cov•et•ed (kŭv′ĭ tĭd) adj. Strongly wished for: *a coveted award.*

craft (krăft) or (kräft) n., pl. **craft.** A boat, ship, aircraft, or spacecraft.

crag (krăg) n. A steep projection of rock forming part of a cliff, mountain, etc.

craw•dad (krô′dăd) n. *Dialect.* A freshwater animal that resembles a lobster but is much smaller; a crayfish.

cre•vasse (krə văs′) n. A deep crack, as in a glacier; a chasm: *The climbers roped themselves together to cross the crevasse.*

crev•ice (krĕv′ĭs) n. A narrow crack or opening.

cringe (krĭnj) v. **cringed, cring•ing.** To shrink back, as in fear; cower: *He cringed whenever the bully came near him.*

crit•ic (krĭt′ĭk) n. **1.** A person who forms and expresses judgments of the good and bad qualities of anything. **2.** A person whose job is judging and reporting on the worth of something intended as an artistic work or on its performance: *a book critic; a music critic.* **3.** A person who finds fault.

cru•cial (krōo′shəl) adj. Of the utmost importance; decisive: *a crucial decision.* —**cru′cial•ly** adv.

ă pat / ā pay / â care / ä father / ĕ pet / ē be / ĭ pit / ī pie / î fierce / ŏ pot / ō go / ô paw, for / oi oil / ŏo book /
ōo boot / ou out / ŭ cut / û fur / *th* the / th thin / hw which / zh vision / ə ago, item, pencil, atom, circus

crypt (krĭpt) *n.* An underground vault or chamber, especially one that is used as a tomb beneath a church.

cue[1] (kyōō) *n.* A word or signal given to remind an actor or singer to speak, sing, or move in a prescribed way during a performance.

cue[2] (kyōō) *n.* A long, tapered stick used to strike a ball in billiards and pool.

cul·mi·nate (kŭl′mə nāt′) *v.* **cul·mi·nat·ed, cul·mi·nat·ing.** To reach the highest point or degree; climax: *A series of demonstrations yesterday culminated in open rebellion.* —**cul′mi·na′tion** *n.*

cul·tur·al (kŭl′chər əl) *adj.* Of culture: *Paris is the cultural center of Europe.* —**cul′tur·al·ly** *adv.*

cul·ture (kŭl′chər) *n.* Intellectual and artistic activity and the works produced by this: *Our libraries and museums bring culture to the people.*

cu·mu·la·tive (kyōō′myə lā′tĭv) *or* (-lə-tĭv) *adj.* Increasing or growing steadily or in stages. —**cu′mu·la′tive·ly** *adv.* —**cu′mu·la′tive·ness** *n.*

cun·ning (kŭn′ĭng) *adj.* **1.** Sly; crafty; clever: *a cunning scheme. The weasel is a small but cunning animal.* **2.** *Informal.* Charming; cute: *a cunning little child.* —*n.* Slyness; craftiness: *The fox is an animal of great cunning.* —**cun′ning·ly** *adv.*

cur·ren·cy (kûr′ən sē) *or* (kŭr′-) *n., pl.* **cur·ren·cies.** Any form of money in actual use in a country: *Switzerland's currency is one of the most dependable in the world.*

cus·toms (kŭs′təmz) *n.* (*used with a singular verb*). The inspection of goods and baggage entering a country.

da·is (dā′ĭs) *or* (dās) *n.* A raised platform for a throne, a speaker, or a group of honored guests.

dash·board (dăsh′bôrd′) *or* (-bōrd′) *n.* **1.** The panel beneath the windshield in an automobile, containing instruments, dials, and controls. **2.** A screen of wood or leather on the front part of a horse-drawn vehicle to block water, mud, or snow splashed up by the feet of the horse.

dead·pan (dĕd′păn′) *adj. Informal.* Characterized by a blank face that betrays no emotion or amusement: *the comedian's deadpan expression.*

de·bris, also **dé·bris** (də brē′) *or* (dā′brē′) *n.* The scattered remains of something broken, destroyed, or discarded; fragments; rubble.

de·cep·tion (dĭ sĕp′shən) *n.* **1.** The act of deceiving: *practice deception.* **2.** Something that deceives, as a trick or lie.

de·com·pos·ing (dē′kəm pōz′ĭng) *adj.* **1.** Separating or breaking down into component parts or basic elements. **2.** Decaying; rotting.

de·coy (dē′koi′) *or* (dĭ koi′) *n.* **1.** A model of a duck or other bird, used by hunters to attract wild birds or animals. **2.** A person who leads another into danger or a trap. —*v.* (dĭ koi′). To lure into danger or a trap.

de·cree (dĭ krē′) *n.* **1.** An authoritative order; a law; edict. **2.** The judgment of a court. —*v.* **de·creed, de·cree·ing.** To establish or decide by decree.

de·ject·ed (dĭ jĕk′tĭd) *adj.* Low in spirits; depressed: *The boy grew more and more melancholy and pale and dejected.* —**de·ject′ed·ly** *adv.*

del·e·gate (dĕl′ə gāt′) *or* (-gĭt) *n.* A person chosen to speak and act for another person or for a group; a representative; agent.

de·lin·e·ate (dĭ lĭn′ē āt′) *v.* **de·lin·e·at·ed, de·lin·e·at·ing.** **1.** To draw or trace the outline of: *delineate the state of California on a map.* **2.** To describe in detail: *delineate the numerous accomplishments of the organization.* —**de·lin′e·a′tion** *n.*

de·lir·i·ous·ly (dĭ lîr′ē əs lē) *adv.* In a mentally confused or excited way.

de·pos·it (dĭ pŏz′ĭt) *n.* Mineral or sandy material left by moving water.

de·pot (dē′pō) *n.* **1.** A railroad or bus station. **2.** A warehouse or storehouse.

dep·re·cat·ing·ly (dĕp′rĭ kāt′ĭng lē) *adv.* **1.** Disapprovingly. **2.** In a belittling way.

de·pres·sion (dĭ prĕsh′ən) *n.* **1.** A mental state of gloom, sadness, or melancholy. **2.** An area that is sunk below its surroundings; a hollow. **3.** A period of drastic decline in economic activity, marked by widespread unemployment and hardship. **4.** The act of pressing down.

de·pres·sive (dĭ **prĕs′ĭv**) *adj.* In or characterized by a mental state of gloom, sadness, or melancholy.

de·pres·sur·ize (dē **prĕsh′ə** rīz′) *v.* **de·pres·sur·ized, de·pres·sur·iz·ing.** To decrease or take away the normal atmospheric pressure that has been maintained in a compartment (as in an aircraft).

dep·ri·va·tion (dĕp′rə **vā′shən**) *n.* The condition of being kept from the possession or enjoyment of something: *cultural deprivation.*

des·o·late (dĕs′ə lĭt) *adj.* **1.** Having little or no vegetation; barren. **2.** Having few or no inhabitants; deserted: *a desolate wilderness.* **3.** Lonely and sad; wretched; forlorn: *a child with a desolate air.* *—v.* (dĕs′ə lāt′) **des·o·lat·ed, des·o·lat·ing. 1.** To make desolate, especially to lay waste to: *A fire desolated the forest.* **2.** To make lonely, wretched, etc. **—des′o·late·ly** *adv.*

det·o·nate (dĕt′n āt′) *v.* **det·o·nat·ed, det·o·nat·ing.** To explode or cause to explode: *detonate bombs.* **—det′o·na′tion** *n.*

de·trac·tor (dĭ **trăk′tər**) *n.* Someone who says uncomplimentary things about, belittles, or slanders another.

de·void (dĭ **void′**) *adj.* **—devoid of.** Completely lacking; without.

dex·ter·i·ty (dĕk **stĕr′ĭ** tē) *n.* **1.** Skill in the use of the hands or body. **2.** Mental skill or adroitness; cleverness.

di·a·dem (dī′ə **dĕm′**) *n.* A crown or ornamental band worn on the head as a sign of royalty.

di·am·e·ter (dī **ăm′ĭ** tər) *n.* **1.** A straight line segment that passes through the center of a circle or sphere with both of its ends on the boundary. **2.** The measure of such a line segment.

differential (gear). An arrangement of gears that allows one turning shaft to drive two other shafts at any two differ-

ent speeds as long as the sum of the speeds of the driven shafts is constant.

di·lat·ed (dī **lā′tĭd**) *or* (dĭ-) *or* (**dī′lā′tĭd**) *adj.* Made wider or larger.

din·gy (dĭn′jē) *adj.* **din·gi·er, din·gi·est.** Drab: *a dingy room.* **—din′gi·ly** *adv.* **—din′gi·ness** *n.*

dis·band (dĭs **bănd′**) *v.* To break up and separate: *disband an orchestra.*

dis·cern (dĭ **sûrn′**) *or* (-**zûrn′**) *v.* **1.** To detect or make out (something that is not clear or easily recognizable to the eye or mind): *We could discern only a heap of rocks.* **2.** To make out the distinctions of or differences between; distinguish: *discern fact from rumor.*

dis·co·theque (dĭs′kə **tĕk′**) *or* (dĭs′kə **tĕk′**) *n.* A nightclub that offers dancing to amplified recorded music.

dis·gorge (dĭs **gôrj′**) *v.* **dis·gorged, dis·gorg·ing. 1.** To bring up and discharge from the throat or stomach; vomit. **2.** To pour forth or throw up.

dis·in·te·grate (dĭs **ĭn′tĭ** grāt′) *v.* **dis·in·te·grat·ed, dis·in·te·grat·ing.** To break or cause to break into separate pieces.

dis·lodg·ment (dĭs **lŏj′mənt**) *n.* The condition of being moved or forced out of position.

dis·man·tle (dĭs **măn′tl**) *v.* **dis·man·tled, dis·man·tling.** To take apart: *dismantle a piano.*

dis·patch·er (dĭ **spăch′ər**) *n.* A person who is employed to control the departure and movements of trains, taxicabs, or delivery trucks or to route telegraph communications: *a radio dispatcher.*

dis·pel (dĭ **spĕl′**) *v.* **dis·pelled, dis·pel·ling.** To make disappear by or as if by scattering; drive away: *This explanation should dispel their doubts.*

dis·pen·sa·ry (dĭ **spĕn′sə** rē) *n., pl.* **dis·pen·sa·ries. 1.** An office in a hospital, school, or other institution where medicines and medical supplies are given out. **2.** A public institution that provides medical treatment and medicines; a clinic.

ă pat / ā pay / â care / ä father / ĕ pet / ē be / ĭ pit / ī pie / î fierce / ŏ pot / ō go / ô paw, for / oi oil / ŏŏ book /
ōō boot / ou out / ŭ cut / û fur / *th* the / th thin / hw which / zh vision / ə ago, item, pencil, atom, circus

dis·rep·u·ta·ble (dĭs rĕp′yə tə bəl) *adj.*
1. Not having a good reputation: *a disreputable place of business.* **2.** Not respectable in appearance or character: *His manner of dress was casual to the point of being disreputable.* —**dis·rep′u·ta·ble·ness** *n.* —**dis·rep′u·ta·bly** *adv.*

di·ver·gent (dĭ vûr′jənt) *or* (dī-) *adj.*
1. Drawing apart from a common point; diverging. **2.** Differing: *widely divergent views on the subject.* —**di·ver′gent·ly** *adv.*

di·vine (dĭ vīn′) *adj.* Of, from, or like God or a god: *divine love. "To err is human, to forgive divine."* —**di·vine′ly** *adv.*

doc·u·ment·ing (dŏk′yə mĕnt′ĭng) *adj.* Providing proof or supporting with evidence: *documenting report.*

dog·ged (dô′gĭd) *or* (dŏg′ĭd) *adj.* Not giving up easily; willful; stubborn: *dogged efforts to qualify for the swim team.* —**dog′ged·ly** *adv.* —**dog′ged·ness** *n.*

do·gie (dō′gē) *n.* In the western United States, a motherless or stray calf.

dom·i·nance (dŏm′ə nəns) *n.* The condition or fact of having the most influence or control.

dom·i·nate (dŏm′ə nāt′) *v.* **dom·i·nat·ed, dom·i·nat·ing. 1.** To control, govern, or rule by superior power or strength; be dominant in position or authority: *No country can dominate the world.* **2.** To occupy the most prominent position in or over: *Wheat fields dominate the landscape of the region.* —**dom′i·na′tion** *n.*

douse (dous) *v.* **doused, dous·ing. 1.** To plunge into liquid; immerse: *douse the shirts in clean water.* **2.** To make thoroughly wet; drench: *They doused their friends with a garden hose.*

dram (drăm) *n.* **1.** A unit of weight equal to 0.0625 ounce. **2.** A unit of apothecary weight equal to 60 grains.

dras·tic (drăs′tĭk) *adj.* Violently effective; extreme or severe: *drastic measures to curb inflation.* —**dras′ti·cal·ly** *adv.*

draw (drô) *n.* **1.** An act of drawing. **2.** An advantage; edge. **3.** A contest ending in a tie. **4.** A natural drainage basin; gully.

dread (drĕd) *n.* A great fear, as of something about to happen: *They lived in dread of attack.* —*v.* To be in terror of; fear greatly. —*adj.* Inspiring great fear: *the dread sharks.* —**dread′ed** *adj.*: *a dreaded disease.*

dy·nam·ic (dī năm′ĭk) *or* **dy·nam·i·cal** (dī năm′ĭ kəl) *adj.* Energetic; vigorous: *a dynamic President.* —**dy·nam′i·cal·ly** *adv.*

dys·en·ter·y (dĭs′ən tĕr′ē) *n.* An infection of the lower intestines that produces pain, fever, and severe diarrhea.

eb·on·y (ĕb′ə nē) *n., pl.* **eb·on·ies.** The hard black or blackish wood of a tropical tree, used especially for piano keys. —*modifier: an ebony cabinet.* —*adj.* Black: *ebony hair.*

ee·rie, also **ee·ry** (îr′ē) *adj.* **ee·ri·er, ee·ri·est. 1.** Inspiring fear without being openly threatening; strangely unsettling; weird: *The entire countryside was bathed in an eerie crimson light.* **2.** Supernatural in aspect or character; mysterious.

e·lat·ed (ĭ lā′tĭd) *adj.* Made happy or joyful.

e·lec·tri·fi·ca·tion (ĭ lĕk′trə fĭ kā′shən) *n.* The wiring or equipping (of a room or building) for electric power.

e·lude (ĭ lood′) *v.* **e·lud·ed, e·lud·ing. 1.** To slip away from; evade: *The answer eludes me.* **2.** To escape understanding or detection by.

em·a·nate (ĕm′ə nāt′) *v.* **em·a·nat·ed, em·a·nat·ing.** To come or send forth, as from a source or origin; issue or emit: *Sweet sounds emanated from a hidden cove.*

em·bank·ment (ĕm băngk′mənt) *n.* A mound of earth or stone built up to hold back water or to support a roadway.

em·bry·o (ĕm′brē ō′) *n., pl.* **em·bry·os.** An organism in its earliest stages of growth.

em·u·late (ĕm′yə lāt′) *v.* **em·u·lat·ed, em·u·lat·ing.** To strive to equal or excel, especially through imitation. —**em′u·la′tion** *n.*

en·a·ble (ĕn ā′bəl) *v.* **en·a·bled, en·a·bling.** To give the means, ability, or opportunity to do something: *Science has enabled humanity to probe the secrets of the universe.*

en·dur·ance (ĕn doŏr′əns) *or* (-dyoŏr′-) *n.*
The ability to withstand strain, stress,
hardship, use, etc.: *Climbing that mountain is a real test of a person's endurance.*

en·dure (ĕn doŏr′) *or* (-dyoŏr′) *v.*
en·dured, en·dur·ing. **1.** To undergo;
bear up under: *The early settlers of America endured great hardships.* **2.** To continue to exist; last: *Her name will endure
forever.* **3.** To bear with tolerance; put up
with: *I can no longer endure your
rudeness.*

en·fold (ĕn fōld′) *v.* **1.** To surround with a
covering: *enfold a pillow in a pillowcase.*
2. To embrace: *He enfolded her in his
arms.*

en·roll (ĕn rōl′) *v.* To sign up; register;
enter; enlist: *enroll people in the army.*

en·train (ĕn trān′) *v.* To board or put on
board a train.

en·trust (ĕn trŭst′) *v.* **1.** To turn over
(something) for safekeeping, care, or
action: *entrust a sale to a broker.* **2.** To
charge (someone) with a task or responsibility involving trust: *entrust someone
with a difficult assignment.*

ep·ic (ĕp′ĭk) *n.* A long poem or literary
work about heroic characters who perform outstanding deeds. —*adj.* **1.** Of or
resembling an epic: *an epic poem.* **2.** Like
something described in an epic; tremendous: *an epic achievement.*

ep·och (ĕp′ək) *n.* **1.** A unit of geologic time
that is a division of a period. **2.** A particular period in history marked by certain
important events or developments; an
era: *the epoch of space exploration.*

e·qui·lat·e·ral (ē′kwə lăt′ər əl) *adj.* Having all sides equal, as a geometric figure.
—**e′qui·lat′er·al·ly** *adv.*

es·cort (ĕs′kôrt′) *n.* **1.** One or more persons
accompanying another to give protection
or guidance or to pay honor. **2.** One or
more planes, ships, etc., accompanying
another or others to provide protection.
—*v.* (ĭ skôrt′). To accompany as an escort: *Police escorted the President.*

es·sence (ĕs′əns) *n.* The quality or qualities
of a thing that give it its identity: *The
essence of democracy is faith in the people.*

etch (ĕch) *v.* **1.** To eat away (metal, glass,
etc.) with or as if with acid. **2.** To make (a
shape or pattern) on metal by dissolving
parts of it with acid. **3.** To practice the art
of etching.

e·ter·nal (ĭ tûr′nəl) *adj.* Unaffected by
time; lasting; timeless: *Rome, the Eternal
City.* —**e·ter′nal·ly** adv.

et·i·quette (ĕt′ə kĕt′, -kĭt) *n.* The body of
prescribed social behavior.

ex·act·i·tude (ĭg zăk′tĭ toŏd′) *or* (-tyoŏd′)
n. The condition or quality of being
exact.

ex·ca·vate (ĕks′kə vāt′) *v.* **ex·ca·vat·ed,
ex·ca·vat·ing.** **1.** To dig or dig out; hollow out: *The workers excavated the
swimming pool. Archeologists excavate
for many years trying to find ruins.* **2.** To
uncover by digging; expose to view: *They
excavated the ruins of Pompeii out of lava
under which it had been buried.*

ex·e·cu·tion·er (ĕk′sĭ kyoŏ′shə nər) *n.*
Someone who executes a condemned
person.

ex·empt (ĭg zĕmpt′) *adj.* Freed from a
duty or obligation required of others;
excused: *exempt from criticism.*

ex·hi·bi·tion (ĕk′sə bĭsh′ən) *n.* A display
for the public, as of art works, industrial
products, etc.: *a museum exhibition.*

ex·hil·a·rate (ĭg zĭl′ə rāt′) *v.* **ex·hil·a·
rat·ed, ex·hil·a·rat·ing.** **1.** To make
very happy; elate: *Challenges can both
exhilarate and frighten us.* **2.** To refresh;
invigorate: *Cold northern air exhilarates
us.* —**ex·hil′a·ra′tion** *n.*

ex·ploit (ĕk′sploit′) *n.* An act or deed, especially a brilliant or heroic feat. —*v.*
(ĭk sploit′). **1.** To make the greatest
possible use of; turn to advantage: *exploit the
nation's timber resources; exploit an idea.*
2. To make use of selfishly or unethically.

ex·ploi·ta·tion (ĕk′sploi tā′shən) *n.*
1. The act of exploiting: *the exploitation of*

ă pat / ā pay / â care / ä father / ĕ pet / ē be / ĭ pit / ī pie / î fierce / ŏ pot / ō go / ô paw, for / oi oil / oŏ book /
oō boot / ou out / ŭ cut / û fur / *th* the / th thin / hw which / zh vision / ə ago, item, pencil, atom, circus

our oil reserves. **2.** The use of another person for selfish purposes: *the exploitation of free labor.*

ex·qui·site (ĕk′skwĭz ĭt) *or* (ĭk skwĭz′ĭt) *adj.* Of special beauty, charm, elegance, etc.: *an exquisite vase.* **—ex′qui·site·ly** *adv.*

ex·tro·vert (ĕk′strə vûrt′) *n.* A person whose interest tends to center on other people and things rather than on his or her own inner thoughts and feelings.

ex·u·ber·ance (ĭg zoo′bər əns) *n.* **1.** The condition or quality of being lively and joyous. **2.** An overflow; lavishness.

fac·et (făs′ĭt) *n.* **1.** One of the flat, polished surfaces cut on a gem to catch the light. **2.** A separate side or aspect of anything: *the many facets of a problem.*

fal·ter (fôl′tər) *v.* **1.** To perform haltingly; lose strength or momentum: *The engine faltered.* **2.** To speak hesitatingly; stammer. **3.** To waver in purpose or action; hesitate.

fam·ine (făm′ĭn) *n.* A shortage of food that results in widespread hunger and starvation.

farce (färs) *n.* **1.** A comic play with a story and characters greatly exaggerated to cause laughter. **2.** Something that is ridiculous or laughable, especially something supposed to be serious.

fas·tid·i·ous·ly (fă stĭd′e əs lē) *adv.* In a manner that is careful in all details: *fastidiously wiped her fingers.* **—fas·tid′i·ous** *adj.* **—fas·tid′i·ous·ness** *n.*

fault (fôlt) *n.* In sports, a bad service, as in tennis. **—v.** To commit such a fault.

feat (fēt) *n.* An outstanding deed or accomplishment; an exploit: *The new bridge is a remarkable feat of engineering.*

fend (fĕnd) *v.* To defend oneself from; repel; resist: *He used an oar to fend off the sharks.*

fierce (fîrs) *adj.* **fierc·er, fierc·est. 1.** Wild and savage; ferocious: *a fierce beast; the fierce roar of the lion; a wild stallion with fierce eyes.* **2.** Extreme in degree; intense: *fierce loyalty.*

fi·nance (fĭ năns′) *or* (fī′năns′) *n.* **1.** The management and use of funds. **2.** fi-nances. Money resources; funds: *His finances were getting low.* **—modifier:** *finance charges.* **—v.** **fi·nanced, fi·nanc·ing.** To provide funds or capital for.

flail (flāl) *n.* A tool for threshing grain, consisting of a long wooden handle and a shorter, free-swinging stick attached to its end. **—v.** To thresh or beat with or as if with a flail.

flank (flăngk) *v.* To be placed or situated at the side of: *Two chairs flanked the couch.*

flare (flâr) *v.* **flared, flar·ing.** To burst out like a flame: *Tempers flared during the discussion.*

flay (flā) *v.* **1.** To strip off the skin of: *flay a deer.* **2.** To strike with force, as if to skin. **3.** To criticize or scold harshly.

fledg·ling, also **fledge·ling** (flĕj′lĭng) *n.* A young bird that has just grown its flying feathers and is learning to fly.

fleet[1] (flēt) *n.* **1. a.** A group of as many warships as are needed for a major operation, under the command of an admiral. **b.** The entire navy of a government. **2. a.** A large number of boats, ships, etc., operating as a more or less organized group: *a fishing fleet.* **b.** A large group of vehicles operating under one management: *a fleet of taxicabs.*

fleet[2] (flēt) *adj.* **fleet·er, fleet·est.** Moving or able to move swiftly; nimble: *a fleet animal.* **—v.** To move or pass swiftly: *clouds fleeting across the sky.* **—fleet′ly** *adv.* **—fleet′ness** *n.*

flex·i·ble (flĕk′sə bəl) *adj.* **1.** Capable of bending or being bent; supple; pliable. **2.** Capable of or responsive to change; adaptable; *flexible plans.* **—flex′i·bil′i·ty** *n.* **—flex′i·bly** *adv.*

flo·ra (flôr′ə) *or* (flōr′ə) *n.* The plants of a particular region or time period: *desert flora.*

flus·ter (flŭs′tər) *v.* To make nervous, excited, or confused: *The staring faces flustered her.*

fol·ly (fŏl′ē) *n., pl.* **fol·lies. 1.** Lack of good sense or judgment; foolishness. **2.** A piece of foolishness, as a silly idea, plan, or action.

for·ay (fôr′ā′) *or* (fŏr′ā′) *n.* **1.** A sudden raid, expedition, or invasion, as to fight someone. **2.** A first attempt or venture in

some field: *her opening foray into politics.*
—*v.* To make a raid, as for plunder.

fore‧bear (fôr′bâr′) *or* (fōr′-) *n.* A person from whom one is descended; ancestor.

fore‧stall (fôr stôl′) *or* (fōr-) *v.* To prevent, put off, or cut off by taking effective action in advance: *He tried to forestall any more questions.*

foul (foul) *adj.* **foul‧er, foul‧est.** **1.** Offensive to the taste, smell, etc.; rotten; putrid: *a foul flavor; a foul smell.* **2.** Dirty; filthy: *foul hairs of the stray dog.* **3.** Morally offensive; wicked: *foul deeds.*

frag‧ile (frăj′əl) *or* (-īl′) *adj.* Easily damaged or broken; brittle: *a fragile piece of crystal.* —**frag′ile‧ly** *adv.* —**fra‧gil′i‧ty** (frə jĭl′ĭ tē) *n.*

fraught (frôt) *adj.* Filled; laden; loaded: *Every moment is fraught with significance.*

fray¹ (frā) *n.* **1.** A fight; brawl; battle. **2.** A contest or dispute.

fray² (frā) *v.* To make or become ragged, worn, or raveled at the edge so that loose threads show.

free lance. A person, especially a writer, editor, artist, or musician, who does not work for one employer only but sells his or her services to several employers as those services are needed. —*modifier:* (**free-lance**): *a free-lance job.*

fren‧zy (frĕn′zē) *n., pl.* **fren‧zies.** Wild excitement or a display of emotion suggesting madness, often accompanied by vigorous or violent activity: *lemmings gone mad and dashing about in a blind frenzy.*

fri‧ar (frī′ər) *n.* A man who is a member of certain religious orders.

fric‧tion (frĭk′shən) *n.* **1.** The rubbing of one object or surface against another. **2.** A force that acts to resist or retard the relative motion of two objects that are in contact. **3.** A conflict or clash, as of persons having differing beliefs or personalities. —**fric′tion‧al** *adj.*

fru‧gal (frōō′gəl) *adj.* **1.** Thrifty in managing money; not wasteful: *a frugal person.* **2.** Costing little or not very plentiful.

frus‧trate (frŭs′trāt′) *v.* **frus‧trat‧ed, frus‧trat‧ing.** To prevent from accomplishing a purpose or goal.

fume (fyōōm) *v.* **fumed, fum‧ing.** **1.** To produce or give off fumes. **2.** To feel or show anger or agitation; seethe. —*n.* Any smoke, vapor, or gas, especially one that is irritating or that has an unpleasant odor.

fu‧ror (fyōōr′ôr′) *or* (-ōr′) *n.* A noisy outburst of anger, disapproval, enthusiasm, etc., as in a crowd; an uproar: *The mob reacted with furor.*

fu‧sil‧lade (fyōō′sə lād′) *or* (-läd′) *or* (-zə-) *n.* **1.** The discharge of many guns at the same time or in rapid succession. **2.** Any rapid outburst: *a fusillade of insults.*

fu‧tile (fyōōt′l) *or* (fyōō′tīl′) *adj.* Having no useful result; useless. —**fu′tile‧ly** *adv.*

gait (gāt) *n.* A way of walking or running. —*v.* **1.** To lead (a show animal) to demonstrate the way it carries itself and moves. **2.** To demonstrate proper carriage and movements while being so led.

gal‧le‧on (găl′ē ən) *or* (găl′yən) *n.* A large three-masted sailing ship of the type much used by Spain during the 16th century.

gal‧lows (găl′ōz) *n., pl.* **gal‧lows‧es** *or* **gal‧lows.** **1.** A framework with a suspended noose, used for execution by hanging. **2. the gallows.** Execution on a gallows or by hanging.

ga‧lore (gə lôr′) *or* (-lōr′) *adj. Informal.* In great numbers; in abundance: *bargains galore.*

game‧cock (gām′kŏk′) *n.* A rooster trained for fighting.

gan‧gren‧ous (găng′grə nəs) *adj.* Dead and decayed, as the tissue in a living body, due to injury, disease, or failure of the blood supply.

gar (gär) *n.* A freshwater fish with a long, narrow body, sharp teeth, and long, narrow jaws.

ă pat / ā pay / â care / ä father / ĕ pet / ē be / ĭ pit / ī pie / î fierce / ŏ pot / ō go / ô paw, for / oi oil / ŏŏ book /
ōō boot / ou out / ŭ cut / û fur / *th* the / th thin / hw which / zh vision / ə ago, item, pencil, atom, circus

garb (gärb) *n.* Clothing or way of dressing: *sailor's garb.* —*v.* To clothe or dress: *The judge was garbed in his robes.*

gas·e·ous (găs′ē əs) *or* (găs′yəs) *or* (găsh′əs) *adj.* Of, concerning, or existing as a gas: *The entire sun is in a gaseous state.*

gauge (gāj) *n.* **1.** A standard or scale of measurement. **2.** A standard dimension, size, etc.: **a.** The distance between two rails on a railroad. **b.** The size of the barrel of a shotgun. **c.** Thickness or diameter, as of sheet metal or wire.

gaunt (gônt) *adj.* **gaunt·er, gaunt·est. 1.** Thin and bony; haggard; emaciated: *a gaunt face.* **2.** Bleak and desolate; stark: *the gaunt, forbidding mountains enclosing the bleakness of Death Valley.* —**gaunt′ly** *adv.* —**gaunt′ness** *n.*

gaunt·ed (gôn′tĭd) *adj.* Having been made gaunt or having become gaunt.

gid·dy (gĭd′ē) *adj.* **gid·di·er, gid·di·est.** Having a lightheaded or whirling sensation; dizzy: *He was giddy with thirst.* —**gid′di·ly** *adv.* —**gid′di·ness** *n.*

gild (gĭld) *v.* **gild·ed** *or* **gilt** (gĭlt), **gild·ing.** To cover with a thin layer of gold: *gild the frame of a mirror.*

gill¹ (gĭl) *n.* **1.** The breathing organ by means of which fish and certain other water animals take oxygen from the water. **2.** One of the thin, closely crowded bladelike parts on the underside of a mushroom cap.

gill² (jĭl) *n.* A unit of volume or capacity used mainly for liquids. It is equal to 4 ounces or 7.216 cubic inches.

gilt (gĭlt) *adj.* Covered with a thin layer of gold, such as gold leaf or gold-colored paint, applied to the surface: *ornate gilt picture frame.*

gir·dle (gûr′dl) *n.* A belt, sash, or the like, worn at the waist.

glint (glĭnt) *n.* **1.** A brief flash of light; a sparkle: *a cold glint in her eyes.* **2.** A faint or brief indication; a trace: *a glint of rising hate.* —*v.* To gleam or flash; sparkle: *Vermilion Creek, glinting like quicksilver in the moonlight.*

gloat (glōt) *v.* To look on or consider with great pleasure or with selfish or spiteful satisfaction.

glock·en·spiel (glŏk′ən spēl′) *or* (-shpēl′) *n.* A musical instrument consisting of a series of metal bars tuned to the tones of the chromatic scale. It is played by being struck with two light hammers.

goad (gōd) *n.* A long stick with a pointed end used for prodding animals. —*v.* To prod with or as if with a goad.

grant (grănt) *or* (gränt) *v.* **1.** To give or allow (something asked for): *grant a request.* **2.** To confer or bestow (a right, privilege, etc.) by a formal act: *The Constitution grants certain powers to the Supreme Court.* **3.** To admit as true; acknowledge: *I'll grant that he looks a lot better now.* —*n.* **1.** The act of or an example of granting. **2.** Something granted: *His grant covers five acres.*

grate¹ (grāt) *v.* **grat·ed, grat·ing.** To make or cause to make a harsh grinding or rasping sound by rubbing: *He grated the two rocks together.*

grate² (grāt) *n.* A framework or network of parallel or interwoven bars or wires, used to block an opening or to separate things by straining them.

grav·i·ty (grăv′ĭ tē) *n.* **1.** The force that the earth or another celestial body exerts on any small mass close to its surface. **2.** Seriousness; importance: *It was then that the gravity of our deed fell upon us.*

great·coat (grāt′kōt′) *n.* A heavy overcoat.

grim·ace (grĭm′əs) *or* (grĭ mās′) *n.* A facial contortion expressive of pain, disgust, etc. —*v.* **grim·aced, grim·ac·ing.** To make a grimace.

grip (grĭp) *n.* **1.** A tight hold; a firm grasp: *a good grip on the steering wheel.* **2.** A manner or power of grasping. **3.** A part designed to be grasped and held; a handle. **4.** Control; power. —*v.* **gripped, grip·ping.** To grasp and maintain a hold on; seize firmly.

gru·el·ing (grōō′ə lĭng) *adj.* Exhausting.

gull·er·y (gŭl′er ē) *n.* A breeding place of gulls.

gul·ly (gŭl′ē) *n., pl.* **gul·lies.** A ditch or channel cut in the earth by running water, especially after a rain.

gum·bo (gŭm′bō) *n., pl.* **gum·bos.** A thick soup with okra and other vegetables and meat or seafood.

hack¹ (hăk) *v.* **1.** To cut with heavy and irregular blows; chop roughly with an ax, knife, etc.: *He hacked off a branch of the tree. They hacked their way through the jungle.* **2.** To cough roughly and harshly. **3.** To strike the arm of (an opponent), especially in basketball. —*n.* **1.** A rough, irregular cut or notch. **2.** A chopping blow. **3.** A rough cough. —**hack′er** *n.*

hack² (hăk) *n.* **1.** A horse or a horse and carriage for hire. **2.** A worn-out, over-worked horse. **3.** A person, especially a writer, who does routine work for hire. **4.** *Informal.* A taxicab. —*adj.* **1.** Done by or working as a hack: *hack work; a hack writer.* **2.** For a taxi or taxis: *a hack stand.*

hack·a·more (hăk′ə môr′) *or* (-mōr′) *n.* A halter with a wide band that can be low-ered over a horse's eyes, used in breaking horses to a bridle.

hal·loo (hə lōo′) *interj.* A word used to get someone's attention: *"Halloo!" she shouted.* —*n.* A shout or call of "halloo": *He gave such a halloo that everyone came running from the castle.* —*v.* **hal·looed, hal·loo·ing.** To shout "halloo."

har·assed (hăr′əst) *or* (hə răst′) *adj.* Bothered by repeated interruptions, at-tacks, etc.

har·row·ing (hăr′ō ĭng) *adj.* Distressing; agonizing: *a harrowing experience.*

hasp (hăsp) *or* (häsp) *n.* A hinged fastener that is passed over a staple and secured by a pin, bolt, or padlock.

haunch (hônch) *or* (hänch) *n.* **1.** The hip, buttock, and upper thigh of a person or animal: *The dog settled back on its haunches.* **2.** The loin and leg of an ani-mal as used for food.

haunt (hônt) *or* (hänt) *v.* **1.** To visit or inhabit in the form of a ghost or other supernatural being. **2.** To linger in the mind: *The thought has haunted me ever since.* **3.** To visit often; frequent. —**haunt′ing** *adj.: a haunting melody.* —*n.* A place that is visited often: *a favorite haunt of artists.*

haz·ard (hăz′ərd) *n.* **1.** A chance of being injured, lost, etc.; danger; risk: *Space travel is full of hazards.* **2.** Something or someone that is likely to cause harm; a possible source of danger: *a fire hazard.*

He·brew (hē′brōo) *n.* **1.** A member of the Semitic people claiming descent from Abraham, Isaac, and Jacob; an Israelite. **2. a.** The Semitic language of the ancient Hebrews, in which most of the Old Testa-ment is written. **b.** The modern form of this language, which is the language of Israel. —*adj.* Of the Hebrews or their language.

heist (hīst) *v.* **1.** *Slang.* To rob; steal. **2.** *Di-alect.* To hoist; lift. —*n.* *Slang.* A rob-bery; burglary.

hemp (hĕmp) *n.* A tall plant with stems that yield a tough fiber used for making rope, cord, etc.

her·i·tage (hĕr′ĭ tĭj) *n.* Something passed down from preceding generations; leg-acy; tradition: *Every country has its heri-tage of folk music.*

hi·er·o·glyph·ic (hī′ər ə glĭf′ĭk) *or* (hī′rə-) *or* **hi·er·o·glyph·i·cal** (hī′ər ə-glĭf′ĭ kəl) *or* (hī′rə-) *adj.* Of or written in a system of writing, especially that used in ancient Egypt, in which pictures or symbols are used to represent words or sounds. —*n.* **1.** A picture or symbol used in hieroglyphic writing. **2. hieroglyphics.** Hieroglyphic writing.

hogs·head (hôgz′hĕd′) *or* (hŏgz′-) *n.* **1.** A large barrel or cask, especially one that holds from 62 to 140 gallons. **2.** Any one of several measures of liquid volume or capacity ranging from 62.5 gallons to 140 gallons, especially one equal to 63 gallons.

hoop·la (hōop′lä′) *or* (hōop′-) *n.* *Slang.* Noisy or confusing commotion or pub-licity: *hoopla of a convention.*

hust·ler (hŭs′lər) *n.* **1.** One who is active and energetic. **2.** *Informal.* One who ob-tains business, money, etc., by energetic activity; one who works busily and quickly.

ă pat / ā pay / â care / ä father / ĕ pet / ē be / ĭ pit / ī pie / î fierce / ŏ pot / ō go / ô paw, for / oi oil / ŏŏ book / ōō boot / ou out / ŭ cut / û fur / *th* the / th thin / hw which / zh vision / ə ago, item, pencil, atom, circus

hys·te·ri·a (hĭ stĕr′ē ə) *or* (-stîr′-) *n.* An extreme, uncontrollable fear or other strong emotion.

i·de·al·ism (ī dē′ə lĭz′əm) *n.* The practice of seeing or representing things as being in perfect form rather than as they usually exist in real life. —**i·de′al·ist** *n.*

i·den·ti·ty (ī dĕn′tĭ tē) *n., pl.* **i·den·ti·ties.** The condition of being a certain person or thing and definitely recognizable as such.

id·i·o·cy (ĭd′ē ə sē) *n., pl.* **id·i·o·cies. 1.** A condition of extreme mental retardation. **2.** Foolish behavior.

ig·no·ra·mus (ĭg′nə rā′məs) *or* (-răm′əs) *n., pl.* **ig·no·ra·mus·es.** An ignorant person.

im·pact (ĭm′păkt′) *n.* **1.** The action of one body striking against another; collision. **2.** The effect of something on the feelings or mind of the reader, spectator, etc.: *emotional impact.*

im·par·tial (ĭm pär′shəl) *adj.* Not favoring either side; unprejudiced: *an impartial witness.* —**im·par·ti·al′i·ty** (ĭm′pär-shē ăl′ĭ tē) *n.* —**im·par′tial·ly** *adv.*

im·pass·a·ble (ĭm păs′ə bəl) *adj.* Impossible to travel across or over: *a deep, impassable gorge.* —**im·pass′a·bil′i·ty** *n.* —**im·pass′a·bly** *adv.*

im·per·cep·ti·bly (ĭm′pər sĕp′tə blē) *adv.* In a way that is not capable of being perceived by the senses or the mind; very slightly.

im·ple·ment (ĭm′plə mənt) *n.* A tool, utensil, or instrument used in doing a task: *farm implements.* —*v.* (ĭm′plə-mĕnt′). To put into effect; carry out: *techniques and material for implementing an idea.* —**im′ple·men·ta′tion** *n.*

in·can·ta·tion (ĭn′kăn tā′shən) *n.* **1.** A formula of words or sounds recited or chanted to produce a magical effect. **2.** The act of reciting or chanting such a formula.

in·com·pat·i·ble (ĭn′kəm păt′ə bəl) *adj.* **1.** Not compatible; not in harmony or agreement: *incompatible colors.* **2.** Not capable of living or working together happily or smoothly: *incompatible roommates.* —**in′com·pat′i·bil′i·ty** *n.*

in·cor·po·ra·tion (ĭn kôr′pə rā′shən) *n.* **1.** The forming of a legal corporation. **2.** A combining or blending into a unified whole; the process of uniting.

in·cor·ri·gi·ble (ĭn kôr′ĭ jə bəl) *or* (-kŏr′-) *adj.* Not capable of being corrected or reformed. —*n.* A person who cannot be reformed. —**in·cor′ri·gi·bil′i·ty** *n.* —**in·cor′ri·gi·bly** *adv.*

in·cre·du·li·ty (ĭn′krĭ dōō′lĭ tē) *or* (-dyōō′-) Disbelief or astonishment.

in·cu·bate (ĭn′kyə bāt′) *or* (ĭng′-) *v.* **in·cu·bat·ed, in·cu·bat·ing. 1.** To warm and hatch (eggs), as by the heat of a parent bird's body or an artificial source of heat. **2.** To develop; grow. —**in′cu·ba′tion** *n.*

in·dus·tri·al·ist (ĭn dŭs′trē ə lĭst) *n.* A person who owns or runs a large industrial enterprise.

in·ef·fi·cient (ĭn′ĭ fĭsh′ənt) *adj.* Wasteful of time, effort, materials, fuel, or energy: *an inefficient clerk; an inefficient machine.* —**in′ef·fi′cient·ly** *adv.*

in·ept (ĭn ĕpt′) *adj.* **1.** Lacking skill or competence: *an inept actor.* **2.** Inappropriate: *an inept suggestion.* —**in·ept′ly** *adv.*

in·eq·ui·ty (ĭn ĕk′wə tē) *n., pl.* **in·eq·ui·ties. 1.** Lack of justice; unfairness. **2.** An instance of unfairness or injustice.

in·gen·ious (ĭn jēn′yəs) *adj.* **1.** Clever at devising things; creative: *an ingenious inventor.* **2.** Showing originality and resourcefulness: *an ingenious idea.* —**in·gen′ious·ly** *adv.*

in·grate (ĭn′grāt′) *n.* An ungrateful person.

in·junc·tion (ĭn jŭngk′shən) *n.* **1.** An order or command. **2.** A court order prohibiting or requiring a specific course of action.

in·jus·tice (ĭn jŭs′tĭs) *n.* **1.** Lack of justice; unfairness. **2.** A specific unjust act; a wrong.

in·su·late (ĭn′sə lāt′) *or* (ĭns′yə-) *v.* **in·su·lat·ed, in·su·lat·ing.** To prevent the passage of heat, electricity, or sound into or out of, especially by surrounding or lining with something that blocks such a flow. —**in′su·lat′ing** *adj.*: *fiber glass insulating material.*

in·tact (ĭn tăkt′) *adj.* Not impaired, injured, or damaged.

in·ter·mi·na·ble (ĭn tûr′mə nə bəl) *adj.* Having or seeming to have no end; endless: *a seemingly interminable ball game.* —**in·ter′mi·na·bly** *adv.*

in·ter·mit·tent·ly (ĭn′tər mĭt′nt lē) *adv.* Not continuously.

in·tern (ĭn′tûrn′) *n.* A recent graduate of a medical school who is undergoing supervised practical training. —*v.* **1.** (ĭn′tûrn′). To train or serve as an intern. **2.** (ĭn tûrn′). To detain or confine, especially in wartime: *intern a ship.* —**in·tern′ment** *n.*

in·ter·pret·er (ĭn tûr′prĭ tər) *n.* **1.** A person who orally translates a conversation or speech from one language to another. **2.** A person who explains or expounds on a certain subject.

in·tim·i·date (ĭn tĭm′ĭ dāt′) *v.* **in·tim·i·dat·ed, in·tim·i·dat·ing.** To frighten or restrain by or as if by threats: *The advancing forces did not intimidate the Romans.* —**in·tim′i·da′tion** *n.*

in·tone (ĭn tōn′) *v.* **in·toned, in·ton·ing.** *v.* **1.** To recite in a singing voice. **2.** To utter in a monotone. —**in·ton′er** *n.*

in·trep·id (ĭn trĕp′ĭd) *adj.* Brave, bold, and fearless; showing courage: *the intrepid pioneers.* —**in′tre·pid′i·ty** *n.* —**in·trep′id·ly** *adv.*

in·tri·cate·ly (ĭn′trĭ kĭt lē) *adv.* In a way that is complicated in structure, pattern, etc.: *an intricately-made bracelet.*

in·trigue (ĭn trēg′) *v.* **in·trigued, in·tri·guing.** **1.** To catch the interest or arouse the curiosity of; fascinate: *The mystery of hibernation has long intrigued biologists.* **2.** To plot or scheme secretly: *rivals intriguing against one another.* —**in·tri′guing** *adj.: an intriguing puzzle.* —*n.* (ĭn′trēg′) *or* (ĭn trēg′). **1. a.** Plotting or scheming carried on in secret. **b.** A secret plot or scheme. **2.** A secret love affair.

in·tu·i·tion (ĭn′tōō ĭsh′ən) *or* (-tyōō-) *n.* **1.** The power of knowing or understanding something instantly, by instinct, without having to reason it out or to get proof. **2.** A perception based on insight or instinct.

in·val·u·a·ble (ĭn văl′yōō ə bəl) *adj.* Of a value greater than can be measured; very valuable: *invaluable art treasures; his invaluable help.* —**in·val′u·a·bly** *adv.*

in·ven·to·ry (ĭn′vən tôr′ē) *or* (-tōr′ē) *n., pl.* **in·ven·to·ries.** **1.** A detailed list, as of goods or possessions. **2.** The process of making such a survey or list. **3.** The supply of goods on hand; stock. —*v.* **in·ven·to·ried, in·ven·to·ry·ing, in·ven·to·ries.** To make an inventory of.

in·vul·ner·a·ble (ĭn vŭl′nər ə bəl) *adj.* Not capable of being hurt, wounded, attacked, etc.: *an invulnerable warrior; an invulnerable fort.* —**in·vul′ner·a·bil′i·ty** *n.* —**in·vul′ner·a·bly** *adv.*

is·sue (ĭsh′ōō) *v.* To come out; flow out: *Water issued from the broken pipe.*

jae·ger (yā′gər) *or* (jā′gər) *n.* Any of several sea birds that snatch food from other birds.

jaun·diced (jôn′dĭst) *or* (jän′-) *adj.* **1.** Affected with jaundice. **2.** Showing or feeling jealousy, envy, etc.; prejudiced.

jaun·ty (jôn′tē) *or* (jän′-) *adj.* **jaun·ti·er, jaun·ti·est.** Having a carefree, self-confident air: *a jaunty gait.* —**jaun′ti·ly** *adv.*

jos·tle (jŏs′əl) *v.* **jos·tled, jos·tling.** To bump, shove, push, or brush against in passing or in a crowd.

joust·ing (joust′ĭng) *or* (jŭst′ĭng) *or* (jōōst′ĭng) *adj.* Used in a combat between two knights on horseback armed with lances and wearing armor.

knave (nāv) *n.* **1.** A dishonest, crafty man: *He played the knave in our business dealings.* **2.** *Archaic.* A male servant: *a lowly kitchen knave.* **3.** A playing card, the jack.

knoll (nōl) *n.* A small, rounded hill; a hillock.

ă pat / ā pay / â care / ä father / ĕ pet / ē be / ĭ pit / ī pie / î fierce / ŏ pot / ō go / ô paw, for / oi oil / ŏŏ book /
ōō boot / ou out / ŭ cut / û fur / *th* the / th thin / hw which / zh vision / ə ago, item, pencil, atom, circus

lan·guor·ous·ly (lăng'gər əs lē) *adv.* In a manner that is listless or lazy.

lap·is laz·u·li (lăp'ĭs lăz'yo͝o lē) *or* (-lăzh'o͝o-) *n.* An opaque, deep-blue mineral that is used as a gemstone.

legal tender. Currency, or money, in certain denominations or amounts that may legally be offered and must be accepted in payment of a debt.

leg·gings (lĕg'ĭngz) *n.* A leg covering of cloth or leather, usually extending from the waist or knee to the ankle.

lem·ming (lĕm'ĭng) *n.* A short-tailed animal of northern regions, related to the rats and mice.

le·thal (lē'thəl) *adj.* Causing or capable of causing death: *a lethal weapon.* —**le'thal·ly** *adv.*

lev·er·age (lĕv'ər ĭj) *or* (lē'vər-) *n.* **1.** The action or mechanical advantage of a lever. **2.** Power to act effectively.

li·chen (lī'kən) *n.* A plant consisting of a fungus and an alga growing in close combination and forming a crustlike, scaly, or branching growth on rocks and tree trunks.

lin·e·age (lĭn'ē ĭj) *n.* **1.** Direct descent from a particular ancestor; ancestry. **2.** All of the descendants of a particular ancestor.

lock·et (lŏk'ĭt) *n.* A small, ornamental metal case for a picture, lock of hair, or other keepsake, usually worn on a chain around the neck.

lode·stone (lōd'stōn') *n.* A magnetized piece of magnetite.

loi·ter (loi'tər) *v.* **1.** To stand about idly; linger. **2.** To go slowly, stopping often. —**loi'ter·er** *n.*

loll (lŏl) *v.* **1.** To move, stand, sit, or rest in a lazy way: *lolling about in dungarees at home.* **2.** To hang or let hang loosely or laxly: *The hunted wolf's quivering tongue lolled.*

long·spur (lông'spûr) *or* (lŏng'-) *n.* Any of several birds of northern regions, having brownish feathers and long-clawed hind toes.

lore (lôr) *or* (lōr) *n.* **1.** Accumulated fact, tradition, or belief: *sea lore.* **2.** Knowledge gained by experience, tradition, or study.

lor·ry (lôr'ē) *or* (lŏr'ē) *n., pl.* **lor·ries.** *British.* A motor truck.

loupe (lo͞op) *n.* A small magnifying glass usually set in an eyepiece and used by jewelers and watchmakers.

low·er·ing (lō'ər ĭng) *adj.* Moving down to a lower level: *the lowering sun.*

lu·mi·nous (lo͞o'mə nəs) *adj.* Giving off light, especially self-generated rather than reflected light; shining: *a luminous sign; luminous eyes.*

lus·trous (lŭs'trəs) *adj.* Having a gloss or sheen; gleaming: *lustrous Oriental silk.* —**lus'trous·ly** *adv.* —**lus'trous·ness** *n.*

mack·i·naw (măk'ə nô') *n.* A short coat of heavy woolen material, usually plaid.

mael·strom (māl'strəm) *n.* **1.** A large and violent whirlpool. **2.** A situation that resembles such a whirlpool in violence, turbulence, etc.: *caught in the maelstrom of war.*

mag·ne·to (măg nē'tō) *n., pl.* **mag·ne·tos.** A small alternator that works by means of permanent magnets, used to generate the electricity for the spark in some engines.

mag·ni·tude (măg'ni to͞od') *or* (-tyo͞od') *n.* Greatness, as of position, size, influence, etc.: *the magnitude of one's achievements.*

maim·ing (mām'ĭng) *n.* An instance of disabling, usually by depriving of the use of a limb; a crippling act.

main·mast (mān'məst) *n.* The principal mast of a sailing ship.

man·ger (mān'jər) *n.* A trough or open box in which feed for horses or cattle is placed.

ma·ni·a (mā'nē ə) *or* (mān'yə) *n.* **1.** A form of mental disturbance associated with psychosis, in which a patient becomes excessively active and gay and experiences a rapid stream of changing ideas. **2.** An intense desire or enthusiasm for something; craze: *He has a mania for stamp collecting.*

man·tle (măn'tl) *n.* *Ornithology.* The wings, shoulder feathers, and back of a bird, when differently colored from the rest of the body: *the pearl-gray mantle of the herring gull.*

mar·i·time (măr′ĭ tīm′) *adj.* **1.** Located on or near the sea: *a maritime province.* **2.** Of shipping or navigation: *maritime law.*

ma·ter·nal (mə tûr′nəl) *adj.* **1.** Of a mother or motherhood: *a maternal instinct.* **2.** Inherited from one's mother: *a maternal trait.* **3.** Related to through one's mother. —**ma·ter′nal·ly** *adv.*

maul (môl) *n.* A heavy hammer with a long handle, used to drive stakes, piles, or wedges.

med·i·ta·tion (měd′ĭ tā′shən) *n.* The process of thinking deeply and quietly: *sat by his window, lost in meditation.*

mem·brane (měm′brān′) *n.* A thin, flexible layer of tissue that covers surfaces or acts as the boundary between adjoining regions, structures, or organs in the body of an animal or plant.

Mer·cu·ry (mûr′kyə rē). The Roman god who served as messenger to the other gods and presided over the realms of commerce, travel, and thievery.

met·al·lur·gist (mĕt′l ûr′jĭst) *n.* A person who specializes in the science and technology of extracting metals from their ores and making useful objects from the metals.

mete (mēt) *v.* **met·ed, met·ing.** To give a proper share of; distribute; allot: *Zeus meted out rewards for the mighty deeds of heroes.*

me·te·or·oid (mē′tē ə roid′) *n.* Any of a large number of celestial bodies, ranging in size from specks of dust to bodies weighing thousands of tons, that appear as meteors when they enter the earth's atmosphere.

me·thod·i·cal·ly (mə thŏd′ĭ kəl lē) *adv.* In a way that is arranged or done according to a clear plan; systematically: *He methodically inspected the cut diamonds.*

me·tic·u·lous·ly (mə tĭk′yə ləs lē) *adv.* In a very careful, precise way: *She meticulously recorded all her expenses.*

mi·cro·film (mī′krə fĭlm′) *n.* **1.** A film on which written or printed material can be photographed in greatly reduced size. **2.** A reproduction made on microfilm. —*v.* To reproduce on microfilm.

mi·cro·or·gan·ism (mī′krō ôr′gə nĭz′əm) *n.* An organism, such as a bacterium or protozoan, so small that it can be seen only with the aid of a microscope.

mi·cro·wave (mī′krō wāv′) *n.* Any electromagnetic wave having a wavelength in the range between about 300 millimeters and 1 millimeter.

milch (mĭlch) *adj.* Giving milk: *a milch cow.*

mil·dew (mĭl′dōō′) *or* (-dyōō′) *n.* **1.** A kind of fungus that forms a white or grayish coating on plant leaves, cloth, leather, etc., especially under damp, warm conditions. **2.** The coating thus formed. —*v.* To become covered or spotted with mildew.

mil·len·ni·um (mĭ lĕn′ē əm) *n., pl.* **mil·len·ni·ums** *or* **mil·len·ni·a** (mĭ lĕn′ē ə). **1.** A span of one thousand years. **2.** A thousand-year reign of Christ on earth, expected by the early Christians. **3.** Any hoped-for epoch of prosperity and peace. —**mil·len′ni·al** *adj.*

mil·li·ner (mĭl′ə nər) *n.* A person who makes, trims, designs, or sells women's hats.

min·i·mal (mĭn′ə məl) *adj.* Smallest in amount or degree; least possible: *a task requiring minimal labor.* —**min′i·mal·ly** *adv.*

mis·giv·ing (mĭs gĭv′ĭng) *n.* Often **misgivings.** A feeling of doubt or concern: *She has misgivings about lending him her new car.*

mo·bile (mō′bēl′) *n.* A type of sculpture consisting of parts that move.

molt (mōlt) *v.* To shed (an outer covering such as skin or feathers) for replacement by a new growth: *molt feathers.* —*n.* The act or process of molting.

mon·o·plane (mŏn′ə plān′) *n.* An airplane having a single pair of wings.

mo·not·o·ny (mə nŏt′n ē) *n.* Tiresome lack of variety; dull sameness.

ă pat / ā pay / â care / ä father / ĕ pet / ē be / ĭ pit / ī pie / î fierce / ŏ pot / ō go / ô paw, for / oi oil / ŏŏ book / ōō boot / ou out / ŭ cut / û fur / *th* the / th thin / hw which / zh vision / ə ago, item, pencil, atom, circus

mo·rale (mə **răl′**) *n.* The state of a person's or group's spirits, as shown in confidence, cheerfulness, and willingness to work toward a goal: *The aim of the party was to heighten morale and increase the staff's will to work.*

mosque (mŏsk) *n.* A Moslem house of worship.

mus·ket (mŭs′kĭt) *n.* An old type of long-barreled gun, used before the invention of the rifle.

mus·ta·chioed (mə stăsh′ōd) *or* (-stăsh′ē ōd) *or* (-stä′shōd) *or* (-shē ōd′) *adj.* Wearing a mustache, especially one that is large and full.

mus·ter (mŭs′tər) *v.* To bring or come together; assemble: *mustered the platoon for inspection.*

myr·i·ad (mîr′ē əd) *adj.* Amounting to a very large, indefinite number: *the moon, sun, planets, and myriad stars.* —*n.* A vast number: *myriad job opportunities for the clever graduate.*

nau·se·at·ed (nô′zē ā′tĭd) *or* (-zhē) *or* (-sē-) *or* (-shē-) *adj.* Suffering from a stomach disturbance that causes a feeling of the need to vomit.

neat's-foot oil (nēts′foŏt′). A pale-yellow oil made from the feet and leg bones of cattle and used mostly for processing leather.

ne·go·ti·ate (nĭ gō′shē āt′) *v.* **ne·go·ti·at·ed, ne·go·ti·at·ing. 1.** To confer or discuss (something) in order to come to terms or an agreement: *negotiate a peace treaty.* **2.** To succeed in accomplishing or coping with: *The car negotiated several difficult turns.* —**ne·go′ti·a·tor** *n.*

neu·rot·ic (noŏ rŏt′ĭk) *or* (nyoŏ-) *adj.* **1.** Of, involving, or caused by a disorder of the mind or emotions that results in symptoms such as unreasonable fears, anxiety, depression, fits of anger, and other abnormal behavior: *neurotic symptoms.* **2.** Suffering from or affected by such a disorder: *a neurotic patient.* —*n.* A neurotic person. —**neu·rot′i·cal·ly** *adv.*

nit (nĭt) *n.* The egg or young of a louse, especially of the kind that infests human hair.

non·cha·lant·ly (nŏn′shə **länt′**lē) *adv.* In a way that is, or seems to be, cool, carefree, and casually unconcerned.

no·to·ri·ous·ly (nō tôr′ē əs lē) *or* (-tōr′-) *adv.* **1.** In a way that is known widely and regarded unfavorably; infamous. **2.** In a well-known or famous way.

ob·nox·ious (əb **nŏk′**shəs) *adj.* Extremely unpleasant or offensive.

ob·ses·sion (əb **sĕsh′**ən) *n.* **1.** Full, recurring attention to a fixed idea or emotion. **2.** An idea, thought, or emotion that occupies the mind continually: *Collecting rocks became an obsession.*

oc·cu·pa·tion (ŏk′yə **pā′**shən) *n.* The conquest and control of a nation or territory by a foreign military force: *the occupation of Germany after World War II.* —*modifier:* occupation *forces.*

o·chre or **o·cher** (ō′kər) *n.* **1.** Any of several oxides of iron that occur as minerals. Their colors are yellow, brown, and red, and they are used as pigments. **2.** A yellowish or brownish orange. —*adj.* Yellowish or brownish orange.

of·fense (ə **fĕns′**) *n.* **1.** The act of causing anger, resentment, displeasure, etc. **2.** A violation of a moral, legal, or social code; a transgression, sin, or crime. **3.** Something that offends: *The building was an offense to the eye.* **4.** (ô′fĕns) *or* (ŏf′ĕns′). The act of attacking or assaulting. **5.** (ô′fĕns) *or* (ŏf′ĕns′). In sports, the team in possession of the ball or puck. —**give offense.** To cause anger, displeasure, resentment, etc. —**take offense.** To become angered, displeased, resentful, etc.

o·pi·um (ō′pē əm) *n.* A bitter yellowish-brown drug prepared from the pods of a certain variety of poppy and used as an anesthetic. It is addictive and, in excessive use, fatal.

op·pres·sion (ə **prĕsh′**ən) *n.* The act of oppressing or the condition of being subjected to harsh treatment: *oppression of the slaves.*

op·ti·cal (ŏp′tĭ kəl) *adj.* **1.** Of or having to do with sight: *an optical illusion.* **2.** Designed to assist sight: *optical instruments; optical lenses.*

or·gan·dy, also **or·gan·die** (ôr′gən dē) *n., pl.* **or·gan·dies.** A light, sheer, crisp cotton cloth used for dresses, curtains, trimmings, etc.

or·ni·thol·o·gist (ôr′nə thŏl′ə jĭst) *n.* A scientist who specializes in the study of birds.

out·cast (out′kăst′) *or* (-käst′) *n.* A person who has been excluded from a society or system. —*adj.* Cast out; driven out; rejected.

o·ver·whelm (ō′vər hwĕlm′) *or* (-wĕlm′) *v.* To overcome completely; overpower. —**o′ver·whelm′ing** *adj.: an overwhelming majority.*

pa·lav·er (pə lăv′ər) *or* (-lä′vər) *n.* **1.** Idle chatter, especially that meant to flatter or charm. **2.** A parley between two groups, especially a parley formerly held between European explorers and representatives of local populations in Africa. —*v.* To chatter idly.

par·a·psy·chol·o·gy (păr′ə sī kŏl′ə jē) *n.* The study of things (such as telepathy or clairvoyance) that are not explainable by known natural laws.

par·a·troop·er (păr′ə trōō′pər) *n.* A member of an infantry unit trained and equipped to parachute from airplanes.

pass·a·ble (păs′ə bəl) *or* (pä′sə-) *adj.* **1.** Capable of being passed or crossed: *a passable road.* **2.** Satisfactory but not outstanding; adequate: *a passable job of acting.* —**pass′a·bly** *adv.*

pas·tor·al (păs′tər əl) *adj.* **1.** Of or portraying shepherds or the simple quality of country life: *a pastoral scene.* **2.** Of or having to do with a pastor, or minister.

pa·ter·nal (pə tûr′nəl) *adj.* **1.** Of a father; fatherly. **2.** Received from a father: *a paternal trait in his bone structure.* **3.** Related to through one's father. —**pa·ter′nal·ly** *adv.*

pa·vil·ion (pə vĭl′yən) *n.* **1.** An ornate tent. **2.** An open structure with a roof, used at parks or fairs for amusement or shelter.

pec·to·ral (pĕk′tər əl) *adj.* Of or located in the chest or breast: *a pectoral muscle.* —*n.* **1.** A muscle or organ of the chest. **2.** An ornament or decoration worn on the chest.

ped·i·gree (pĕd′ĭ grē′) *n.* **1.** A line of ancestors; ancestry. **2.** A list of ancestors. **3.** A list or record of the ancestors of a purebred animal.

pem·mi·can (pĕm′ĭ kən) *n.* A food made by North American Indians from a paste of lean meat mixed with fat and berries.

pen·dant (pĕn′dənt) *n.* A hanging ornament, as one worn dangling from a necklace or from the ear.

per·ceive (pər sēv′) *v.* **per·ceived, per·ceiv·ing. 1.** To become aware of through any of the senses, especially to see or hear. **2.** To achieve understanding of: *Try to perceive the meaning of these sentences.* —**per·ceiv′er** *n.*

per·i·scope (pĕr′ĭ skōp′) *n.* Any of several instruments in which mirrors or prisms allow observation of objects that are not in a direct line of sight.

per·sim·mon (pər sĭm′ən) *n.* **1.** An orange-red fruit with pulp that is sweet and edible only when fully ripe. **2.** A tree that bears such fruit.

per·spec·tive (pər spĕk′tĭv) *n.* **1.** The technique of representing objects on a flat surface so that they have the three-dimensional quality they have when seen with the eye. **2.** A picture drawn in perspective. **3.** A viewpoint.

per·turb (pər tûrb′) *v.* To make uneasy or anxious; disturb; upset: *Don't let such a small matter perturb you.*

pes·ti·lence (pĕs′tə ləns) *n.* **1.** A deadly epidemic disease, especially bubonic plague. **2.** An epidemic of such a disease.

pet·ro·la·tum (pĕt′rə lā′təm) *n.* A jellylike, usually colorless mixture of hydrocarbons obtained from petroleum, used in making ointments and lubricants.

ă pat / ā pay / â care / ä father / ĕ pet / ē be / ĭ pit / ī pie / î fierce / ŏ pot / ō go / ô paw, for / oi oil / ŏŏ book /
ōō boot / ou out / ŭ cut / û fur / *th* the / th thin / hw which / zh vision / ə ago, item, pencil, atom, circus

phar·ma·ceu·ti·cal (fär'mə soo'tĭ kəl) or **phar·ma·ceu·tic** (fär'mə soo'tĭk) *adj.* Of pharmacy or pharmacists. —*n.* A pharmaceutical drug, preparation, or product.

phar·ma·cy (fär'mə sē) *n., pl.* **phar·ma·cies.** 1. The methods and techniques of preparing and dispensing drugs. 2. A place where drugs are sold; a drugstore.

phe·nom·e·nal (fĭ nŏm'ə nəl) *adj.* Extraordinary; remarkable: *a phenomenal memory; a phenomenal score.* —**phe·nom'e·nal·ly** *adv.*

phi·los·o·phy (fĭ lŏs'ə fē) *n., pl.* **phi·los·o·phies.** 1. a. The study by logical reasoning of the basic truths and laws governing the universe, nature, life, morals, etc. b. A formal system of ideas based upon such study: *the philosophy of Aristotle.* 2. A personal set of opinions about life, the world, etc.: *"Might makes right" was the tyrant's philosophy.* 3. A basic practical rule or set of rules: *Vince Lombardi's philosophy of coaching.* —*modifier: a philosophy professor.*

pike (pīk) *n.* 1. A long spear formerly used by infantry. 2. Any spike or sharp point, such as the tip of a spear.

pi·lot (pī'lət) *n.* 1. Someone who operates an aircraft or spacecraft. 2. A licensed specialist who steers large ships in and out of port or through dangerous waters. 3. A small-scale experimental model. —*adj.* Serving as a small-scale model for future work: *a pilot project.* —*v.* **pi·lot·ed, pi·lot·ing.** 1. To operate and set the course of (a plane, ship, or vehicle). 2. To direct or lead, as through difficulties.

pinch bar. A bar of iron or steel with a pointed, slightly curved end, used for lifting or prying; a crowbar.

pin·na·cle (pĭn'ə kəl) *n.* 1. A tall, pointed formation, as a mountan peak. 2. The peak or summit of anything: *at the pinnacle of his fame.* 3. A small turret or spire on a roof.

piv·ot (pĭv'ət) *n.* 1. A short rod or shaft about which a related part rotates or swings. 2. A wheeling movement made as if on a pivot: *A quick pivot placed him under the basket, ready for a shot.* —*v.* 1. To swing or turn on or as if on a pivot: *The needle pivots on a jeweled bearing.* 2. To depend on: *The whole project pivots on her ability as a fund raiser.*

placer mine. A mine where minerals are obtained by dredging or washing the deposits of sand or gravel left by a river or glacier.

plain·tive·ly (plān'tĭv lē) *adv.* Sadly; mournfully: *The child cried plaintively.*

plas·tic (plăs'tĭk) *adj.* Capable of being shaped or molded: *Clay is a plastic material.* —**plas·tic'i·ty** *n.*

plun·der (plŭn'dər) *v.* 1. To take booty or valuables from; pillage; rob: *Pirates plundered the coastal city.* 2. To seize wrongfully or by force; steal.

po·ten·tial (pə tĕn'shəl) *n.* Capacity for further growth, development, or progress; promise: *a program to encourage students high in potential but low in hope.* —**po·ten'tial·ly** *adv.*

pre·cau·tion (prĭ kô'shən) *n.* An action or step taken in advance to guard against possible danger, error, or accident: *take safety precautions.*

pre·cip·i·tous (prĭ sĭp'ə təs) *adj.* Like a very steep or overhanging mass of rock, such as the face of a cliff; sloping sharply.

pred·a·tor (prĕd'ə tər) *or* (-tôr') *n.* An animal that lives by capturing and feeding on other animals; a preying animal.

preen (prēn) *v.* To smooth or clean (the feathers) with the beak: *The parrot preened its feathers.*

prem·ise (prĕm'ĭs) *n.* **premises.** Property under a single ownership; someone's land or building: *the school premises.*

pri·or (prī'ər) *adj.* 1. Preceding in time or order: *his prior employment.* 2. Preceding in importance or value: *a prior consideration.* —**prior to.** Before: *Prior to that time, no inspection was made.*

pri·or·i·ty (prī ôr'ĭ tē) *or* (-ŏr'-) *n., pl.* **pri·or·i·ties.** 1. Precedence in importance or urgency: *Safety is given high priority in factories.* 2. Something more important than other considerations: *Her major priority is finding a good job.* —*modifier.* Having priority: *These are the priority items on the list.*

prob·ing (prō'bĭng) *adj.* Investigating or exploring.

prod•i•gy (prŏd′ə jē) *n., pl.* **prod•i•gies.**
1. A person with exceptional talents or
powers: *a child prodigy.* **2.** Something
extraordinary or rare; a marvel: *geysers
and rock formations that are prodigies of
nature.*

pro•file (prō′fīl′) *n.* **1.** A side view of an
object, especially of the human head; a
representation of a human head or other
object seen from the side: *the profile of
Lincoln on the penny.* **2.** The outline of
something: *the jagged profile of the city.*

pro•gres•sion (prə grĕsh′ən) *n.* **1.** Movement; progress: *limbs adapted for progression on land.* **2.** Advancement to a
higher or different stage: *the player's progression from an amateur to a professional.* **3.** A series of things or events;
sequence: *the formal dinner with its progression of great dishes.* **4.** A sequence of
numbers, each derived from the one before by some regular rule.

pro•hi•bi•tion (prō′ə bĭsh′ən) *n.* A law or
an order that prohibits something: *a prohibition on smoking.*

prone (prōn) *adj.* **1.** Lying with the front or
face downward. **2.** Tending; inclined:
prone to make hasty judgments.
—prone′ly *adv.* **—prone′ness** *n.*

pro•o•ri•ent•ed (prō′ôr′ē ĕn′tĭd) *adj.* Familiar with and giving attention or importance to professionals rather than to
amateurs.

prop•a•gan•da (prŏp′ə găn′də) *n.* The
communication of a given doctrine to
large numbers of people, especially by
constantly repeating the doctrine and by
giving only information that supports it:
*Government-controlled radio can be an
instrument of propaganda.*

pro•spec•tive (prə spĕk′tĭv) *adj.* Possible:
prospective customers. **—pro•spec′tive•ly**
adv.

pros•per•ous (prŏs′pər əs) *adj.* Econom-
ically successful; enjoying wealth or profit: *prosperous cities.* **—pros′per•ous•ly**
adv.

pro•to•type (prō′tə tīp′) *n.* **1.** A first or
early example of something, on which
later examples are based or judged: *Edi-
son's invention factory was the prototype
of modern engineering laboratories.*
2. The first full-scale model to be constructed of a new type of vehicle, machine, etc.: *the prototype of a new jet
airplane.*

Prov•i•dence (prŏv′ĭ dəns) *n.* God.

prov•o•ca•tion (prŏv′ə kā′shən) *n.* **1.** The
act of provoking; incitement. **2.** An action
that provokes anger or aggression:
*Sharks will sometimes attack people with-
out provocation.*

psy•chi•cal (sī′kĭ kəl) *adj.* **1.** Of the
human mind or psyche. **2. a.** Of extraordinary or apparently supernatural processes, such as extrasensory perception or
mental telepathy. **b.** Of, produced by, or
affected by such processes. **—***n.* A person
who is apparently responsive to supernatural phenomena; a psychic. **—psy′
chi•cal•ly** *adv.*

psy•cho•log•i•cal (sī′kə lŏj′ĭ kəl) *adj.*
1. Of psychology. **2.** Of or derived from
the mind or emotions. **3.** Capable of in-
fluencing the mind or emotions: *psychological persuasion.* **—psy′cho•log′i•cal•ly**
adv.

psy•chol•o•gist (sī kŏl′ə jĭst) *n.* **1.** A scientist who specializes in psychology. **2.** A
psychotherapist.

psy•chol•o•gy (sī kŏl′ə jē) *n., pl.* **psy•
chol•o•gies.** **1.** The scientific study of
mental processes and behavior. **2.** The
emotional characteristics and behavior
associated with an individual, group, or
activity: *the psychology of war.* **3.** Action
or behavior, often subtle, intended to
persuade or manipulate: *You used poor
psychology in showing your anger.*

pul•ver•ize (pŭl′və rīz′) *v.* **pul•ver•ized,
pul•ver•iz•ing.** **1.** To pound, crush, or
grind into tiny particles; reduce to powder or dust. **2.** To become powder or
dust. **—pul′ver•i•za′tion** *n.*

ă pat / ā pay / â care / ä father / ĕ pet / ē be / ĭ pit / ī pie / î fierce / ŏ pot / ō go / ô paw, for / oi oil / ŏŏ book /
ōō boot / ou out / ŭ cut / û fur / *th* the / th thin / hw which / zh vision / ə ago, item, pencil, atom, circus

purge (pûrj) *v.* **purged, purg·ing. 1.** To rid of what is considered undesirable or harmful: *purge society of every possible evil.* **2.** To rid (a nation, political party, etc.) of persons considered undesirable, especially by harsh methods. —*n.* The act or process of purging.

purl (pûrl) *v. Dialect.* In surfing, to allow the nose of a surfboard to dip so deep that the board is greatly slowed down or actually submerged.

Py·thag·o·ras (pǐ thăg'ər əs). A Greek philosopher of the sixth century B.C.

quail[1] (kwāl) *n., pl.* **quail** or **quails.** Any of several rather small, plump, short-tailed birds with brownish feathers.

quail[2] (kwāl) *v.* To lose courage; cower: *Harvey's dog looks ferocious, but it quails at the sight of a stranger.*

quar·ry[1] (kwôr'ē) *or* (kwŏr'-) *n., pl.* **quar·ries.** An open excavation from which stone is obtained by digging, cutting, or blasting.

quar·ry[2] (kwôr'ē) *or* (kwŏr'ē) *n., pl.* **quar·ries. 1.** An animal hunted or chased. **2.** Anything pursued in a similar manner.

quartz·ite (kwôrt'sīt') *n.* A metamorphic rock that is formed by the compression of sandstone.

qua·ver (kwā'vər) *v.* To speak in a quivering voice or utter a quivering sound.

quet·zal (kĕt säl') *n.* A brilliant green and red Central American bird of which the male has very long tail feathers.

queue (kyōō) *n.* **1.** A line of people awaiting their turn. **2.** A long braid of hair that hangs down the back.

quick·sil·ver (kwĭk'sĭl'vər) *n.* The element mercury.

qui·nine (kwī'nīn') *n.* **1.** A bitter, colorless drug derived from certain cinchona barks and used to treat malaria. **2.** Any of various drugs or chemicals that are derived from quinine.

rab·ble (răb'əl) *n.* **1.** A noisy, unruly crowd or mob. **2. the rabble.** The common people, often regarded with contempt.

rat·i·fy (răt'ə fī') *v.* **rat·i·fied, rat·i·fy·ing, rat·i·fies.** To approve and thus make officially valid; confirm: *ratify an amendment to the Constitution.* —**rat'i·fi·ca'tion** *n.*

ra·tion (răsh'ən) *or* (rā'shən) *n., pl.* **ra·tions.** Food issued or available to members of a group: *a soldier's rations.*

rau·cous (rô'kəs) *adj.* **1.** Loud and harsh: *raucous cries.* **2.** Boisterous; disorderly: *their raucous party yesterday.* —**rau'cous·ly** *adv.* —**rau'cous·ness** *n.*

re·buff (rĭ bŭf') *n.* An unfriendly reply or response to an offer or proposal of a course of action; a blunt refusal or snub. —*v.* To refuse bluntly; repel.

re·cede (rĭ sēd') *v.* **re·ced·ed, re·ced·ing.** To move back or away from a limit, point, or mark: *after the flood had receded.*

reck·on·ing (rĕk'ə nĭng) *n.* **1.** The act or process of counting, calculating, or computing. **2.** The determination of the position of a ship, airplane, or other craft by calculation.

re·con·noi·ter (rē'kə noi'tər) *or* (rĕk'ə-) *v.* **1.** To make a survey or inspection of, as in preparation for something. **2.** To make a military exploration of an area.

re·coup (rĭ kōōp') *v.* To regain a former favorable position.

re·fract (rĭ frăkt') *v.* To cause the path of (light or other radiation) to bend or deflect by its passing through or meeting the boundary of a different medium such as water or glass.

ref·uge (rĕf'yōōj) *n.* **1.** Protection; shelter: *seeking refuge in the castle.* **2.** A place of protection or shelter: *a wildlife refuge.*

registered letter. A letter that has been officially recorded by the post office.

reg·is·trar (rĕj'ĭ strär') *or* (rĕj'ĭ strär') *n.* An official of a college, corporation, etc., who is responsible for keeping records.

re·in·force (rē'ĭn fôrs') *or* (-fōrs') *v.* **re·in·forced, re·in·forc·ing.** To make stronger by or as if by adding extra support to: *reinforce a bridge.*

re·lief (rĭ lēf') *n.* The projection of a sculptured figure from a flat background. —*modifier: a relief carving.* —**in relief.** Carved, drawn, etc., so as to project or seem to project from a flat background.

re•mu•da (rĭ mōō′də) *n. Southwestern U.S.* A herd of horses from which ranch hands select their mounts.

ren•dez•vous (rän′dā vōō′) *or* (-də-) *n., pl.* **ren•dez•vous** (rän′dā vōōz′) *or* (-də-). **1.** A prearranged meeting: *a rendezvous of the explorers in the wilderness.* **2.** A designated place for a meeting. —*v.* **ren•dez•voused** (rän′dā vōōd′) *or* (-də-), **ren•dez•vous•ing** (rän′dā vōō′ĭng) *or* (-də-), **ren•dez•vous** (rän′dā vōōz′) *or* (-də-). To meet together or cause to meet together at a certain time and place.

rep•ri•mand•ed (rĕp′rĭ mănd′ĭd) *adj.* Severely or officially scolded.

res•in (rĕz′ĭn) *n.* Any of several clear or translucent yellowish or brownish substances that ooze from certain trees and plants and are used in liquid or hardened form in varnishes, lacquers, and for many other purposes.

res•in•ous (rĕz′ə nəs) *adj.* Of, containing, or resembling resin: *a resinous substance.*

res•o•lu•tion (rĕz′ə lōō′shən) *n.* **1.** The state or quality of being firm of purpose. **2.** The act of making a firm decision to do something. **3.** The process or capability of making the individual parts of an object visible and distinguishable from one another. **4.** A course of action determined or decided upon.

re•sume (rĭ zōōm′) *v.* **re•sumed, re•sum•ing. 1.** To begin again or continue after a break. **2.** To assume or take again: *The former prime minister resumed power.*

ret•ro•spect (rĕt′rə spĕkt′) *n.* A review, survey, or contemplation of the past.

rev•el (rĕv′əl) *v.* **rev•eled** or **rev•elled, rev•el•ing** or **rev•el•ling.** To take great pleasure or delight: *He revels in making fun of others.*

rev•er•ence (rĕv′ər əns) *n.* A feeling of awe and respect and often of love.

re•viv•al (rĭ vī′vəl) *n.* **1.** The act or process of bringing back or returning to life or consciousness. **2.** The act or process of bringing back or giving vigor or strength to (something).

re•vul•sion (rĭ vŭl′shən) *n.* A feeling of strong disgust or loathing.

rid•dle (rĭd′l) *v.* To solve or explain.

rig•or (rĭg′ər) *n.* **1.** Strictness; severity: *the rigor with which she pursued her goals.* **2.** A harsh or trying condition or circumstance; hardship.

rig•or•ous (rĭg′ər əs) *adj.* **1.** Full of severe conditions; harsh: *the rigorous physical training of the astronauts.* **2.** Precisely accurate; strict: *a rigorous examination of policy.*

rile (rīl) *v.* To stir up (liquid); unsettle; roil.

rime (rīm) *n.* A frost or coating of grains of ice, as on grass or trees. —*v.* **rimed, rim•ing.** To cover with or as if with rime.

rit•u•al (rĭch′ōō əl) *n.* **1.** The form or order of events followed during a religious or other ceremony. **2.** The group of ceremonies used by a church, religion, tribe, fraternal organization, etc.: *Hindu ritual.* **3.** Any procedure faithfully and regularly followed: *An exercise period was part of her morning ritual.* —*adj.* Of or in accordance with rituals: *ritual dances.* —**rit′u•al•ly** *adv.*

ri•val•ry (rī′vəl rē) *n., pl.* **ri•val•ries.** The effort to equal or outdo another.

rock-elm *adj.* Made from the wood of the American elm, or slippery elm, tree.

rod (rŏd) *n.* A metal bar in a machine: *a piston rod.*

rook•er•y (rŏŏk′ə rē) *n., pl.* **rook•er•ies.** A place where certain birds or animals gather to breed.

ro•sette (rō zĕt′) *n.* **1.** An ornament or badge made of ribbon or silk gathered and shaped to resemble a rose. **2.** Something shaped like a rose, as a rounded cluster of leaves or the clusters of spots on a leopard's fur.

rube (rōōb) *n. Slang.* An unsophisticated country person.

run•a•bout (rŭn′ə bout′) *n.* A small, open automobile or carriage.

ă pat / ā pay / â care / ä father / ĕ pet / ē be / ĭ pit / ī pie / î fierce / ŏ pot / ō go / ô paw, for / oi oil / ŏŏ book / ōō boot / ou out / ŭ cut / û fur / *th* the / th thin / hw which / zh vision / ə ago, item, pencil, atom, circus

sa•ber (sā′bər) *n.* **1.** A heavy cavalry sword with a single-edged, slightly curved blade. **2.** A light, double-edged sword used in fencing. —*v.* To strike, cut, or kill with a saber.

sa•ga (sä′gə) *n.* **1.** A long Scandinavian adventure story of the Middle Ages, telling about historical or legendary heroes, families, deeds, and events. **2.** Any long history or tale.

sage[1] (sāj) *n.* A very wise person, usually old and highly respected. —*adj.* **sag•er, sag•est.** Full of, showing, or noted for wisdom and sound judgment. —**sage′ly** *adv.*

sage[2] (sāj) *n.* A plant with grayish-green, spicy-smelling leaves used as flavoring in cooking.

sal•i•vate (săl′ə vāt′) *v.* **sal•i•vat•ed, sal•i•vat•ing.** To produce or secrete a watery fluid in the mouth. —**sal′i•va′tion** *n.*

san•i•ta•tion (săn′ ĭ ta′shən) *n.* **1.** The study and application of procedures and regulations that are meant to protect public health. **2.** The disposal of sewage and wastes. —*modifier: a sanitation worker.*

sar•coph•a•gus (sär kŏf′ə gəs) *n., pl.* **sar•coph•a•gi** (sär kŏf′ə jī′). A stone coffin.

scan•dal•ous (skăn′dl əs) *adj.* Causing scandal: *scandalous behavior.* —**scan′dal• ous•ly** *adv.* —**scan′dal•ous•ness** *n.*

scep•ter (sĕp′tər) *n.* A staff held by a sovereign as a sign of authority.

scroll (skrōl) *n.* A roll of parchment, papyrus, etc., used for writing documents.

scru•ple (skrōō′pəl) *n.* **1.** Hesitation, or a feeling producing hesitation, based on one's conscience. **2.** A unit of apothecary weight equal to 20 grains. —*v.* **scru•pled, scru•pling.** To hesitate as a result of conscience or principles.

scru•pu•lous•ly (skrōō′pyə ləs lē) *adv.* **1.** Properly; honestly. **2.** In an exacting or conscientious way.

scud (skŭd) *v.* **scud•ded, scud•ding.** To move along swiftly and easily: *the clouds scudding across the sky.* —*n.* **1.** The act of scudding. **2.** Wind-driven clouds, mist, rain, or cloud-like matter.

se•cret (sē′krĭt) *v.* To conceal or hide: *He secreted the letter in his cloak.*

se•cu•ri•ty (sĭ kyŏŏr′ĭ tē) *n.* **1.** Freedom from risk or danger; safety. **2.** Anything deposited or given to guarantee fulfillment of an obligation; a pledge: *The owner insisted that an extra month's rent be given as security.*

seis•mol•o•gist (sīz mŏl′ə jĭst) *n.* A scientist who studies earthquakes and the mechanical properties of the earth.

se•le•ni•um (sĭ lē′nē əm) *n.* Symbol **Se** One of the elements, a substance that can exist as a red powder, a black, glassy material, or a gray crystal, with chemical properties resembling those of sulfur.

self-as•sur•ance (sĕlf′ə shŏŏr′əns) *n.* Confidence or sureness in oneself.

self-suf•fi•cient (sĕlf′sə fĭsh′ənt) *adj.* Able to provide for oneself without help; independent. —**self′-suf•fi′cien•cy** *n.*

sem•a•phore (sĕm′ə fôr′) *or* (-fōr′) *n.* **1.** Any visual signaling device with flags, lights, or movable indicators, as on a railroad. **2.** A system for signaling that uses various positions of the arms or flags. —*v.* **sem•a•phored, sem•a•phor•ing.** To send (a message) by semaphore.

sem•i•nar (sĕm′ə när′) *n.* **1.** A conference at which views and information are exchanged, usually on an academic subject. **2. a.** An advanced course of study for a small group of students who do independent research on a specialized subject. **b.** A meeting of such a group.

sem•i•pre•cious (sĕm′ē prĕsh′əs) *adj.* Designating a gem, such as topaz, amethyst, or jade, that is less valuable than a precious stone.

sen•su•al (sĕn′shōō əl) *adj.* Giving pleasure to the senses or to the body; physically gratifying: *the sensual experience of a warm bath.*

sep•ul•cher (sĕp′əl kər) *n.* A burial vault.

se•ren•i•ty (sə rĕn′ĭ tē) *n.* Peacefulness; tranquillity.

serv•ice (sûr′vĭs) *n.* In tennis, the act, manner, or right of putting the ball into play.

set (sĕt) *n.* In tennis and other sports, a group of games that forms one unit or part of a match.

shang·hai (shăng hī′) *v.* **shang·haied, shang·hai·ing. 1.** To kidnap for forced service. **2.** To force (someone) to do something by deceitful or dishonest means.

sheaf (shēf) *n.* Any collection of things held or bound together; a batch.

shear (shîr) *v.* **sheared, sheared** or **shorn** (shôrn) *or* (shōrn), **shear·ing.** To deprive; divest: *sheared him of all his privileges.*

sheath (shēth) *n., pl.* **sheaths** (shē*thz*) or (shēths). Any tightly-fitting protective covering or structure.

shoal¹ (shōl) *n.* **1.** A shallow place in a body of water. **2.** A sandbank or sandbar. —*adj.* Shallow: *places where the water is shoal.*

shoal² (shōl) *n.* A school of fish or other water animals. —*v.* To come together in or swim in a shoal; to school.

shorn (shôrn) *or* (shōrn). A past participle of **shear.**

shuck (shŭk) *n.* An outer covering, such as a corn husk, pea pod, or oyster shell. —*v.* To remove the husk or shell from.

shut·tle (shŭt′l) *n.* **1.** A train, bus, aircraft, etc., making short, frequent trips between two points. —*v.* **shut·tled, shut·tling.** To move or travel back and forth by or as if by a shuttle.

sig·ni·fy (sĭg′nə fī′) *v.* **sig·ni·fied, sig·ni·fy·ing, sig·ni·fies. 1.** To serve as a sign of: *What does this monument signify?* **2.** To make known: *Janet signified that she wanted to leave early.* **3.** *Dialect.* To make a direct or indirect implication of baiting or boasting in order to make fun of someone's appearance, relatives, or situation.

sil·hou·ette (sĭl′ōō ĕt′) *n.* **1.** A drawing consisting of the outline of something, especially a human profile, filled in with a solid color. **2.** An outline of something that appears dark against a light background. —*v.* **sil·hou·et·ted, sil·hou·et·ting.** To cause to be seen as a silhouette; to outline.

sil·i·con (sĭl′ĭ kən) *or* (-kŏn′) *n.* Symbol **Si** One of the elements, a substance that occurs in crystalline and non-crystalline forms. It is a semiconductor and is used in making transistors, rectifiers, and other solid-state electronic devices. It is also used in making bricks, glass, concrete, pottery, etc.

sim·u·lat·ed (sĭm′yə lā′tĭd) *adj.* Having or duplicating the conditions, appearance, form, or sound of; imitative: *experiments using simulated space flight; a necklace of simulated pearls.*

sin·gles (sĭng′gəls) *n.* A match between two players in tennis and other games: *went on to win every major singles competition in the United States that year.*

sin·glet (sĭng′glĕt) *n.* An undershirt or athletic jersey.

sis·kin (sĭs′kĭn) *n.* **1.** A small sharp-billed finch. **2.** Any of several small birds.

skep·ti·cal (skĕp′tĭ kəl) *adj.* Of or characterized by doubt; doubting or disbelieving: *a skeptical attitude.* —**skep′ti·cal·ly** *adv.*

skir·mish (skûr′mĭsh) *n.* **1.** A minor encounter between small bodies of troops. **2.** Any minor conflict. —*v.* To engage in a skirmish.

slag (slăg) *n.* **1.** The glassy refuse that remains after a metal has been removed from an ore by smelting. **2.** Refuse from a volcano.

slea·zy (slē′zē) *adj.* **slea·zi·er, slea·zi·est. 1.** Thin and loosely woven; flimsy: *a coat with a sleazy lining.* **2.** Of poor quality; cheap; shoddy: *sleazy furniture.* **3.** Vulgar; disreputable: *a sleazy individual.*

slough (slōō) *or* (slou) *n.* **1.** A hollow or depression in the ground, usually filled with mud or mire. **2.** A stagnant swamp, bog, or marsh.

slue (slōō) *v.* To turn, twist, move, or skid to the side.

smelt·er (smĕl′tər) *n.* A device for melting or fusing ores in order to extract the metals they contain.

ă pat / ā pay / â care / ä father / ĕ pet / ē be / ĭ pit / ī pie / î fierce / ŏ pot / ō go / ô paw, for / oi oil / ŏŏ book / ōō boot / ou out / ŭ cut / û fur / *th* the / th thin / hw which / zh vision / ə ago, item, pencil, atom, circus

so·cial·ize (sō'shə līz') *v.* **so·cial·ized, so·cial·iz·ing. 1.** To place under public ownership or control. **2.** To make sociable or friendly in attitude or manners. **3.** To take part in social or group activities. **—so'cial·i·za'tion** *n.*

so·ci·o·log·i·cal (sō'sē ə lŏj'ĭ kəl) *or* (sō'shē-) *adj.* Of or involving sociology, the scientific study of human society and its origins, development, organizations, and institutions.

sod·den (sŏd'n) *adj.* **1.** Thoroughly soaked; saturated: *sodden land.* **2.** Bloated and dull. **—sod'den·ly** *adv.*

sol·i·tude (sŏl'ĭ tōod') *or* (-tyōod') *n.* **1.** The state of being alone or remote from others; isolation. **2.** A lonely or secluded place.

som·ber, also **som·bre** (sŏm'bər) *adj.* **1.** Dark; gloomy: *a somber color.* **2.** Melancholy; dismal: *a somber mood.* **—som'ber·ly** *adv.*

sor·cer·er (sôr'sər ər) *n.* A person who practices sorcery; a wizard.

sor·ghum (sôr'gəm) *n.* **1.** A grain-bearing grass grown as feed for animals and as a source of syrup. **2.** Syrup made from the juice of this plant.

sor·rel[1] (sôr'əl) *n.* Any of several plants with sour-tasting leaves.

sor·rel[2] (sôr'əl) *n.* **1.** A yellowish brown. **2.** A yellowish-brown horse. *—adj.* Yellowish brown: *a sorrel horse.*

spec·trum (spĕk'trəm) *n., pl.* **spec·tra** (spĕk'trə) *or* **spec·trums. 1.** The bands of color seen when white light, especially light from the sun, is broken up by refraction, as in a rainbow or by a prism. **2.** A broad range of related qualities, ideas, or activities: *a wide spectrum of emotions.*

spec·u·late (spĕk'yə lāt') *v.* **spec·u·lat·ed, spec·u·lat·ing. 1.** To think deeply on a given subject; ponder: *speculated that life might exist in outer space.* **2.** To guess. **3.** To buy or sell something, as stocks or land, that involves a risk on the chance of making a substantial profit.

spher·i·cal (sfîr'ĭ kəl) *or* (sfĕr'-) *adj.* **1.** Having the shape of a sphere or nearly the shape of a sphere. **2.** Of a sphere or spheres. **—spher'i·cal·ly** *adv.*

spin·y (spī'nē) *adj.* **spin·i·er, spin·i·est. 1.** Full of or covered with spines; thorny or prickly: *spiny undergrowth; a spiny hedgehog.* **2.** Forming or shaped like a spine or spines: *spiny prickles.*

spon·ta·ne·ous (spŏn tā'nē əs) *adj.* **1.** Happening or arising without apparent outside cause; self-generated. **2.** Arising or occurring voluntarily and from impulse: *spontaneous cheers.* **—spon·ta'ne·ous·ly** *adv.*

spo·rad·i·cal·ly (spô răd'ĭk lē) *adv.* At irregular intervals; in a way that has no pattern or order.

spume (spyōom) *n.* Foam or froth on a liquid. *—v.* **spumed, spum·ing.** To froth or foam.

spunk (spŭngk) *n. Informal.* Spirit; courage: *show spunk.*

sta·tis·tics (stə tĭs'tĭks) *n.* A collection or set of numerical data.

stat·u·ette (stăch'ōo ĕt') *n.* A small statue.

sta·tus (stā'təs) *or* (stăt'əs) *n.* A relative position in a ranked group or in a social system: *high status of a professional.*

ster·e·op·ti·con (stĕr'ē ŏp'tĭ kŏn', stîr'-) *n.* An optical device formerly used to project the enlarged image of a picture.

sto·rax (stōr'ăks', stôr'-) *n.* An aromatic resin obtained from various trees of the genus *Styrax.*

strait-laced (strāt'lāst') *adj.* Excessively strict in behavior; prudish.

strap·per (străp'ər) *n.* A tall, strong, sturdy person.

strat·e·gy (străt'ə jē) *n., pl.* **strat·e·gies. 1.** The science or art of planning a series of actions or maneuvers that will probably be useful in gaining an advantage over an opponent. **2.** A plan of action arrived at by means of this science.

stren·u·ous·ly (strĕn'yōo əs lē) *adv.* In an energetic, forceful way.

string·er (strĭng'ər) *n.* **1.** Someone or something that strings. **2.** A long, heavy bar or timber that connects or supports parts of a structure. **3.** A part-time representative of a newspaper or magazine who is stationed out of town or abroad.

sub·scrib·er (səb skrīb'ər) *n.* A person whose name is signed (to something).

sub·ter·ra·ne·an (sŭb′tə rā′nē ən) *adj.*
1. Situated beneath the earth's surface: *a subterranean spring; a subterranean transit system.* **2.** Hidden; secret: *a subterranean plot.*

sub·tle (sŭt′l) *adj.* **sub·tler, sub·tlest.**
1. So slight as to be difficult to detect or analyze; elusive: *subtle changes.* **2.** Not immediately obvious: *a subtle problem.* —**sub′tle·ness** *n.* —**sub′tly** *adv.*

suf·fice (sə fīs′) *v.* **suf·ficed, suf·fic·ing.**
1. To meet present needs or requirements; be enough or adequate. **2.** To be enough or adequate for: *water to suffice them for three days.*

suf·fo·cate (sŭf′ə kāt′) *v.* **suf·fo·cat·ed, suf·fo·cat·ing. 1.** To choke; smother. **2.** To die from a lack of oxygen. —**suf′fo·ca′tion** *n.*

sulfa drug. Any of a group of synthetic organic compounds capable of inhibiting bacterial growth and activity.

sul·len (sŭl′ən) *adj.* Showing a brooding ill humor or resentment; morose; sulky: *a sullen disposition.* —**sul′len·ly** *adv.* —**sul′len·ness** *n.*

su·perb (soo pûrb′) *or* (sə-) *adj.* **1.** Of unusual quality; excellent: *a superb meal.* **2.** Majestic; imposing: *a superb view.* —**su·perb′ly** *adv.*

su·per·la·tive (sə pûr′lə tĭv) *or* (soo-) *adj.* Of the highest order, quality, or degree: *It was a superlative specimen of crystal.* —*n.* Something of the highest possible excellence.

su·per·no·va (soo′pər nō′və) *n., pl.* **su·per·no·vae** (soo′pər nō′vē′) *or* **su·per·no·vas.** A rare happening in which a star undergoes an extremely large explosion and becomes for a short time a very bright object radiating vast amounts of energy.

sur·vey (sər vā′) *or* (sûr′vā′) *v.* **1.** To look over the parts or features of; view broadly: *surveyed the neighborhood from a rooftop.* **2.** To examine so as to make estimates or criticisms; investigate: *sur-*veyed the damage done by the storm. —*n.* (sûr′vā′). **1.** A view of a broad area, field, or subject. **2.** An investigation or study of a range of persons or things: *a survey of public opinion.*

swathe (swŏth) *or* (swôth) *v.* **swathed, swath·ing. 1.** To wrap or bind with a strip or strips of cloth: *His right ankle was swathed in bandages.* **2.** To cover or wrap with something that envelops: *The rock star was swathed in furs.* —*n.* A band, bandage, or other wrapping.

sym·me·try (sĭm′ĭ trē) *n., pl.* **sym·me·tries.** An exact matching of form and arrangement of parts on opposite sides of a boundary, such as a plane or line, or around a point or axis.

tab·ard (tăb′ərd) *n.* A sleeveless or short-sleeved tunic worn by a knight and embroidered with his coat of arms.

tail·race (tāl′rās) *n.* The part of a millstream through which the water flows below the water wheel.

tam·per (tăm′pər) *v.* **1.** To interfere in a harmful manner: *caught tampering with the switches.* **2.** To bring about an improper situation in a scheming manner: *tamper with the jury.* —**tam′per·er** *n.*

tan·gi·ble (tăn′jə bəl) *adj.* **1.** Capable of being touched: *a tangible product like steel.* **2.** Capable of being understood or realized: *a tangible benefit.* **3.** Concrete; real: *tangible evidence.* —*n.* **tangibles.** Material assets. —**tan′gi·bly** *adv.*

ta·per (tā′pər) *n.* A small or slender candle: *a lighted taper.*

Tar·tar (tär′tər) *n.* A member of the Mongol races of central Asia.

tat·too[1] (tă too′) *n.* **1.** A signal sounded on a drum or bugle to summon soldiers to their quarters. **2.** Any continuous, even drumming.

tat·too[2] (tă too′) *n.* A mark or design made on the skin by pricking and ingraining a permanent dye or by raising scars. —*v.*

ă pat / ā pay / â care / ä father / ĕ pet / ē be / ĭ pit / ī pie / î fierce / ŏ pot / ō go / ô paw, for / oi oil / oo book /
oo boot / ou out / ŭ cut / û fur / *th* the / th thin / hw which / zh vision / ə ago, item, pencil, atom, circus

tat•tooed, tat•too•ing, tat•toos. To mark (the skin) with a tattoo.

tech•nol•o•gy (tĕk nŏl′ə jē) *n., pl.* **tech•nol•o•gies. 1. a.** The application of scientific knowledge, especially in industry and commerce. **b.** The methods and materials used in applying scientific knowledge in this way. **2.** The knowledge that a civilization has available for adapting and using its environment to fit its needs: *the benefits and hazards of advanced technology.*

tem•per•a•ment•al•ly (tĕm′prə mĕn′tl ē) *or* (-pər ə-) *adv.* Of the manner in which an individual thinks, behaves, and reacts in general: *She was calm and temperamentally suited to the pace of her work.*

ten•den•cy (tĕn′dən sē) *n., pl.* **ten•den•cies. 1.** A demonstrated inclination to think, act, or behave in a certain way; propensity: *He has a tendency to write long paragraphs.* **2.** A natural inclination: *a girl with artistic tendencies.*

ten•e•ment (tĕn′ə mənt) *n.* **1.** A building to live in, especially one intended for rent. **2.** A cheap apartment house whose facilities and maintenance barely meet minimum standards.

ter•rain (tə rān′) *or* (tĕ-) *n.* A tract of land, especially when considered with respect to its physical features: *hilly terrain; rugged terrain.*

teth•er (tĕth′ər) *n.* **1.** A rope or chain for an animal, allowing it to move about in a small area. **2.** The range or scope of one's resources or abilities. —*v.* To restrict with a tether.

the•sis (thē′sĭs) *n., pl.* **the•ses** (thē′sēz′). **1.** An idea stated or put forward for consideration, especially by a person who plans to maintain it by logical argument. **2.** A long essay resulting from original research.

tier (tîr) *n.* Any of a series of rows placed one above another.

tin•der•box (tĭn′dər bŏks′) *n.* **1.** A metal box for holding material used to kindle fires.

tinge (tĭnj) *v.* **tinged, tinge•ing** *or* **ting•ing. 1.** To color slightly; tint: *The sunset tinged the sky with red.* **2.** To give a slight trace or touch to; affect slightly: *admiration*

tinged with envy. —*n.* A faint trace of color, flavor, etc.: *There was a tinge of sadness in her remarks.*

ti•ta•ni•um (tī tā′nē əm) *n.* Symbol **Ti** One of the elements, a shiny white metal that is strong, light, and highly resistant to corrosion.

tone (tōn) *n.* **1.** A color or shade of color. **2.** Quality of color.

torch (tôrch) *n.* **1.** A portable light produced by the flame of an inflammable material wound about the end of a stick of wood. **2.** Anything that serves to enlighten, guide, inspire, etc. **3.** *British.* A flashlight.

tow•path (tō′păth′) *or* (-päth′) *n., pl.* **-paths** (-păthz′) *or* (-päthz′) *or* (-păths′) *or* (-päths′). A path along a canal or river used by animals towing boats.

trans•cend (trăn sĕnd′) *v.* **1.** To go beyond or outside the range of: *mysterious happenings that transcend human experience.* **2.** To rise above; surpass; excel: *a painter who has transcended herself in various ways.*

trans•fu•sion (trăns fyoo′zhən) *n.* The direct injection of whole blood, plasma, or other fluid into the bloodstream.

trans•plant (trăns plănt′) *or* (-plänt′) *v.* **1.** To remove (a living plant) from the place where it is growing and plant it in another place. **2.** To transfer (tissue or an organ) from one body or body part to another. **3.** To transfer to and establish in a new place: *The early colonists transplanted their songs as well as their customs to the New World.* —*n.* (trăns′plănt′) *or* (-plänt′). **1.** Something transplanted, especially an organ or piece of tissue transplanted by surgery. **2.** The act or operation of transplanting tissue or an organ: *The doctor performed a heart transplant.* —**trans•plant′a•ble** *adj.* —**trans′plan•ta′tion** *n.*

trav•erse (trăv′ərs) *or* (trə vûrs′) *v.* **trav•ersed, trav•ers•ing. 1.** To travel across, over, or through: *traversed the desert safely.* **2.** To move forward and backward over: *Searchlights traversed the sky.* **3.** To extend across; cross: *A bridge traversed the mountain stream.* —*n.* Something lying across something else, as a beam, a rung of a ladder, etc. —*adj.* Lying or extending across: *a traverse curtain rod.*

treach•er•ous (trĕch′ər əs) *adj.* **1.** Betraying a trust; disloyal: *a treacherous friend.* **2. a.** Not dependable: *He has a treacherous memory.* **b.** Not to be trusted; deceptive; dangerous: *treacherous surf.*

trem•or (trĕm′ər) *n.* **1.** A shaking or vibrating movement: *an earth tremor.* **2.** A rapid, involuntary twitching of muscles.

tres•tle (trĕs′əl) *n.* **1.** A horizontal beam or bar extending between two pairs of legs that spread outward at an angle, used to support a vertical load. **2.** A framework made up of vertical, horizontal, and slanting supports, used to hold up a bridge.

trib•u•tar•y (trĭb′yə tĕr′ē) *n., pl.* **trib•u•tar•ies. 1.** A river or stream that flows into a larger river or stream. **2.** A person, nation, etc., that pays tribute to another. —*adj.* **1.** Flowing into another: *a tributary river.* **2.** Paying tribute: *a tributary kingdom.*

trib•ute (trĭb′yo͞ot′) *n.* Acknowledgment of gratitude, respect, or admiration.

tri•um•phal (trī ŭm′fəl) *adj.* Of, celebrating, or in memory of a triumph: *a triumphal march; a triumphal arch.*

trus•tee (trŭ stē′) *n.* **1.** A person or firm that manages another person's property or assets. **2.** A member of a group or board that manages the affairs of a college, foundation, institution, etc.

tu•ber (to͞o′bər, tyo͞o′-) *n.* A swollen, usually underground stem, such as the potato, bearing buds from which new plant shoots arise.

tug (tŭg) *v.* **1.** To pull at vigorously. **2.** To move by pulling with great effort. **3.** To tow with a tugboat. —*n.* **1.** A strong pull. **2.** A tugboat. **3.** One of two side straps connecting a harnessed animal to a vehicle.

tur•moil (tûr′moil′) *n.* A condition of great confusion or disturbance.

type•face (tīp′fās′) *n.* In printing, the size and style of the characters of type.

ty•phus (tī′fəs) *n.* Any of several forms of an infectious disease caused by microorganisms and characterized generally by high fever, depression, delirium, and red rashes.

ul•ti•mate (ŭl′tə mĭt) *adj.* **1.** Final; last; conclusive: *ultimate defeat.* **2.** Highest possible; greatest: *driving them to a point of ultimate daring.* **3.** Basic; fundamental: *ultimate truths.* —*n.* The final or highest stage or degree; the maximum: *insuring the ultimate in stopping power for their brakes.* —**ul′ti•mate•ly** *adv.*

un•ac•count•a•bly (ŭn′ə koun′tə blē) *adv.* In a way that cannot be explained; mysteriously.

u•nan•i•mous (yo͞o năn′ə məs) *adj.* **1.** Sharing the same opinion: *Critics were unanimous in their enthusiasm for the play.* **2.** Based on complete agreement: *a unanimous vote.* —**u•nan′i•mous•ly** *adv.*

un•can•ni•ly (ŭn kăn′ə lē) *adv.* **1.** In a way arousing wonder and fear; strangely. **2.** So perceptively as to seem supernatural: *uncannily accurate predictions.*

un•de•ci•phered (ŭn′dĭ sī′fərd) *adj.* Not having been changed from a code or cipher to ordinary language; not deciphered; not decoded.

un•du•late (ŭn′jə lāt′) *or* **(ŭn′dyə-)** *or* **(-də-)** *v.* **un•du•lat•ed, un•du•lat•ing. 1.** To move or cause to move in or with a smooth, wavelike motion: *flag undulating in the wind.* **2.** To have a wavelike appearance or form: *undulating hills.*

u•ni•corn (yo͞o′nĭ kôrn′) *n.* An imaginary animal of legend, resembling a horse with a single long horn projecting from its forehead.

un•in•hab•it•ed (ŭn′ĭn hăb′ĭ tĭd) *adj.* Not inhabited; having no residents.

un•rec•on•ciled (ŭn rĕk′ən sīld′) *adj.* **1.** Unable to be friendly again. **2.** Un-

---

ă pat / ā pay / â care / ä father / ĕ pet / ē be / ĭ pit / ī pie / î fierce / ŏ pot / ō go / ô paw, for / oi oil / o͝o book / o͞o boot / ou out / ŭ cut / û fur / *th* the / th thin / hw which / zh vision / ə ago, item, pencil, atom, circus

accepting. **3.** Not in harmony or agreement: *unreconciled differences.*

vac•u•um (văk′yo͞o əm) *or* (-yo͞om) *n.*
1. The absence of matter. **2.** A space that is empty of matter. **3.** A space containing a gas at a very low pressure.

va•moose (vă mo͞os′) *v.* **va•moosed, va•moos•ing.** *Slang.* To leave or go away hastily.

va•por (vā′pər) *n.* Any barely visible or cloudy diffused matter, such as mist, fumes, or smoke, suspended in the air.

vault•ing (vôl′tĭng) *adj.* Resembling an arched roof.

vel•vet (věl′vĭt) *n.* **1.** Smoothness; softness. **2.** The soft covering on the newly developing antlers of deer and related animals.

ve•ran•dah or **ve•ran•da** (və răn′də) *n.* A roofed porch or balcony.

ver•sa•tile (vûr′sə tĭl) *or* (-tīl′) *adj.* **1.** Capable of doing many things well: *a versatile athlete.* **2.** Having varied uses or functions: *a versatile machine.* **—ver′sa•til′i•ty** *n.*

vi•al (vī′əl) *n.* A small glass container for liquids.

vin•di•ca•tion (vĭn′dĭ kā′shən) *n.* **1.** The clearing of accusation or blame with supporting proof. **2.** The justification or proof of the worth of (something).

vo•ca•tion (vō kā′shən) *n.* A profession, especially one for which one is specially suited or trained. **—vo•ca′tion•al** *adj.*

vol•ley (vŏl′ē) *n.* In tennis, a shot made by striking the ball before it touches the ground.

waist•coat (wĕs′kət) *or* (wāst′kōt′) *n.* *Chiefly British.* A vest.

wan•ly (wŏn′lē) *adv.* Weakly or faintly.

wax (wăks) *v.* To become gradually larger, more numerous, stronger, or more intense: *the moon waxed and waned.*

wean (wēn) *v.* **1.** To cause (a young child or other young mammal) to become accustomed to food other than its mother's milk. **2.** To cause (someone) to give up a habit, interest, etc.

wedge (wĕj) *n.* **1.** A block of metal or wood tapered in a triangular shape designed to be inserted into a crack or crevice and used for splitting, tightening, lifting, etc. **2.** A triangular thing, piece, or formation: *a wedge of pie.* **3.** Something serving to split or divide or to push or force a way in like a wedge: *The issue drove a wedge between the party leaders.* **—v.** **wedged, wedg•ing.** **1.** To split, force apart, or fix in place with or as if with a wedge. **2.** To crowd, push, force, or squeeze into a limited space: *wedge into a compact car.*

whet (hwĕt) *or* (wĕt) *v.* **whet•ted, whet•ting.** **1.** To sharpen (a knife or other cutting tool); hone. **2.** To make more keen; stimulate: *Cooking odors always whet my appetite.*

whip•poor•will, also **whip-poor-will** (hwĭp′ər wĭl′) *or* (wĭp′-) *or* (hwĭp′ər wĭl′) *or* (wĭp′-) *n.* A brownish bird of the North American woodlands that is active by night and has a repeated three-syllable call that sounds like its name.

wick•er (wĭk′ər) *n.* Flexible twigs or shoots, as of a willow tree, woven into a material used for baskets, summer furniture, etc.

wing•spread (wĭng′sprĕd′) *n.* The distance between the tips of the extended wings, as of a bird, insect, or airplane: *the 3.6 meter wingspread of a wandering albatross.*

with•ers (wĭth′ərz) *pl. n.* The highest part of the back of a horse or similar animal, between the shoulder blades.

wiz•ened (wĭz′ənd) *adj.* Shriveled; withered: *wizened old owl.*

wol•ver•ine (wo͝ol′və rēn′) *n.* A flesh-eating animal of northern regions, having thick, dark fur and a bushy tail.

wry•ly (rī′lē) *adv.* **1.** In a way that is twisted or bent to one side. **2.** With a twisted expression of distaste or displeasure: *remarked wryly.*

year•ling (yîr′lĭng) *n.* An animal that is one year old or between one and two years old.

yield (yēld) *v.* To give in; submit: *yielded to her arguments.*

Index

AUTHORS AND TITLES

LITERARY TYPES

ARTICLES

PERSONAL NARRATIVES AND BIOGRAPHIES

PLAY

POEMS

STORIES

Art Credits

Illustrators: pp. 12–22, JOHN F. WHALLEY; pp. 23–31, JOHN D. DAWSON; pp. 41–44, tables by ANCO, art by GEORGE ULRICH; p. 46, ANCO; pp. 48–58, JUDITH DUFOUR LOVE; pp. 59–65, JOE ISOM; p. 66, PAUL GOBLE; pp. 72–73, DAVID MCKEE; pp. 74–91, JOEL SNYDER; pp. 92–93, STEPHEN GAMMELL; pp. 94–105, DANIEL E. FLANAGAN; p. 106, RONALD LEHEW; pp. 108–109, ANCO; pp. 110–112, graphs by ANCO, art by GEORGE ULRICH; pp. 121–125, ELIZABETH CLEAVER; pp. 126–139, MERYL HENDERSON; pp. 129, 133, 137, border motifs by CHRISTINE CZERNOTA; p. 140, Reprinted from *Eskimo Songs and Stories* translated by Edmund Field. Illustrations by Kiakshuk and Pudlo. Copyright © 1973 by Dell Publishing Co., Inc. Used by permission of the publisher, Delacorte Press/Seymour Lawrence; pp. 141–142, DAVID MCKEE; pp. 148–161, DOUGLAS SNOW; p. 162, PAT WONG; pp. 180–185, MARILYN BRAATEN; pp. 186–192, CHARLES MCVICKER; p. 193, MARIA TERMINI; pp. 194–207, ROBERT OWENS; pp. 208–209, DAVID MCKEE; pp. 210–220, LINDA STRAUSS EDWARDS; pp. 221–226, GARY FUJIWARA; pp. 227–235, DIANE DE GROAT; p. 236, PAUL GOODNIGHT; pp. 239, 241–244, MARILYN FALLON; pp. 248–256, JOHN HOLDER; pp. 257–259, JENNIE WILLIAMS; pp. 260–276, LESLIE H. MORRILL; pp. 277–278, DAVID MCKEE; pp. 284–295, JOSEPH SMITH; p. 297, ATI FORBERG; pp. 298–309, PAUL S. WEINER; pp. 311–313, GEORGE ULRICH; pp. 315–316, charts by ANCO, art by GEORGE ULRICH; pp. 318–325, ALEXANDER FARQUEHARSON; pp. 326–334, HARU WELLS; pp. 335–351, RICHARD LOEHLE; pp. 352–353, DAVID MCKEE; p. 354, PATRICIA JOHNSON; pp. 364–369, DOROTHEA SIERRA; p. 370, DAVID WIESNER; pp. 371–379, TROY HOWELL; pp. 380–384, JOHN F. WHALLEY; pp. 386–387, 389–391, DICK SANDERSON; p. 404, JOSEPH LOW; pp. 405–416, CHARLES CARROLL; pp. 417–418, DAVID MCKEE; pp. 424–439, FLOYD SOWELL; pp. 440–443, WILLI K. BAUM; pp. 444–453, HAL FRENCK; p. 454, MARC BROWN; pp. 465, 469, GEORGE ULRICH; pp. 471–481, BONNIE UNSWORTH, designer; pp. 482–499, CAROL SCHWARTZ; pp. 500–501, DAVID MCKEE; pp. 502–503, MARK CORCORAN; pp. 507, 510, JOAN E. PALEY; pp. 514–523, JUDITH GOETEMANN; pp. 530–536, BARBARA BASCOVE; pp. 537–539, PAUL M. BREEDEN; pp. 545–561, LISA ALIPRANDO; p. 562, RICHARD E. BROWN; pp. 563–564, DAVID MCKEE.

Photographers: pp. 32–33, JOHN SHAW/BRUCE COLEMAN; pp. 34–35, STEPHEN J. KRASEMANN; pp. 36–37, KATHY BUSHUE/WILDERNESS PHOTO-GRAPHICS; pp. 38–39, DAN DAVIDSON; p. 39 (top) ALASKA WILDLIFE FILMS; p. 46, Editorial Photocolor Archives; pp. 68–69, Courtesy of National Collection of Fine Arts, Smithsonian Institution; pp. 95, 100–101, 104, TOM MAHONEY, photos from *The Longest Auto Race* by George Schuster and Tom Mahoney; p. 115, MORTON BEEBE/Photo Researchers, Inc.; p. 118, JACK MANNING/NYT PICTURES; pp. 163, 167, 169, 171, OZZIE SWEET; p. 177 (left) LYNN STONE/Animals, Animals; p. 177 (right) RALPH REINHOLD/Animals, Animals; p. 179, BACKROADS/Editorial Photocolor Archives; p. 186, ORVILLE RAND/Charles Woolley Collection; p. 190, Culver Pictures, Inc.; p. 355, photography by Egyptian Expedition, The Metropolitan Museum of Art; pp. 358, 361, 363, LEE BOLTIN and The Metropolitan Museum of Art; p. 382, California Historical Society; p. 393 (left) JERRY WACHTER/Focus on Sports, (right) Focus on Sports; pp. 398–399, Wide World Photos; p. 402, Courtesy of National Baseball Hall of Fame and Museum, Inc.; p. 455, JOSEPH L. BRENNAN; p. 457, WARREN BOLSTER; pp. 458–459, 460, WERNER STOY/Camera Hawaii; p. 471, MITCHELL B. REIBEL/Focus on Sports; pp. 475, 477, KEVIN GALVIN/Photo Sports; p. 541, Henri Matisse, SELF-PORTRAIT AS AN ETCHER, c. 1903, etching and drypoint, printed in black, plate: 5 5/16″ × 7 7/8″, Collection, The Museum of Modern Art, New York, Gift of Mrs. Bertram Smith; p. 542, Henri Matisse, VIEW OF COLLIOURE AND THE SEA, 1911, oil on canvas, 24 3/4″ × 20 3/8″, Collection, The Museum of Modern Art, New York, Bequest of Nelson A. Rockefeller; p. 543, Henri Matisse, HORSE, RIDER, AND CLOWN, Plate 5 from JAZZ, Paris, Tériade, 1947, Pochoir, Sheet, 76 1/4″ × 25 1/4″, Collection, The Museum of Modern Art, New York, Gift of the artist.

Book cover, title page, and magazine covers by WINONA TAYLOR.